TRANSFER OF WATER RESOURCES KNOWLEDGE

Proceedings of the

FIRST INTERNATIONAL CONFERENCE

ON TRANSFER OF

WATER RESOURCES KNOWLEDGE

September 1972, Fort Collins, Colorado, U.S.A.

Edited by

Evan Vlachos

WATER RESOURCES PUBLICATIONS

Fort Collins, Colorado, U.S.A.

1973

For information and correspondence:

WATER RESOURCES PUBLICATIONS

P.O. Box 303, Fort Collins, Colorado 80521

*TC
401
.I6
1972*

TRANSFER OF WATER RESOURCES KNOWLEDGE

This publication is printed and bound by LithoCrafters,
Ann Arbor, Michigan, U.S.A.

TABLE OF CONTENTS

iii

ACKNOWLEDGMENTS

The Planning and Organizing Committees for the First International Conference on Transfer of Water Resources Knowledge express their sincere appreciation to the United States Agency for International Development for their sponsorship. Without their financial support, Grant No. AID/csd-3617, it would have been impossible to organize and develop the program. Recognition is also given to UNESCO for providing partial travel support for several foreign participants.

Other co-sponsors of the Conference included: American Society of Civil Engineers, Section of Hydrology of the American Geophysical Union, International Association of Hydrological Sciences, U.S. National Committee for the International Hydrological Decade, and Colorado State University. Their interest in supporting the meeting as co-sponsors was greatly appreciated.

The contributions from the authors, general reporters, session chairmen, general speakers, technical editors, and those who offered discussion during the meeting is also gratefully acknowledged. Without their interest in the transfer of knowledge and full cooperation and contributions it would have been impossible to have had a meaningful conference and to publish these proceedings.

Everett V. Richardson   V. Yevjevich
Director of Conference   Chairman of Planning Committee

FOREWORD

    The diversified papers of this volume are indicative
of the concern for the transfer of knowledge. The conference
opened with a two-fold approach to aspects of transfer,
namely:

    - The transfer of knowledge from developed to developing
      countries.

    - The transfer of knowledge from research to practice.

    Indeed, the general argument in the original conception
of the conference can be summarized in the following simplified
diagram which can guide us into an understanding of the
various sessions of the conference both in terms of regional
concern and organizations and also in terms of the interrelated
emphasis on theory, research, and practice.

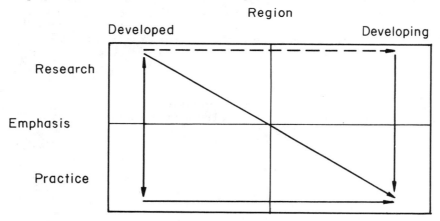

    Simplified as the above remarks and arrows may be in
attempting to clarify the overall thrust of the conference,
there are at the same time some major underlying difficulties
in understanding the major parameters involved in these
transfers of knowledge. One concerns the problems involved
in the distinction between "developed" and a whole host of
terms describing the other countries, such as "underdeveloped,"
or "developing," or "less developed," or "Third World." Not
only are such terms difficult to define, but also "underdevelopment" is not a general condition of any given country,
since it may refer to circumstances describing a particular
region and pockets of underdevelopment within a developed
nation. The conference seems to be adopting the term

"developed to developing regions," a compromise extending our
narrow horizon of national identification.

Another major concern explicated in the above simplified
diagram has to do with the one-way direction of the transfer
of knowledge from developed to developing nations. One may
even describe such a preoccupation as a form of "intellectual
imperialism." However, no particular country has a monopoly
on water knowledge. We need to underline from the beginning
the reversibility of transfer and the experience to be gained
from "developing" nations in offering traditional wisdom and
tested ways of utilizing water that may be of use even for
conditions of advanced technology. In this respect, there is
also an insidious danger involved in the blind faith to the
foreign consultant, even at the expense of excellent local
authorities whose opinion seems to rate lower than any imported
authority (even when imported consultants may be considered
as third-rate professionals in their own country). Thus, we
may now extend our argument running throughout the present
volume to include the much larger question of the transfer
of knowledge and develop a scheme which incorporates the
mutual benefit from an emerging general pool of knowledge and
the steps involved in the transmission and adoption of water
resources knowledge:

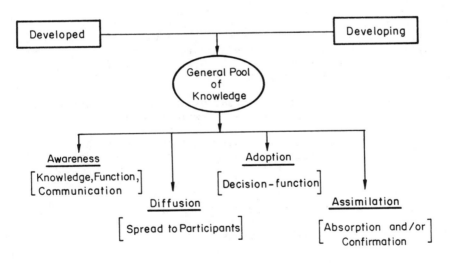

As this simplified diagram indicates, the present
collection of papers raises major points about the overall
process of communicating and transferring knowledge and about
the important linking mechanisms between transmitters and
receivers. More important, it points out to such important

elements of the process, as the source, methods, channels, receiver, and short- and long-range effects of the communicated knowledge.

At the same time, the above diagram and more or less simplified expression of the major concerns in the volume need to be understood in the context of different levels of analysis and training environments which in turn require different modes of transfer of knowledge. This means more specifically three different levels affecting planning and education and the general approach of transferring water resources level. The first may be considered as the macro-level which incorporates high level training and it revolves around issues of planning and policy implementation. The second, may be referred to as the meso-level or a middle level of analysis, involving partially elementary principles of planning, but also much more field work and intermediate methods of transfer. Finally, we may include a micro-level or a low level of practical analysis and training, concerning itself mostly with application and the use of knowledge in everyday circumstances. The various papers of the conference reflect the concern with all these levels of analysis from the highest levels of planning and international experience to the much more concrete micro-level of everyday application.

However, more central throughout the various papers of the present volume are crucial questions reflecting the concern with specific methodologies of the transmission of knowledge. With the help of the authors we may raise a number of vital questions which characterize also the overall preoccupation of the conference:

1. What is to be transmitted, namely the distinction between hardware versus software information.

2. How is knowledge to be transmitted, namely the specific strategies and tactics or the methodologies and mechanisms that make transfer of knowledge more effective.

3. Who will transmit, or the types of persons and organizations usually carrying out activities associated with the transfer of water resources knowledge.

4. When is information to be transmitted, exemplifying preoccupation with the diachronic or long-range character of an effective transfer of knowledge and the concern with the various levels of the process of communication and information absorption.

5. Why transfer of knowledge, i.e., the concern with the
    overall goals of development and the larger purposes
    to be achieved through the introduction of new
    knowledge from developed to developing regions.

The last question is one of extreme relevance that seems
to underline the writing of most of the writers in this
volume; namely, the concern with the normative requirements
of the transfer of knowledge and the goals to be achieved from
efforts of planned change.

The above point brings us then into two major concerns
and underlying issues that seem to characterize the specific
discussions concerning the transfer methodology in the various
papers and discussions of the conference. A distinction
between direct exchange of information versus a step exchange
which is required especially in order to avoid the tremendous
data explosion of recent years by differing users, efficiently
and effectively, to the appropriate sources of data:

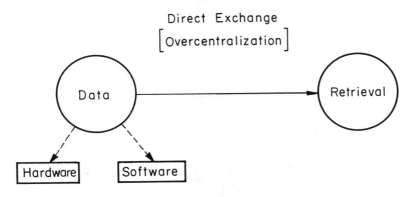

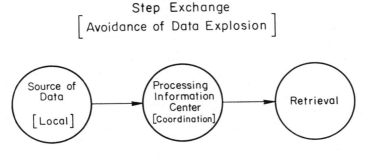

In such differentiation in the process of data transferring
and knowledge utilization, we may be thinking both in terms of
hardware and software information and in accordance with the

need for avoiding problems of overcentralization as contrasted with aspects of coordinating appropriate information, relevant to the requirements of a particular region or problem.

Another major point throughout the conference and the papers included herein, has to do with the general theme of what "research to practice" really implies. While the conference addressed itself primarily to a simple distinction of how research relates to everyday practice we need to extend our argument and our intellectual horizon beyond that particular point in order to include the significance of the research and practice to specific action programs or to the actual users of this knowledge (together with all questions reflecting our concern with public participation). This is why a final diagram may be useful in summarizing the extension of this horizon in the process of the transfer of water resources knowledge:

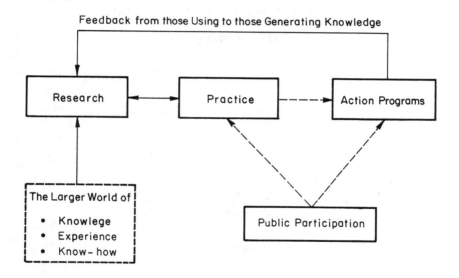

This diagram although not specifically referred to in any of the papers of this volume is a combination of both the discussions and many of the items brought forward in the papers, panels, and round-tables of the conference. We must think of a more complete system that reflects the continuous interface of research and practice and their relationship to the much larger and more important question of what do these two concerns mean for specific action programs and to the wider public participation beyond the immediate concerns of the specialists. These concerns are part of continuous questions raised throughout the conference as to the major aspects involved in a cogent, systematic transfer of water resources methodology.

In this respect, then, we may conclude the foreword by bringing forward as a conclusion a number of questions which the authors and participants of the conference seem to continuously have raised.

1. How do we gain insight from failures as well as from successes?

2. What structural and institutional supports are required for a simulating transferred knowledge?

3. What are the facilitators and/or constraints for transfer for both transmitting and receiving regions?

4. How does transfer of knowledge diffuse within a particular region or within certain populations?

5. What does field practice and action programs entail? How long? Where? For whom?

6. What is the connection between transfer of knowledge and systemic planning?

7. What is the role, if any, of public participation and its relationship to research and practice?

8. What are some of the specific forms and experiences of benefitting from the transfer of knowledge from developing to developed regions?

9. Are there dangers from "over-transferring of knowledge"? Do we need, perhaps, intermediate levels of knowledge (or methodologies of knowledge) as well as of technology in order to achieve a balanced and equitable development?

Hopefully, a number of these questions will also be raised and analyzed during the Second International Conference on Transfer of Water Resources Knowledge to be held in the summer of 1977. Such questions need to be answered if we are to re-examine traditional means of transfer of knowledge or if we are to introduce innovative schemes of knowledge exchange. One thing, however, seems to stand out rather clearly in the various papers of the conference: Transfers of knowledge without any other major socioeconomic changes, without deep transformations in both the social structure and the commitment of professionals to a wider horizon under the specific cultural conditions of each country and region, will be exercises in futility, abortive transplants, and continuous sources of frustration for well-meaning technologists.

WELCOME ADDRESS by PRESIDENT A.R. CHAMBERLAIN
of COLORADO STATE UNIVERSITY
on THE OCCASION of
THE FIRST INTERNATIONAL CONFERENCE ON TRANSFER
OF WATER RESOURCES KNOWLEDGE

It is my pleasure to officially welcome you to Colorado State University for the First International Conference on Transfer of Water Resources Knowledge. As professionals you have been involved in information transfer in the water resources area for over 50 years. It is interesting to note that we now record the first international conference on the subject in which you have been engaged for many years. That is perhaps in recognition that at last we have available the technological tools, as well as, and this I believe is more significant, the social motivation to pursue more meaningfully than ever before, a translation of our technical knowledge into social action.

I would say that there is an easy way to solve many of these problems; that is for a few more of you to run for political office through whatever form of government you have and get in charge. The solutions would be identified and implemented quickly. I do not say that as facetiously as it might imply. In this country, for example, it is very unusual to find people such as engineers and scientists in political positions of public policy-making. I believe more of them should seek that kind of role and thereby become more a party to the level of public policy decision-making.

But let us argue how we are going to get the job done. Some of you have already observed our audio-visual facility in this building and have seen some of the adjunct facilities around the campus to support the transfer of knowledge. I would like to suggest that the entire activity in which you are proposing to engage is really continuing education. National studies both in this country and abroad have amply demonstrated that by the turn of the century some seventy to eighty percent of all continuing education activities will be done via educational technology, both hardware and software. This is an arena in which we, in fields such as engineering, are still not prone to see the true potential that is available to us with the present technology.

You are undoubtedly aware of the technical developments in your own field of engineering, but I suspect you are not adequately receiving the communication capability under the concept of continuing education of which educational technology is already capable and will increasingly carry out in the coming two or three decades. I would hope you will give some thought into the probable circumstance that instead of meeting in sessions like this, by the end of the century you can have conferences like this every day of the week, any place in the world, in any kind of geographic setting, and in class sizes or conference sizes from one to one thousand, on practically any element of technology in which you have an interest. Educational technology is not going to simply be a tool for conveying programmed knowledge to you. It will be able to manage the environment in which you carry out your own personalized learning experience. This holds perhaps the greatest promise of all in our arena of conveying water resource technology among nations, among people, and across disciplines.

The institution that is serving as your host feels that it has a high stake in developing information transfer systems in this particular region. We feel from the work that we have done to date, and from that done in conjunction with a number of other institutions both in this country and abroad, that it is appropriate to make the kind of investments that you have seen here and that you can see over in our computer-assisted instruction experimental laboratory. These significant investments enable us to pursue both the positive and the negative aspects of educational technology as a part of the information transfer resource available to our society. We are absolutely convinced that whether the discipline is sociology, economics, physics, engineering, or anatomy, there is a portion of the learning experience that can be handled more effectively by technology than by a direct one-to-one or a one-to-twenty relationship of professors to students, or science to scientists. As an insititution, then, this is a part of our perception of our purpose as well as the traditional on-campus role.

I would like briefly to tell you something about this institution. We now have roughly 17,000 students under a restrictive admissions program. We are working on a planned growth that will ensure that the institution's enrollment will not exceed 20,000 students. In other words, we are presuming in terms of educational effectiveness of the scope of the activities we have, and in terms of economic efficiency, that an enrollment of about 20,000 students in ten major program areas, of which engineering is one, constitutes the optimum size for this institution. We have received significant support of this concept through all the levels of our state government.

In carrying out these programs, we will continue to have about the same distribution of total enrollment that we now have, which includes approximately eighty-five percent undergraduate students and fifteen percent graduate enrollment. Our freshman class now runs fifty percent young women and fifty percent young men. CSU's graduate programs are about fifty percent non-resident students, coming from more than 60 foreign countries. We expect this general relationship of students from all 50 states and from 60 to 70 foreign countries to continue. Of course, all of the facility planning, all of the faculty planning, and all of the curricular planning is oriented to this educational mission, which is only a part of the total higher education offerings existing within the state of Colorado.

As one of the land-grant institutions in the United States, we feel that no longer are we working in an arena of just trying to respond to educational opportunities for the thousands that may be knocking at the door. We are now working in an arena of a carefully prescribed set of goals, a carefully prescribed set of activities, that permits a degree of quality planning rather than just quantity planning which was not possible even five years ago. I believe this is highly relevant to the concept of information transfer in such fields as water resources. We need to give more attention to the aspects of the quality of what we are doing in the total social context in which we are functioning, rather than solely to the quantity of activities that we might be able to carry out.

As you pursue your particular conference objectives, I would hope that you will take the opportunity to get acquainted with more of the staff of your host campus. We have formulated our objective with respect to water resources in an interdisciplinary context in which the goals of the departments of Economics and of Political Science, the College of Forestry and Natural Resources, the College of Agricultural Sciences, and the College of Engineering have been defined to achieve this broader understanding of our natural resources and their effective management and utilization.

Again I welcome you to the campus and wish for you a very successful conference. Some of you, of course, have been on the campus a number of times before, and I would invite those of you for whom this is the first visit, to put Colorado State University on your list for an annual visit or a biannual visit. Have a good conference.

OPENING REMARKS

By

V. Yevjevich
Professor of Civil Engineering
Colorado State University
AT THE FIRST CONFERENCE ON TRANSFER
OF WATER RESOURCES KNOWLEDGE

September 14, 1972

Ladies and Gentlemen:

The First Conference on Transfer of Water Resources
Knowledge is being held at this university because both the
knowledge transfer and the production of knowledge are the
basic purposes of a high-learning institution. The Conference
fits excellently the university objectives, namely, to transfer
knowledge by educational and other processes, and to produce
new knowledge for various social objectives. No modern and
high level educational systems can persist without being
challenged by the inquiry of the unknown. For creating the
new knowledge and for developing the corresponding technology,
the transfer of knowledge from research to practice, and from
developed to developing regions is as much an obligation of
universities as it is of any other national or international
organization involved in the knowledge transfer.

The opening remarks at this Conference would be incomplete
without looking at it from two points of view, namely, why to
use the subject of water resources as an example of knowledge
transfer, as it is the case at this Conference, and what aspects
of the knowledge transfer should have the major stress in
discussions.

The water resources technology belongs to one of the
oldest technologies that man has developed. Present social
requirements put emphasis on proper conservation, development
and control of water resources, with a search for optimal
social consequences. Very large capital investments go into
various aspects of water resources use and control all over
the world. As a consequence, the example of water resources
is pertinent in studying the knowledge transfer.

Though the transfer of knowledge can be conceived only
as the retrieval and dissemination of published literature in
the most efficient way, this Conference is not conceived with
the only or even the major stress on that aspect of transfer.
The emphasis is rather on the knowledge transfer from research
to practice, and from developed to developing regions of the
world.

The transfer from research to practice cannot be conceived only as a one-way street. Basically, practice is the major, but not the only, source of subjects for investigation, research, and development. As an example, some problems may be conceived as pertinent for research activities and technologic developments for which the present practice may not even be relevant. Who could anticipate various environmental problems, subject at present to data collection, investigation, research and technologic development, ten years ago only from the practice at that time?

Similarly, the knowledge transfer from developed to developing regions is not a one-way street. It may be difficult to find even the least developed region, from which something cannot be learned and transferred to the most developed region. However, the subject of knowledge transfer, as conceived for this Conference, presumes that the bulk of the transfer is and should be from the developed to the developing regions of the world. The word "regions" is used here instead of the word "countries", because numerous are examples for which two regions of the same country can be far apart in development and in the application of the available world knowledge. The time is proper to drop the concept of dividing the world into developed and developing countries, and instead make the distinction into the developed and developing regions, thus transcending national boundaries. In a more and more integrated world market, the international boundaries may often be less important than the boundaries between the developed and developing regions.

A large investment is annually made by the world into data procurement, various investigations, research activities and technologic developments on water resources. Some estimates of this annual expenditure is as high as a half billion U.S. dollars. These estimates depend on which activities are included into the concept of knowledge necessary for the planning of conservation, development and control of water resources. The final product of this investment are: pools of various data, multitude of investigation reports, and published works from research activities and technologic developments. At present, they exponentially increase with time. Taking into account all presently available useful information, and the non-obsolete knowledge on water resources, this represents a value of several billions of dollars invested. The value of knowledge being produced annually is likely commensurate with the total annual investment by the world in water resources development and control, and the total usable and accumulated knowledge at present is also likely commensurate with the total past investments into water resources systems.

No society can or should continue to support permanently any type of activity without accounting in some way for the returns of the investment. It is safe to postulate that the accountability will be more and more enforced in the near future of what is being produced in the data collection, investigation, research and development phases of modern water resources technology. In anticipating a strict social control of the production and application of the water resources knowledge, the basic criteria may be how this knowledge is transferred and applied to socially useful purposes. The legitimate human curiosity to know and to discover is best supported and promoted by showing that it is also very useful for those who pay for the efforts to discover and know. Therefore, a good prospect for this continuous support must be based on an efficient transfer of knowledge to useful social objectives.

In a world of more and more published works, the first question is how to assess what is the new knowledge. This evaluation is relatively a difficult task not only because of difficulties in assessing what the obsoleteness of knowledge is, but also because of subjective influences both by individuals or institutions. A powerful figure builds a philosophy of approach, often carried on for decades by his influence. A team of specialists in an organization may institutionalize a concept, an idea, a method or approach, and until the major promoters of the team are retired, new philosophies are not likely to emerge from that organization. The inertia thus produced may be, however, a stabilizing factor against the volatile and superficial innovations, but at the same time they can be the most stifling factors of the scientific and technologic progress. Basic criteria and procedures are necessary for selecting what is and what is not a new knowledge, and which existing knowledge is not obsolete. It is likely that both the objective and subjective factors will continue to interplay for some time in decisions on what is the new and/or non-obsolete knowledge. Therefore, before transferring knowledge, it must be accepted as worth transferring.

The scientific and technologic progress in disciplines of applied side--which are of old human concern like disciplines underlying the development of water resources--will depend highly on how the presently prevailing concepts, methods and approaches are challenged in a reasonable way. To make a parallel with the medical profession, as some physicians like to tell, the truths of medicines are shortlived because they are replaced by the better truths, while the medical superstitions live for centuries.

The new knowledge may be transferred either by the generating party, or it may be independently implemented by the user. However, numerous are examples of the best transfer when both the producer and the user jointly make efforts to apply it. It is safe to postulate the hypothesis that the full partnership of knowledge producer or holder and the knowledge user can accomplish a high efficiency in its transfer.

A multitude of ways have been used in transferring the knowledge from developed to developing regions. This Conference will analyze their various aspects and it would be superfluous to review them in these opening remarks. However, two points are worth stressing.

First, the political decision makers at various levels in developing regions should be made well aware that a tremendous wealth of accumulated knowledge is available nearly free for assimilation and application to problems of their regions. Several developed countries have used this wealth wisely in the past in order to raise their economies above the level of the user only, to levels of both the user and producer of the world knowledge.

Second, without basic nuclei of high level scientists and professionals of an important discipline in a developing region-- who are able to assimilate, adapt, improve and apply the available world knowledge--the knowledge transfer to developing regions cannot be the most efficient. Regardless of all international and bilateral attempts on knowledge transfer to developing regions, only the viable institutions and the competent specialists in developing regions can be the most efficient vehicles of knowledge transfer in the long run.

It seems the proper time at present to put stress on the bilateral and multilateral cooperations of institutions and individuals from developed and developing regions for knowledge transfer, rather than continue various approaches of direct technical or scientific assistance.

The knowledge transfer, as analyzed by authors and general reporters for this Conference, covers the subjects of high social interest. They will be also reviewed by a panel discussion on Saturday morning. You, the participants, may find the attendance of this Conference the most stimulative, if you contribute by discussion, your experience and raise the pertinent and provocative questions to authors, general reporters and panelists.

In the name of the Planning and Organizing Committees of this Conference, we wish to all of you present at this meeting a successful and rewarding participation.

CONCLUDING REMARKS

By

E.V. Richardson
FIRST CONFERENCE ON TRANSFER OF WATER RESOURCES KNOWLEDGE
Colorado State University

We started this conference on the concept of transfer of knowledge from research to practice, feedback from practice to research and the transfer from developed to developing regions and the feedback from this. However, it is clear from the panels and the two days of discussion that other types of knowledge transfers are important. One is the transfer of knowledge to the lay public. Professor Gilbert White eluded to this; however, because his remarks were colored with some criticism of we engineers, some people may not have heard his message. Another is the transfer of knowledge on the problems that exist in the developing areas that we need to find solutions for, and a third are the tools used in the transfer process. At our next conference, we need to broaden our discussion on the transfer of knowledge to include these.

We discussed the use of publications in the knowledge transfer, the need for dissemination of publications, and the value of information retrieval systems. However, there was some suggestions that publications are not utilized in the developing regions. One person says that we need to keep the channels open so that users can get publications free; another says, well, if they don't pay for them, they don!t use them. My experience has been that engineers in the developing areas want and need free publications. When I travel in the developing areas of South America or Asia, I find the young engineers want these publications; they read them. In fact, it scares me a little, the way they accept some of these articles we publish. Some of the material they're reading -- they shouldn't be! We need to do a better job of editing and culling. This is particularly true of the professional societies. Many of the engineers in the developing areas haven't been trained to scrutinize literature, and they accept written information as the gospel and try to utilize the information. I am not so concerned about a publication that presents old information as new -- rediscovery of the wheel -- as I am about poor, misleading, or false knowledge.

I find that if the young engineer or planner has a problem they go to the library. I can quote example after example where young engineers have gone in and done a beautiful job of solving a problem by utilizing the literature. Therefore, publications and their retrieval are vital and we should be building up libraries.

Those engineers and scientists who are active in the developing areas and in transfer of knowledge are dedicated and capable. They take a personal interest in the problems and they care. This was brought out both in the Conference and the preceding Symposium. However, one thing was not stressed, which should have been. Mr. Paul-Marc Henry stated that we are in a hurry, but he did not really emphasize why we were such. In a conversation with him, he made a statement that illustrates why we are concerned and in a hurry. If there is a drought next year in India, people will die. This will be true no matter what the world tries to do. The world's population is growing faster than the capacity of the world to feed them. A year with marginal food production because of weather, or governmental policies causes untold misery. Two years can result in a catastrophe. The shortage of food is further illustrated by the fact that the U.S. is selling bushels of grain to the Soviet Union and China. At this time the U.S. is not utilizing it's total capabilities for food production. However, the U.S. can only increase our food production within finite limits. What is the future two years, ten years from now? Population is increasing and will continue to increase even with effective birth control. These are the reasons we are concerned and in a hurry (population growth, food production).

Our reasons for being in a hurry are not getting to the public, and we need to transfer our concern to the public. This comes back to the point which I want to emphasize; that is, that we as technicians and engineers, or even as policy makers and planners, are not getting our message to the public. This is one reason why the environmentalists are taking us to task; they don't understand what we are trying to do. That is why they call us the "stream destroyers, destroyers of the environment;" they are not getting the message. It is our responsibility to inform the public. It is not the responsibility of the social scientists, political scientists, or anyone else; they can help, but it all comes back to us. We have been too concerned with our technology and not concerned enough with the transmission of technology.

I think with this I will close. We have been quite pleased with the attendance and interest of the participants. Discussions have gone on after the closing of each session. I hope that our proceedings will justify all the words and efforts that have gone into the last 2 1/2 days. I further hope that in 1977 we can have another Transfer of Water Resources Knowledge Conference, building on the results of this Conference.

MAJOR ADDRESSES DURING THE CONFERENCE

- *W.S. BUTCHER - "Water Resources: Facing The Challenge of Today and Tomorrow"*

- *G.E. SCHWEITZER - "From Research to Reality"*

- *G.F. WHITE - "Prospering with Uncertainty"*

WATER RESOURCES RESEARCH:
FACING THE CHALLENGES OF TODAY AND TOMORROW*

By

William S. Butcher
Chairman, Committee on Water Resources Research
Office of Science and Technology
Executive Office of the President
Washington, D.C.

The President's budget for Fiscal Year 1973 calls for
expenditure of almost four billion dollars ($3.909 billion)
for water resources related developments, which represents
an increase of almost one hundred percent since 1970 when
the corresponding budget figure was $1.883 billion. From
present indications this figure will probably expand in the
years ahead due principally to increased spending on waste
water disposal through the construction grant program of
the Environmental Protection Agency. The expansion of that
program which has taken place already and which will continue
in the future has been added on to a federal water resources
program which has been expanded modestly over the years. At
the present time this other part of the program represents
something over two billion dollars. However, to this must
be added the considerable expenditures of State and local
governments in investments in water supply and waste water
facilities.

Traditionally and appropriately it has been part of this
nation's strategy in dealing with its water resource problems
to have included within that a significant research program
which today is represented by a federal expenditure of almost
a hundred and fifty million dollars per year. While this
Federal expenditure on water resources activities is far
from the total in that field, this is not true for research
on water resources where the Federal expenditure represents
the majority of that research effort in the nation. Just
what proportion it represents of the total research effort
depends on one's definition of the field. The Federal
research effort certainly represents something on the order
of ninety percent of the total government water research
effort counting State, local and Federal government in total.

This large Federal program is one of the many fragmented
government efforts that cut across a number of mission
oriented agencies. In the water resources field one can
identify twenty one Federal agencies which have water resources
research programs ranging from the large involvement of the
Department of the Interior, the Environmental Protection
Agency and the Department of Agriculture to the less extensive
efforts of the U.S. Army Corps of Engineers down to the other

*Luncheon Speech - First International Conference on Transfer of
Water Resources Knowledge.   3

agencies that have an important but for them, a subsidiary interest in water resources research.

Within an overall effort of this magnitude there is the possibility that some duplication might occur as well as there are opportunities for cooperation between agencies. These were recognized in the water resources field when the President's Science Adviser, in his capacity as Chairman of the Federal Council for Science and Technology, set up in 1963 the Committee on Water Resources Research with the broad charge to coordinate the overall Federal program in water resources research. Coordination can result from a highly integrated and managed effort. This approach would require considerable expenditure of staff time as well as the necessary authority for the manager. Alternatively the management by exception concept can be used where programs which are appropriate, well-managed, and clearly not over-lapping are virtually left alone and attention is directed to opportunities to institute cooperative efforts between agencies and to guard against wasteful duplication. This latter course has been the approach taken by the Committee on Water Resources Research.

Is There a Program of Federal Water Resources Research?

In the sense of a highly managed, integrated effort in water resources research there is no Federal program but rather a collection of individual agency programs, each pursuing an objective which is related to the mission of the agency undertaking the effort. Prior to the enactment of the Water Resources Research Act in 1964 it was a mistake to think there was a Federal program in water resources research. However, the enactment of that legislation was with the understanding that the research supported would be generally responsive to the needs of the water resources field and not narrowly related to the mission of the sponsor-ing agency, namely the Department of the Interior. Through this the Federal effort has been integrated to a large extent. As you know, the program of water resources research supported through that office is carried out by many universities and contractors throughout the country. I regard it as a gap-filling mechanism.

With the cooperation of the Committee on Water Resources Research, a short range assessment is made of where added research efforts are needed to round out the program and fill in any gaps which may occur in and between the mission-oriented activities of the federal agencies. Many gaps have been identified by the Office of Water Resources Research and money accordingly directed to this. One of these is the Urban Water Resources Research Program, which has had strong support from OWRR and OWRR in this has had the backing

of the Committee on Water Resources Research. This is just
one example of an identified area which was not being pursued
by a federal agency but was seen as an important one in the
overall spectrum of water resources research needs of the
nation.

Is There a Goal for Our Water Resources Research Program?

In a sense of a goal or end point which will be arrived
at, there is no goal. Trying to actually define a goal of
a research program can be an exercise in futility although
we could express the goal of our program as being to provide
the research necessary to assure an appropriate water resources
program for the nation. Such a goal statement is not very
helpful in judging a specific research project. Research
projects therefore must be judged on a more pragmatic basis
which recognizes that water is not an end in itself but a
means to an end. That end may be a better quality of life
for our people through better food and fiber supplies, through
enhanced recreation opportunities, protection from flood
hazards, etc.

In its simplest form, the notion of water resources
would seem to refer to making use of the water as a physical
entity in a consumptive way as we might with other resources
which are allocated and used up. But water is a multi-
purpose renewing resource and increasingly the capacity of
water to assimilate the wastes of our civilization is becoming
important to us. That assimilation capacity is a resource
which also can be allocated, however, the allocation of that
resource and the management of the demands placed upon it
raise complex issues in our overall water resources management
strategy which merit attention of research.

In other contexts, water and the management of it is
just one of the many parts of a highly complex situation.
For instance, in an urban area, water affords opportunities
for recreation at the same time flood plain zoning is a
response to a water resource problem, and through this a water
resource policy can infringe on land use policy. Also in
urban areas, the problems of water supply, drainage, and
waste disposal are all magnified on account of the concentration of population yet even then water management is only
one facet of the urban complex.

Over the years we have evolved in Federal government
and other places an allocation of responsibility for the
various activities involved in handling our water resources
and the research related to it. From a distance this would
appear to be a fairly stable pattern, but at closer quarters
we can see this is in a continual state of flux.

The Federal Water Resources Research Effort

The magnitude of the Federal research effort can be seen from two different viewpoints. First, there is the size of the total effort in water resources research. This has responded in greater or less degree as the other Federal activities in research have prospered or otherwise. Today it is higher than its ever been, being approximately one hundred fifty million dollars per year. The justification of that figure being larger or smaller must be related to the overall Federal budget and the various competing demands on the finite Federal purse. Naturally those within the field of water resources research are always well aware of new opportunities for spending research dollars which are expected to have a high payoff in terms of results and the effect of those results on the efficiency of Federal activities in water resources. Secondly, others see water quality research planning, urban water resources research, etc., all as separate problems each having its own justification for the present and proposed funding levels. Within our research effort in water, the distribution of the funds which are devoted to water resources research is perhaps a more important issue than the overall sum of these efforts. Under some idealized system of allocation of community resources we would allocate our total resources in such a way as to maximize our goal. While we can pursue rational approaches as far as they will go, they will never take us to a final answer in allocating community resources, Federal resources, or even water resources research dollars. I believe that the best way in which we can allocate our research dollars is to use the past as our guide, and rely on informed judgment, which should be fortified with whatever facts can be made available.

Over a period of time we have evolved a distribution of our research dollars, allocating it between applied research where the payoff may be confidently expected and pure research where the payoff is less immediate in both time and possibly place. In the Federal government, while the research that is carried out is mission oriented and nominally noncompeting, it should not be overlooked that there is an element of competition between Federal agencies. This is a healthy, vitalizing force to the extent that it exists today. For instance, in many ways the missions of the Bureau of Reclamation and the Corps of Engineers involve similar problems in building major water retaining structures. This competition provides a stimulus for excellence and from a community point of view, is an important motivating force. Similarly, the water quality related aspects of water quality planning and construction and the relationship of this to comprehensive planning of water resources can involve both the Corps of Engineers and the Environmental Protection Agency. While the activities in all of these agencies represent good professional practice,

there are discernable differences in approach and these
differences are supported by their respective adherents.
Technological progress results from this interaction.

Without sounding complacent, I believe that the water
resources research in the United States is equalled by no
other nation. Obviously,somebody is doing something right.
We have a good system, we shouldn't try to change it just
for the sake of change.

If we look back over water resources research, we can
see that from year to year the Federal programs change by
incremental amounts. New topics come into agency programs,
some topics rise in importance and others fall. The fact that
a problem is falling in research support can indicate one of
two things. Either the research goal has been achieved or
a reassessment of the funds previously invested in that topic
are considered to be better reinvested elsewhere.

While incremental change takes place from year to year
in Federal research, it should be noted that big changes in
research support or whole new programs have not come from
within the agencies by internal processes but rather have
come from the outside through legislative or political action.
For instance, the program of the Office of Saline Water
represented a step-function in the funding of federal water
resources research. This came through legislative action.
Similarly, the Office of Water Resources Research was set
up through legislative action. Water resources issues
presently before the congress similarly could produce step-
functions in the funding of water resources research.
Candidates for this kind of action might be the Water Pollution Control Act Amendments of 1972, and the drinking water
legislation as well as the Environmental Institute proposal
all of which await final Congressional action.

Setting Water Resources Research Priorities

As part of the Committee on Water Resources Research's
attention to our overall posture in water resources research,
it has been decided that a statement reflecting current 1972
opportunities for research should be made. For quite some time
now the Committee has been considering making a major statement
on research priorities and has experimented with a number of
ways for grappling with this. It first examined in depth a
number of specific problem areas looking at the on-going
research and the problems that it should be addressing.
Examining some of the parts of water resources research will
give a great deal of knowledge about those parts but the
Committee recognized that the totality of the problem should
also receive some attention. Accordingly, the Committee
examined the feasibility of a systematic examination of

needed research. This approach is intellectually appealing and the Committee did over a period develop a method which it believes could achieve that end. However, lacking the resources to pursue research needs in this rational but experimental manner the Committee has logically fallen back on organizing the best informed opinion and synthesizing this into a comprehensive review. This process is presently going on.

In considering the question of research priorities, COWRR has implicitly developed a number of fundamental concepts on which this is based. First, while there are important problems ahead in water resources, there are no crisis which cannot be handled by suitable and timely action. This has been the case in the past and it is believed that this kind of balance can be maintained in the future. Secondly, this process of keeping our water resource problems at bay has not been achieved by inaction but by constant action. One is reminded of the Queen in Alice in Wonderland who had to run as hard as possible to stay in the same place. Thirdly, that the notion of a research "need" can be misleading if that research need implies necessity for the research. Rather, I prefer to talk about research opportunities as a means of developing research priorities. Today we can carry out all of the functions we need to in water resources at some cost in energy, money, or degradation of the environment. If through research we can reduce these costs and the expected reductions are in excess of the research costs then this is an opportunity worth grasping. If we do not grasp it and the opportunity is lost, the community thereby undergoes considerable cost. Some of the costs we might incur through a strategy of this kind are incalculable if there is no way back such as, if the environmental quality of a particular place would be destroyed and a means of restoring it does not exist. Sometimes a research opportunity is the last link in an important chain and unless this last link is forged the whole value of the chain is unavailable to us. However, if there is only one last link in a chain we should beware of justifying all links as if they were last links otherwise we are guilty of double counting the benefits.

In talking of a research program we should be careful not to confuse the problems to which we should like to have an answer but see no way ahead, with problems that are eminently researchable. A good research program cannot be built out of important problems if they are not amenable to research. The alchemists of old who wanted to transmute lead into gold and those who yearned for the perpetual motion machine were addressing important problems which if they could be solved would be very valuable. However, for us at least in the terms they saw them, these are not problems and have no place in a research program. In other words, a

8

research program should consist of things which are at least
believed to be achievable. Achieving them may be a very
exacting task and we may even set our sights somewhere alittle
beyond where we think we can in fact get with today's technology.
But reality is what we work with and we must be controlled by
in setting our research goals.

Problem Identification

Thinking about what is our whole water resources strategy
is so large a problem that it can best be approached by
partializing it - by looking at the pieces and examining each
in some detail. But what are the appropriate pieces into which
to break our water resources research effort? Some years ago
the Committee on Water Resources Research set up ten categories
into which it divides the efforts of the various Federal
agencies. These are: (1) the nature of water, which deals
with water as a substance; (2) water cycle, which is essentially
the hydrological cycle; (3) water supply augmentation and
conservation; (4) water quantity management and control; (5)
water quality management and protection; (6) water resources
planning; (7) resources data; (8) engineering works; (9)
manpower grants and facilities; and (10) scientific and
technical information. For comparing various mission-oriented
agency programs, these categories have proved quite useful
and are used in each annual report of the Committee on Water
Resources Research. However, as a framework for seeing
research problems, they have not been all that useful, as
some problems will cut right across the categories. For
instance, urban water resources research is involved in a
number of categories, as is comprehensive planning for
water quantity and quality management. The problem of heated
water discharge is likewise related to several of these
categories, and so on. Thus the Committee has developed a
problem-oriented look at the field while bearing in mind the
usefulness of the categories for cataloging, recording,
budgeting and the like.

Before coming to problems which appear to be the most in
need of attention at this time it should be noted what control the Committee on Water Resources Research has over
Federal spending. There is no overall manager of federal
water resources research and probably there should not be one.
Our heterogenous, pragmatic way of dealing with problems,
using COWRR to give some semblance of order, and using OWRR
and possibly other agencies to fill the gaps is a system which
for all its shortcomings does work. In this context, who
listens to COWRR's pronouncements? The Committee on Water
Resources Research is in effect a coordination body which
simply offers advice, not about agency roles but focuses on
problems in water resources which require research. It has
no power to direct agencies to devote their attention to

these nor has it any direct influence on the budgetary
process which diverts funds to these topics. However, COWRR
believes that the respect for and the force of its opinion,
means that it is listened to and to the extent that it strikes
a responsive chord is taken notice of. COWRR is also the
source of much informal advice received by the Executive
Office of the President, through its Chairman who has always
been a member of the President's Science Adviser's staff.

If asked COWRR would say that the overall level of effort
put in Federal water resources research could be profitably
expanded as there are many research topics of importance which
require research funding and which are not presently receiving
it to the extent they should. The problems that seem important
from the 1972 perspective will clearly be an outgrowth of
problems in the past. In 1966 "The Ten Year Program of
Federal Water Resources Research" saw that additional research
would be very effective and very productive in the field of
water resources planning. This statement resulted in more
effort being diverted to that particular area. At the same
time, additional needed effort in water pollution control
technology was also identified. Research on conservation of
water in various uses were seen as an important area of
research, as payoff could be great in terms of water saved.
In 1966 COWRR well ahead of the fad of the 1970's saw that the
ecological impact of water development merited increased
attention, as well as another piece of that same problem
namely the effect of man's activity on water. These are the
water resource interactions which now we would see as
environmental impact.

The cost of any project in water or otherwise will greatly
affect whether or not we will be able to purchase it within
a limited budget. Efforts to reduce costs will increase the
availability of water resource developments and additional
research on this topic was pressed by the Committee in 1966.
At that time too, attention was drawn to the potential of
unconventional or far out ideas which at first sight might
seem unlikely of early application but which in fact contain
the germ of a good idea. What was far out in 1966 is probably
still far out, although ideas do attain a measure of
respectability over a period of time.

What then is COWRR's assessment of the 1972 priority
items for water resources research? Water resources technology
for handling and dealing with water as a physical entity is
fairly mature art. However, refinements are still available
and I know we will go on to make important developments in
the handling of our water resource both as regards surface
water as well as our ground water resource where our technology
is less mature at this time.

What also seems important are the interactions between our water activities with other related activities. Water planning in isolation makes little sense. Planning is for a social purpose and results in the expenditure of money. Hence, the socio-economic issues in resources planning are important yet they are understood only dimly. Another part of that interaction is that of water resources planning with land use planning particularly in the urban area. Water resources is just a part of the urban problem - a very important part - and those of us who have expertise in water resources handling must learn to work with and appreciate the problems that are special to the urban areas as well as being able to meet those general water problems which are often seen in their most extreme form in urban areas. Another important problem for the future is the impact of water resources developments of all kinds, both from quantity and quality points of view on other parts of our environment. All these topics are related to the planning process and research is needed so that water resources planning can be both efficient in itself and take into account all of the interactions which are inevitable in the realization of a water resources plan.

The Federal Government is presently spending and will probably spend even more on water quality hardware. The magnitude of this program as being comparable to the space program, is scarcely recognized by many people. However, as it will be dispersed across the nation instead of being centralized it probably will retain a low profile even when the spending is much greater than now. However, it represents a great investment in technology and it is important that the technology purchased be the best that we are able to provide. Spending Federal dollars on white elephants is something we must avoid to the greatest extent possible. At the same time our concern for healthy drinking water in face of the increasing problems posed by exotic chemicals in our environment means that additional research will be needed to take care of the increasing problems that providing a good drinking water supply is bringing.

Even though we are some way from the limits of our total water resource we are still using a considerable percentage of the water we have available especially in the areas where irrigation is developed. If we could save some of that water by more water efficient practices, then these conservation means would make a lot more water available. The opportunities for saving water in the agriculture sector are large. In the same way, more recycling of industrial water could also produce important changes if we can find cost effective ways of improving our technology there.

Hydrology is a topic which has received a great deal of research and the process, at least from some points of view, is fairly well understood. However, the predictive ability we have in hydrology is still something which would be very valuable to us if it could be improved. Research clearly is the way ahead here.

This country is undergoing increasing problems of erosion of its lands and sedimentation of its streams. Compensating, at least in part, for some of the sedimentation by dredging is a costly operation and the degradation of our land is important too. This can be seen as a water quality problem; an interactive problem between land and water use that has considerable environmental impact. Research is needed to enable us to get better control over this problem.

Our investment in water resources hardware has been increasing over the years and our stock of this has been going up all the time. The operating and maintenance and costs of the facilities on an annual basis is becoming a larger and larger part of our water resources budget. While operation and maintenance costs may seem mundane, the opportunities for savings here are becoming greater as the expenditures increase. Operation and maintenance encompasses a multitude of problems and research in this area could help us keep down the cost of operating and maintaining our water resources facilities.

Water resources research as well as water resources activities all depend on data collected in the field. This country has had an on-going data collection program for many years. It is a costly program and it is important that we have one that is responsive to our present and prospective future needs. Research on just how much data should be collected for present and future demands in view of the uncertainties of the future, is very important, as is the development of instrumentation to make that data collection more effective and more immediate.

Earlier on it was mentioned that research is not an end in itself but a means to an end. Perhaps the most important end is improving professional practice by making available new and better ways to achieve our objectives or making new objectives available that were previously not sought because they were not available. The results of research are zero unless they find a place in either future research or in practice. To disseminate research results we have a number of conventional processes whereby we do this formal instruction, professional association, continuing education, etc. Over the years we have given a great deal of attention to technology transfer, research dissemination, or whatever term you prefer. Additional research on the processes of

12

research dissemination is important if our research program is to have a logical link to professional practice. There are many innovative actions we could take in technology transfer in addition to the more traditional ways most of us have used. The advanced state of water resource technology shows that our system does in fact work but I am convinced there are opportunities to make it work better.

Any discussion of technology transfer is incomplete if it takes account simply of transfer of research to our professionals within the United States. There is an international dimension which should not be overlooked. The international Hydrological Decade which goes from 1965 to 1974 and which focused on scientific research has in effect been a technology transfer mechanism of considerable importance. Through other multi-national programs in the water field such as the 1967 Water for Peace Conference, or the recent UN Conference on the Human Environment research dissemination on topics to an international scale has taken place. While the technology transfer content of these conferences has been a part of its objective, we have recently in this country developed a number of bi-lateral agreements with foreign countries. The most recent ones of these is that between the U.S. and the USSR. Under this there are to be cooperative activities in water resources. Through this program it seems likely that both countries are going to be intimately involved in a mutual action oriented program which indirectly is going to transfer some of our technology to them and some of their technology to us. While the objectives of such programs are mutual research or mutual activities, in effect these are technology transfer programs using the pattern of getting two parties who wish to interact in technology transfer, to work together on a joint problem. This is the mechanism which will also be very effective in technology transfer on the national scene.

In conclusion, our water resources research program in the past was a pragmatic response to agency problems, at least from the Federal point of view. This program was rather fragmented but these fragments have been built into a structure by explicit actions of the Federal government. The Federal government through coordination effort tends to keep an eye on where this heterogeneous program ought to be going and which gaps should be filled in. Periodically statements are made on problem areas which are under-programmed and one such statement is in the final stages of preparation at this time. Some of the topics that appear to be candidates for featuring in that report have been mentioned.

FROM RESEARCH TO REALITY

BY

Glenn E. Schweitzer
Director, Office of Science and Technology
Agency for International Development

Science and the Needs of the Day

"Science can only give us the tools in a box ... but of
what use to us are miraculous tools until we have mastered
the human, cultural use of them?" These words of Frank Lloyd
Wright aptly describe the theme of this symposium -- to transfer the potential of dramatic scientific achievements of
recent years into practical benefits for all of us.

A pragmatic approach to relating science to society now
permeates all aspects of our governmental science policy and,
as reflected here in Colorado, is adding a new dimension to
scientific meetings throughout the world. The President's
March 16th message on science and technology stated the issue
quite succinctly:

"The mere act of scientific discovery alone is not
enough. Even the most important breakthrough will have
little impact on our lives unless it is put to use -- and
putting an idea to use is a far more complex process than
has often been appreciated. To accomplish this transformation, we must combine the genius of invention with
the skills of entrepreneurship, management, marketing
and finance."

Many scientists believe that Government bureaucrats are
becoming overzealous in their efforts to demonstrate the
benefits of science by attempting prematurely to translate
research results into practical reality. The purists will
argue that there is no better way to sacrifice the quality of
research than to subvert legitimate basic inquiry into more
glamorous applied activities of immediate payoff. However,
most of us will agree that we have been long overdue in our
attempts to focus the relatively untapped warehouse of research results more sharply on everyday needs.

During the past several days you have been addressing
many of the pressing problems of more effective utilization
of our planet's water resources -- resources essential to
sustain life. The dual aspects of this symposium -- trans-

*Banquet Speech - First International Conference on Transfer of
Water Resources Knowledge.

lating laboratory experience to practice and transferring research results from developed to developing areas -- wound around the hydrology theme underscore the very down-to-earth orientation of this audience.

My remarks this evening will be limited largely to the transfer of skills and knowledge from developed to developing countries, recognizing that the transfer is usually a two-way street with the developed countries gaining more than they realize from collaborative efforts. However, I will not confine my comments to hydrology but rather talk about the scientific enterprise in somewhat broader terms.

A Technology Transfer Framework

While technology is but one of the determinants of the rate and direction of development, it is frequently a key determinant as to the competitiveness of products, the commercial viability of processes, and the efficient utilization of capital and manpower resources. In changing their traditional methods, the developing countries often have to use the immediately available technologies, even when they are unsuited to their economic and social conditions. They might otherwise forego important development opportunities since they lack the capability for devising an indigenous technology or for appropriately adapting one from foreign sources. At the same time, the transfer of technologies from the advanced countries often has built-in mechanisms and time elements which hinder modification or adaptation. Domestic policies in the developing countries and the conditions attached to foreign aid frequently make capital available on subsidized terms and thus encourage excessive use of scarce resources of capital and underutilization of abundant manpower resources. Among the consequences of adoption of inappropriate technologies have been the growing lack of capital, particularly foreign exchange, the rapidly increasing rate of unemployment, and the inability to develop industrial skills at the rate required.

With regard to technology transfer through the private sector, it is tempting to argue that the best hope for the developing countries lies in their acquisition of technologies that are already applied in more advanced countries, and that it is a mistake and waste of their resources for them to go for research and technical development on their own. There are several reasons, however, why the developing countries clearly should not rely entirely on foreign sources of technology, although they can continue to gain great advantages by using private investment and licensing and the many other means of acquiring foreign know-how.

15

It is difficult for a country that does not itself possess a certain number of trained scientific and technical personnel to know what usable technology exists elsewhere, to understand it, to adapt it to the country's special needs or peculiar conditions, to repair and maintain the necessary equipment, or indeed to operate it. If a country builds up its own scientific and technical capacity, it is in a much better position to utilize what exists elsewhere. Lack of appropriately trained persons is often an obstacle to the wider application of technology that is already known and to some extent used in a country. In addition, each country is better able to hold its place in international competition if it has the capacity to introduce innovations (new products or less costly methods of production) based on existing technology.

Finally, the foreign technology is often adapted to very different basic conditions, such as a relative shortage of labor, abundant supplies of capital and a large market. Developing countries, facing almost diametrically different conditions, will often find that a variant of the technology of the developed countries, or perhaps an altogether different technology, is more suited to their conditions. But the choice of an appropriate technology is not readily achieved by a country that lacks indigenous research and development facilities. This research and development structure needs to be heavily weighted towards the problems of production. In many cases, existing institutions need to be brought into closer relation with the country's actual agriculture and industry, and new institutions should, from the beginning, be strongly oriented towards local practical problems and to meeting the needs of local users.

Not the least of the reasons for developing countries to develop their own scientific and technological base for adapting, disseminating and as necessary inventing technologies is that it provides them with a more secure technical and psychological base for expanding productive private trade and investment relations with the more developed countries. The developed countries have the strongest and stablest economic relations with countries in this situation.

Technical Information as a Technology Transfer Mechanism

Technical information has often been called the lifeblood of development by information specialists. Clearly, technical information can serve an important function in technology transfer. However, its impact on development has frequently been sharply limited due to inadequate screening of information that is available, failure to package the information in bundles that can be digested and used, and absence of dissemination mechanisms that can facilitate access to information by the users. More often than not, it is assumed that all types of technical information are needed and will be useful in developing countries and that a flow of information can not help but solve problems. But this assumption needs to be questioned.

When is technical information really needed and when is it just nice to have? Our current experience in developing countries indicates that as long as technical information is provided free, the appetite is unlimited, but as soon as even a very modest surcharge is imposed, the demand falls off rapidly. While foreign currency restrictions pose an obstacle to acquiring publications, there are modest funds available in almost every country for technical information and if a document is sufficiently important, funds will be found.

On the other hand, technical information should play an important role in the formal and informal education process. Information in support of education must be subsidized. However, I would argue that in this area also there has not been as judicious a use of available funds in the selection process as there might be.

It would seem that a fundamental principle of the technology transfer strategy of developed countries should be to facilitate developing country access to the relevant results of the hundreds of billions of dollars which have been invested in research and technology during the past 25 years. The printed word should play a key role in such a strategy. If the printed word is to be most useful, however, it must be collected and presented in such a way that it can be useful to specialists in developing countries who are faced with a whole set of different socio-economic conditions that exists in the environment where the research was carried out. Also, technical information should be used as but one element of the overall technology transfer package -- a package that should feature personal interaction between the developed and developing country specialists. Such interaction is essential to point the way to the most useful information sources, to clarify the subtleties of the printed word, and to make technical information truly useful.

Absorptive Capacity of the Developing Countries

As we all know, the extent that developing countries use research and technology developed abroad is directly related to the "absorptive capacity" of these countries -- the readiness and capability of specialists and institutions to adapt, apply, and disseminate the technology. This capacity is important whether the technology is being transferred in the form of equipment, as technical information, or through exchanges of people. It embodies a capability to recognize the alternative technical approaches that are or could be available; to choose the technology that makes the most sense technically, economically, and socially; if necessary, to adapt the technology to local conditions; to understand the direct impact and the more subtle long-term impacts of the technology; and to operate and maintain the technology.

The institutional orientation is often the decisive aspect of a developing country's capability to absorb technology. For example, there are a large number of developing country students at most of our universities. Right now, there are more than 12,000 developing country engineering students at U. S. graduate schools. But are their courses of study truly of relevance to interests back home, or will they give further impetus to the brain-drain? While it is difficult for a U. S. university on an institutional basis to make sudden changes in the orientation of the content of its academic curriculum, individual professors and instructors can introduce elements into their courses which will enrich the experiences of developing country specialists and allow them to return home better prepared to face the realities of development.

Many of our university professors maintain collaborative linkages with a large number of researchers abroad, including colleagues in developing countries. The substantive aspects of these linkages -- exchange of technical reports, joint research efforts -- can do much to influence the orientation of research activities in developing countries.

Last year, A.I.D. initiated a new program entitled, "Scientists and Engineers in Economic Development," carried out with the assistance of the National Science Foundation. Under this program, U. S. university professors can apply for financial support for travel and research in developing countries, provided the host institution will pay local costs and the proposed activities are relevant to the host country's development priorities. We have been pleased indeed by the excellent response to this program -- a response characterized by determination on the part of the U. S. scientists to bend their expertise to development priorities, and a readiness on the part of developing countries to share the costs of the program. Therefore, we are doubling the size of the program this year.

Bringing Remote Sensing Down to Earth

Remote sensing can serve as a specific example to elaborate some of the previous points.

Many papers have been written in recent years about the potential of remote sensing for development. Until very

18

recently, most of these were cast in vague terms and rested largely on an intuitive conviction that this new technology has many high pay-off applications. With the launching of the ERTS-A satellite, a closer look is now being directed to the utility of this technology. However, even if the information to be acquired can be shown to be of the highest priority, the data will be of little use unless the developing countries are equipped to interpret and use it in an integrated fashion with overall developmental activities.

We now know that even the poorest countries can participate in satellite programs. It is not true that computers, air conditioned rooms, and elaborate equipment are essential components of a program to derive useful data from satellite imagery. When properly designed, experiments can be carried out on a low cost budget, and I am optimistic that future operational satellite programs will similarly provide for participation by countries which are short on investment resources. A well trained hydrologist, geologist, or agriculturist with minimal photo interpretation experience should be able to derive some useful information from satellite imagery using only a light table and manual plotting equipment. Indeed one of the advantages of satellite imagery is the concentration of large quantities of data on a single photograph, thus easing the correlation and scanning aspects of data reduction and interpretation problems. In short, I am not suggesting that expensive interpretation equipment is an unnecessary luxury. Rather, there are alternative approaches-- well known to you--which can be effectively employed with a little imagination, perseverance, and determination. Relatively primitive data interpretation techniques can be particularly useful when existing information is in extremely short supply.

Eighteen countries where A.I.D. conducts programs have approved experiments aboard the ERTS satellite. Let me just cite the case of one country--namely, Mali--to illustrate how a nation long on aspirations but short on trained talent and investment resources hopes to benefit from the imagery. As you know, NASA will provide black and white prints, color mosaics, and transparencies to the ERTS investigators. Malian scientists--several hydrologists, geologists, and agriculturists--using only a light table will search the imagery for leads to mineral deposits, underground water recources, and flood patterns of the Niger River, as well as breeding grounds for desert locusts and other agricultural applications. Given the dearth of currently available data in useable form about the country, it seems clear that even the raw satellite imagery will in itself upgrade considerably the quality of geological, hydrological, and cartographic maps currently available. Interpreted data taken from the imagery should provide the basis for the investment of very limited but still significant financial resources in specific projects supported by the Government of Mali and by external assistance agencies.

With regard to low cost aircraft programs, clearly the expense of acquiring and operating the aircraft is an essential investment that is far from insignificant. Perhaps the greatest hope in reducing this expense is that military agencies throughout the developing world are gradually becoming interested in using their planes for development as well as security purposes. Under these circumstances civil agencies may be able to obtain aircraft services at acceptable costs. The problem then is outfitting the aircraft and carrying out well planned programs designed to provide useful data. Mounting cameras in a pressurized or unpressurized hull of a plane or in a wing pod, installing the camera triggering and control devices, and adapting appropriate navigation equipment to correlate aircraft location with photographic targets are important, but the techniques are well known and should not be expensive--at least in terms of foreign currency requirements. More critical are the selection of the camera and the approach to data interpretation which will provide information of genuine interest to the user organization. There are clearly tradeoffs between the type of camera employed, the altitude of the aircraft, the ground resolution desired, and the quantity and form of the data to be analyzed. Thus, in designing low cost aircraft programs, the alternatives of all elements of the entire system from data acquisition to final usage should be carefully considered.

We have recently initiated an experimental aircraft program on the island of Bali. The Indonesian Government is providing an Aerocommander which will be modified to carry relatively inexpensive, multi-spectral equipment. A modest, on-the-job training program should enable the Indonesians to interpret effectively the data to be acquired during the next 18 months in conjunction with ERTS imagery and ground truth data. While this project is principally an experiment to demonstrate the utility of low-cost aircraft programs in a developing country environment, we anticipate there will be substantial spinoff benefits for Indonesia which has given priority to integrated development of the resources of Bali.

Implications for the Science and Technology Community

Research for the sake of research is running into rougher weather every year, particularly in international development circles. No one will deny the value of research as an educational tool. However, research proposals funded on the basis of discovery of the unknown are becoming more and more scarce. There is a saying that research goes with the money, and the money is tending to congregate either around sharply oriented basic research or applied research and development.

With regard to technology transfer, scientists too often argue that their job should be limited to presentation of an idea, but that it is up to someone else to translate the idea into economic and social betterment. The economists and the users of technology, on the other hand, argue that scientists don't provide them with a usable product. It is up to the scientists to reach out in their concerns beyong the confines of science and technology, all the way to the utilization of research results if necessary. If one must divert some of his energy from doing the job he is best trained to do--the job of investigation--so be it. The scientific community has a unique sense of coherence that has largely excluded the economists and the users of technology. Now the scientific community is gradually beginning to have an effective extension arm, and this is an encouraging sign for international development.

The stakes are too high for science to become a cemetery for ideas. Rather science must be a breeding ground for infectious applications.

PROSPERING WITH UNCERTAINTY *

By

Gilbert F. White
Institute of Behavioral Science
University of Colorado

The coupling of concern with hydrologic matters on the one hand and application of knowledge to practical affairs on the other, comes at a peculiarly appropriate time in our contemporary history. It is a time, judging from my exposure to work of national governments in a number of countries, in which the regard and confidence which have been extended to those involved in water management in the design, construction, and operation of water projects is subject to a new kind of questioning. There is a new prudent criticism on the part of many sectors and constituencies which heretofore have been generally enthusiastic and supporting of the water management enterprise. This situation is reflected in the fact that the U.S. Commissioner of Reclamation in the last few years, for the first time since the Bureau of Reclamation was established in 1902, has been subject to very severe criticism, and to a defeat on a major development project proposed for the Colorado River. Ten years ago, knowledgeable people in the United States would have said that there never would be that kind of a defeat for a project that had been as carefully proposed and shepherded as was that for the two dams in the Colorado. Similarly, there now is widespread questioning in the press as to the wisdom of there having been undertaken a series of major water storage projects in the tropical world. There has been an outbreak, not only in the United States but also in other parts of the world, of articulate criticism of conventional practices with respect to stream channelization and water storage.

Perhaps this is an exaggerated view of the current situation. I think not. We have witnessed in the early 1970's a remarkable change in the regard in which water management is held. I think this peculiar situation results from a conjunction of at least five streams of thought on the world scene.

One reason is that while the sophistication of scientific investigation and engineering analysis and design has proceeded with rapidity and strength in many specialized sectors of resources management, the skill to make integrated investigations of the whole bundle of problems that are presented in any given resources management undertaking has not kept pace. In June 1972, Hurricane Agnes was the largest single natural disaster in terms of dollars damage cost in the history of the United States. It had its greatest impact in areas of the middle and north Atlantic drainage basins and the upper Ohio, which had been the subject of careful investigation and

---

*Joint Banquet Address with the Second International Hydrology Symposium.

elaborate construction programs dating from the passage of the federal Flood Control Act of 1936. Most of you know the circumstances of this disaster which some estimate reached the proportions of $3,000,000,000 in that short period of five or six days. Works which had been constructed to standard project flood dimensions were overtopped by seven feet in some places. Tens of thousands of people were evacuated, and the property damage was widespread.

Why could we have a disaster of those proportions after thirty years of careful engineering investigations, construction, and operation? It was not, I suggest, the weakness of engineering design and operation. It was a concentration upon special aspects of those engineering programs that so obscured the significance of complementary works in the field of flood warnings, land use regulations, flood proofing, and insurance that the net effect of many of the works ended up to be negative rather than positive as had been anticipated by the designers. We had with good intention and elaborate outlay of funds marshalled technical skills which because of their specialized nature and their failure to be related to complementary works were self defeating in reducing the toll of losses to the nation.

The tropical cyclone of November, 1970 occurred two years before on the shores of the Bay of Bengal which was the greatest disaster of recent decades outside the United States. There too, tremendous damage to property resulted in great loss of life. Also I think it can be said from the reports that are available, there had been careful, industrious engineering design and construction activity. There had been a highly efficient meteorological forecasting service in certain sectors. But the net effect of the application of those works was to build up the susceptibility of Bangladesh to loss of property and life of unprecedented proportions.

Whether one agrees that the engineering designs were proper designs or as thoughtful as they might have been, I think one could not disagree that the effect of concentrating on special sectors of them had, in fact, exacerbated the loss of life and property. I have in mind one small area, the islands of Char Jabbar which had been protected with levees which did not withstand the height of the incoming waters. Many of those responsible for the design will argue that they had never intended that those works would be able to withstand winds, surges, and tides of the combination that was experienced. But what was tragic about this area was that 20,000 people had been encouraged by the construction of these works to move into a hazardous zone in the desperate search for production which predominates in Bangladesh. When the cyclone hit, the accurate forecast was never broadcast. The radio station went out of activity at 11:00 p.m. according to its normal program. However, had the forecast been broadcast, there was virtually nothing that many occupants of the area could have done, for the engineering work had not provided for places of refuge, for roads of egress, nor for any kind of detailed plans for people to take intermediate sorts of emergency measures. On this one small island, 6,000 people died that night.

The Agnes and Bangladesh tropical cyclones are the two most recent and dramatic cases of the failure of specialized, internally adequate engineering enterprises. They should not be regarded as being eccentric exceptions. They reflect, rather, a general trend which one can observe in many parts of the world. Progressively increasing social losses from natural hazards of flood, drought, and other disasters of geophysical origin have, in fact, been encouraged by the construction of engineering works of a specialized character.

Along with this fact, we must place a second one which appears to be a paradox at first glance. It is that the more refined is our scientific knowledge about the nature of the world, the more uncertain is our future. Each technical development, each small nudge on the boundaries of knowledge increases our uncertainty as to what will happen next. To the extent that we open up new alternatives, to the extent we increase the number of situations in which human judgment must be exercised, to the extent we make it possible for something to go wrong, then we become less certain about what the future will bring. We must recognize that an inevitable penalty of all of the research in which we are engaged is to increase uncertainty.

How do we live with increasing uncertainty? One could take a more optimistic view and ask how do we prosper in the face of uncertainty? I'd like to come back to this when I consider one of two possible sorts of actions we ought to appraise.

A third factor at work on the world scene is that the pace of economic development in many developing countries (we should be careful not to classify developing countries as though they were all alike) is depressingly slow. In a few cases it is negative, in a number of cases it is stationary, and in many cases it is far below the expectations generated in the hopeful period of the first United Nations development decade. Not only is the pace of development low, but the gap between the rich and the poorer nations grows at an accelerating rate, so that at the end of the development decade, the absolute gap between the rich and the poor has widened in most instances far beyond the total income of the poor nations. We

24

must recognize quite soberly that we do not see any easy or early way of accelerating the rate of growth in the low income countries or of closing the gap. For the moment both trends continue.

This is highly important for those who are interested in droughts and floods, because it has been shown by some recent analyses at Clark University and elsewhere that in developing countries the proportion of the national income that is affected by fluctuations of natural phenomena amounts in some instances, to as much as two and two and one half percent. It is roughly twice as much as in high income countries. The resultant fluctuations can spell as much as half the net gain that hopeful proponents of economic growth can expect in a year. To the extent that these countries depend on water management works to buffer the effects of drought and flood, they risk the possibility of severe setbacks with extremely meager margins.

Related to this is a fourth factor, which need be mentioned only briefly, and this is the sense of environmental crisis. In some quarters it is regarded as kind of perogative or privilege of the affluent. It is nevertheless widely held in many intellectual circles around the world. It had led to questions being asked about resources management which heretofore were not posed in a serious and probing fashion. The question of what alternatives to heavy engineering investments is now raised earnestly. The question of what are the full consequences, social and ecological, of a particular project. This question is now asked with persistence whereas only six years ago they were stated, if at all, in a rather casual and at times almost trivial way. I am sure that we are all aware of this change. But are we fully aware of the new responsibility it puts on the scientist and technician involved in water development? The responsibility is to answer the questions of what are the alternatives, and what are the full consequences, knowing that in almost every instance we cannot provide a clear, unequivocal answer. In most cases the answer must be expressed in probability or uncertainty terms.

Related to this is the fifth point. It is the increased demand upon technical and professional circles to consult with the people who are directly affected by the resources management project that is being planned. In the United States, we call this community participation. We have had to adjust a very complicated set of technical procedures over the past six years to providing explicitly for consultation with groups concerned. Overseas, some observers have perhaps accurately called this the beginning of the "post-patronizing era." We had colonialism, and then we had a post-colonial period, but post-colonial may be better termed the patronizing period. We are moving out of patronizing into a relationship of equality and collaboration. These did not prevail as long as professionals in high income countries thought of themselves as sharing their know-how, helping people do things the way they do them, and building up educational and technical capacity by their standards. This change, too, is leading people in developing countries to ask different questions of the experts than they would have thought of posing as recently as ten years ago.

What does one make of these trends if one shares the belief that they are at work and that they account for a basic revision in the stance of the professional engineer or scientist on the world water scene? They suggest two kinds of efforts that it seems to me we are all going to have to make in the years immediately ahead. One I would call an effort to map reliability and the other an effort to chart routes to achieve goals.

Good topographic sheets often carry at the bottom a small inset showing the relative reliability of the observations on which this is based. We see much less frequently on reports in the water field figuratively smaller maps that show the relative reliability of the findings presented as professional judgments. I've had occasion in the last year, in connection with a review of experience with stream channelization in the United States, to observe this. One picks up a report from a confident, responsible agency on a proposed channelization project. It contains an estimate of expected flows of water in the stream to be channelized. It also contains estimates of necessary alterations of channel cross section and pattern in order to accommodate these flows. What it rarely does is indicate that the estimate of flow in terms of either historical record or some sort of stochastic analysis, is of quite a different order of reliability than the hydraulic estimate of changes required in the stream channel. The kinds of models we have for predicting channel characteristics are of a basically different character than the models we use in certain hydrologic analysis. Do we find that in a report? And if we find it is it in a form that anyone who is not a member of the fraternity can understand? While dealing with quite different levels of reliability we have not been effective in conveying this difference to those who must make or judge decisions. We need now to cultivate improved ways of explaining differences in reliability.

Inevitably, this leads us to trying to explain the concept of probability and uncertainty. How do we do this? I remember talking to a man on the flood plain of the Housatonic River, after the floods of 1955, who was building a house on the foundations of the house that had been swept away by the first

26

flood that summer. I asked if he thought there was any risk
involved in building again on that place, and he said no, that,
as a matter of fact, he had a very good friend in the U.S.
Geological Survey who had assured him that there had been two
floods that summer with a return interval of one hundred years.
He didn't intend to build a house that would last two hundred
years he said, and he felt quite safe about the enterprise.
That is plain misinterpretation of adequate information,
poorly communicated. There are other factors involved in
interpretation.

I asked a man building a new apartment building on the
Boulder flood plain if he thought there was any risk of flood.
He replied he had no risk at all. I asked him if he knew about
the flood of 1894. He said, of course, he knew about it, the
flood of 1894 had come up chest-high where he was standing. How
then, I said, could there be no risk. Well, he said there will
be no risk, because he would sell the building within six
months. From his standpoint, he was entirely correct. How do
we interpret to him or to the society that is going to bury
their dead and pay $5,000 at 1% interest loans to people who
occupy that building after the next flood that there was no
risk.

We know too, that people confronted with threats for
which they have no ready means of coping, deny the threat. The
best known of these threats is a nuclear bomb. One simply
doesn't discuss it. If pressed, people may move from denial
to a special kind of interpretation. Some years ago a
colleague at the University of Chicago asked people at the
busiest shopping intersection if they thought there was any
chance that there some day would be an atom bomb explosion in
that area. About half replied there might be an explosion and
the remainder were uncertain. Then the question asked was,
if there were to be an explosion, where do you think you would
be three days later? At this point there was no real uncertainty in response: 95% of the respondants said that
three days later, they would be helping bury the dead.

People have other modes of response: They fasten on to a
deterministic explanation such as floods occurring every ten
years, droughts every seventeen years, and so on. That does
a great deal to reduce tension and stress. If we are more
professional, we may have something like a maximum probable
flood which eliminates a great deal of the uncertainty as to
the possibility of there being a larger event. How do we
explain this to others?

The first question I would like to leave with you is, how
do we improve our means of figuratively drawing a kind of
reliability map when we bring our findings and recommendations

to those who must make choices. This applies not only in the hydrologic field, but in biological and related physical fields.

The second question grows out of this and has to do with a sort of network analysis. For a number of years I have worked on studies of side effects of large reservoirs in tropical areas of Africa. In each of these cases, including Lake Nasser, Kariba, and Kainji and so on, the UNDP organized interdisciplinary investigations to identify the consequences and deal with them. An extremely difficult part of this exercise-quite aside from getting the ichthyologist to talk to a hydrologist when there is a sociologist present-is tracing out what the professional investigator assumes to be the causitive links that will assure the application of the findings which he generates.

There is a strong tendency, having arrived at the best available judgment as to the probable occurrence of floods at a certain magnitude to leave it up to somebody else to make use of the estimate. In turn, whoever makes use of the estimate, say in the design of a spillway, then expects that somebody else will deal with the problem of what will happen downstream when that amount of water passes over the spillway. Whoever deals with the channel downstream, will expect someone else to cope with the question of social readjustment to these flows of water. I have yet to find in a comprehensive engineering document a precise charting of what it is assumed will have to be done all the way along the line in terms of both technical and social readjustments in order to attain the social aims that project is expected to serve. It can be done: the essential paths of analysis can be identified. But it is an extraordinarily rare practice. It needs to be done regularly and systematically.

Many of us suffer from the complaint from which the proverbial economist suffered. Three professors are on the desert island, they have only one tin of food, and they can't get into it. The physicist says, I will build a fire and heat it so it will explode. The engineer says he will take it to the top of a big rock, and drop it. The economist says I can think of something much better than that, now first assume we have a can opener. In a sense, most of us follow the same practice, we assume somebody else is going to do something, usually rationally. This may seem to dispose of our responsibility. We now need-recognizing it will take long and is extremely difficult-to find a practicable way each time we produce a report to show all steps that are necessary to achieve the aims which we claim to advance. Each step will involve a probability estimate. Thus, the estimate of reliability goes hand in hand with charting the routes to social goals. We are going to have to learn to live much more intelligently with probability and uncertainty. The more all of us work, the greater the amount of uncertainty we shall have to live with. The trick and the challenge is to learn to prosper with it.

SESSION I

PRINCIPLES AND MECHANICS OF INFORMATION RETRIEVAL

Chairman: E.V. Richardson

Rapporteur: Donald C. Taylor

● *The section concerns itself with some general principles of information storage and retrieval and the development of systems for information exchange and communication. The bibliographical explosion and the need for timely and easily accessible information provide the basis for the establishment of specialized centers and services. A special case of the application of economic analysis in the paper of Warford and Whitford serves as an example of the transfer of economic theory to practice.*

SESSION I: PRINCIPLES AND MECHANICS OF INFORMATION RETRIEVAL

Rapporteur: Donald C. Taylor
Manager, Research Services
American Society of Civil Engineers

At a major agricultural education center like Colorado
State University, often called a "cow college," it seems to me
it would have been more appropriate to call this a conference
on information insemination rather than dissemination. It
would not only have demonstrated more aggressive intention on
the part of the Conference Planning Committee, but also made
it more interesting for the reporters.

The purpose of this session is to discuss the principles
and mechanics of information retrieval. This will be done
considering the need for water resources information systems,
by reviewing descriptions of various types of information
retrieval systems currently in operation and by examining
methods by which new information is developed and placed
into practice.

The availability of information storage and retrieval
systems is like eating ice-cream. If you have never had it
you never want it, but once you have had it you always want it.
Only one to two decades ago, except perhaps in the medical and
biological science areas, there were very limited information
storage and retrieval systems available on a continuing basis
to the physical science, engineering and social science
communities. There were, of course, traditional efforts made
to produce bibliographies, listings of research in progress,
reports on specific areas of interests, state-of-the-art
reports and many other one time special effort projects. All
these services were very useful and practical when the extent
of available literature was small for any one subject area and
did not change substantially over several years.

With the information explosion bibliographical and other
information listings became out of date almost as soon as the
work to prepare them was completed and they were published.
Computerized systems of information exchange changed this
picture by offering a method of greatly reducing the time span
of assembling and printing current bibliographical and other
information listings. With the advent of computers, and
trained managerial and professional people capable of understanding and exploiting them, we are in fact approaching a
time when information systems are not only available, but they
are becoming economically cheaper to use than not to use.

Pioneer efforts for the development of information
systems were often conducted in the face of a great deal of
opposition from top management and budget controllers who said

31

things like, "Let's not spend time and money on things others are doing, let's use it to get our own job done." What they are now finding out is that their own job gets done faster, cheaper and better by a full awareness of other related successful and unsuccessful efforts on the same problem. In other words, now that they have all tasted ice-cream they are finding they cannot do without it.

The Need for Information Exchange

In their paper on "Economic Analysis and Municipal Water Supply in Developing Countries," Warford and Whitford [1]* point out a typical problem in regard to the reluctance to use up-to-date management techniques due to lack of understanding and therefore mistrust of new ideas and procedures. Under present methods of information transfer it would take at least a whole generation of newly educated professionals and a change of top management to even allow the consideration of change in procedures. Better, lower cost, readily available and accepted systems of information retrieval would not only shorten the time between the application of research to practice, but also promote a more widespread use of accounting and other management processes. Already accepted in other areas, these benefits would be valuable in more developed countries as well as, and even more so, in less developed countries.

In the First International Conference on Transfer of Water Resources Knowledge, we are going to find that there are many tested and operable systems of information storage and retrieval that are available in developed countries. The same needs exist, if not even more so, in lesser developed countries. In many cases since the systems mechanics have been worked out it would not take more than an extension of present services available in developed countries to serve others. If ways of doing this feasibly and economically can be inspired at this First Conference it has the potential for making a most valuable contribution to everyone in the world concerned with water resources development.

The transfer of water resources knowledge in general can take on the form of personal visits on the one hand to highly automated selective dissemination systems on the other. The purpose of this session is to deal with those systems and problems thereof that are geared to provide a continuing standardized service that many users can interpret and employ in their various areas of practice. These type of systems usually require substantial investments in time and money to establish them as a useful service and continue their operation while there is a need for the service. Before the decision to

*Numerals in parentheses refer to corresponding items in the Brief Summaries of Session papers attached.

develop and employ them is made, considerable soul searching
has to take place on the part of the investor and the user.

The purpose of more effective information exchange is
two-fold. One is that it provides more efficient use of
already available information thereby eliminating duplication
of effort and the second is that it provides a mechanism for
identifying gaps in knowledge and thereby determines research
needs on problems that are important to those in practice.
(Note: Duplication of research is not always inefficient or
bad. If the cost of finding information even with an operating
information retrieval system is more than doing the research
in the first place, then except for the waste of a researcher's
time as a resource, it may be just as easy to do the research
over.)

In their paper on "Research Implementation, a Coordinated
Approach," Bagley, Riley and Lawrence [2] discuss the system
by which research is defined, conducted and brought into
practice so that the most benefit is made of established needs
for information. Solutions therefore will have a built-in
communication channel back into practice. Figure 1 of their
paper shows the system clearly. The system and problem
described by the authors is aimed more at relatively short term
applied research efforts with direct communication between the
user of knowledge and the researcher. It therefore presumes
that through research, answers can be found before the mission
is abandoned or alternative solutions have been selected. The
system as described can be interpreted more broadly in terms
of different degrees of applied or basic research. In more
basic cases the mission, for instance, instead of being the
building of a dam might be the building of certain types of
dams or even more basic the philosophy of the use of dam
system vs. other alternatives to the control of water.

The broader the problem or mission, the longer the time
frame of the research and the more random is the production of
new knowledge. For these purposes, information systems play
an uncontested role in the dissemination of new knowledge.

Functions of Information Centers

There seem to be two major functions of information
storage and retrieval systems and probably several variations
and combinations of each. One function is to provide
accessibility to bibliographic information including information on research in progress. The other function is to provide
accessibility to data, numeric or factual, from either point
or continuous sources. This data may be either for planning
(short and long term) or for real time use. The requirements
for operation of information processing facilities to meet
each of these needs is much different even though an informa-

tion center may serve both of these purposes for the same
clientele.

In the first case the information document is the center
of attention. In it may be data or facts for the information
gatherer to use but it is usually not specifically cited or
made available to a data seeker. In the second case, data is
important and the documents are secondary. In fact in many
instances data is stored and made available without being
incorporated into prepared documents. Information center
operators might consider ways in which to specifically help
the data seeker locate original or comprehensive data listings
by incorporating clues to its availability through additional
key words or key word systems designed for this purpose.

Documentary type information can be not only on material
that is published and available in some form but also on
information that is being produced such as research in
progress. The same abstracting and indexing services that are
used for one type of material can be used for the other. As
long as the information is identified as to what it is, it
can also be stored and retrieved together. A user then knows
what is available and what is being developed and where.

Storage and Retrieval Systems - The operation of any
computerized information storage and retrieval system depends
on a standardized abstracting and indexing system which by its
very nature can be expensive and time consuming. The key to
lower cost systems of the future is source abstracting and
indexing by the author upon presentation of the paper. Prior
to the achievement of a high percent of self-prepared author
abstracts and indexes, information services are faced with
these responsibilities and related costs if they are to
provide the service level required.

Dissemination of Information - Systems of information
dissemination vary from the production and publication of
extensive catalogues for mass use by everyone in the field
to the provision of specialized services to individuals by
such means as selective dissemination. In between these two
extremes lie the production of bibliographies, abstract
journals and state-of-the-art reviews. Catalogues on the one
hand provide a service at low cost per person but low visibility per person to find what he needs. Selective dissemination
provides a high cost but high visibility per person served.

Examples of Operating Information Systems - In his paper
on "Water Resources Scientific and Technical Information
Display, Storage and Retrieval." Jensen [3] describes the
operations of the Water Resources Scientific Information
Center (WRSIC) of the Office of Water Resources Research of
the U.S. Department of Interior. A part of their overall

system which was developed in cooperation with other input
centers is called the General Information Processing System
(GIPSY). The search techniques and use of this system is
described in Figs. 1, 2, 3, 4 and 5 of the paper. This
system provides a means for serving generalized audiences as
well as answering individual inquiries on request.

In his paper on "The Information Science Approach to
Transfer of Knowledge," McBirney [4] discusses the development
of information science, and its components and services. He
described an individualized selective dissemination service
provided by the Bureau of Reclamation for its employees. In
addition to abstracting and indexing publications, the Bureau
of Reclamation program carefully selects material that is to
be referenced in the system thereby reducing input and output
costs. Also important is that each user is catalogued
according to his own key word descriptions thereby being a
distinctive individual to the computer and system that serves
him.

Data Information Systems

Data systems vary considerably depending on the use of
the data. Use might be for the functions of planning, design,
operational control, operation analysis, and research. Data
systems are usually designed to fit the functional need.
While serving one functional need well, a data system does
not necessarily serve another. Operational control for instance requires the immediate receipt, processing and
retransmittal of information in real time while information for
long range planning may be the steady accumulation, analysis,
and display of information over periods of hours, days, months
or years.

Information systems for data in general belong in two
categories as explained by Jensen [3]. One is for numeric
data and the other is for alphabetic and narrative data.
Numeric data information storage and retrieval has had a
history of successful application. The storage and retrieval
of alphabetic and narrative data requires detailed care on the
part of the indexer and close interaction with the user.
These factors and others make retrieval relevance of this kind
of data highly unpredictable and unstable. Most of the work
of WRSIC is concerned with alphabetic and narrative data.

In their paper on "Transmitting Water Resources Information By A Time-Share System," Keyes, Telfer and Glass [5] have
presented a successful application of a numeric data information retrieval system. While this system was designed to
serve the purpose of special research it could be expanded to
provide information for planning, design and the needs of
real time forecasting. Figure 1 of the paper is a schematic
depicting present weather data handling systems.

The conclusion of the authors brought out the following observation: 'The concept of the environmental network has been successfully demonstrated in the Project Skywater program. The computer services and products offered by the CSS time system can grow to meet the needs of the users."

"All sensitive activities such as forest fire control, flood forecasting, air pollution forecasting and control and a host of other functions requiring special weather or hydro-meteorological information and display can benefit from a user oriented, real-time environmental data system. Only an addition of real-time surface weather data, hydrologic data, certain kinds of ecological data and other information are required. An increased number of users of the system will create a more cost effective operation and justifies the vast expense involved."

Global Transfer of Information

Desirous as it may be, the global transfer of water resources information is not without problems. McBirney [4] points out that even in developed countries information centers are not consistent in their services. The magnitude of the problem of information transfer in the world, he points out, is shown by analogy to the extent of world agricultural documentation service. "A 1969 survey by the European Atomic Energy Community (Luxemburg) revealed there were 514 secondary agricultural documentation services with total output of 1.5 million references... Of the services analyzed, 50 countries are involved in 22 languages."

Conclusions

There are real demonstrated needs for transfer of information on a global basis. These needs are such that retrieval systems can be devised in many shapes and forms to meet basic as well as advanced criteria for information transfer. The needs are for bibliographic information as well as numeric, alphabetic and narrative data. Tested operative systems exist among developed countries for storing retrieving and disseminating all types of water resources information. There are costs involved in developing and operating retrieval systems but there are also immediate and potential benefits to their use. While water resources information needs of different groups vary extensively, McBirney [4] points out the following general points that are basic for everyone concerned to follow:

1) Everyone has an obligation to limit the input of information to relevant and unduplicated material.

2) All papers and reports should be author-indexed and author abstracted.

3) Assuring understanding of the contents of papers and reports should be the principal objectives of any author.

4) A socially responsible consciousness should exist at all times in developing usable information systems that will suit most adequately the needs of the user in his context of operation and knowledge.

Brief Summaries of Session Papers

For these summaries, the abstract or synopsis prepared by the author was used when adequate. In some cases revision was made by the writer to amplify or clarify the points of the author.

1. Warford and Whitford, "Economic Analysis and Municipal Water Supply in Developing Countries."

Transfer of new information from research or activities of others into practice is time consuming, frustrating and different. This paper discusses some of the difficulties involved in applying economic theory to the practical problems faced by municipal water supply authorities, with particular reference to conditions in developing countries. Possibly in reaction to the sometimes impracticable, over-theoretical recommendations of academic economists, one school of thought contends that economic theory is inadequate to cope with the numerous social and technical constraints that are characteristic of this industry. It is argued, however, that certain basic economic principles are so crucial and so relevant to this field that there is ample scope to adapt theory to suit the practical circumstances of the industry, and that compromise solutions can be reached that are likely to yield considerable benefits. The problem is to use economics in a way that is palatable to the industry - this in turn means not only that it should be sensible but it should clearly be seen to be sensible.

The foregoing is illustrated by particular reference to pricing and investment policies. A brief discussion of the principles and problems of implementing marginal cost pricing is followed by an outline of how a practically feasible approximation to the theoretical ideal can be achieved. The role of benefit-cost analysis and of "shadow pricing" in project design, selection, and construction is then briefly discussed, with particular attention to the unemployment and acute foreign exchange problems that are typical of developing countries. The political, institutional and social barriers to the adoption of economically efficient pricing and investment rules constitute a theme that runs throughout this paper.

37

2.   Bagley, Riley, and Lawrence, "Research Implementation, a Coordinated Approach."

Ideally, the two regions of research and practice are linked by two-way information channels which convey research needs, or user problems, to the scientist and research knowledge to the user. Without well-developed linkage channels, research programs tend to be fragmented and inconsistent with user needs, while users fail to apply currently available knowledge to meet the problems which they face. The paper suggests some of the problems associated with the effective two-way flow of information between the research and practice regions, and presents possible techniques for implementing this flow. Recommendations for the improvement of communication are made, and specific examples are cited based on the experience of the authors. There has apparently been a tendency in the past to treat the various components of the system, namely: 1. research, 2. practice, and 3. linkage, as independent entities rather than as an integrated system which provides for the effective flow of information within the system as a whole. In summary, the paper examines this problem, suggests some solutions, and gives some specific examples of the effectiveness of the suggested solutions.

3.   Jensen, Raymond A., "Water Resources Scientific and Technical Information Display, Storage, and Retrieval."

The purpose of this paper is to discuss information storage and retrieval activities currently being conducted by the Water Resources Scientific Information Center of the Office of Water Resources Research in the U.S. Department of the Interior and their implications, to describe the information base that is being compiled, to describe the software retrieval program being used with this data base, and to present some examples of searches used to produce topical bibliographies and to answer specific queries.

The use is stressed of university water resources research groups as input centers to convert information collected in performing their own research to a common format which when merged, will comprise a comprehensive and searchable information base. The integration of this input, and that received from other sources, by these groups into a state-of-the-art review is discussed. The eutrophication information center at the University of Wisconsin Water Resources Research Center (paper by L. Zweifel) is an example which is reviewed. The general information processing system (GIPSY) utilized by the prototype network recently established by the Water Resources Scientific Information Center of the Office of Water Resources Research with terminals at the University of Wisconsin,

Cornell University, and the University of North Carolina is discussed. GIPSY is a search program plus a set of utility programs which operate in batch or tele-processing mode from remote terminals. The use of GIPSY in the online reactive mode is discussed along with the generating of topical bibliographies.

The advantages and disadvantages of computer-based information transfer, their general use, their impact and their future are discussed in light of the authors' experiences.

4. McBirney, Warren B., "The Information Science Approach to Transfer of Knowledge."

In general terms the information science approach to facilitating the transfer of knowledge is discussed. Use of abstract bulletins, selective dissemination of information, bibliographies, state-of-the-art reviews, microforms, and retrieval are reviewed. The operational scientific information program of the Bureau of Reclamation is described in its application of the computer for dissemination and retrieval. A brief view is given of feasible methods for providing scientific information to developing countries as compared to more modern societies.

5. Keyes, Telfer, and Glass, "Transmitting Water Resources Information By A Time-Share System."

Many of the Division of Atmospheric Water Resources Management (DAWRM), Bureau of Reclamation's contractors have a need for a real-time data system in order to conduct weather modification field experiments and/or operations or to evaluate their projects during post analyses. These contractors can obtain weather, precipitation or streamflow information in various degrees of reliability, usefulness and costs from several sources -- direct from NOAA, USGS, weather consultants and DOD (Navy, Army and Air Weather Service) sources.

To reduce the cost and increase the reliability of data vital to the contractor's operations, the DAWRM explored the feasibility of providing high quality, low-cost data to all concerned from a centralized source.

A time-share computer system to transmit water resources information has been described by the authors. The basic system consists of a central processing unit, terminal locations, input data locations, and output data location or users. The system has been used by the Jemez Atmospheric Water Resources Research Project (JAWRRP) but could be expanded to include real-time forecasting or design in any atmospheric water resources program.

ECONOMIC ANALYSIS AND MUNICIPAL WATER SUPPLY IN
DEVELOPING COUNTRIES

By

Jeremy J. Warford* and Peter W. Whitford*
International Bank for Reconstruction and Development
Washington, D.C.

Synopsis

This paper discusses some of the difficulties involved in
applying economic theory to the practical problems faced by
municipal water supply authorities, with particular reference
to conditions in developing countries. Possibly in reaction
to the sometimes impracticable, over-theoretical recommendations of academic economists, one school of thought contends
that economic theory is inadequate to cope with the numerous
social and technical constraints that are characteristic of
this industry. We argue, however, that certain basic economic
principles are so crucial and so relevant to this field that
there is ample scope to adapt theory to suit the practical
circumstances of the industry, and that compromise solutions
can be reached that are likely to yield considerable benefits.
The problem is to use economics in a way that is palatable to
the industry - this means that it should not only be sensible
but also be seen to be sensible.

We illustrate the foregoing by particular reference to
pricing and investment policies. A brief discussion of the
principles and problems of implementing marginal cost pricing
is followed by an outline of how a practically feasible
approximation to the theoretical ideal can be achieved. The
role of benefit-cost analysis and of "shadow pricing" in
project design, selection, and construction is then briefly
discussed, with particular attention to unemployment and
acute foreign exchange problems that are typical of developing
countries. The political, institutional, and social barriers
to the adoption of economically efficient pricing and investment rules constitute a theme that runs throughout this
paper.

Introduction

The obstacles faced in implementing the findings of
scientific and technological research and of transmitting
technological knowledge and innovation from developed to

---

*The opinions expressed in this paper are those of the authors
and should not be attributed to the Bank.

40

developing countries are often considerable. However, they
rarely match the difficulties surrounding attempts to introduce
economic theory into decision-making in the municipal water
supply field. Indeed, it is likely that, while technological
innovations are often seized upon avidly by water utility managers, the economic implications of those innovations may be
entirely ignored. This is due in part to an undue reliance upon financial criteria for decision-making, the lack of communication between economists and the industry, and the fact that
organizational responsibility for pointing out these economic
implications is ill-defined. More important, this reluctance
to make use of economic analysis is explained by the political
and social sensitivities that are aroused by recommendations
that result from the application of economic theory to
municipal water supply.

This paper discusses these difficulties and points to
ways in which economic theory can be of practical use to the
water supply industry. The paper is restricted to economic
aspects of municipal water supply[1]; it does not deal with the
more general issues of water resources development. It is also
aimed at the peculiar problems faced by developing countries,
although the principles to be discussed have rarely been adopted
in the water supply field, even in the developed world, due
to their controversial nature.

In fact, one school of thought contends that economic
theory is irrelevant in view of the complex nature of the
political, social, and technical constraints that are
associated with the financing and supply of water for human
consumption. This view has been encouraged by the sometimes
highly theoretical but impractical recommendations of academic
economists. However, by applying and modifying certain basic
economic principles to deal with the crucial issues confronting
the industry, a good deal can be accomplished. We illustrate
this with particular reference to pricing and investment
policies, showing why implementation even of modest improvements
is so difficult.

The World Health Organization has made an estimate of the
investment needed for the decade 1971-80 in order to provide
piped water, by household service or public standpipe, to the
total urban population of the developing world. This would
require a capital investment of about US$9 billion.[2] While
talking of "needs" or "requirements" is intellectually suspect,

---

1/We are not referring here to engineering economics, which is
   the use of discounted cash flows to choose between alternative investments.

2/"Water Supply and Sewerage: Sector Working Paper," World
   Bank, Washington, D.C., October 1971.

this figure does give some idea of the magnitude of the task facing water planners in the developing countries and of the need to avoid wasteful use of the scarce resources within these countries.

Obstacles to the Introduction of Efficient Pricing

Economic Efficiency and Marginal Cost Pricing - An economically efficient policy is one that maximizes the real income benefits which accrue to a society, without considering the way in which those benefits are distributed. Stemming from this definition is the proposition that the price of any service or commodity supplied by a public body should be equated to the cost of producing an additional unit of it or, in other words, to its marginal cost. If consumers are willing to pay a price that exceeds marginal cost, it means that they place a value on the marginal unit consumed that is at least as great as the cost to the rest of society of producing that unit: output and consumption should, therefore, be expanded. If, on the other hand, the market clearing price (the price at which supply just equals demand) is less than marginal cost, it can be assumed that there is oversupply of the commodity: the cost of additional output exceeds the benefits.

An important distinction must be drawn between purely accounting costs and real (or economic) costs. The former, which could include repayment of past loans, simply represent a transfer of income within society. Efficiency in resource allocation dictates that these "sunk costs" (costs incurred in the past) be ignored for pricing purposes for they represent no net loss, or avoidable cost, to society as a whole. On the other hand, the resources employed in the construction and operation of a particular project represent, at the time of employment, real costs, in terms of opportunities foregone for investment elsewhere. The price charged for the good or service concerned should clearly incorporate recovery of such costs if they are incurred as a result of additional consumption.

There is, therefore, a fundamental difference between the economist's approach to pricing and the accountant's. Indeed, we would argue that a basic obstacle to achieving an efficient allocation of resources in this and in other public utility fields is the unquestioning reliance upon historical, financial data for decision-making. Such data frequently does not re-present the real costs and benefits to the community that the utilities are supposed to serve. Since the achievement of financial objectives by a public utility is presumably not an end in itself, the undue attention given to accounting con-ventions is detrimental to the contribution that the industry could make to economic and social welfare. This will sub-sequently be illustrated.

42

"Lumpiness" - There are a number of practical problems
surrounding the introduction of marginal cost pricing. Marginal cost pricing is most easily applied where output of the
commodity concerned can be expanded in small increments.
Frequently, however, capital investments in water supply are
"lumpy" i.e. only large increments of supply are technically
feasible. For example, increasing the supply of water may
require a new dam or a major addition to a treatment plant. In
such cases, the definition of marginal cost depends on the
time horizon chosen. For a system with excess capacity,
marginal cost is merely the additional operating costs for an
additional unit of output - the short-run marginal cost. When
capacity has to be extended to allow additional consumption,
however, marginal cost includes the necessary investment costs,
the long-run marginal cost. Strict application of marginal
cost pricing in the context of "lumpy" investments would imply
large and sudden fluctuations in price; these would be difficult
to justify to the water utility let alone to the consumers.

Perhaps one reason why utility managers have not taken
economists seriously is that their recommendations sometimes
seem to be impractical. The marginal cost controversy is a
case in point. The strict adherence to marginal cost pricing,
with its consequent price fluctuations, recommended in the
best known book on the economics of water supply[1] seems to
have done economics some harm in the eyes of the industry.
However, in other contexts, economists have suggested average
incremental cost pricing as a more practical suggestion. Under
this policy, price is set equal to the average cost of producing
water from the most recent or the next feasible investment -
a compromise solution that can do the job reasonably well.

Difficulties of Measurement - It is often said that the
major obstacle to implementing marginal cost pricing is the
difficulty of measuring marginal cost. However, this difficulty
is more apparent than real. Estimation of future supply costs
can still provide a reasonably accurate signal for investment.
It is still to be preferred to the present accounting methods of
attempting to recover an arbitrary mixture of sunk costs, expected future costs and costs which measure not the burden on
society but that felt privately by the water utility.

This last constitutes the real measurement problem. It
arises because water supply is such an important part of the
social infrastructure that it should be operated with

1/J. Hirshleifer, J. C. de Haven and J. W. Milliman, Water
    Supply: Economics, Technology and Policy, University of
    Chicago Press, 1960

particular attention to the public welfare. One consequence of this is that the financial interests of the water utility should be subordinate to the interests of society as a whole, and that pricing policies should ideally recognize the so-called "external" effects of water production and consumption. These effects may or may not be relevant for economic efficiency, depending on whether or not they represent a net gain (or loss) to society.

An external effect is one which is felt by parties other than the buyers or sellers of a particular commodity and which, in a competitive market situation, would not be reflected in the price of that commodity. An external benefit would arise if water consumption by one individual is of benefit, perhaps because of his improved health or the reduced risk of fire, to his neighbor. In such a case, optimal pricing would require a price equal to marginal cost minus the benefits to others that accrue from marginal consumption.

Efficiency in pricing and investment is unaffected by purely "pecuniary" external effects - transfers in income or kind resulting from the supply of a commodity between members of the same society. Thus, a water supply project that stimulates industrial development, thereby yielding net gains to a particular region of a country, will not be justified on the grounds of economic efficiency if the result is merely to attract industry and reduce gains by an identical amount in other regions. Nevertheless, purely transfer effects such as these, which cannot be evaluated in monetary terms, may sometimes be accepted as legitimate social objectives, overriding the losses in efficiency that might result from a given policy.

It is not inevitable that efficiency and other criteria should conflict. Thus, if subsidization of water consumption encourages industrial development in a depressed region, income distribution arguments for such a policy may be reinforced by efficiency considerations. This might be so, for example, where the subsidy results in a transfer of activity, without undue loss of productivity, from a region of high employment, where the value of labor in other uses is high, to an area where it may be near zero.

The foregoing gives some idea of the tremendous difficulties involved in measuring external effects. The task of disentangling real and purely transfer effects is particularly awesome: externalities, almost by definition, are difficult to estimate, and any decision involving the redeployment of resources or the redistribution of income will invariably set off a complex chain reaction involving repercussions in other parts of the economy. This process is clearly a barrier to the introduction of an efficient pricing policy and it would be idle to pretend that precise answers or recommendations can be achieved from analysis of these effects. However, there is evidence that they are sufficiently important to warrant detailed analysis.

It is rare that a government would think this way, and there is usually no agency or department with responsibility for carrying out this kind of research. Of course, it would be unreasonable to expect managers of water utilities to do so: they are judged solely by their performance in supplying water and achieving certain narrowly specified financial targets for their organizations. There is no reason why they should be concerned with general economic development, income distribution, and external benefits, particularly when these objectives may be in conflict with their own goals. However, the achievement of financial targets by a water utility is, as far as society as a whole is concerned, not an end in itself, but rather the means of accomplishing an end which ultimately approximates economic efficiency.

Marginal Cost Pricing and Profitability - Strict application of marginal cost pricing would result in an enterprise making financial losses when average costs of supply are falling (i.e. when marginal cost is less than average cost) and the problem of financing such losses has been a traditional preoccupation with economists. However, in most cases, the reverse situation applies: water supply costs around the world are rising, as more distant and lower quality sources must be tapped and as the quality of service is upgraded.[2] In such cases, a price equal to the long-run marginal cost will result in the water utility making a profit.

Ironically, this situation would be frowned upon in countries where loss-making is regarded as politically quite acceptable. It is often difficult to convince government officials of the value of conventional average cost pricing, leading to a "normal" rate of return on investment. Raising charges to cover even operation and maintenance costs is difficult enough: the introduction of marginal cost prices, which require only that people pay the real resource cost of their consumption, would normally require a radical change in social attitudes.

Average incremental cost pricing was mentioned above as a means whereby prices can be adjusted periodically to reflect

---

[2] It may be true that, when a small system is being expanded, economies of scale may be important and result in a falling marginal cost. However, for large cities, these economies of scale are typically more than offset by increased transmission and treatment costs.

the average costs of technically feasible new investments. In the usual situation, where average costs are rising, profitable operation will result and price increases will be moderate and irreversible. Thus, this policy could be more readily put into operation than strict marginal cost pricing.

Water "Requirements" and Metering - The basic obstacle to the application of economy theory to water supply investment decisions is the attitude that "requirements" for water exist that must be met at all costs. This attitude probably stems from the fact that water is essential for life and should therefore not be subject to the laws of supply and demand. However, the fraction of domestic water use that is used to sustain life is minute and for most of the other uses consumption is sensitive to the price of water as well as to many other socio-economic variables. These factors are rarely analyzed when forecasts of future consumption are made.

It is undeniable that water supply is a social service in that it aims to reduce disease and improve standards of living. It is also true that in many countries the lowest income groups cannot afford to pay the full economic cost of water supply, even for the public standpipe service, which is usually the only type of service available to them. However, it is important to state explicitly the amount of subsidy considered reasonable from social considerations and who should provide it, the taxpayers of the country as a whole or the richer consumers of the city. Economic pricing rules should then be applied to those able to pay the full cost.

The use of economically efficient pricing presupposes that all consumers' services are metered, a condition that does not apply in many developing countries. When the marginal cost of water to the consumer is raised from zero to a positive number, he will reduce his consumption, if he behaves rationally, until the value in use of the last unit of consumption reaches the price charged. This reduction in consumption reduces variable costs and may allow system expansions to be deferred. Besides, these tangible benefits are the less easily quantified management benefits of being able to measure consumption and thus give a rational basis for leak detection and future network design. Against these benefits must be set the costs of installing, maintaining, and reading the meters. As the cost of obtaining water rises, it may be expected that the benefits of metering will increase.

Arguments against metering are often based on purely financial grounds, i.e. the effect of metering on the revenues of the enterprise. This confusion of financial and economic thinking results in proposals such as: it is best to meter poor properties first because high revenues are already obtained from the property tax on bigger properties. It is also argued that metering will lower the consumption of the poorer people below what is necessary to maintain public health. Even if this could be demonstrated, it could be easily prevented with an explicit subsidy.

In this section, we have described a pricing policy that approaches economic efficiency more nearly than conventional methods. Such policies are particularly relevant for developing countries, where the penalties incurred by a misallocation of resources, in terms of growth foregone elsewhere in the economy, are of crucial importance. However, recommending such a pricing policy does not mean that it should be blindly followed as it says nothing about distributional effects. However, it does provide a yardstick, against which the economic implications of proposed pricing policies can be measured. Too often marginal cost pricing is not even considered.

Obstacles to the Use of Benefit-Cost Analysis

Benefits - Where direct charging for water is not feasible (i.e. where the costs of metering are deemed to exceed the benefits brought about by reducing consumption, deferring investment and saving operating costs), the willingness of consumers to pay for water cannot be used as an indicator of the need to invest in additional capacity. This also applies to some degree where there are large external effects. Indirect methods of evaluating project benefits are required in these circumstances. However, techniques to do this are poorly developed because of the widespread acceptance of the "requirements" approach, referred to earlier.

It is generally accepted that the real problems of benefit-cost analysis are found in the measurement of benefits and, where consumers' willingness to pay cannot be used, this is more true of municipal water supply than of other types of water resource investments. Actual revenues from metered water sales provide only a minimum estimate of the economic benefits, as they generally leave a considerable consumer's surplus i.e. many consumers would have been willing to pay more than the actual price of water. Another method of assessing benefits is to equate them to the cost of the next cheapest investment. Great care must be used to ensure that this is a real alternative. We have already mentioned that it is rare for governments to assign responsibility to any particular agency for analysis of the external impacts of water supply, and that utility managers have little incentive to do this themselves. However, one approach is to use the housing market as a proxy for the water market to determine how much consumers really value water. This is estimated from the amount that they bid for houses that are served with a

47

piped supply. Preliminary results of a study done on behalf
of the World Bank demonstrate that the effect of water and
sanitation facilities on house prices may be considerable.
Of course, this is something that water supply engineers have
been saying, but have not demonstrated in a statistically
rigorous way. The advantage of property value studies is that
they point to equitable and economically efficient ways of
financing water supply and sanitation services, particularly
where metering is inappropriate. Moreover, they give some
idea as to the extent to which water supply projects can and
should be developed in the face of rising costs.

Another way of measuring benefits is the estimation of
the public health benefits of a safe, dependable water supply.
This is an area where data on changes in mortality and morbidity
from water-borne and water-associated diseases are very sketchy
and consumer behavior is an unreliable guide. Some think that
the benefits are so obvious that research is not necessary,
while others consider them so difficult to isolate that it is
useless to try to quantify them. Moreover, it is not clear
whether public health benefits, of which the consumer may
be unaware, should be additional to or an alternative measure
of benefits measured in the market place.

The benefits are by no means obvious; however, the
highly complex task of trying to determine the impact of water
supply is worth the effort, in view of the billions of dollars
that are spent on this activity in the name of public health.
Furthermore, benefit-cost analysis, which measures all effects
in monetary terms, must be seen not as a decision-making rule
but as one piece of information necessary to making sensible
expenditure decisions. Thus, although we might agree that
money should be spent to achieve certain humanitarian or other
goals, even when the costs exceed the benefits of such action
from an economic viewpoint, we would still argue that the
decision to do so can only be a sensible one if the policy-
maker is apprised of the economic consequences of his decision.
One reason why economics is frowned upon by those concerned
with public health matters is the belief that its use is
necessarily at odds with humanitarian principles. This is
clearly not so, but this viewpoint is one more obstacle that
has to be overcome if economic analysis is to be taken
seriously in the water supply field in developing countries.

Costs - Although benefit measurement probably poses the
greatest challenge to economists, we believe that much work
also needs to be done on the cost side where the value is
likely to be even greater. The central issue here is "shadow
pricing," its relevance for water supply projects in developing
countries, and the institutional, financial, and technical
obstacles to its introduction.

As we have already pointed out, investment decisions should be based on economic not financial costs. Economic costs are equivalent to social opportunity costs, that is, the value of the goods and services given up because of the employment of resources in the water supply project.

In many countries, the wage rate for labor is significantly higher than the minimum necessary to induce the man to work. If the labor employed on the project would otherwise be un-employed, then its opportunity cost is zero. If the workers would be otherwise employed in agriculture, their shadow wage is the value of their agricultural output. Typically, in developing countries, the shadow cost of unskilled labor is well below its financial cost while the reverse might be true for certain skilled workers.

The opportunity cost of capital should not be the utility's borrowing rate, which may be arbitrarily set by the Government, but a rate equivalent to the rate of return on capital in the private sector, adjusted for taxes. Foreign exchange should be valued at its natural market rate rather than one based on exchange controls and other artificial means of rate support.

Similarly, the economic cost of land is the value of the net output foregone by using it for the water supply project. Quite often this will approximate its market cost.

These divergences between financial and economic costs are far greater in developing than in developed countries. Developing countries are characterized by massive unemployment and overvalued local currency. Failure to "shadow price" these factors, plus the availability of government or overseas capital at interest rates below the opportunity cost of capital will tend to distort the choice between labor and capital-intensive methods of construction and operation. This will be critically important for components such as dams, tunnels, trenching, treatment plant automation, and the local manufacture of materials and equipment.

Obstacles to the Use of Shadow Pricing - 1. Developing countries are eager to utilize new technology from developed countries but this is generally of a labor-saving type. Commonly, such techniques will show financial savings but economic losses.

2. If the application of shadow pricing were to result in the selection of a project of higher financial cost than otherwise, it would not be equitable to charge the consumers for this increase, since the economic benefits accrue to the whole nation. On the other hand, it would probably be diffi-cult to convince the Government that the choice based on shadow pricing was in its best interest.

3. International consulting firms are not familiar with labor-intensive methods and are unlikely to recommend their use. They will tend to consider only the methods with which they have had experience in their home countries. Foreign contractors are unlikely to have the necessary experience in large-scale labor management necessary to implement labor-intensive methods.

4. Even if a selection based on shadow pricing is attempted, severe difficulties of calculation remain, the solutions of which would require the employment of economists for feasibility studies.

5. If social opportunity costs were to be used in bid comparison, the procedure to be used in evaluation would need to be carefully explained in the invitation to bid.

6. Labor-intensive methods tend to be more time-consuming than capital-intensive methods. However, this can be allowed for in the usual present worth analysis.

7. Probably the greatest problem will be the communication gap. Engineers and accountants find it difficult to believe that one method can be more expensive than another yet more efficient. On the other hand, economists have done little to explain their concepts and terminology or to gain sufficient practical knowledge of water supply to be able to suggest areas in which their theories could be most usefully employed.

As far as we are aware, shadow pricing has never been explicitly applied in the municipal water supply field. It might be expected that it will find its most beneficial use in developing countries, where financial costs are grossly distorted. However, the obstacles we have just discussed are going to be difficult to overcome.

Conclusion

In view of the rapidly increasing costs of water and the tremendous backlogs in supply in developing countries, it is particularly important to ensure that the allocation of supplies among consumers and the selection, design, and construction of projects are determined in accordance with sound economic principles. The paper has illustrated this and demonstrated some of the obstacles to the implementation of economic principles.

It is important, however, to stress once more that although economically efficient policies - which have nothing to say about equity or income distribution - are not necessarily the "right" ones to be followed. What we do insist is that the course of action which is likely to be economically efficient should at least be known, and that departures from that course of action should be made as a result of an explicit analysis of the efficiency losses entailed. This would encourage distributional and equity goals to be achieved at the least cost to society. Currently, no such analysis is made at all.

We have noted the reasons for resistance to the introduction of marginal cost pricing - or some variant thereof. These stem largely from the entrenched position of accountants in the public utilities field, with their emphasis on financial rather than economic costs, the difficulties of measuring external effects, the political implications of higher prices and high profits that would be a common result of implementing this principle, and the fact that in most countries there is no one with a clearly defined responsibility for analyzing the wider effects of water supply on economic development, income distribution, and so forth.

Moreover, not only is adherence to economic pricing principles at odds with the "requirements" approach, but also is the need to evaluate the benefits of water supply projects. Benefit measurement, unless it can be used to reinforce the notion that water supply is underrated by those responsible for allocating funds from national budgets, is unlikely to be popular with the industry. On the cost side, we have singled out shadow pricing as being of significant importance to the development of the industry, particularly with regard to the characteristic economic problems of developing countries. Obstacles to its introduction are many, but we would argue that economists should not give up hope of getting their ideas accepted. If they are prepared to modify - but not sacrifice - theory to suit the practicalities of real life and to ensure not only that their ideas are sensible, but are clearly seen to be sensible by practitioners in the field, they may yet achieve something. However, large changes will not be accomplished overnight.

RESEARCH IMPLEMENTATION, A COORDINATED APPROACH

By

Jay M. Bagley, Director   J. Paul Riley
Utah Water Research Lab   Utah State Water Research Lab
Utah State University   Utah State University

and

Daniel F. Lawrence, Director
Utah Division of Water Resources
Department of Natural Resources

Synopsis

Ideally, the two regions of research and practice are linked by two-way information channels which convey research needs, or user problems, to the scientist and research knowledge to the user. Without well-developed linkage channels, research programs tend to be fragmented and inconsistent with user needs, while users fail to apply currently available knowledge to meet the problems which they face. The paper suggests some of the problems associated with the effective two-way flow of information between the research and practice regions, and presents possible techniques for implementing this flow. Recommendations for the improvement of communication are made, and specific examples are cited based on the experience of the authors. There has apparently been a tendency in the past to treat the various components of the system, namely: 1. research, 2. practice, and 3. linkage, as independent entities rather than as an integrated system which provides for the effective flow of information within the system as a whole. In summary, the paper examines this problem, suggests some solutions, and gives some specific examples of the effectiveness of the suggested solutions.

The Problem of Research Implementation

Today's resource planning and management problems are so complex, and the short and long term social consequences of actions so important to assess that water resource planning and management entities cannot function effectively without a viable research arm or ready access to a research resource. Ideally, there should be a close interaction and easy flow of ideas between the research and application phases. Unfortunately, transition from research development to useful application or implementation remains a problem area. Promising developments often falter or founder because the organizational and communicative patterns which link research with application are not adequately established.

The problem of effective communication, or interface, between scientists and users was set out recently by Dr. D. Wynne Thorne, Vice President for Research at Utah State University, as follows: "Preliminary attempts to involve our most capable scientists in assisting industry, formulating public policy, and assuming leadership in action programs have emphasized a dilemma which we believe is common to most universities trying to assume a more vigorous public service role of this nature. Communication between scientists and industrial, public, and private group leaders is often difficult because frames of reference, and even word meanings, differ among the individuals."

At first consideration, it might appear that organizational unification, which provides the research arm "in-house", may overcome many of the impediments to effective utilization of research results. Several potential advantages can be cited for combining the research function with the planning and development, or user, function in a single organization. Some of these advantages are: (1) an increased awareness and acceptance by researchers of principal user goals; (2) a more rapid recognition of user problems and corresponding budgetary allocations to initiate priority work; (3) greater mobility of people between research and mission components; and, (4) full communication between researcher and user through all stages of research to ultimate use.

In reality, there are many factors which impede effective realization of the potentials of organizational unification. The unification of the research and planning-management functions in a single organization does not automatically achieve the results which surficially appear so evident. For example, a recent review of the overall program of the U.S. Forest Service by the General Accounting Office (GAO) concluded that the findings from the Forest Service's research program were not being effectively incorporated into the management of forest lands. On the other hand, the establishment of the Office of Water Resources Research, with a direct tie to university research resources, seems to acknowledge the fact that new ideas and technology can be successfully transplanted from one organization to another--or from separate research organizations to user organizations. There are many offsetting advantages and unique circumstances which complicate any meaningful contrast of the effectiveness of translating research results to practical use under unified or separated organizational arrangements.

The object here is not to detail the advantages and disadvantages of "in-house" versus "out-of-house" research. Both approaches have a distinctive yet complementary role, and both require effective communication between the researcher and the user. The point is that there are multi-levels of planning and management having widely differing degrees of complexity and social interaction. Each must have access to research resources and research results. While planning-management organizations may vary greatly in size and areal and legal jurisdiction, they all possess a certain commonality in that today's problems are seldom without inter-disciplinary associations. Small action groups may lack the ability to organize a coherent research effort around a problem of a multidisciplinary nature. Consequently, small planning-management organizations which cannot maintain, on a full-time basis, the many specialties that might be needed, would find considerable advantage in collaborating with a research organization having a substantial pool of specialists in both the "hard" and "soft" sciences.

Ideally, the two regions of research and use are linked by effective information or communication channels which convey clear definitions of research needs or user problems, to the scientist and research knowledge to the user. Without well-developed linkage channels, research programs tend to be fragmented and inconsistent with user needs, while users fail to apply currently available knowledge to meet the problems which they have.

Communication Between Research and Practice

The system of communication between the user and the researcher is illustrated in schematic form by Fig. 1. The planning and management, or user, functions shown near the top of the diagram are mission oriented. The success of the user in meeting mission objectives frequently is limited by problems which arise both from a lack of sufficient basic information and from the application of specific research results. The question then is one of attempting to solve these user problems by transmitting them to the researcher whose functions are depicted at the bottom of the diagram of Fig. 1. The loss of problem definition and resolution between the user and the researcher is represented by the diagram as information "filters". The smaller the amount of information that is removed by these filters, the more clearly defined are the problems as they reach the researcher, with the result that research programs tend to be increasingly less fragmented and more consistent with user needs. On the other hand, information loss in this channel between the user and the research functions causes a distortion of research needs as viewed by the researcher. Under this situation research programs usually are not adequately geared to solve the problems of the user.

In a similar manner, research results are transmitted with a greater or lesser degree of information loss from the researcher to the user. The user might not have sufficient background and experience, for example, to fully understand

and utilize the research information as it is being presented.
On the other hand, inconsistencies might exist between needs
as viewed by the user and information as being supplied by the
researcher. This loss of research information through the
transfer process to the user is represented by the diagram of
Fig. 1. The potentially useful report collecting dust on the
sponsor's desk is a typical example of this kind of information
loss between the research and use functions.

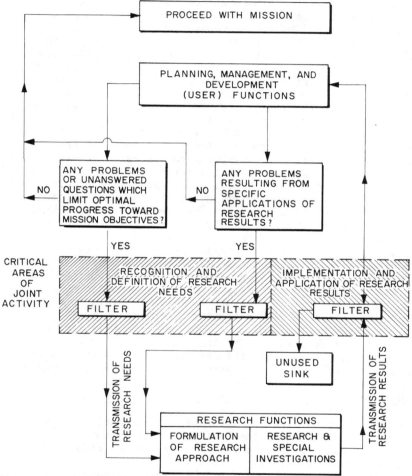

Fig. 1. A schematic diagram depicting the communication
channels between the research and application functions in society.

Figure 1 includes two shaded areas which encompass the
three filters near the center of the diagram. The shading is
intended to represent critical areas of joint user-researcher
activities involving (1) the recognition and definition of
research needs, and (2) the implementation and application of

55

research results. It is recognized that these joint activities can, and indeed should, extend to some degree across the entire diagram from the user to the research functions. However, well-developed and well-coordinated joint user-researcher activities at the interface between the user and research functions is vital for a minimum information loss through the communication links.

The establishment and maintenance of the organizational and communication linkages between research and the user or application functions has the same problems and advantages regardless of whether these two basic components are separate or unified in one organizational structure. Frequently, for example, administrative policies tend to optimize the performance of only one segment of the system, for example, research output, but at the same time provide little motivation for the researcher to perform well in the vital area of communications. The advantages of effective communication to the research functions are that the exposure to viewpoints and ideas from the planning-management component temper the research approach and orientation toward more practical considerations. There is, therefore, less tendency for the research to become narrow or myopic. Also, a close interchange develops in the researcher improved insight into the social, political, and institutional framework within which his results must be implemented. Needless to say, it is important that research thrusts not be surreptitiously biased by emotion or political advocacy. Political and intellectual neutrality need to be preserved. On the other hand, users such as planner-manager personnel benefit from close interaction with research through the intellectual stimulation that finds creative expression and innovation in the applications arena. Further, this interaction develops in the user a greater appreciation and awareness of technological limitations and possibilities, and gives him a more realistic understanding of the potentialities of research and of its practical limitations in terms of such items as time and budget constraints and assurances of success.

Some Examples of Successful Research Implementation

Figure 1 depicts the vital two-way communication links between the researcher and the user. If this communication is effective, each is able to play an equally important and integrated, mutually-supportive role in formulating solutions to the problems of the user. The following two examples of successful coordination between the researcher and user functions are taken from recent experiences involving researchers at Utah State University.

1. The first example involves a cooperative study between Utah State University (the researcher) and the Utah State Division of Water Resources (the user) which

entailed the development of a simulation model of the
hydrology of the Bear River basin, an interstate
stream within the three states of Wyoming, Idaho,
and Utah. Through frequent meetings and discussions
both the Division and The University were involved
in the conceptualization stages of the study. During
these stages a common understanding was reached as to
(1) the kinds of answers required from the model; (2)
the time and space resolution to be used in the model,
and (3) the limitations of available data and additional data needed. Throughout the course of the
study, a Division man with previous experience in
computer modeling spent an average of two days each
week at the University campus. Thus, all questions
which occurred during the study were solved jointly.
When the model was completed, the report and computer
program constituted more than a "black box" to the
Division because its personnel fully understood the
model, including its capabilities and limitations.
Since that time, not only has the Division independently applied the model to many planning and
management studies involving the water resources of
the Bear River basin, but also has been able to
expand and further develop the model as needed. In
this case, a highly effective utilization of research
knowledge has been achieved.

2. The second example is similar to the first in that it
involves a cooperative study between the University
and the U. S. Bureau of Reclamation for the development of a water resource management model of the
Provo River basin in central Utah. This study has
involved rather detailed considerations of both
surface and groundwater hydrology, and has required
that other constraints be included, such as water
rights and reservoir operating rules for multi-
purpose development. For this reason, counterpart
teams of professionals were established at both the
University and the Provo District Office of the
Bureau. Each of these two teams consisted of a
"prime contact" man and of individuals having particular areas of expertise, such as surface water
hydrology, ground water hydrology, and water resource
management. Throughout this cooperative study, which
is now nearing completion, there has been a high
degree of interchange through numerous meetings and
discussions both at the University and at Bureau
offices in Provo. Early in the study the team from
the University spent several days in the District
Office in Provo discussing various aspects of the
model development, and in processing and evaluating
available data. In the later phases of the study the

Bureau team has spent approximately two to three days each month with the University team at the Utah Water Research Laboratory. The model was developed, tested, and "debugged" on the hybrid computer facilities available at the laboratory. However, the USBR District Office in Provo (like Utah State University) is equipped with a remote terminal to the Univac 1108 digital computer at the University of Utah in Salt Lake City. Therefore, in order to facilitate operational studies by Bureau personnel, the model subsequently was jointly reprogrammed to run on the Univac 1108 digital computer. The teams from the University and the USBR have worked closely in developing and testing the model, and since then jointly have conducted several management studies involving water resource use and development in the Provo River basin, and the relationship of this resource use to the Central Utah Project being planned by the USBR. Personnel of the Bureau team now are thoroughly acquainted with the model and its development procedure, and are capable of applying it to various kinds of management studies in the future. This study also has served to demonstrate that close cooperation between researchers and users, and the rapid feedback which it promotes, can lead to a highly effective application of research results.

Some Specific Recommendations for Successful Research Implementation

Under the two following recommendations the areas of joint user-researcher activity represented by shading in Fig. 1 would be expanded to include both the user and research functions. The two examples of successful research implementation cited in the previous section contain elements of both recommendations.

1. The effective transfer of a research finding tends to be a unique problem. The best approach in any instance is determined by the specific characteristics of both the research result and the using component. It is probably most effective if the original researcher, or the developer of a research result, is able to team with the implementing or using group and to follow his brainchild into testing, adaptation, and final utilization. A successful pattern of technology transfer would involve people moving with the idea from research to implementation. Provision for researchers to extend their work to implementation phases, and opportunities for resource planners and managers to familiarize themselves with new technological advances through workshops, seminars, or other less formal

arrangements, could enlarge and enrich the experiences and perspectives of both groups, and thus accomplish effective coordination.

2. Communication can be achieved by bringing applications people into the research environment on a temporary basis to learn new technology and to work jointly with research in testing and adapting. For effective interaction and coordination of research and user activities each segment must be able to consider the other as an extension of its own staff. Whether under unified or separate institutional structures, organizational policies should make such interaction easy. There is a need to foster mobility of people between and within organizations to reduce the structural, ideological and intellectual barriers between research and application. Admittedly, some difficult administrative problems might exist in implementing this recommendation, but in most cases the creative advantages of improved research and its application would outweigh the disadvantages.

WATER RESOURCES SCIENTIFIC AND TECHNICAL INFORMATION
DISPLAY, STORAGE, AND RETRIEVAL

By

Raymond A. Jensen, Manager, Water Resources Scientific
Information Center, Office of Water Resources Research,
U.S. Department of the Interior, Washington, D. C., USA

The purpose of this paper is to discuss information storage
and retrieval activities currently being conducted by the Water
Resources Scientific Information Center of the Office of Water
Resources Research in the U. S. Department of the Interior and
their implications, to describe the information base that is
being compiled, to describe the software retrieval program
being used with this data base, and to present some examples
of searches used to produce topical bibliographies and to
answer specific queries.

Synopsis

University water resources research groups are used as
input centers to convert information collected in performing
their own research to a common format which, when merged, will
comprise a comprehensive and searchable information base. The
integration of this input, and that received from other sources,
by these groups into a state-of-the-art review is discussed.
The eutrophication information center at the University of
Wisconsin Water Resources Research Center (paper by L. Zweifel)
is an example which is reviewed. The general information processing system (GIPSY) utilized by the prototype network
recently established by the Water Resources Scientific Information Center of the Office of Water Resources Research with
terminals at the University of Wisconsin, Cornell University,
and The University of North Carolina is discussed. GIPSY is
a search program plus a set of utility programs which operate
in batch or tele-processing mode from remote terminals. The
use of GIPSY in the online reactive mode is discussed, along
with the generating of topical bibliographies.

Input

The Water Resources Scientific Information Center (WRSIC)
was established under the authorization for water resources
research, training, and information dissemination provided by
the Water Resources Research Act of 1964, and started operational functions in the fall of 1967. The objective of the WRSIC
is to disseminate scientific and technical information to the
water resources community. In common with other information
or documentation centers, one of the first WRSIC tasks was to
establish sources of information input. Several major sources
of such input have been initiated. One of the most significant
of these is input received from the 51 state water resources

research institutes and centers. These centers, under agreements with the Office of Water Resources Research, abstract and index the documents which they produce by completing a precoded WRSIC abstract form for each document. Similarly, agreements have been reached with most Federal water resources agencies. In these latter agreements, WRSIC agrees to provide services to the agencies in return for copies of their water resources documents with completed abstract forms. These forms, as in the case of the state water resources research institutes, must be completed using the WRSIC format and WRSIC's terms from its water resources thesaurus.

The largest source of input, representing approximately 90% of the total WRSIC input, is from the literature centers of competence or information analysis centers. WRSIC receives input from seven such centers which it supports: The University of Arizona's center on arid lands water resources, the University of Florida on Eastern water law, the University of Chicago on metropolitan water resource management, one at the University of Wisconsin on water resource economics, one at Cornell University on policy models for water resource systems, one at University of Wisconsin on eutrophication, one at the National Water Well Association on water well construction technology, and one on public water supply treatment technology at the American Water Works Association. WRSIC also supports one in the U. S. Geological Survey on surface and groundwater hydrology and one at AEC's Oak Ridge National Laboratory on water related aspects of nuclear radiation and safety. WRSIC also receives cooperative support from the Environmental Protection Agency which enables literature center of competence input to be received from: Battelle Memorial Institute on methods of chemical and biological identification and measurement of pollutants, from Iowa State University on livestock waste, from the Oceanic Research Institute on coastal pollution, from Vanderbilt University on thermal pollution, from the University of Texas on wastewater treatment, from the University of Washington on water quality requirements for special water and marine organisms, and from the American Water Works Association on water treatment wastes.

The last and newest source of input for WRSIC has been from a large discipline-oriented abstracting service: Biological Abstracts. We have initiated arrangements whereby Biological Abstracts monitors its service to select references in specified areas of water resources, adds indexing terms to these references and transcribes the data onto the WRSIC precoded input form to enable processing for the WRSIC information base, and for display in published form as part of Selected Water Resources Abstracts. We are expecting to receive an additional 4,000 abstracts in Selected Water Resources Abstracts this year through this means. This we hope, will enable readers of Selected Water Resources Abstracts to avoid the necessity of searching Biological Abstracts as well as Selected Water

Resources Abstracts and, will improve WRSIC's coverage of
non-English language literature in the specified subject
areas. Eventually it is planned to provide similar service
to users by incorporating the input from other major discipline-
oriented secondary abstracting services.

Centers of Competence

As we have shown WRSIC has approached the problem of
establishing a comprehensive and exploitable information base
by looking for literature centers of competence in universities
where literature is already being reviewed in support of
research and persuading these competent groups to adopt the
common standards for abstracting and indexing required by
WRSIC for input. This use of university research groups as
input centers to convert information collected in performing
research to a common format, and which, when merged, comprises
a comprehensive searchable information base, has proven to be
very successful. At the beginning it was predicted that there
would be substantial overlap and duplication between various
research groups because of the overlapping nature of water
resources projects in general. This has not proven to be the
case. However, as the number of input centers utilized by
WRSIC becomes greater, the problem may become more serious.
The integration of the input received by one center with that
received from other sources into a state-of-the-art review
is one of the benefits from this approach to input processing.
This essentially converts the activity of an input or literature center of competence, as described by WRSIC, into an
information analysis center in which output services are
provided at the center as well as input to the WRSIC.

Eutrophication Information Center

The Eutrophication Information Center at the University of
Wisconsin Water Resources Research Center (paper by L. Zweifel)
is an example of a WRSIC literature center of competence, or
input processing center, which is also an information analysis
center. It has integrated input in an output series of state-
of-the-art and critical reviews and has provided reference
services and bibliographic services to a number of state and
Federal agencies and citizens in Wisconsin, and elsewhere, on
problems associated with eutrophication. To provide this output, it draws heavily on the accumulated expertise developed
by the research programs at the University of Wisconsin, and
the engineering library, for a full panoply of information
services to researchers and research managers in the area of
eutrophication. This center has received additional support

from the Environmental Protection Agency, the Department of Agriculture, and the Soap and Detergent Association.

Output Services

Briefly, WRSIC output services consist of Selected Water Resources Abstracts which appear twice monthly, contain approximately 650 abstracts in each issue during the current year, and have cumulative indexes in December, by subject, author, organization, and accession numbers. An accumulated quarterly report of OWRR research reports is also produced. primarily for use within its program. The annual Water Resources Research Catalog is published with the help of Smithsonian Science Information Exchange. The current volume has over 6,300 research project descriptions. We have produced various state-of-the-art reports. Among these are one on metropolitan water resources management, two on aspects of eutrophication, one on institutional aspects of water resources development and one about to be published on water well construction technology. We have also produced various topical bibliographies, such as storm water runoff and the effects of heated effluents on aquatic life. The Water Resources Thesaurus has recently been published in its second edition and is generally used by various groups both in providing input to WRSIC and in organizing local document collections by water resources research organizations within the U. S. and abroad.

Information Retrieval System

The WRSIC information retrieval system, formally known as GIPSY or General Information Processing System, is one of several new and exciting computer search programs developed to aid searchers and compilers of large to medium files to store, retrieve, manipulate, and format information more rapidly and effectively. WRSIC has tested a number of software systems and is still testing others, but the one about which we are the most knowledgeable, and which has been more used in an operational sense, is the system developed at the University of Oklahoma by Dr. James Sweeney. We are testing and demonstrating for several reasons: (1) to give greater depth of search (2) to enable coordination of terms, (3) to manipulate data and reorder our formats, (4) to provide quick response, (5) to enable convenient current searching of our data base, and (6) to provide a hard copy printout. This WRSIC reactive system comprises a search program plus a set of utility programs. Searches are batched or teleprocessed from remote terminals. The system accepts variable fields, variable length records made up of codes, numbers, text, etc. All data elements are searchable, and the retrieved records may be printed in pre-defined formats. Retrieved records may also be used as inputs to other programs. The computer commands for the search program are simple, as can be seen by Fig. 1. On the left are the

computer commands; on the right is a list of the searchable
parts of the abstract used by WRSIC. The select command
gives the user the opportunity to list the variables which he
desires to search. The iterate command enables the user to
select a set of variables. Print is a command which prints the
entire abstract entry. The list command provides for printing
selected portions of the entry. Copy gives a preformatted
entry. Dump simply puts the search on tape. Sum is numerical
addition. Define is the tutorial that tells what the commands
mean. Sort enables one to sort alphabetically and numerically
in ascending or descending order. Back enables one to go back
to a previous subset of the data base. And message is a command
that enables communication with the computer center that is
running the system. The searchable parts of the abstracts are
exactly as they appear fully displayed in Selected Water
Resources Abstracts. The record begins with the accession
number followed by the field and group classification categories,
the organizational affiliation of the author, the title, the
personal authors, the citation, which is in most cases a
journal, the project number, descriptors or words that appear
in the Thesaurus, identifiers or words that do not appear in the
Thesaurus, and the text of the abstract itself. The search
procedure appears in Fig. 2. The operator begins by formulating
the question and developing a search strategy in the form of a
Boolean statement or a set of statements. The proper strategy
is developed only with experience and insight, and it requires
some prior knowledge of the data base, the way in which it was
assembled and its contents indexed. By experience we have
found that persons who are not familiar with the data base
need to have their search strategy formulated by someone who
is knowledgeable in indexing techniques. The user then specifies
the variables and the Boolean statement or logic he wants to
apply to these variables. The file is searched and search
statistics are then displayed. The user can react to these,
and if he is satisfied with them, he can proceed; if not, he
can go back and specify a new set of variables and logic.
Being satisfied, he prints either, at the terminal or computer
center printer, the entire entry or subset of it. Again, if
he is satisfied, he can accept this result or he can go back and
formulate a new and different question that more nearly meets
his needs. The WRSIC currently uses this system in several
different ways. It is used in the batch mode by storing the
data base in the computer of the Department of the Interior's
U. S. Geological Survey. It is also used in remote batch with
the same computer. In addition, a demonstration and network
data base is stored in the computers at the University of
Oklahoma in Norman and at Oklahoma State University in Still-
water.

Network

During this calendar year we have established a prototype computer search and retrieval network consisting of three direct access terminals. (See Fig. 3). The first is at Cornell University, the second at the University of North Carolina, and the third is at the University of Wisconsin. Two of these terminals are also input centers of competence. This network is in the pilot-operation stage so that we can establish how GIPSY works in a university research environment, the kind of questions that will be asked, the kind of satisfaction that will be received in response to these questions, and the kind of charges that will be necessary to make these centers self-supporting through their state water resources research institutes. Non-Federal users go to these three network centers which serve one of three regions into which the United States has been divided. Federal users go to these network centers or go directly to WRSIC if some prior agreement has been made. We expect eventually to expand this network so as to include terminals connected with the WRSIC data base at all state water resources research institutes.

Examples

The first example is a simple query: "What are the effects of detergents on the American oyster"? (See Fig. 4). The first command given the computer is select. The computer acknowledges with a series of dashes. The next command is Field 5 with delimiters around the five. The first logic statement is A. In other words all references are desired that are in field five which is the water quality field. The computer responds and says that the search is beginning. After a short lapse of time, the computer comes back with search statistics. It searched 37,354 abstracts and selected 10,562, labeled subset one. The computer again asks if the user wishes to iterate. The user responds "yes" and lists the first variable as the descriptor, oyster, with delimiters around it. Again the logic statement is A. The computer searches the 10,562 abstracts and selects 207, designated subset 2. The computer lists its search statistics and again asks if the user would like to iterate. The user says "yes" and lists the keywords, "A American oyster" in the abstract and "B detergent" in the abstract. The logic statement is A and B ($is used as the ditto mark). The computer begins the search and searches the 207 abstracts. It finds 0 having the two terms in common, with 3 on American oyster and two on detergents. Computer again asks does the user wish to iterate? The user says "no"; he wants to go back. The computer asks what subset? The user specifies subset 2. This time the descriptor "oyster" and the descriptor "detergent" are listed. The logic statement again is A and B. The search of the 207 abstracts produces a

65

subset with three in it satisfying both variables. In other words there are 207 on oyster and three on detergents. The computer asks if the user wants to iterate again? He says "no"; he wants to list. The computer comes back and asks whether the user want to list on terminal or printer. The answer is t for terminal. The computer asks the user to enter the labels which he wants printed, and the user replies with the title and the number. The titles are shown in Fig. 4. All are abstracts relevant to the effects of detergents on the American oyster. In order to review a full abstract, the command "iterate" is given. The computer asks the user to specify a subset number, and he again goes back to "three". He asks for W70-06696 which is one of the 3 abstracts just located. The logic statement is A. The computer finds that abstract and asks the user if he wishes to iterate again? He says "no", but states that he would like to print. The computer asks whether to use the terminal or the printer. The user specifies the terminal. As one can see from the Figure, the entire abstract is printed up to the point where the printer was stopped.

Another example of using the WRSIC computer search and retrieval system is in the production of topical bibliographies. A specific example of this is a bibliography on arsenic and lead (Fig. 5). The user command is select and the field searched again is field (5), which is the water quality field in the water resources research categories. The logic statement is A and 42,920 abstracts are searched with 15,036 being selected to produce subset one. The computer listed its search statistics and was told to iterate again. The field this time was 6E which is the category for water law and institutions. The logic statement was "not A", and the computer selected 12,735 of the original 15,036 so that 2,301 abstracts on water law were eliminated. Again the computer was instructed to iterate and asked to search the abstract for "arsenic" and for "lead." The logic statement was A or B. It searched the 12,735 and found 216, 49 of which were on arsenic and 171 on lead. Again the computer was instructed to iterate and told to search the abstract for "lead" within one word of "to" in order to eliminate the phase "lead to" which would be confused with the metal "lead." The logic statement was "not A." The 216 were searched and 109 satisfying this relationship were found and designated subset 4. There were 107 "lead to's" eliminated. The computer was instructed to print, and it subsequently printed the 109 abstracts on arsenic and lead, the first of which is shown in the figure. This example comprised the main bibliography section of a publication on arsenic and lead. In addition, the computer was used to generate a key-word-in-context index which takes the terms from the descriptor and identifier fields of each of the abstracts and permutes them in the form of an index. A computer-produced author index is added, and in some bibliographies, a set of relevant notices of research in progress statements is added to round out the comprehensiveness of the bibliography for better service to the user.

Computer-Based Information Transfer Systems and Their Impact

In the case of numeric data, there is a history of successful applications of information transfer systems because of the fact that data are precise, measurable, and generally free of semantic and syntactic ambiguity. No intermediary is necessary in transfer because of the nearly 100% coincidence between the request and the data containing the potential answer. However, in the Water Resources Scientific Information Center we are more concerned with the transfer of alphabetic or narrative data. The application is difficult and challenging because of (1) the nature of the data, (2) the semantic and syntactical problems, (3) the large mass of data and the resulting costs for manipulation, (4) the narrative approach to data searching and the resultant subjective pitfalls, and (5) the virtual impracticality of the direct approach to data so that an interface is required in the form of a knowledgeable mediator. The opportunities for such a system are: (1) once the data has been rendered machinable, no subsequent processing is necessary; (2) the data can be reformatted in a variety of ways with no additional effort or expense: (3) independent accessibility from a number of locations becomes possible; (4) the information is transferable to other programs with little added intervention; and (5) the information is displayable in a variety of formats, including high quality print, without the need to restructure the file each time. Limits are as follows: (1) cost is the biggest factor since, in an interactive system, the file must be "on" constantly, demanding large amounts of dedicated memory (also a large amount of data has to be moved to reach a specific answer). (2) mediation between the user and the file is essential for effective use. (3) excellence is required in indexing so that the abstract concepts as well as concrete specifics can be retrieved with equal effectiveness. (4) retrieval relevance is highly unpredictable and unstable. Retrieval of abstractions (such as sociological aspects of water resource planning) is impossible in an unindexed system and relatively haphazard in well-indexed files. Considering the potentials of such systems as the WRSIC retrieval system and the impact generally, it is our feeling that we are moving closer to full text storage of documents and therefore nearer to a true information center rather than a document center. Desk-side access terminals will become increasingly available to water resources educators, managers, and researchers. This availability will enable direct file input from the terminal as well as direct receipt of the output results of file searches.

67

References

GENERAL INFORMATION PROCESSING SYSTEM APPLICATION INFORMATION,
by Charles H. Addison, Duane Coney, Margaret Jones, Robert
W. Shields, and James W. Sweeney. University of Oklahoma
Science Series, Monograph IV, March 1970.

GENERAL INFORMATION PROCESSING SYSTEM REMOTE TERMINAL USER'S
GUIDE, By Charles H. Addison, Phillip W. Blackwell, Wayne
E. Smith, Robert W. Shields, and James W. Sweeney, Uni-
versity of Oklahoma Information Science Series, Monograph
No. 3, March 1969.

GIPSY Computer Retrieval of Geologic Literature, by Phillip
W. Blackwell, Jack L. Morrison, and Wayne E. Smith, Jr.,
Oklahoma Geology Notes, Vol. 29, No. 1, February 1969,
p. 6-13.

1971 ANNUAL REPORT, Cooperative Water Resources Research and
Training. Office of Water Resources Research, U. S.
Department of the Interior, December 1971, 335 p.

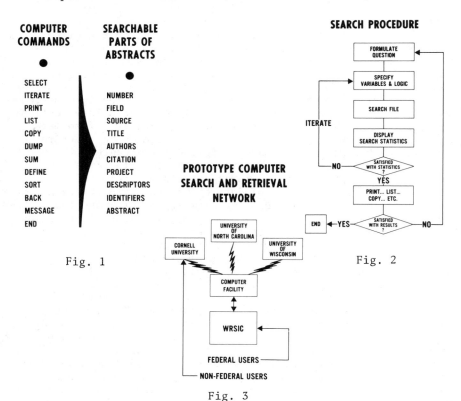

Fig. 1

Fig. 2

Fig. 3

WHAT IS THE EFFECT OF DETERGENTS ON
THE AMERICAN OYSTER?

m SELECT

c ....

m A. FIELD < 5 >

m LOGIC A

c SEARCH BEGINNING

c SEARCHED 37354

c SELECTED 10562 SUBSET 1

c VARIABLES SATISFIED

    A 10562

c ITERATE?

m YES

m A. DESCR < OYSTER >

m LOGIC A

c SEARCH BEGINNING

c SEARCHED 10562

c SELECTED 207 SUBSET 2

c VARIABLES SATISFIED

    A 207

c ITERATE?

m YES

m A. ABSTR < AMERICAN OYST >

m B. S < DETERGENT >

m LOGIC A and B

c SEARCH BEGINNING

c SEARCHED 207

c SELECTED 0 SUBSET 3

c VARIABLES SATISFIED

    A 3

    B 2

c ITERATE?

m NO

m BACK

c SPECIFY SUBSET NO.

m 2

m A. DESCR < OYSTER >

m B. S < DETERG >

m LOGIC A and B

c SEARCH BEGINNING

c SEARCHED 207

c SELECTED 3 SUBSET 3

c VARIABLES SATISFIED

    A 207

    B 3

c ITERATE?

m NO

m LIST

c ....

c TERMINAL OR PRINTER?

m T

c ENTER LABEL (S)

m TITLE

m NUMBER

m

c TITLE EFFECTS OF 'SOFT' DETERGENTS

    OF THE AMERICAN OYSTER (CRA

ACCESSION NO. W70-08696

TITLE: BIOLOGICAL EFFECTS OF SURFAC
    ANIMALS.

ACCESSION NO. W71-11651

TITLE: EFFECTS OF SYNTHETIC SURFACT
    (M. MERCENARIA) AND OYSTERS

ACCESSION NO. W71-12307

m ITERATE

c ....

SPECIFY SUBSET NO.

m 3

m A. NUMBER < W70-06696 >

m LOGIC A

c SEARCH BEGINNING

c SEARCHED 3

c SELECTED 1 SUBSET 4

c VARIABLES SATISFIED

    A 1

c ITERATE?

m NO

m PRINT

c TERMINAL OR PRINTER?

m T

EFFECTS OF 'SOFT' DETERGENTS ON EMBRY
    (CRASSOSTREA VIRGINICA),
    BUREAU OF COMMERCIAL FISHERIES
    ANTHONY CALABRESE, AND HARRY C.
    1966 PROCEEDINGS OF THE NATIONAL
    JUNE, 1967. 3 TAB, 6 REF.

DESCRIPTORS
*LINEAR ALKYLATE SULFONATES, *
MORTALITY, *TOXICITY, GROWTH RA
EMRYONIC GROWTH STATE, LARVAL

IDENTIFIERS
*CRASSOSTREA VIRGINICA, DETERGEN

ABSTRACT
    EXPERIMENTS WERE DESIGNED TO
    AND LARVAE OF A STANDARD LINEA
    COMMERICAL LIQUID LAS DETERGEN
    DEGRADATION PRODUCTS OF LAS.

    (SJOLSETH AND KATZ WASHINGT

FIELD 05C WATER RESOURCES
    OFFICE OF T
    U.S. DE

    ACCESSION

Fig. 4

PRODUCING A BIBLIOGRAPHY ON ARSENIC AND LEAD

```
m   SELECT
m   A FIELD   <5>
m   LOGIC  A
c   SEARCHED   42920
c   SELECTED   15036  SUBSET  1
c   VARIABLES SATISFIED
        A  15036
m   ITERATE
m   A FIELD   <6E>
m   LOGIC  NOT A
c   SEARCHED   15036
c   SELECTED   12735  SUBSET  2
c   VARIABLES SATISFIED
        A  2301
m   ITERATE
m   A. ABSTR   <ARSENIC>
m   B. S       <LEAD>
m   LOGIC  A OR B
c   SEARCHED   12735
c   SELECTED   216  SUBSET  3
c   VARIABLES SATISFIED
        A  49
        b  171
m   ITERATE
m   A. ABSTR <LEAD> WI1 <TO>
m   LOGIC  NOT A
c   SEARCHED   216
c   SELECTED   109  SUBSET  4
c   VARIABLES SATISFIED
        A  107
m   PRINT
```

ARSENIC ACCUMULATION BY FISH IN LAKES TREATED WITH SODIUM AR
  NEW YORK STATE DEPT. OF HEALTH, ALBANY. DIV. OF LABORATORI
  WILLIAM W. ULLMANN, ROBERT W. SCHAEFER, AND WALLACE W. SAM
  J WATER POLLUTION CONTROL FED, VOL 33, NO 4, PP 416-418, A
  REF.

DESCRIPTORS
  *AQUATIC WEED CONTROL, *ARSENIC COMPOUNDS, *FISH, *H
  *SODIUM ARSENITE, AQUATIC PLANTS, CHEMICAL ANALYSIS,
  NEUTRON ACTIVATION ANALYSIS, NEW YORK, SEDIMENTS, WA
  ALKALINITY.

IDENTIFIERS
  CALICO BASS, CASSADAGA LAKE(NY), CHAUTAUQUA LAKE(NY)

ABSTRACT
  AUTHORS INVESTIGATED CONCENTRATIONS OF ARSENIC IN WA
  (CALICO BASS) IN THREE NEW YORK STATE LAKES, TWO OF
  SUBJECTED TO SODIUM ARSENITE TREATMENT FOR SUBMERGED
  METHODS FOR LAKE WATER WERE NOT DESCRIBED, BUT RESID
  DETERMINED BY NEUTRON ACTIVATION ANALYSIS. FINDLEY L
  MILLIGRAM LITER) CONTAINED ARSENIC CONCENTRATION OF
  MILLIGRAMS LITER BEFORE SPRAYING, 7.0 MILLIGRAMS LIT
  AFTER SPRAYING IN MAY 1958, AND 1.5 MILLIGRAMS LITER
  SPRING 1959, CONCENTRATION HAD RETURNED TO PRETREATM
  CHAUTAUGUA LAKE (ALKALINITY 256 MILLIGRAMS LITER) C
  MILLIGRAMS LITER BEFORE TREATMENT IN JUNE 1959. AFTE
  ARSENICAL (4.5 HOURS), CONCENTRATION OF 0.45 MILLIGR
  FOUND WHICH DIMINISHED TO 0.04 TO 0.04 MILLIGRAMS LITER AFT
  UNTREATED CASSADAGA LAKE (ALKALINITY 64 MILLIGRAMS
  ARSENIC CONCENTRATIONS FROM 0.04 TO 0.10 MILLIGRAMS
  PRECEDING STUDY. IN CASSADAGA AND CHATAUQUA LAKES ME
  WAS LOWER THAN DETECTABLE LIMIT (0.10 MUCROGRAMS GRA
  AUTHORS ATTRIBUTE HIGHER RESIDUES IN FINDLEY LAKE FI
  0.28-056, MAXIMA 0.31 1 0) TO PERSISTENCE OF RESIDU
  ALL FISH EXAMINED, ARSENIC WAS LESS THAN THAT REPORT
  EDIBLE MARINE FISH. (EICHHORN WIS)

FIELD 05B 02H   WATER RESOURCES SCIENTIFIC I
                                  OFFICE OF WATER RESOURC
                                  U.S. DEPARTMENT OF TH

                                  ACCESSION NO W6

Fig. 5
```
```

THE INFORMATION SCIENCE APPROACH TO
TRANSFER OF KNOWLEDGE

By

Warren B. McBirney
Chief, Engineering Reference Branch
Bureau of Reclamation
Denver, Colorado
USA

Synopsis

The information science approach to facilitating the transfer of knowledge is discussed in general terms. Use of abstract
bulletins, selective dissemination of information, bibliographies, state-of-the-art reviews, microforms, and retrieval are
reviewed. The operational scientific information program of
the Bureau of Reclamation is described in its application of
the computer for dissemination and retrieval. A brief view is
given of feasible methods for providing scientific information
to developing countries as compared to more modern societies.

Introduction

Long ago, the existence of an information explosion was
recognized, graphed, debated, and given lengthy rhetorical
treatment. In the past 15 years, much experimentation has
taken place with regard to managing the explosion, and we have
seen a proliferation of methods and experimental techniques
designed to cope with a phenomenon that remains largely an
unsolved problem in developed countries. The proliferation is
perhaps a necessary adjunct to an eventual synthesis of worthwhile systems and a reduction in the number of avenues one may
travel toward a "best" approach to his own particular problem.

In the United States, the availability of intellectual and
computer resources could be looked upon as simultaneously the
solution to the problem and the cause or aggravator of it. The
intellect is responsible for growth in scientific information
output, as well as design and use of computer hardware and
software for handling it.

Within the context of this conference, the most that can
be said regarding the transfer of knowledge, it seems to me,
is that the opportunity to acquire knowledge is implicit in the
transfer of information from one practitioner to another
through some medium (written or oral), but whether it becomes
actual knowledge with the recipient is a matter dependent upon
his concentration. Suffice it to say that the party of the
first part may have knowledge which he wishes to impart to a
party of the second part, but it only becomes knowledge when

71

the first party expresses his information meaningfully in such a manner as to permit mental synthesis into knowledge by the second party. Also, to make a peripheral point, many opportunities exist in the transfer process for an undesired diminution in quality.

In the sections that follow, an attempt will be made to summarize some of the means by which information can be transferred, conventionally and in sophistication. The success of the efforts will have considerable impact on both developed and developing countries, but more on the latter since their needs are the greater.

Abstracting and Indexing Reports

One of the simplest ways to call attention to the contents of an article and a report is to provide an abstract in which principal findings are concisely summarized. A prospective reader may quickly scan the abstract to decide whether the full article may be of sufficient interest to justify committing time to read it. Document contents can also be represented by assigning definitive words in index fashion. These are variously called keywords, descriptors, or identifiers. Choosing such terms is a precision matter, since a reviewer could easily be misled by terms of secondary importance.

Abstracting and indexing are becoming near-requirements in the scientific community. If properly done, they are time-saving tasks for all prospective readers. Many review publications will announce an article through quoting the abstract and index terms. The index terms are frequently used as input to computerized data bases, along with the complete bibliographic reference.

Abstract Bulletins

One of the most easily compiled information sources is the abstract bulletin. This medium has been used since 1830, and has done much to relieve the individual researcher from examining full size documents in libraries. It also brings to his attention many more references than could be expected in most libraries.

The abstract is usually supplemented by a short list of keywords defining document content. These may be drawn from a thesaurus of terms developed to facilitate indexing, or the author's vocabulary as an expert in his field. Whenever a thesaurus is a professional product conforming to standards for such words, its use is much preferred, particularly when the indexing terms are to be used in a computerized retrieval system. However, any indexing is preferable to none, and is a valuable supplement to the abstract.

Researchers are finding that abstract journals are not always the answer to their prayers, especially as they expand in volume. Some measure of control may be had in making content more specialized, or in so devising categories that a reviewer need search only a small portion of any one issue. This solution is not without some measure of risk because the bulletin editor may not always categorize correctly or cross-reference accurately.

Another approach is to issue a bulletin more frequently, such as every two weeks instead of monthly. While the physical size is reduced thereby, the gain may be somewhat psychologically offset by receiving twice the number of bulletins.

Bibliographies and State-of-the-art Reviews

A more specific type of information resource is the bibliography, a product of conventional and special libraries alike. It is more often generated upon request, although libraries and information centers which sense a developing need for topical bibliographies do not wait for demand.

The researcher frequently asks for or compiles a bibliography as a prelude to beginning a new study or extending an existing one. A frequent complaint is that a comprehensive bibliography may require in preparation too great a proportion of the time to be committed to the entire study. Unless the compiler is either the researcher himself or quite competent in the subject field, a great amount of time may actually be consumed, beyond the limits of good sense. Nevertheless, a bibliography that is conscientiously used can be an overall timesaver and a definite economic benefit.

The state-of-the-art review is truly a high-priced bibliography, but it goes a significant major step beyond by way of evaluating studies on an individual basis and then, in an environment of competence, summarizing the current state of investigations. Only compilation by the prospective researcher himself could improve on it as a valuable tool pointing the way toward continuing research. Both of these products suffer with the passage of time, and must be updated to survive. Also, both are greatly dependent upon having adequate resources upon which to draw for the initial listing and eventually providing copies of complete references listed therein. Librarians the world over rarely discard a bibliography, because of its potential value and cost in compiling.

Computerized Information Retrieval

Most of today's information centers are dependent upon the capabilities of computer programming. Tape, drum, or disk equipment provide the storage medium for bibliographic

references, abstracts, and index terms. Some of the larger
systems even support complete text searching capability, but
the more common are less sophisticated. A cathode ray tube
display is frequently coupled with the computer so that there
can be interaction of user and the data base.

Peripheral equipment may include tape output, printer,
plotter, and various types of microforms. The more common of
the last is the microfiche, usually a positive or negative film
containing 60, 98, 200, or up to 1,000 frames of information in
a 4- by 6-inch area. The microfiche is read on an enlargement
viewer, some of which have printing capability.

The data base may be queried in a great many ways--some
by keyword input, punchcard input, paper tape input, and direct
keyboard input. Combinations of keywords responding to AND, OR,
and NOT instructions frequently provide access to limit the
response to the most narrow of specifics.

Obviously, the computer provides a readily accessible
storage volume that cannot be matched by manual or other memory
systems. But a data bank can only respond with what is already
in storage, and the skill used to place references in storage
has a significant influence on what information can be recalled.
This is particularly true when keywords are depended on for
access, because inadequate or inaccurate indexing of a reference
may leave it irretrievable.

A data bank must be a living thing to be viable, continually
supplemented with new material and without gaps in time. What
starts out to be a servant can eventually become a master in the
sense that as it grows, it becomes more valuable and thereby
demands more input to sustain its value.

Selective Dissemination of Information

The word "selective" is the key to this concept, a method
of giving a system user only what he wishes to see and will
devote time to read. In the broadest sense, the title on a
book facilitates selection through visual comparison with other
titles and one's memory concerning current needs or desires.
Today's connotation encompasses sophisticated computer techniques
for matching a user's very specific interests with the contents
of certain documents, where both have been indexed from the same
vocabulary (thesaurus). Only those references meeting defined
criteria are announced to the prospective user.

Other selection techniques do not require a controlled
vocabulary, but the matching process is similar.

SDI service for individuals is expensive if one considers
only input and dissemination costs. More difficult to quantify,

however, as a counterbalancing credit, is the value of successful selectivity avoiding waste in time on the user's part in
finding worthwhile references and screening out imperfect ones.
One frequent compromise is to provide SDI for group interests
so that 5 to 10 persons receive a single announcement of references meeting their collective interests. This approach usually
requires acceptance of more general references, and submerges
the needs of individuals.

Some SDI systems are coupled to a loan service for those
documents wanted in full. Others merely announce them, with
the user left to his own local resources in getting them.

Microforms

Photographic means have been applied to providing a
systems user with a reduced-size copy of each pertinent
reference. Duplication and mailing costs are thereby reduced,
but lower costs on one end of the process may be offset by
significant costs for the recipient to get the reference to a
readable size again. Roll film in 16 mm and 35 mm has been
used, as well as strip film and 35-mm aperture cards, the
latter with single frame or 4 frames per card. A more common
microform for narrative material is the microfiche, available
in several sizes but the most common is 4 by 6 inches with 60,
98, 200, or up to 1,000 frames.

Obviously, a microfiche frame is too small to be read with
the unaided eye, and a reader or reader-printer is required.
Large information centers are able to accommodate the machine
costs of blowback equipment fairly easily, but small libraries
or technical organizations cannot often afford the initial
hardware investment. Advantages to using fiche are inherent
in their size, the number of pages that can be included on
each fiche, low duplicating costs, and (following purchase of
the reader-printer) low full-size copy costs.

Bureau of Reclamation Scientific Information System

In 1963, Reclamation recognized that greater sophistication was needed in keeping its scientists and engineers up to
date in their respective fields. The press of everyday assignments was too great to expect them even to scan the large
volumes of available literature in attempts to maintain their
levels of expertise. Consequently, an organizational component
was created with the mission of screening and disseminating
pertinent scientific literature. Today it consists of selective
dissemination of information (SDI) and retrieval systems for
over 1,900 employees, from the journeyman level to supervisors
and managers.

For those of you not familiar with Reclamation programs, we are a planning, design, construction, and operating agency interested in all phases of water resources development, acting in concert with objectives of the proposed Department of Natural Resources. The range of interest includes dams, canals, pipelines, power generation and transmission, municipal and industrial water supplies, water quality, environmental matters, and atmospheric water resources management.

The Bureau is most widely known for such structures as Hoover Dam, Glen Canyon Dam, the All-American and San Luis Canals, and Grand Coulee Dam (soon to be the world's largest source of hydropower). Among Federal agencies, ours is unique in one respect of interest to the taxpayer - about 89 percent of the costs of Reclamation projects are eventually repaid to the Treasury by water and power users.

The Bureau employs about 2,500 engineers and scientists throughout the 17 Western States. Our Engineering and Research Center is located in Denver, Colorado, staffed by 1,200 employees, including over 650 engineers and scientists. Technical supervision of design and administration of construction contracts, by which over 99 percent of all Bureau constructions is performed, are directed from Denver, as well as a viable research program whose products are finding application throughout the world.

In addition, Reclamation operates now in an atmosphere demanding the multi-disciplinary approach to water resource development; economic alternatives taking into account inter-basin factors as contrasted to the older, more limited intra-basin considerations. Demographic trends affect the need for water resources, and result in technically challenging problems associated with new sources of water potentially available through desalination of brackish and sea waters, the increase of atmospheric water yields, and geothermal sources.

The SDI system operates, then, to satisfy the needs of employees in this wide spectrum of interests. Input originates from many sources, and a great volume of materials is scanned each month. Over 625 periodicals are reviewed along with technical society journals, Federal and state research reports, foreign publications, and translations. Thirty-six percent of the input to this current awareness program consists of preprints of papers, 34 percent are articles from periodicals, 22 percent are reports and monographs, and 8 percent are translations. About 19 percent of the input originates in Reclamation. Our emphasis has been on preprints and unpublished reports because in this way valuable information can be made available long before it would otherwise appear in more formal print.

With a controlled vocabulary in the form of a Thesaurus of Water Resources Terms--numbering over 6,500 keywords--pertinent documents are indexed. Correspondingly, the professional interests of each system user are defined with terms from the same Thesaurus. Selection of keywords is made by trained engineer-literature specialists who index the documents as well as narrative statements of interest furnished by each user.

A computer is programmed to match document contents to the user's interests, and he is furnished an SDI card on which are given an abstract, the bibliographic reference, and index information. A return portion permits his ordering a loan copy of the full document and includes a declaration as to how close the document announced fitted his interests.

A unique feature of the program concerns a desk retrieval system. With the return portion of the card removed, the SDI card may be mounted, abstract toward the reader, in shingle fashion on a profile heading sheet. The user's personal set of keywords is printed across the top of this sheet, for easy reference to the keywords causing dissemination. The desk retrieval system enables the user to perform a limited manual search for document references previously furnished to him.

Because the SDI system is selective by design, the majority of documents used as input each month do not come to each user's attention. Thus, without some alternative means to give visibility to these materials, the user would be denied access to items of peripheral interest or those totally unrelated to his primary field. Therefore, an abstract bulletin called RECAP is provided periodically on an organizational basis and contains all inputs to the SDI system. Any employee of Reclamation may request loan copies of documents from RECAP, whether an SDI participant or not.

We study the responses of users in the SDI system to establish monthly patterns and predict long-term trends. Analyses of keyword usage on cumulative bases make possible meaningful revisions of our Thesaurus. Similar analyses of users' interest profiles indicate terms which should be eliminated in favor of adding new ones more in line with their needs. Other informal studies reveal subject areas needing greater attention.

No system should operate for very long without giving the customer a chance to speak his piece. We have had two user's surveys, both giving the respondent opportunities to provide answers to questions and to comment at length if he desires. The most recent survey was conducted by a component not directly connected with system activities to ensure a detached evaluation. The summary report said, in part, "It is evident from the returns that the SDI system meets with widespread acceptance, stimulates a much higher interest in current technical literature than would otherwise exist, and even by itself is effective as a means of keeping Bureau personnel informed of new technical developments." More specifically, 97 percent of the respondents said the SDI system was moderately to very effective in keeping them informed in their fields of interest.

Over the last 9 years, the SDI input, supplemented extensively by thousands of other references, has become a data base of useful importance. The base may be manipulated in several ways to retrieve answers to search questions. We can address the base with keywords only (up to 6) to make the output very selective, and to provide the user with any combination of bibliographic references, keyword listings and abstracts that he wishes. Cost is currently between $20 to $30 per search.

Considerations in Global Transfer of Information

Despite the fact that information science techniques have been developing for over 25 years, information centers in the so-called developed countries still do not exhibit any except the most general common characteristics in regard to the processing of information. Thus, at this stage, it seems presumptuous to suggest specific approaches to any global schemes that would uniformly serve all or the majority of countries.

Only in 1971 was the first international conference held to study the feasibility of a world science information system. Under the acronym of UNISIST, the Director-General of UNESCO authorized a study with the International Council of Scientific Unions (ICSU) on this matter.

To illustrate the magnitude of this self-imposed problem, consider just the number of world agricultural documentation services and their diverse approaches to serving their users. A 1969 survey by the European Atomic Energy Community (Luxembourg) revealed there were 514 secondary agricultural documentation services with total output of 1.5 million references. Of these, 150 issue titles only, 378 issue titles and abstracts, 237 have subject indexes, 248 have author indexes, 450 produce serially published output, 31 services are mechanized with machine-readable tape available from 18 services, and 66 services offer retrieval to search questions. There are 100 card services issuing 348,000 references per year. Of the services analyzed, 50 countries are involved in 22 languages. It should be apparent that we are a long way from unifying the exchange of information mechanisms in the world.

Several points can be made in regard to facilitating the transfer of information. First, each of us has an obligation to limit the input of information which eventually becomes a

part of the overall problem. Only papers and reports of substance should be written, and once written the material contained therein should not be rewritten for some other outlet
just for the sake of building a seemingly impressive literary
effort.

Second, all papers and reports should be author-indexed
and -abstracted. Information centers will never have the
complement of personnel needed to do this for the entire
scientific community. Failure to include an abstract often
means that a paper gets little visibility because abstract
journals frequently will not include just bibliographic
references.

Third, it is important to remember that being able to
assure understanding of the contents of papers and reports
should be the principal objective of any author. If we write
with such complexity that only the best informed can understand, we may impress our immediate colleagues but we miss the
great bulk of the potential audience. In a social sense,
the needs of less articulate and experienced engineers and
scientists in developing countries should be met. We do not
need to re-invent the wheel, for example, each time that
transportation equipment is discussed, but neither should
authors confound the reader with ego-building displays of
personal knowledge for no good purpose.

And fourth, I believe that all of us should develop, if it
doesn't exist already, a consciousness of social responsibility.
In personal contacts, discussions at international meetings,
and in the work of advisory teams the transfer of information
should take into account the expertise of the user, the
economics of the area to be involved, and the level and extent
of technology available to use the information.

Assuring the continuous flow of information on a global
basis could be a major step toward removing some of the
disparities that exist among nations and contribute to tensions.

TRANSMITTING WATER RESOURCES INFORMATION
BY A TIME-SHARE SYSTEM[1]

by

Conrad G. Keyes, Jr., Associate Professor, New Mexico
State University, Las Cruces, New Mexico, USA.

Ray T. Telfer, Research Meteorologist, Division of
Atmospheric Water Resources Management, Bureau
of Reclamation, Denver, Colorado, USA.

Alabama Glass, Marketing Representative, Computer
Sharing Services, Denver, Colorado, USA.

Synopsis

A time-share computer system to transmit water resources
information has been described by the authors. The basic
system consists of a central processing unit, terminal locations, input data locations, and output data locations or
users. The system has been used by the Jemez Atmospheric Water
Resources Research Project (JAWRRP) but could be expanded to
include real-time forecasting or design in any atmospheric
water resources program.

Introduction

Many of the Division of Atmospheric Water Resources Management (DAWRM), Bureau of Reclamation's Contractors have a need
for a real-time data system in order to conduct weather modification field experiments and/or operations or to evaluate their
projects during post analyses. These contractors can obtain
weather, precipitation or streamflow information in various
degrees of reliability, usefulness and costs from several
sources--direct from NOAA, USGS, weather consultants and DOD
(Navy, Army and Air Weather Service) sources.

To reduce the cost and increase the reliability of data
vital to the contractor's operations, the DAWRM explored the
feasibility of providing high quality, low-cost data to all
concerned from a centralized source.

Project Skywater Environmental Data Network

The design and implementation of the environmental network
has been reported by Telfer (1972) and is depicted schematically
in Fig. 1. Functionally, this network has been very flexible

---

[1]System used under Contract No. 14-06-D-6803 with the Division
of Atmospheric Water Resources Management, Bureau of Reclamation.

and has been used for a variety of tasks by the Jemez Atmospheric Water Resources Research Project (JAWRRP). However, Telfer (1972) has stated the main purposes of the system to be:

1. Purvey National Meteorological Center data and derived products to the contractors on a real-time basis.
2. Provide a pool of computer programs and a data base to enable the DAWRM to exploit computer technology economically in all of the weather modification experiments and/or operations.

The heart of the environmental network is the Computer Sharing Services facilities in Denver, Colorado. Figure 2 shows the Honeywell/G.E.-400 series computer that has been used for at least two years.

The main time-sharing system, the Honeywell/G.E.-440, is a medium-to-large-scale general purpose digital computer dedicated entirely to time-sharing.

The communications system used in transmitting data from Suitland, Maryland to Denver is a Honeywell 316. This is a small scale, high speed communications system.

Because of the accessibility, via teletypewriter locations across the Western United States, to its data base and pool of computer programs, the environmental network has been very useful in developing, testing and implementing a variety of mathematical or physical models used for the design or forecast of weather modification activities in experimental, pilot and operational projects.

Input Information

Rawinsonde (upper air) data can be transmitted into the system from either Suitland, Maryland (computer-to-computer) or from any of the field projects (teletypewriter terminals-to-computer). A series of computer programs is available to process the rawinsonde data, store them in individual files and store the output individual files on the disc storage. Other input data, i.e., the JAWRRP data used in a non-parametric statistical evaluation, can be placed in disk storage files or on magnetic tape along with the output information needed for future designs or operations. Telfer (1972) presented 56 forecast gridded fields of data that are also transmitted from Suitland and stored in the CSS computer. The areal coverage of this grid is basically the Western half of the United States, but can be expanded to include most of North America.

The Cuba, New Mexico upper air data and the 6-hour mean areal precipitation data used in the evaluation of the effect of winter seeding in the northern New Mexico weather modification project, as reported by Keyes, et.al. (1972a and 1972b), were

81

actually processed on the time-share system. The processing procedure will be described by Keyes, et.al. (1972c) at a later conference.

Computer Programs

The Computer Sharing Services catalog of computer programs (2) contains numerous standard and specialized subroutines or files that are used by some of the field projects. Since a user number accounting system is used, all field projects can also develop computer programs that are needed in their actual operations or in post analyses of their projects.

Each rawinsonde from either Suitland or any project can be processed in a variety of computer programs that have been developed by the DAWRM or its contractors. Telfer (1972) and Pederman (1970) have mentioned these programs in the past and they are given in Fig. 3.

Keyes, et.al. (1972a and 1972c) reported the computer programs that have been developed by the Northern New Mexico project (JAWRRP) for use in data processing and evaluation of the winter seeding. Figure 3 also gives a list of these file names used in the environmental network.

Output Information

Much information can be obtained by the user for forecasting operations on weather modification projects:
1. Variety of displays of the forecast grid fields of data (i.e., 500-mb temperature, 12-hour 500-mb height, etc.)
2. A plot of multiple fields on an expanded scale grid for the user's area of interest. This gridded output can be isoplethed by the user. However, Telfer (1972) has suggested that the gridded data are most useful when used directly as input to additional physical models that produce predicted upper air soundings, profiles, etc. (see Fig. 4).
3. The sizes of clouds which produce more rain from an ice phase seeding and also the sizes of clouds which will produce less rain if such seeding takes place (Telfer, 1972).
4. Use of predicted information from the convective models to predict particle growths when various sizes of hygroscopic particles are disseminated beneath the clouds.

---

[2]Computer Sharing Services Time-Sharing Reference Manual.

The Colorado State University analysis program (written for a CDC 6400 computer) was made available and rewritten for the GE-400 time-share system.

The precipitation processing files are used in a series to give the results needed in the evaluation program. An example of the mean areal 6-hour precipitation rates appears in Fig. 5.

Conclusions

The concept of the environmental network has been success-fully demonstrated in the Project Skywater program. The computer services and products offered by the CSS time-share system can grow to meet the needs of the users.

All sensitive activities such as forest fire control, flood forecasting, air pollution forecasting and control and a host of other functions requiring special weather or hydro-meteorological information and display can benefit from a user oriented, real-time environmental data system. Only an addi-tion of real-time surface weather data, hydrologic data, cer-tain kinds of ecological data and other information are required. An increased number of users of the system will create a more cost effective operation and justify the vast expense involved.

References

Keyes, C. G., Jr., J. V. Lunsford, F. D. Stover, D. Rottner and R. D. Wilkins; Interim Progress Report No. 5, July 1, 1971 through December 31, 1971; Engineering Experiment Station, New Mexico State University, February 28, 1972.

Keyes, C. G., Jr., D. Rottner, F. D. Stover and R. D. Wilkins, An Evaluation of the Results of Four Years of Randomized Seeding in Northern New Mexico, Reprint of the Third Conference on Weather Modification, Amer. Met. Society, Rapid City, June 26-29, 1972.

Keyes, C. G. Jr., R. D. Wilkins and F. D. Stover, Data Processing Techniques Used in Evaluating Weather Modification Projects, Preprint of Eighth Annual American Water Resources Associa-tion Conference, AWRA, St. Louis, October 31, 1972.

Pederman, W. A., The Utilization of the Computer for Operational Weather Modification, Technical Note No. 1, The Weather Modification Research Project, The University of Denver, 1970.

Telfer, Ray T., Project Skywater Environmental Data Network, Weather Analysis and Forecast Conference, Portland, May, 1972.

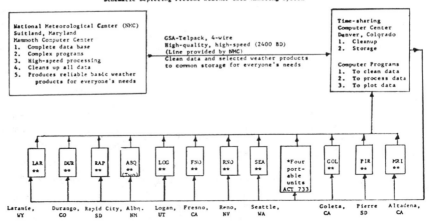

Fig. 1. Schematic depicting present weather data handling system.

Fig. 2. T/S system.

1. ANALYSIS (ANAL)

2. SECTIONAL CHARTS (SECTNL) (RAYPLT)

3. CROSS SECTION (XSEXN)

4. RAOB (RAOB)

5. CONVECTIVE MODEL (CONVECT)

6. CSU OROGRAPHIC MODEL (CSUMOD)

7. HIRSCH MODEL (SDGPCM)

8. 12-HR FCST SOUNDING (TPRAOB)

LIST OF OPERATIONAL PROGRAMS (JAWRRP)

1. STATISTICAL EVALUATION OF SEEDING (NSTAT)

2. DAILY PRECIPITATION GENERATION FOR ALL STATIONS (PCPOUT)

3. MEAN AREAL 6-HR PRECIPITATION RATES (PCP6HR)

Fig. 3. Example of operational programs within the environmental network.

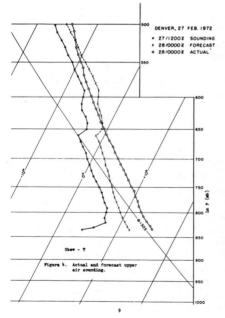

Figure 4. Actual and forecast upper air sounding.

MEAN AREAL 6 HR PRECIPITATION RATES

DATE	AU	PER	MAPR	MRPR
681113	1	3	55	55
681113	2	4	393	393
681114	3	1	202	210
681114	4	2	239	248
681114	5	3	10	10
681114	6	4	0	0
681115	7	1	0	0
681115	8	2	33	35
681115	9	3	250	259
681115	10	4	151	157
681116	11	1	2	2
681116	12	2	0	0
681116	13	3	10	10
681116	14	4	48	64
681117	15	1	3	6
681117	16	2	19	38
681125	17	3	0	0
681125	18	4	0	0
681126	19	1	0	0
681126	20	2	0	0
681128	21	3	171	171
681125	22	4	232	232
681129	23	1	2	17
681129	24	2	0	0
681201	25	3	193	193
681201	26	4	112	112
681202	27	1	5	7
681202	28	2	19	27
681202	29	3	22	31
681202	30	4	1	1
681203	31	1	0	0
681203	32	2	0	0
681216	33	3	0	0
681216	34	4	0	0
681217	35	1	0	0

AU - THE ANALYSIS UNIT NUMBER
PER - THE PERIOD OF DAY (GMT), 2=1200, 3=1800
MAPR - THE MEAN AREAL 6 HR PRECIPITATION RATE
MRPR - THE MEAN REPORTING STATION 6 HR PRECIPITATION RATE

Fig. 4. Actual and forecast upper air sounding.

Fig. 5. Mean areal six hour precipitation rates as outputed by the time-share system.

DISCUSSION by W. W. Doyel*

In discussing data and information storage and retrieval
two items need stressing: the purpose for putting the data
and information into the system; and the need for and use of
the data - and the actual input. The proper data must be
acquired and available to the user. The data must be in
compatible form, of comparable quality, accessible and
retrievable. Many data will not be in machine-readable form
but must still meet this criteria. Software packages can be
developed fairly easily to manipulate data, but handling data
or information that does not meet much, either current or
anticipated is useless. Stress must be also placed on user
requirements - the system must be responsive. The trend today
is away from the central repository to storage at local or
regional level with indexing as the access mechanism. Also,
overall environmental systems are under consideration or
development, which will include local centers for various data
from various disciplines. The proposed National Environmental
Information System (Dingell Bill) is now in conference committee
in Congress. The RALI system is now under development within
the Interior Department. Initial action in establishing the
National Water Data Exchange (NAWDEX) has been taken by the
U.S. Geological Survey. Various states and universities also
are developing environmental information systems. It is the
development of these systems to where they are responsive
and the assurance that the data and information entered into
them will satisfy user needs that is important - not the
development of the mechanics per se - which is being done,
and is a much simpler matter to resolve.

DISCUSSION by John Miller**

Mr. Browzin has made an interesting suggestion. It is
true as he suggests that much research work is published
in a form difficult for practicing engineers and administrators to use. I doubt that any committee however constituted
can provide the standardization he seeks. The best solution
for gaining acceptance of good ideas and rejection of bad is
the marketplace of practice. There is a need for publication
devoted most to application, or more emphasis on application
in present publications. Perhaps a partial solution would
be a requirement that all articles in present publications
have a good summary which presents the essential elements of
the assumptions, methods and applications with a minimum
of mathematics. This would enable many more practicing
engineers to use new developments.

---

*U.S. Geological Survey

**Office of Hydrology W21, National Weather Service

DISCUSSION by Sie Ling Chiang*

In spite of the existing difficulties of communication between people of different background, both "jargons" and "redundancy" are unavoidable. "Jargon" provides shortcut for communication and "redundancy" provides necessary overlapping of knowledge so that people of different disciplines can communicate. Therefore, it is up to educators as well as individuals involved to decide what type of people they want to produce or to be, and prepare for it.

DISCUSSION by B. S. Browzin**

The number of published research papers of high quality, many of which are of practical interest, is so large that the practicing engineers cannot select the papers which he may successfully use to improve the design. Even if he spends enough time for search of pertinent research papers, he often will face another obstacle. Many, if not most of papers, are written rightfully in a scientific language and with mathematical formulations which are difficult for understanding by many engineers, particularly by those educated in schools not emphasizing scientifically oriented engineering programs. In addition, most authors of research papers do not extend their argument up to explaining how to use the results obtained in their research. Rarely numerical examples are added to facilitate a quick understanding of the method. The two obstacles create a gap between the research and engineering; aboundness of publications and insufficient emphasis on applications of results obtained in the research by the authors.

This gap could be closed by providing the engineers by certain users manuals for the new methods. Out of the abundant research, the best new methods must be selected and recommended by a body of experts. The selected methods must be presented to the engineers in users manuals written on the basis of original authors papers but with the inclusion of numerical examples and computer programs.

The duty of selecting papers could be taken by ASCE, AGU, government agencies, and by the large private firms with cooperation of the universities. The writing and the editing of the manuals could be performed on a volunteer basis by experts. At the same time, the publishing must be supported by certain financial funds. The selections of hydrologic topics could be the beginning of such a program.

*Bureau of Engineering, Pa. Dept. of Environmental Resources

**Ebasco Services, Inc., 2 Rector Street, New York, New York.

DISCUSSION by Daniel F. Lawrence*

Research and research use is a two-way street, i.e., the lines of communications must be kept open. At the same time there is urgent need to keep current on a common definition of what we mean by "The Real World."

Users must be motivated to "read the literature" and to be aware of knowledge available; and researchers must be motivated to recognize the need to produce "usable" finished product.

DISCUSSION by Peter W. Whitford**

Re: Reporter's Summary, Session I, p. 2, paragraph 2

The reference to "accounting processes" is misleading as the major thrust of the paper of Dr. Warford and myself was to point out the need to apply economic theory rather than accounting practices. However, in fact, the introduction of modern accounting systems is one of the major concerns of the World Bank in its municipal water supply activities. Although the Bank is actively interested in expanding the role of economic analysis in urban water supply, opportunities for applying such theory as exists have not been extensive to date.

---

*State Capitol, Salt Lake City, Utah

**World Bank, Washington, D. C.

SESSION II

NATIONAL AND INTERNATIONAL TRANSFER EXPERIENCES

Chairman: E.V. Richardson

Rapporteur: Allen Agnew

● *The range of experiences offered in this section illustrate the variety of concrete cases connecting research and practice in different cultural settings. Together with the papers of Sessions V and VI, they represent the vast array of water resources knowledge application and exchange and the benefits derived from cooperative programs.*

Rapporteur: Allen F. Agnew
Director, State of Washington Water Research Center
and Professor of Geology
Washington State University
Pullman, Washington, U.S.A.

In studying the five papers prepared for this session, I
was impressed by the fact that they seem to fall into four
categories--(1) two describe existing institutional entities
enabling people from many countries to share knowledge, (2)
one reports on a major river basin that needs attention, and
seeks knowledge from other experts, (3) one recounts a success
story of transfer of knowledge developed in one country to
another, and (4) one discusses institutional constraints that
hamper the transfer of knowledge regarding resource planning
and management, from a developed to a developing country. Let
us examine them in this order, although it is not the order
in which they are scheduled to speak.

<u>Developing Cooperative Research Programs for Flood Control in
Brahmaputra Valley</u> is a straightforward account by S. N.
Gupta, Commissioner of the Ganga Basin of the Ministry of
Irrigation and Power of India, New Delhi. Mr. Gupta tells us
that the Government of Assam created a Flood Control Commission
(of which he was a member) in July, 1970, to study flood problems
of the valley and to prepare a master plan for flood control.
The complexity of the river system and its meteorological
environment makes this a challenging river basin. A comprehensive research program is being planned jointly by the
Directorate of the Central Water and Power Commission of India
and Colorado State University's Hydrology and Water Resources
Department, through the National Science Foundation of the
U.S.A. Mr. Gupta's counterpart at Colorado State University
is Professor V. Yevjevich. Mr. Gupta hopes that participants
at this conference will provide suggestions regarding the
planning of the ten proposed studies. This is a case of
information transfer requested via the <u>conference</u> route.

The ten studies "required" for the master plan for flood
control, as listed by Mr. Gupta are:
    i. Prediction of flood stages and discharges at vulner-
able locations. Evaluation of effect of "rate of bed and flood
rise" on the stage-discharge relation.
    ii. Determination of water-surface profiles along existing
and proposed levees.
    iii. Investigations of levee-alignment problems with regard
to bank erosion.

iv. Determination of effect of increase in flood heights caused by reduced valley storage due to levee construction.

v. Determination of backwater effect on levee system in tributaries.

vi. Determination of flood-inundation areas on main stream and tributaries, and devising measures to protect them.

vii. Evolving flood-control structure designs that are efficient, economical, and safe, and determining their most suitable locations.

viii. Development of basin-wide plans for flood control and for coordinated operation of the flood-control works.

ix. Improving drainage channels in tributary basins.

x. Evolving combinations of structures (levees, spurs, and revetments) for achieving channel stabilization in the tributary as a whole from the foothills to its juncture with the Brahmaputra. Studying the development of cut-offs to shorten stream lengths and reduce flood heights.

In addition to reminding Mr. Gupta that one can never achieve immunity from floods (management and partial control, yes) and to disagree that floods are baffling (if carefully studied), I wish to raise the following questions:

Regarding "i","bed and flood rise" is unclear. I think he means the rise in bed and water surface profiles, because he discusses the gradual, long-term rise under 3.3. Is this correct?

Regarding "ii",since both longitudinal and cross profiles are important, those two words should be inserted.

Regarding "ix",recently in the U.S.A. we have been re-examining the matter of stream channelization and straightening, with the result that the civil engineering fraternity has been divided into two camps--those who favor it, and those who oppose it. Some of the issues are like those given in Mr. Gupta's Nos. iii, iv, and v. This particular matter deserves thorough discussion.

Regarding "x",if Mr. Gupta means all of the tributaries, I agree; on the other hand, if he means just one tributary, I question why and how this one will be selected. In either case, I think the question should be discussed along with "ix".

One of my colleagues at Washington State University, Dr. John F. Orsborn, who is Director of the Albrook Hydraulic Laboratory, reminds me that section 4.1 is weak where it states that the Brahmaputra River "does not conform to any defined laws of hydraulics;" on the contrary, it is very busy obeying these hydraulic laws. Mr. Gupta's last sentence in 4.1 states the case very well. Also, in line 1 of 7.4 doesn't Mr. Gupta mean _flow_ data rather than just _flood_?

Application of Hydrogeological Data to Long-Term Economics of Growing Sugar Cane in Venezuela is a case history by L. C. Halpenny, consultant for Water Development Corporation of Tucson, Arizona, U.S.A., and Dr. A. Dupuy P., general manager of Haciendas of Central El Palmar, San Mateo, Venezuela. In this technical paper we learn how a hydrogeological problem of overdraft was solved, by the conjunctive use of surface water and ground water. This is a matter of the _application_ of knowledge perfected in one area, to the solution of a problem in another area, thus involving the _geographical_ transfer of knowledge from the U.S.A. to Venezuela. I think that the authors should have stressed the integrated surface water-ground water management aspects of the project; I found as deficiencies the fact that they omitted information on stream flow quantity and quality, and the relationship of Lake Valencia's hydrology to the project.

Puerto Rico: A Case Study of Water Resource Technology Transfer is an excellent presentation by William E. Nothdurft, of the Department of Public Works of the Commonwealth of Puerto Rico; Mr. Nothdurft tellingly describes some of the barriers to information transfer--political and institutional barriers that must be overcome if the transfer process is to succeed. He sets the stage by describing the theoretical framework, and then discusses the Puerto Rican experience as it fits into that framework. His discussion presents us with the problems of transferring knowledge _from the developed to the developing areas_, but I feel that these problems are just as great in transferring knowledge within a so-called developed area. More of this, later.

Mr. A. D. Pobedimsky, of the United Nations' Economic Commission for Europe, describes the experience of the UNECE Committee on Water Problems in the area of _Transfer of Knowledge in Water Resources from Research to Practice_. The Committee, which was established in 1967, constitutes a forum for considering the more comprehensive problems related to overall socio-economic policies and planning in the water-resources field. The work of the Committee will be carried out in accordance with ten-year and five-year work programs. It will _prepare studies_ for circulation, _convene seminars and symposia_, and carry out _study tours_, thus engaging in several mechanisms of information transfer.

Mr. Larry D. Stephens, Executive Secretary of the U.S. Committee on Irrigation, Drainage, and Flood Control, noted that since it was established in 1950 it has provided a forum for engineers, scientists, and water users to exchange knowledge. His paper, entitled The Role of the International Commission on Irrigation and Drainage in the Transfer of Water Resources Knowledge, shows that this information-transfer process was intended for peers only. The biennial congresses and publications are mechanisms used by ICID. Membership in the ICID permits one to enjoy also the quarterly Newsletter and the ICID Bulletin. This represents an unusual kind of information transfer--the participating members are 61 countries, whose single representatives have the major task of transferring information to all interested individuals in their own countries; how well the representatives do their jobs in information transfer back home provides a measure of the degree of success of this organization.

I raise the question: How well is the process of information transfer being carried out between the official representative and the interested and qualified "engineers, scientists, and water users"? And, who are the "Water users"; more engineers and scientists? (The eighth Congress, in Varna, Bulgaria this year, was attended by about 700 engineers and scientists, from 45 countries; thus the Congresses constitute an impressive forum for information transfer).

Now, to return to the matter of how transfers are brought about. This involves (1) having something to transfer, (2) the physical mechanics or mechanisms of transfer, (3) the language of transfer, and (4) the institutional mechanisms for transfer.

We must begin with the premise that we do have something to transfer--an idea, a bit of data, interpretations of data, recommendations, etc.

A wide variety of transfer mechanisms exist, and more use could be made of some of them. All involve certain of our senses, particularly sight and hearing. The audio-visual area of our educational institutions has developed at a great rate during the past several years, as new techniques were devised, tested, and perfected. In this area equally important strides have been made by private industry and government, both of which use audio-visual mechanisms to reach their several different publics.

And this leads us to the third item of transfer that I mentioned--language. Whether language is verbal, computer, musical pantomime, or affects other senses such as smell, it must be common to both the person transferring and the person receiving. If verbal, the common language may be that of a nationality--say, English or Russian--or it may be that of a discipline--say economics. Rapid translation is available for the non English or the non Russian-speaking person, but we do not have such service for the non-engineer who wants to know what the engineer is talking about.

Language of the discipline, then, is a major barrier to the transfer of information to users not familiar with that discipline. This means that every person who deals with the planning and management of a natural resource such as water must make a special effort to understand the discipline of the other person, and he must make an equally great effort to communicate his ideas so they are understandable by persons unfamiliar with his discipline. The ICID, therefore, which undoubtedly does an excellent job of communicating with its public of engineers and scientists, must make a concerted effort if it is to communicate with other "water users"-- government officials and others who are not engineers and scientists. Similarly, the UN/ECE Committee on Water Problems, which examines socio-economic policies and planning, would have a much larger task if it were to attempt to communicate also with scientists and engineers who are not conversant with sociology and economics.

Now, I have saved the largest barrier until the last. As Mr. Nothdurft states so well in his paper, information transfer from developed to developing areas must take place in an environment of two different but overlapping systems. On the one hand, transfers take place within (intra) a system or institutional management structure and, on the other, transfers take place from an external source into (inter) a given system or structure. The efficiency of the intra system, he says, depends largely on the level of managerial sophistication of the structure. The efficiency of the inter system, however, depends upon the institutional flexibility of the initiating system and on the absorptive capacity of the receiving system.

The within (intra) system has barriers in developing areas, Nothdurft says, because many such areas have no cultural orientation or tradition favoring rational policy making. He continues, "The extreme cultural alterations, resulting from a very rapid development process...are often not paralleled by equal changes in the behavioral patterns and structural characteristics of the policy makers and organizations..." At the risk of destroying Mr. Nothdurft's illusion, I should like to suggest to the participants of the Conference that developed countries--at least democratic ones such as the United States of America--have similar barriers, although the reasons may be different. Despite the fact that we base our operations on "modern technology" and have a verbal disposition toward "comprehensive planning," we have not yet solved adequately the problem of incorporating the desires of the public into policy making. Thus in the U.S.A. we are presently engaged in numerous efforts, and are testing numerous mechanisms to overcome this barrier of inadequate public involvement in decision making.

The into (inter) system, as Mr. Nothdurft points out, has barriers related to inflexibility--both the sender and the receiver must be capable of modification. And, because this process is two-way, such adaptive modifications must take place at both the initial stage of transmission and at the feedback stage. I should stress, here, that there should be many feedback stages--thus we should think of the process of feedback as a virtually continuous one.

This problem of institutional inflexibility, he says, applies most directly to the source--the technologically advanced country. "The transfer of water resource knowledge is severely hampered by the tendency of the transfer source to rely on standardized and often inapplicable...procedures and...frameworks." This inflexibility correctly raises questions regarding the relevance of projects developed within such framework. It would be far more valuable to use "a program approach linked to the overall development goals of the region rather than a project-by-project approach." I feel that this excellent statement must be emphasized again and again.

Nothdurft raises an even more important point when he declares that the steady transfer of new and sophisticated technological input does not necessarily constitute an improvement in the capability of a system of a developing country to manage a resource; there is a point of diminishing returns for a system that is capable of absorbing only so much technological input, when it is forced to absorb more. The application of the most advanced technologies, he says, is of little value where the existing data base does not match the level of sophistication required by the new technology. However, my colleague Dr. Orsborn disagrees with his statement (page 6, paragraph 4 of Mr. Nothdurft's paper) that lack of ability to generate a sophisticated stage-discharge recurrence interval has kept Puerto Rico from applying the flood-plain regulations transferred from the U.S.A.; these regulations, Dr. Orsborn feels, can be applied with less than sophisticated information although, admittedly, more sophisticated would be better.

"The single most important characteristics which distinquishes developing regions from those that are more technologically advanced in terms of water resource planning and development," Mr. Nothdurft continued, "is the relative level of uncertainty with regard to policy, planning, and economic variables." Accordingly, the proper application of the older technology might produce greater benefits in attaining resource-management objectives in the less-complex system

of a developing country than would a steadily increasing level
of sophistication of technology. Although many people feel
that bigger is better and that more sophisticated is better,
that the modern is better, I agree with Mr. Nothdurft that
there is a limit. Progress is great, but let us be sensible
about it.

In conclusion, this session provides us, through the
conference mechanism of information transfer, with illustrations of several ways to bring such transfer about. It provides stories of success and of hope, but it also cautions us
that not all methods appropriate for a developed area are
equally appropriate for a developing one.

I have raised questions wherein I disagree with the
authors--not only because of our different philosophies
and different backgrounds, but also perhaps because I do not
understand exactly what they are trying to communicate to me.
Therefore, I hope that the discussion in this session will
be both vigorous and constructive, for we shall all grow
thereby.

I commend the authors and their organizations for their
past successes and their plans for the future, and I feel
that we are especially indebted to Mr. Nothdurft for presenting
us with a framework for understanding why even the best plan
may not succeed, because of institutional barriers.

DEVELOPING A COOPERATIVE RESEARCH PROGRAM
FOR FLOOD CONTROL IN BRAHMAPUTRA VALLEY

By

S. N. Gupta*
Member (Investigation, Planning and Design),
Brahmaputra Flood Control Commission
Assam

Synopsis

The mighty Brahmaputra river in the northeastern region of
India causes unprecedented flood and erosion problems. The
people in the valley have to face vast devastation and untold
misery during each flood season. The Government of Assam
created a Flood Control Commission in July 1970 to study flood
problems of the valley and prepare a master plan for flood
control. The complex Brahmaputra system has unique hydro-
meteorological environment. A comprehensive cooperative
research program is being planned by Hydrology Directorate
of Central Water and Power Commission, India and Hydrology
and Water Resources Wing of Colorado State University, Fort
Collins, to study the problems. The Brahmaputra river and its
problems are detailed in this paper.

Introduction

Every nation has flood problems. Man has fought with
floods through ages. He has been devising flood control
measures to protect towns, villages, industries, and agriculture lands on streams that overflow their banks and cause
vast devastation and untold human misery. Although a lot of
human endeavor has been put in to achieve immunity from floods,
individual river basins continue to present flood problems
which are baffling. In India, the two major river basins, the
Ganga and the Brahmaputra, have always been subjected to the
fury of floods. Every year, floods cause huge damage to the
states of Uttar Pradesh, Bihar, West Bengal, and Assam which
lie within these two basins. In the particular case of Brahmaputra, flood control has been practiced mainly by the construction of levees both along Brahmaputra and its fifty north and
south bank tributaries. However, judicious location of levees
which would least interfere with the individual river regime
and thus afford hydraulicand structural stability to these
levees is yet a matter of research. Owing to a variety of
meteorological factors, the pattern of flooding and sediment

---

*Now Commissioner, Ganga Basin, Government of India, Ministry
of Irrigation and Power, New Delhi.

transport in Brahmaputra and its tributaries is largely
unpredictable. The magnitude of the problem is so vast that
it requires considerable research. A cooperative research
program is being planned by Hydrology Directorate of Central
Water and Power Commission in collaboration with the Hydrology
and Water Research Wing of Colorado State University, Fort
Collins, to study the flood and sediment problems of Brahmaputra
basin and devise measures for their efficient control. In this
paper, a brief description of Brahmaputra valley and its problems is given with a view to invite suggestions from world
hydrologists and hydraulicians for planning and developing a
research program for the control of Brahmaputra valley floods.

The Brahmaputra Basin

The Brahmaputra is one of the largest rivers of the world.
It is the east flowing river of the Himalayas and winds its way
through northeastern part of India. It is 2880 km long; 1600
km length lies in Tibet, 160 km in Arunachal, 720 km in Assam
and nearly 480 km in Bangla Desh and then falls into the Bay
of Bengal. It drains an area of 580,000 km^2. This mighty
river carries a flood flow of 62,300 m3/s and flows over a
width of 6 to 9 km. During its journey in Assam valley, as
many as 30 tributaries join along its north bank and 20
tributaries along its south bank (Fig. 1). These carry discharges ranging from 1415 m3/s to 14,150 m3/s.

The Assam region is characterized by hills, mountains,
and valleys. The total area of the State is about 122,000 km^2
of which the riverine area comprises 12 percent. The Brahmaputra basin is an east-west elongated narrow river basin having
a width varying from 80 to 88 km. The topographical features
considerably influence rainfall distribution in the basin. The
rainfall in northeastern frontier region is as high as 6350 mm
whereas lower down, it reduces to 1780 mm.

The Brahmaputra is a braided river all along its length
in Assam; its flow divides into a number of interlacing channels
separated by sandy islands, big and small. The river bed and
banks are built of fine alluvial soil with rock protrusions at
places. The sediment transported by the river consists of the
same grade of material. Its bed slope varies from 1 in 3600
to 1 in 5500 in upper reaches; it is 1 in 7000 in middle reaches
and 1 in 10,000 in lower reaches. The maximum flood rise at
Dibrugarh (Upper Assam) where the river is wide (width 3900 m)
and shallow, is 4.5 m whereas at Gauhati (Lower Assam) where
the river is narrow (width 1370 m) and flows in a single
channel, the flood rise is 10.5 m. The Brahmaputra basin in
general and its northern part in particular, receives sediment
from the Himalayan range in the north where weathering and
erosion of soft rocks are considerable. In addition, northeastern India is an active seismic zone; earthquakes of varied

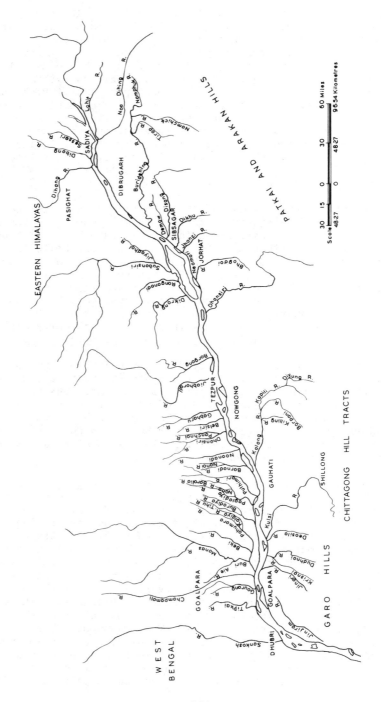

Figure 1. Brahmaputra and its Tributaries.

100

intensity are frequent. Such earth movements have and may in
the future alter the gradient of the river. A study of Brahmaputra channel regime reveals that there is a gradual rise in
river bed levels at Dhubri, Gauhati, and Tezpur (Central and
Lower Assam); there was an abrupt rise of 3 m after the earthquake of 1950 at Dibrugarh (Upper Assam).

Floods in Brahmaputra Valley

The monsoon rains in Brahmaputra valley start in April
and continue till the end of October; the heavy rainfall
months are June to September. The three tributaries namely
Dehang, Dibang, and Lohit emerging from the Himalayan range
form Brahmaputra as it enters Assam. The rainfall in the
catchments of the three tributaries initially contributes to
the flood flows of Brahmaputra in its head reaches. Thereafter,
the flood of 30 north bank tributaries and 20 south bank tributaries all along its length join Brahmaputra and as a result,
its flow swells. The pattern and intensity of rainfall in the
tributary catchments are largely responsible for varying intensities of flood flows in these tributaries, and when these join
flood waters of Brahmaputra, the entire flood pattern of the
river system becomes unpredictable. The flood gauges observed
at Dibrugarh, Tezpur, Gauhati, and Dhubri during the years of
high floods in the valley for the monsoon period of June to
September, amply show this irregular trend (Fig. 2).

Likewise, the flood flows in two problem north bank
tributaries namely, Subansiri and Pagladiya, show an irregular
trend owing to varying pattern and intensity of rainfall in the
catchments of these tributaries (Fig. 3).

The flood waters of Brahmaputra and its north and south
bank tributaries spill over their banks and inundate large
areas in the valley. Owing to gradual rise of bed levels of
Brahmaputra and many of its tributaries, the flooding in the
valley has increased. The backwater flow from the Brahmaputra
into the tributaries at the outfall largely floods the areas
adjoining them. In addition, the long duration of high floods
in Brahmaputra and extensive spilling of flood waters on banks
cause large flood pockets which are difficult to drain. This
greatly disrupts the normal life of the valley and has largely
affected the economic prosperity of the region.

Apart from the topographical and meteorological factors,
another unusual factor is the frequent occurrence of seismic
disturbances in this geologically recent and unstable region.
These seismic disturbances do not allow the rivers to stabilize
their regime and carry the flood waters within their sections.
The sections of the rivers are constantly adjusting to the
varying amount of silt load being brought by the rivers which
either reduces the channel capacity or forces the rivers to

101

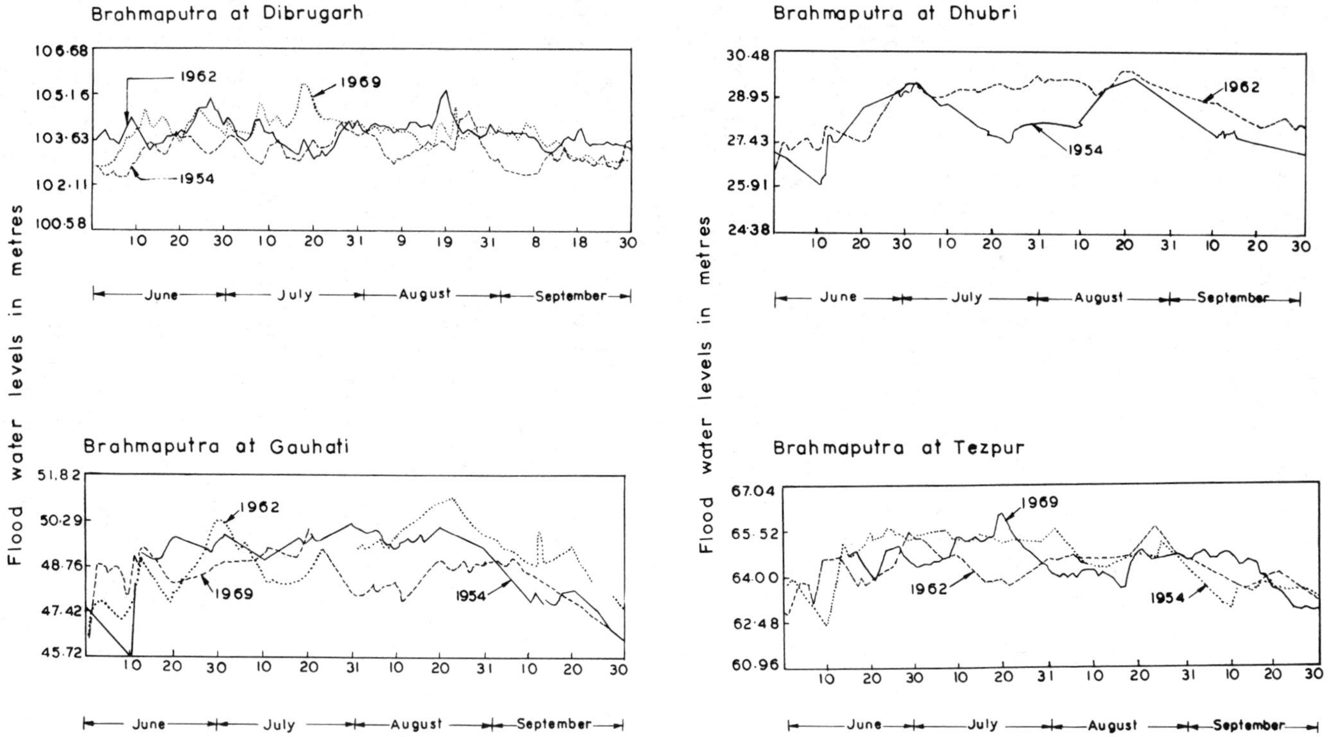

Figure 2. Gauge-Hydrographs of Brahmaputra at Dibrugarh, Dhubri, Gauhati and Tezpur.

102

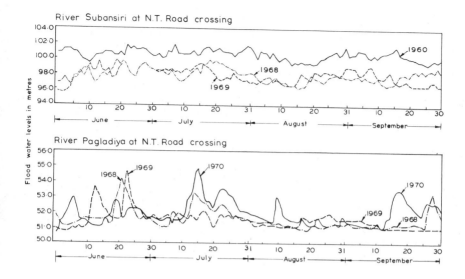

Figure 3. Gauge-Hydrographs of River Subansiri and River Pagladiya at N.T. Road Crossing.

change their courses altogether. This further aggravates the problem of flooding in the valley.

Bank Erosion in Brahmaputra Valley

It is characteristic of braided rivers that their bed and banks are subjected to scour and erosion owing to variation in sediment discharge at different flood stages, adverse curvature of flow, and unfavorable shifting of shoals in their vicinity. The flood waters of Brahmaputra move freely over a vast expanse of 6 to 9 km, spilling over the banks at places and getting deflected by natural rock protrusions within the alluvial banks. Combined with this, the north and south bank tributaries empty themselves into the Brahmaputra all along its length. All these situations accentuate the velocities of flow along the banks in a manner which does not conform to any defined laws of hydraulics. In addition, sediments brought by them introduce varying flow patterns in the main river. As a result, the river banks are mercilessly eroded in long lengths ranging from 1.5 km or more. Erosion makes no distinction between north and south bank, it attacks both, depending upon the prevailing curvature of flow. The width of erosion varies from 150 to 460 m or more in any flood season. Thus, the control of bank erosion is a formidable problem.

103

The bank erosion along meandering tributaries is as serious as that along Brahmaputra. It is a natural phenomena that most tributaries travel downstream owing to variation in silt charge and discharge; the resulting curvature of flow, combined with spill flow over the banks, causes erosion of banks at the outer curves of the loops especially at their exit. The protection of valuable agricultural lands and habitation which are threatened on account of this bank erosion, poses serious problems in the valley.

Hydro-Meteorological Data for Brahmaputra Valley

For any flood control scheme, the availability of adequate hydro-meteorological data is the first necessity. There are as many as 300 rainfall stations in Assam valley where rainfall data is available for 30 to 50 years. Their number and location fall short of the requirements for proper study of flood hydrology of Brahmaputra and its tributaries. However, some studies have been attempted with the help of this data to predict flood situations in the valley.

Three gauge and discharge sites were established at each of the tributaries: one near the foothills, one in the middle reaches, and one in the lower reaches in the backwater zone. Suspended sediment load is observed at each of the discharge sites. There are 5 gauge sites on Brahmaputra and one discharge and sediment site at Gauhati, where the river is now bridged with rail-cum-road bridge. This data has been used for the study of flood flow patterns and intensities in the Brahmaputra and its tributaries.

The Contour survey of the riverine area aggregating 10,310 km^2 is available. Aerial photography and spot heighting of the entire riverine area aggregating about 28,500 km^2 is also available. The compass survey of Brahmaputra in its entire length of 720 km in the valley was carried out in 1970-71, and cross sections of the river at intervals of 8 km were taken. Similar surveys are in progress for tributaries.

It is recognized that hydro-meteorological data for Brahmaputra valley is inadequate for requisite analysis. However, the development of new concepts of interpretation with the aid of models from inadequate hydrologic data should serve for initiation of the proposed studies.

The Brahmaputra Flood Control Commission

The colossal problem of floods, erosion, and drainage congestion in the Brahmaputra valley calls for drawing up of a Master Plan for flood and erosion control in the first instance and thereafter, phased implementation of the plan. With a view to achieve this objective, the Government of India

104

and the Government of Assam created a three-tier organization
during May - July 1970, comprising the Brahmaputra Flood
Control Board, the Brahmaputra Flood Control Commission, and
a Board of Technical Consultants. The Flood Control Board is
a high powered policy making body with the Union Minister for
Irrigation and Power as its Chairman, and it will decide
priorities in the implementation of the various flood control
projects. The Commission is a full time organization for
preparing a comprehensive plan of flood control of the valley
and for execution of works. The Board of consultants is
constituted to advise the Commission on complicated problems
which arise during investigation, planning, design, and
construction of works.

The Brahmaputra Flood Control Plan

The Master Plan for Brahmaputra Flood Control will
comprise flood control plans for each tributary basin. This
will include dams, levees, channel improvement and stabilization, and tributary basin improvement.

Dams for Flood Moderation - The Himalayan range presents
favorable sites for the construction of dams on various tributaries of Brahmaputra valley. But the major bottleneck is the
seismicity of the region which stands in the way of this
attempt. It is proposed to investigate two sites, viz., on
river Dihang, the main source of Brahmaputra, and on river
Subansiri, as these play a major role in contributing to the
flood flows of Brahmaputra in head reaches.

Levees - This device is effective to contain flood flows
within a river. Scientific embanking of a tributary from its
emergence near the foothills up to its outfall into Brahmaputra
is a hazardous task because of the limitations imposed by the
local people who are not prepared to part with their lands
along proposed alignments of such levees. All the same, the
aim should be to evolve the best alignment and section of a
levee both for hydraulic and structural stability. The
planning will involve construction of new levees in unembanked
reaches, raising and strengthening of existing levees, and
retiring such existing levees which constrict the free passage
of flood flows.

Channel Improvement and Stabilization - Bank erosion is a
chronic problem both on main Brahmaputra and its meandering
tributaries. It has not been possible to improve the regime
of the main river channel or tributaries and stabilize their
banks with known methods of river training practiced in the
valley, such as stone, revetments, stone, pile, and timber
spurs. In addition, bottom paneling technique (vertical
submerged screens placed in the stream), originally developed
by the National Hydraulics Laboratory, Chatou was tried at 5

105

places on the Brahmaputra river to improve the river regime.
Of these, two resulted in failure, while the other three seemed
to be successful. Further, it is proposed to improve river
channel with the help of suction dredging. Two dredgers are
being obtained for this purpose, and these will come into
operation from 1973.

Tributary Basin Improvement - At present, the tributary
basins get flooded from spill flows of tributaries and from
rainfall within the basin. A number of drainage channels
exist in the basin area, but these remain clogged with silt
and debris and must be improved for their proper functioning.
To drain these waterlogged areas, sluices are proposed for the
tributary and Brahmaputra embankments at suitable locations.

The study of Brahmaputra flood hydrology is a big challenge
to the present generation of hydrologists, geologists, and soil
conservationists. Each discipline has to play a dominant role
in the study of the flood characteristics of the Brahmaputra.
The study should establish, both on the basis of available data
and proposed data, the sequence and severity of meteorological
and hydrological events that are responsible for the occurrence
of significant floods at key points in the valley. The analysis
of observed rainfall data will yield runoffs that account for
floods on the Brahmaputra river and the tributaries. The Indian
Meteorological Department has already processed a scheme for
setting up a hydro-meteorological organization within the
framework of Brahmaputra Flood Control Commission for observation and analysis of hydro-meteorological data to establish
rainfall-runoff relationships for tributaries and to evaluate
storms that produce significant floods both on tributaries and
on the Brahmaputra.

The analysis of observed flood data at tributary gauging
stations will lead to the determination of infiltration
indices, recession curves, base flows, and unit hydrographs,
and at Brahmaputra gauging stations, flows contributed by
major drainage areas, discharge frequency curves and storage
discharge relationships in backwater leveed areas, for use in
flood routing. The analysis of rainfall and observed flood
data will help to accurately forecast floods in the valley.
The Central Water and Power Commission has already set up a
Flood Forecasting Unit which forecasts flood stages at
Dibrugarh, Gauhati, Goalpara, and Dhubri. As more flood data
becomes available at other key stations on the Brahmaputra,
forecast units will become more informative and effective.

Channel stabilization to control bank erosion on
Brahmaputra and the tributaries, is another challenging task.
A number of considerations, factors, and variables are involved
in any channel stabilization project; most of these are related
to modifications in channel width, depth, channel roughness,

and velocities either maximum or dominant. The channel energy slope should be amenable to improvement within the limits of maximum and minimum slopes due to channel shape, bed material load, channel alignment, discharge and other natural factors. The channel geometry will vary with the pattern of runoff hydrograph; the frequency and duration of all flows have a strong influence on the configuration of the channel and the stability of the banks. The rate of rise or fall of a stream should also be taken into account since this affects the rate and pattern of sediment movement and particularly the bed load. A critical study of such hydraulic data on various tributaries and Brahmaputra will suggest what type of channel stabilization devices such as revetments, spurs, dikes, and others should be tried in particular situations to achieve the desired goals.

Hydrological and Hydraulic Model Studies of Brahmaputra Valley

Water resources development has been the natural goal of man through the ages. In early days, intuition was his guide in dealing with complicated flow phenomena and finding solutions. Now these are investigated by means of simulation techniques on hydraulic and hydrological models. During the past quarter century, hydraulic model science has developed to be an indispensable tool for the design of flood control structures and river training devices. A large number of hydraulic research laboratories developed all over the world, notably the U.S.A., Germany, and U.S.S.R. India has also made substantial progress in developing hydraulics laboratories to evolve designs of complicated structures related to the execution of river valley projects; most of the States have full fledged laboratories to solve their own problems.

For Brahmaputra basin, the following studies must be carried out for preparing a master plan for its flood control:

i)   Prediction of flood stages and discharges at vulnerable situations on the main river and its tributaries. Evaluation of effect of rate of bed and flood rise on the stage-discharge relation.

ii) Determination of water surface profiles along existing and proposed levees for vulnerable floods.

iii) Investigations of problems of levee alignment with respect to bank erosion.

iv) Determination of the effect of increase in flood heights as a result of reduction in valley storage due to the construction of levees.

v)   Determination of backwater effect on tributary levee system as a result of floods in Brahmaputra.

vi) Determination of areas on main stream and tributaries that will be inundated by floods and devising measures to protect the same.

vii) Evolving efficient, economical, and safe designs for flood control structures and determining most suitable locations for these structures.

viii) Development of basin-wise plans for flood control and coordinated operation of flood control works.

ix) Improving drainage channels in tributary basins.

x) Evolving a judicious combination of levees, spurs, and revetments for achieving channel stabilization in the tributary as a whole from the foothills to its outfall into Brahmaputra. Also, a study of the development of cut-offs to shorten stream lengths and reduce flood heights.

Study of Brahmaputra Flood Hydrology on a Mathematical Model With the Aid of Computers

The availability of high speed computers of large capacity makes it possible to simulate the performance of relatively complex river basin systems for periods of any desired length. Simulation on computer has, therefore, become a new technique of river basin analysis which gives answers to flood flows and optimum utilization of water resources for complicated systems which have not been possible hitherto.

Design, construction, and operation of a mathematical model for Brahmaputra basin will provide a unique tool for the study of complex flood phenomena in the valley. It will reveal the pattern of flooding of Brahmaputra as a result of flooding of various tributaries. It will show on which tributaries flood control reservoirs should be built for effective lowering of flood stages in Brahmaputra. It will reveal the effect of the existing levee system on tributaries and the main river and will indicate in what manner a future levee system should be projected. It will also depict how river training measures should be devised to least interfere with the channel regime and, at the same time, control bank erosion. It will help in planning drainage channel improvement and correct location of sluices for relieving waterlogging in tributary basins.

U. S. National Science Foundation Cooperative Research Project Between India and U. S. A.

Mr. V. Yevjevich, Professor-in-Charge, Hydrology and Water Research Program, Colorado State University, Fort Collins,

U.S.A., stated to Dr. K. L. Rao, Union Minister for Irrigation and Power, India, in April 1971 that for the first time, the U.S. National Science Foundation has obtained the counterpart dollars for supporting cooperative research between the U.S.A. and seven other countries with counterpart dollar funds, and India is one of them. He suggested that a research project on floods would solve practical flood problems of large Indian rivers.

Dr. K. L. Rao conveyed to Prof. Yevjevich that he welcomed the idea of a proposed cooperative research program. He suggested that the study of hydrology of Brahmaputra river would be a suitable subject for the cooperative research program as they were facing a number of complex flood problems in the control of the Brahmaputra and its tributaries originating in the Himalayas which caused considerable havoc in the narrow Brahmaputra valley in Assam.

This paper has been prepared in an attempt to provide a base for preparing and developing a cooperative research program for the control of floods in the Brahmaputra. It is hoped that useful suggestions will be forthcoming from scientists and engineers attending the First International Conference on transfer of water resources knowledge to plan the proposed studies.

The initiative for the cooperative research project on Brahmaputra Flood Hydrology has come from Prof. V. Yevjevich, Hydrology and Water Resources Department, Colorado State University, Fort Collins. I, as his counterpart in India, express my deep appreciation for his efforts in framing the project proposals. I feel sure that this unique collaboration will greatly enhance the scope of developing applied hydrology research in India.

Acknowledgment

Mr. P. C. Jain, Deputy Secretary and Mr. S. P. Kaushish, Assistant Secretary, Central Board of Irrigation and Power have made useful suggestions in defining the flood problems on Brahmaputra and in preparing figures for the paper. Their assistance is gratefully acknowledged.

APPLICATION OF HYDROGEOLOGICAL DATA TO LONG-TERM
ECONOMICS OF GROWING SUGAR CANE IN VENEZUELA

By

L.C. Halpenny
Water Development Corporation
Tucson, Arizona

and

Dr. A. Dupuy P.
Central El Palmar
San Mateo, Venezuela

Synopsis

Transfer of hydrogeological knowledge from research to
practice and from developed to developing regions has been
successfully achieved beginning in 1959 under a cooperative
effort between consulting hydrologists and sugar cane growers
in Venezuela. The program was begun by Central El Palmar,
within the area drained by Rio Aragua in the State of Aragua,
Venezuela. The area is intensively farmed with irrigated
agriculture, of which a substantial portion is sugar cane. The
water supply for irrigation is obtained partly from stored
surface-water runoff and partly by pumping wells. In 1962 a
similar program was begun by Central Yaritagua along Rio Turbio
in the States of Lara and Yaracuy.

The initial objective of the program was to detect changes
in groundwater levels from which predictions could be developed
as to whether or not the groundwater system was being overdeveloped. This early-warning system indicated in 1962 that
Tocoron sub-area in Aragua State was being overdeveloped, and
arrangements were made to reduce pumping and to divert more
surface water to the area.

As the work progressed, improvements in techniques of well
drilling and development resulted in increased well yields and
reduced water costs. From collection of cost data, it was
possible to determine the actual cost of irrigation water for
each ton of sugar cane and each ton of refined sugar from each
farm. Evaluation of water-supply data made it possible to
refine the consumptive use calculations for planning future
irrigations. Optimum cane yield results when 200 cubic meters
of total water supply is available for each metric ton of cane
produced.

The program has clearly demonstrated usefulness of applying
hydrogeological data in developing an agricultural "factory"
that will produce maximum crop yields at minimum cost. Similar
programs would probably be practicable for other large-scale
agricultural operations.

Introduction

Central El Palmar was constructed in 1955 and, at the time of construction, was one of the largest and the most modern sugar mill and refinery in the world. The factory is near the town of San Mateo in the State of Aragua, Venezuela. Sugar cane for processing at Central El Palmar is grown in the valley of Rio Aragua and along the eastern and southeastern side of Lake Valencia (see Figure 1). During approximately half of each year the rainfall is inadequate to support growth of sugar cane; thus irrigation is essential. The irrigation supply is derived mainly from groundwater supplies and secondarily from surface water impounded in reservoirs. In 1959 the principal stockholders of Central El Palmar made a decision to employ modern techniques of hydrology to insure that an adequate irrigation supply could be provided indefinitely. Beginning in July 1959 a program was established to monitor water levels in wells, to determine whether or not the ground-water supply at each hacienda was capable of sustaining annual irrigation demand or was overdeveloped.

This paper describes the evolution of the initial objectives into a sophisticated annual appraisal of the economics of irrigation of sugar cane.

Hydrologic Balance at Haciendas

The program as developed began with monthly measurements of the depth to static water level in all wells at each hacienda for a period of 12 months to determine the amplitude of seasonal changes in water level. The work was done by personnel of Central El Palmar, using steel tapes. Measurements were made to the nearest centimeter. All wells at the hacienda were shut off for a minimum of 24 hours before measurements are made. After a 12-month record was developed, the frequency of measurements was reduced to twice each year, once at the end of the irrigation season (May) and once at the end of the rainy season (October). Samples of water from each well were collected twice a year for chemical analysis on the same schedule as the water-level measurements.

The discharge pipe at each irrigation well was equipped with a connection for a pitot tube and with a device for easy attachment of an orifice plate. Measurement of well discharge was made twice each irrigation season, once near the beginning and once near the end of the season. Hour meters were installed at each irrigation well. Using the well discharge, measured in liters per second, and the record of number of hours each well is operated, the monthly and annual volume of water produced was then calculated.

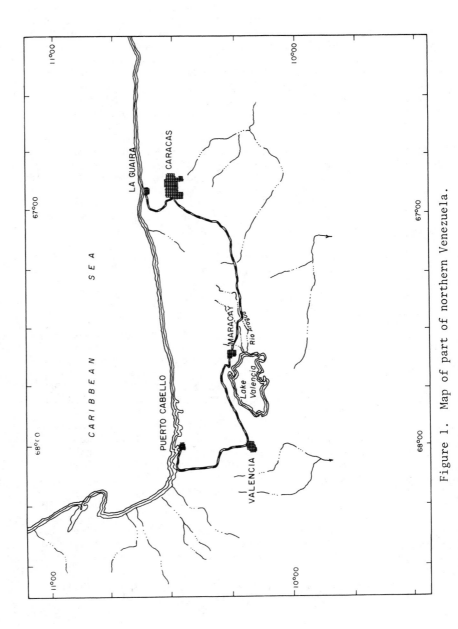

Figure 1. Map of part of northern Venezuela.

Knowing the volume of water produced and the resultant effect of this production upon groundwater levels made it possible to monitor the aquifer characteristics at each hacienda with satisfactory precision.

By 1962 it became apparent that the demand for irrigation water at the Tocoron group of haciendas could not be sustained indefinitely by pumping from wells; the water table was declining at a rate of about 1 meter per year. Calculations were made to determine the annual volume of surface water required to offset reduced groundwater withdrawal under a balanced regime. By March 1963, arrangements were made for importation of canal water and reduction of groundwater pumpage. After the water table had recovered, the amount of surface water used was reduced slightly and groundwater pumpage was increased. The haciendas are now irrigated on a planned combination of groundwater and surface water that keeps the water table neither too high nor too low.

Problems did not arise at the other haciendas until the rainy season of 1967 when rainfall was substantially lower than normal. Water levels in wells did not recover to normal stage owing to lack of recharge. A review of precipitation records was made and a conclusion was reached that a second dry year could be tolerated if the pump settings were lowered as needed. Rainfall was above normal in the 1967-1968 water year, and water levels at most haciendas recovered satisfactorily. A second season of low rainfall occurred in 1971, and water levels at the beginning of the 1971-1972 irrigation season were again lower than is considered desirable.

Well Construction, Development, and Maintenance

After the hydrologic monitoring program was well under way, attention was directed to well yields and well drawdowns. The objective was to abandon marginal wells and to construct new wells which would be efficient and economical. All of the wells were drilled by rotary method. Casing perforations were torch cut, and the wells were gravel packed. Casing diameters were 14-inch and 16-inch. The first change made was to improve the quality of the gravel used for gravel packing. A search was made all over northern Venezuela for a source of gravel comprised of rounded siliceous material. The best source was found on the Orinoco River at Ciudad Bolivar. A stockpile was established there consisting of double-screened materials in the size range between 1/8 and 1/2 inch. The truck which delivers sugar to Ciudad Bolivar brings back a load of gravel to Central El Palmar.

The program of cutting perforations was standardized as to width of cut, length of cut, and number of cuts per meter of casing, with the objective of enabling water to enter the casing freely without substantial loss of hydraulic head.

Improvements in well development were established and implemented. With thorough and complete well development, a well produces sand-free water with a maximum yield and a minimum drawdown.

The work done at a well, when the discharge was measured twice a year, was supplemented by measuring depth to pumping water level and by measuring the unit rate of power or fuel consumption. With these data several parameters could be evaluated. The drawdown is the difference between depth to static water level and depth to pumping water level. The specific capacity is the discharge divided by the drawdown. The overall efficiency of the well is the ratio of actual power or fuel needed to lift water from the pumping water level to land surface compared with theoretical power or fuel demand with no friction loss. If the cost of operating a well increases, there are three possible reasons for the increase:

1. If the aquifer is overdeveloped and the water table has declined, total pumping lift increases and the pumping cost increases.

2. If the static water level remains the same but the depth to pumping water level increases, the specific capacity of the well decreases. This means that the well has deteriorated, not the aquifer, and that redevelopment of the well is required to restore the original specific capacity.

3. If the depth to static water level and the depth to pumping water level remain the same but the power or cost increases, the pumping unit is in need of repair.

Consumptive Use of Water

Availability of data on annual volume of water used for irrigation at each hacienda soon led to the question of whether too much or too little water was being used to grow the sugar cane. Specifically, how much total water supply is required each and every month of the year to maintain the cane in optimum condition? Calculations were made to determine the consumptive use demand on a monthly basis. The data for each hacienda - total rainfall and total irrigation supply - were computed by months and compared with the theoretical monthly demand. Cane production, in tons per hectare, was compared with water supply, hacienda by hacienda. It was found that too much water was being used at some haciendas and not enough at others, and adjustments were made to provide an

114

irrigation supply in accordance with the monthly water requirement.

It was found that optimum cane yield results when 200
cubic meters of total water supply is available for each
metric ton of cane produced.

Agricultural Economics

When the program of installing hour meters at the wells
and making monthly readings was started, data of monthly power
or fuel consumption at each well were also recorded. Thus,
annual data were available for power/fuel cost and, for each
hacienda; these were expressed in units of cost per hectare of
sugar cane and cost per ton of cane produced.

Data were available on cost to construct a well and to
equip it with a pumping unit, and these could be amortized
and expressed as an annual cost per hacienda.

For the past 4 years data have been collected as to the
cost of maintenance and repair for each well. For each
hacienda, data are also being recorded for the cost of
maintenance and repair of the irrigation system (canals,
laterals, canal lining, field leveling, etc), and for the cost
of labor for irrigation. It is now possible to determine the
total cost for irrigation at each hacienda on a semi-annual
basis. These data are expressed as cost per hectare of cane
under cultivation and cost per ton of cane produced.

Summary

In less than 10 years, a complete program of data collection and evaluation relating to all aspects of water supply has
been developed and implemented by the staff at Central El
Palmar. The program is operated by company personnel functioning
in close cooperation with management and the consultant. There
has been a successful transfer of hydrogeological knowledge from
research to practice and from a developed to a developing region.

It is now possible to know with certainty in which areas
the groundwater is underdeveloped, fully developed, or overdeveloped; which wells are efficient and which are not; whether
well problems are related to the aquifer, to well deterioration,
or pump deterioration; how much irrigation water is needed at
each hacienda; and the total annual cost for water per hectare
of cane under cultivation and per ton of cane harvested. With
this knowledge the haciendas are being operated as agricultural
factories designed to produce maximum crop yields at minimum
cost. Similar programs likely would be found practicable for
other large-scale operations.

PUERTO RICO: A CASE STUDY OF WATER RESOURCE TECHNOLOGY TRANSFER

By

William E. Nothdurft *
Area of Natural Resources
Department of Public Works
San Juan, Puerto Rico

Synopsis

The transfer of water resources knowledge from developed to developing areas involves two distinct but overlapping conceptual systems: Intra-System Transfers, transfers from point to point within a given system or institutional management structure; and Inter-System Transfers, transfers from some external source into a given system or institutional management structure. The efficiency of intra-system transfer depends to a large degree upon the level of managerial sophistication of the institutional structure. The efficiency of inter-system transfer depends upon the institutional flexibility of the initiating system and the absorptive capacity of the receiving system. This paper discusses the theoretical framework of these transfers and the barriers to their efficient functioning in the water resource management institutional structure of one developing area: the Commonwealth of Puerto Rico.

Technology Transfer: A Theoretical Framework

Improving resource management capability, whether we are concerned with developed or developing regions, involves two basic conceptual issues. Formulated as questions, they are: how adequate are the mechanisms for the transfer and application of existing technologies within the institutional management system; and, how capable is the existing institutional system of absorbing and implementing new management technologies?

Approaching these two issues requires a clear and functional definition of the process of technology transfer. In the formal language of information science, technology transfer is frequently conceptualized as a process occurring within a given transfer "space," and having both vertical and horizontal components, axes, or dimensions. Vertical components encompass the research and development phase; horizontal components encompass the application and impact phases.[1]

---

*Presently with New England River Basins Commission, Boston, MA.
[1]Wilkinson, Kenneth P., "Diffusion of Technology and Political Information: What Theory Do We Have?" Proceedings of the National Symposium on Social and Economic Aspects of Water Resources Development. AWRA, Cornell University, 1971, p. 2.

In discussing the transfer of water resource knowledge from developed to developing regions, we are concerned with activity along the horizontal dimension of the technology transfer process. More specifically, in the light of the two conceptual issues raised above, we are concerned with transfers from point to point within a given system (in this case a developing institutional resource management structure), and transfers from an external source into the system (from developed to developing regions). For the sake of simplicity, we might term the first case "intra-system transfers," and the second case "inter-system transfers."

Significant barriers exist in both cases which serve to frustrate the movement, absorption, and subsequent implementation of recently developed water resource knowledge. The barriers, or inefficiencies, in intra-system transfers are closely related to the level of managerial sophistication in the institutional structure. On the other hand, inefficiencies in inter-system transfers can generally be attributed to institutional inflexibility on the part of either the transfer recipient (as is generally the case), the transfer source, or both; and the incapacity of the recipient system to absorb new inputs.

Barriers to Intra-System Transfers - The level of managerial sophistication within the system, that is, the efficiency with which intra-system transfers of information, knowledge or technology are made, can, in part at least, be determined by the degrees to which existing knowledge, systematic programming, and rational techniques are utilized in policy making.[2]

Many developing areas have no cultural orientation or tradition in favor of rational policy making, i.e., the systematic evaluation of alternative methods of achieving desired goals. The extreme cultural alterations resulting from a very rapid development process, whether politically (i.e., through revolution) or economically (i.e., through rapid industrialization) induced, are often not paralleled by equal changes in the behavioral patterns and structural characteristics of the policy makers and organizations within a given institutional system. The resulting barriers and inefficiencies to the transfer of information or knowledge and, in our case, the management of resources, is thus largely unavoidable, though they clearly contradict both the desire often declared by developing states to base their operations on "modern technology" and their verbal disposition toward "comprehensive planning."[3]

---

[2]Adapted from Yehezkel Dror, Public Policymaking Reexamined (San Francisco: Chandler Publishing Co., 1968), pp. 108-109.
[3]Ibid.

Barriers to Inter-System Transfers - The efficiency with which inter-system transfers of information, knowledge, or technology are made, that is, transfers from developed to developing regions, depends to a very great extent on the institutional flexibility of both systems, and the absorptive capacity of, and relevance of the transfers to, the receiving system. In the language of classic communication theory, both the sender (or source or encoder), and the receiver (or destination or decoder) must be capable of adaptive modification if the message, in this case new techniques of water resource management and development, is to be effectively transferred. Moreover, because the process is two-directional, adaptive modifications are necessary at both the initial transmission stage and at the feedback stage to insure continuing or long-term relevance of the transfer itself.

The problem of institutional inflexibility applies most directly to the transfer source--the technologically advanced country. The transfer of water resource knowledge is severely hampered by the tendency of the transfer source to rely on standardized and often inapplicable norms, procedures, and developmental and planning frameworks. As an example, multilateral lending institutions, such as the World Bank group or the Inter-American Development Bank for instance, tended at least initially to adopt standard U.S. project evaluation procedures. Economic feasibility studies for irrigation projects have been conducted in developing regions throughout the world based on standard Bureau of Reclamation procedures. The inflexibility of these institutional procedures raises legitimate questions as to the relevance of projects developed within such a framework. It would be far more valuable, in terms of investment efficiency, to assess water resource development feasibility using a program approach linked to the overall development goals of the region rather than a project-by-project approach based on inflexible and inapplicable institutional procedures.

Of more potential importance to the issue of inter-system transfer efficiency, is the question of whether a steady transfer of new and sophisticated technological input necessarily constitutes an improvement in the capability of a developing system to manage or develop a resource. Stated differently, at what point does a given institutional system, which is currently capable of absorbing a given level of technological input, begin to yield diminishing returns when forced to absorb even more sophisticated technological inputs? The application of the most advanced technologies and analytic techniques, for instance, is of little value where the existing data and information base does not match the level of sophistication required by the new technology. It makes little sense to improve program output by five or ten percent through sophisticated technological or analytic inputs when the potential gains are negated by policy, planning or economic variables. And the single most important characteristic which distinguishes developing regions from those that are more technologically advanced, in terms of water resource planning and development, is the relative level of uncertainty with regard to policy, planning, and economic variables. The proper application of what might be termed "old technology" or analytic methods might produce greater benefits for the attainment of resource management objectives in the inherently less complex system of developing countries than would result from steadily increasing the level of sophistication of technological inputs. Inter-system transfer efficiency, therefore, depends less upon the isolated efficiency of a given technology, than upon the ability of the receiving system to absorb and implement that technology.

The transfer of water resources knowledge from developed to developing regions, then, functions at two distinct, yet overlapping, levels: intra-system and inter-system. An understanding of the normative functions of each of these systems in the technology transfer process is essential if the results of recent world-wide investments in water resources research and development are to be successfully transmitted to and implemented by developing regions. The theoretical framework having been established, it would now be valuable to investigate how these two systems function within the water resource management institutional structure of one rapidly developing region: the Commonwealth of Puerto Rico.

Puerto Rico: A Case Study in Water Resource Technology Transfer

The enormous strides is socio-economic development made by Puerto Rico in the last twenty years are well known. Under a vigorous industrialization program, heavily supported by U.S. capital, the Island has been transformed from a poor, almost exclusively agricultural society to a prospering urban-industrial society with the highest per capita income in Latin America. These achievements, and the Island's formal relationship with the United States, would appear to exempt it from consideration under the classic definition of a developing area.[4] However, the assumption that these advances have been paralleled by similar advances in institutional or managerial sophistication and that it is therefore capable of a high level of transfers of water resource knowledge is, for the most part, incorrect. As a consequence of this mistaken assumption, the technology transfer process is even more

---

[4] For a discussion of a "model" developing state, see Dror, p. 105.

complex in Puerto Rico than in many so-called "model developing states" where the assumption is never made. Despite advances on many fronts, barriers exist in Puerto Rico, and specifically in the institutional structure for water resource management and development, which serve to significantly decrease the efficiency of intra- and inter-system transfers of technology. Moreover, they are barriers which are now, or will soon be, common to many other developing states.

A Brief Assessment - Puerto Rico's burgeoning urban population and its continuing rapid rate of industrial development have placed increasingly heavier demands on its water resource base. While rainfall is abundant, averaging 75 inches on an Island-wide basis, it is unevenly distributed, ranging from 200 inches in the northeast rain forest to 35 inches in the southwest coastal plain. The upland portions of the Island's 17 catchment areas are small, steep, and disturbed, while the coastal plains are narrow, flat and heavily developed. While on the one hand water supply shortages are a serious problem on the south coast, severe flooding occurs regularly on the north coast. In addition, the water resource planning, management, and development institutional structure is severely fragmented, with responsibilities spread among several Commonwealth and Federal agencies. Moreover, while the development of the Island has long been guided by an executive level Planning Board, water and related land resource problems have traditionally held a low priority.

Intra-System Transfers in Puerto Rico - As stated earlier, the facility with which intra-system transfers of information are made, and therefore the efficiency with which the institutional structure manages the resource, depends to a great degree upon the level of managerial sophistication of the policy makers and agencies that make up the system. There are many reasons why the current level of managerial sophistication in Puerto Rico frustrates rapid intra-system transfers.

Over the years, the assignment of managerial authority for resource management has followed a piecemeal or crisis-by-crisis approach, rather than any comprehensive plan. As a result, water resource management responsibilities are extremely fragmented: water supply activities are conducted by the Aqueduct and Sewers Authority, water quality by the Department of Health, flood control works by the Department of Public Works, flood plain zoning and regulations by the Planning Board, to cite only a few examples. This fragmentation directly effects the efficiency of intra-system transfers. Fragmented authority leads to noncomprehensive problem analysis, which results in piecemeal single-purpose development, which only serves to reinforce the rigidity of the fragmented structure. Efficient transfers within such a structure are highly unlikely.

In attempts to improve the efficiency of resource management activities, the Commonweath has depended primarily on organizational structure changes. In 1968, an Area of Natural Resources was created as a sub-unit of the Department of Public Works and charged with the operational responsibility of resource planning and management for the Island. In 1970, an executive level Environmental Quality Board was created with sweeping planning, policy-making and enforcement powers. However, neither one of these organizational structure modifications included the phasing out of the fragmented resource management responsibilities of existing agencies. Consequently, both agencies were additionally charged with the somewhat onerous task of "coordinating" the activities of a variety of other agencies. With only minor exceptions, the fragmentation, with regard to water as well as other resources, remains intact, with the longer-established agencies often jealously guarding their territories of responsibility.

It is unlikely that these or any other structural changes are likely to improve the efficiency of resource management, as long as they are perceived as threats by established agencies. It is more likely the case that they will significantly decrease the efficiency of intra-system transfers. Nevertheless, on June 20 of this year, the Governor signed a new law, creating a Department of Natural Resources, to strengthen the existing Area of Natural Resources, and to bring together some of the fragmented resource management authority. While this most recent change certainly represents at least a partial success at raising the level of managerial sophistication, most of the important functions remain fragmented and in the hands of other agencies. Further, the negative effects of the power struggles which went on throughout the process of revising and passing the law are likely to be felt for some time.

In addition to problems which can be attributed directly to structure, the institutional framework of Puerto Rico's resource management system is often unresponsive as a direct result of the Latin tradition of strong executive leadership. Having power concentrated at the top of each administrative unit results in a highly inflexible (though certainly well protected) decision making environment, one which does not lend itself to efficient transfers of knowledge, information, or technology. Transfers become highly sensitive because policy decisions are viewed as personal rather than institutional. Subordinates in the organizational structure make very few decisions and avoid situations which would force the hand of the executive. Finally, the strong personal identification of the executive with the organizational unit precludes objective, rational decision making. As an example, a high executive in the organizational unit responsible for cleaning up San Juan's polluted Condado Lagoon, is proceeding with

121

the installation of artificial reaerators on the premise
that they will provide sufficient turbulence and oxygen to
break down B.O.D. wastes presently tied up in the bottom muds,
even though the agency's chief environmental scientist has
advised that there is not sufficient basis for proceeding
with such action.

Closely related to the problem of executive power concentration is the issue of political maturity. The political
sensitivity of decisions promotes a tendency toward short-term,
high yield, high visibility programs and thus is a serious
barrier to comprehensive planning. When the commodity at stake
is a scarce resource, the result of this politically stimulated
short-sightedness is critical to the development of the region.
While good plans, politically agreed upon, will receive the
support of the Commonwealth's executive branch, poor plans might
well receive the same enthusiastic support.[5]

The fragmentation and often simultaneous overlapping of
authority, the tendency toward extensive but often nonproductive institutional structure alterations, executive level
power concentration, executive-agency identification and
political maturity problems, tell us much about the level of
managerial sophistication in Puerto Rico's water resource
institutional structure. They constitute significant barriers
to intra-system transfers of available information and technology within the existing institutional structure which cannot
help but have a strong negative impact on the ability of the
system to deal with inputs of new information and technology
through inter-system transfers.

Inter-System Transfers to Puerto Rico - We have noted
that the efficiency of inter-system transfers of water resource
knowledge depends upon the capacity of the management system
to absorb new inputs of technology, and the adaptability of
the technology transferred to meet the level of managerial
sophistication and the developmental needs of the receiving
system.

As discussed above, the capacity of the management system
to absorb new inputs is directly related to the efficiency
with which the system converts existing inputs into management
policy. It is characteristic of most developing countries that
both the quality and quantity of these inputs is insufficient
for rational decision making. Physical, demographic, economic,
climatologic and hydrologic data are generally not available,

---

[5]R. Scott Foster, "Water Resource Management and the Environment: A Comparison of Governmental Approaches in Puerto Rico
and Southeast New England," Proceedings, op.cit., p. 231.

and are very difficult, time-consuming, and expensive to collect[6]. This is not the case in Puerto Rico. Commonwealth and Federal agencies have been collecting valuable data for years. However, as a result of the fragmentary nature of water management authority, these data have been collected and applied, for the most part, only at the individual agency level for single-purpose development. Nevertheless, while perhaps difficult to acquire, the data is at least available. In Puerto Rico, the breakdown in the input-output system occurs at the data analysis level. While abundant data inputs exist, present data analysis and information generation efforts have been and continue to be unrelated to either the priority information needs of the final users of water resources information, or to the broad issues and problems which face the Island.

In the U.S., flood plain management has been developed as a mechanism to reduce flood hazards by changing occupancy patterns. Model flood plain regulations which have been developed at the national level, have been adopted in many states. These same regulations have been instituted by planning authorities in Puerto Rico. However, the analytical capability required to effectively implement the regulations, that is, the ability to generate the sophisticated stage-discharge relationship recurrence interval, and to translate these into principal floodway and overbank storage requirements, has not been developed to a level commensurate with the requirements of the transferred regulations. Thus, unless the receiving system has the capacity to absorb and implement new technologies, the transfer efficiency can be expected to be very low. This is a clear example of how the forced input of sophisticated technologies to a system incapable of absorbing them yields diminishing returns.

On the other hand, diminishing returns, in terms of meeting the long-term developmental needs of a region, can also result from inflexibility of the transfer source. The rigidity of assistance programs, coupled with an increasing need for external sources of aid, occasionally causes a developing region to become committed to water resource development projects which do not precisely meet its perceived needs. Moreover, matching funds are also often committed which might better have been used elsewhere. A case in point is a recent conflict between the Commonwealth and the EPA over what regional emphasis should be made in pollution control efforts.

While the Commonwealth sought to ease the pollution problems in inland rivers in an effort to ease related public health hazards, the EPA wanted to eliminate large discharges

---

[6]Dror, op. cit., p. 116.

in coastal estuaries, specifically San Juan Bay. Whereas
B.O.D. removed per dollar investment would have been larger
in the EPA alternative, it is likewise true that the inland
rivers alternative would have produced greater public health
benefits in terms of reducing hazards due to bilharzia and
other parasitic diseases. The relevance of the B.O.D. removal
per dollar investment yardstick is thus open to serious question as a guideline for achieving Commonwealth goals.

Furthermore, the problem of institutional inflexibility
on the part of the transfer source is not limited or unique
to the Commonwealth-Federal government relationship. An
analogy at the world-wide level is the presumption that large
river basin development projects contribute significantly to
the economic growth of developing countries. Every developing
country seeks a showcase dam project as an illustration of its
level of development. This phenomenon can be attributed, in
part, to the fact that the developed-country bias for large
basin projects has been transferred to developing countries
through international development agencies. Many resource
economists have questioned the efficiency, in terms of alternative opportunities, of the large investment committments
required for such projects.

Conclusion

It should be clear that a fundamental understanding of
the normative functions of both intra-system and inter-system
transfers is essential if the knowledge which has resulted
from recent world-wide investments in water resources research
and development is to be successfully and efficiently applied
to the resource management needs of developing areas. An
examination of the factors which affect the efficiency of these
transfers in Puerto Rico should be of interest in making case
studies of other developing areas to improve the value of.
future transfers.

TRANSFER OF KNOWLEDGE IN WATER RESOURCES FROM RESEARCH TO PRACTICE*

By

Mr. A.D. Pobedimsky
United Nations
Economic Commission for Europe
Environment Division, Geneva

Synopsis

The purpose of this paper is to describe how an international organization (the UN Economic Commission for Europe) transfers knowledge in the field of water resources from research to practice. Among other items discussed, emphasis is placed on the pooling of international experience in the field of water resources development and water quality problems on studies and seminars in this field, and on the transferring of national experience through systematic circulation of technical information. Suggestions are also offered as to the efficient transferral of knowledge by international organizations and the eventual use in national practices.

General

In the member countries of the European Economic Commission, industrial and scientific development, continuing urbanization, as well as the rising standards of living increase water demand on the one hand and water pollution on the other. Thus in the last decade all ECE countries have taken a decisive turn towards planned water resources development. In many of these countries the elaboration and adoption of long-term programs and plans for water resources development are considered an essential factor to economic development.

One of the most typical and important approaches to long-term policy on water and related land resources planning and development is the integrated and comprehensive approach. Taking this into account, the need for an international exchange of experience in this field has been strongly felt by the ECE governments.

For this purpose, in 1967, under the auspices of the European Economic Commission, the Committee on Water Problems was created. While programs related to specific aspects of water economy were undertaken in various UN and other international organizations, the newly established ECE Committee

---

* Experience of the Economic Commission for Europe, Committee on Water Problems (UN ECE)

on Water Problems has been used by Governments as a forum for examining the more comprehensive problems related to over-all socioeconomic policies and planning in the water resources field.

The terms of reference, as well as the field this Committee serves are comprehensive, covering development and use of water resources, qualitative and quantitative aspects. Some of the specific duties of this Body are as follows:

- help to arrange the exchange and diffusion of information and experience on problems of concern in the formulation and application of Governmental water policies and exchange of experience on water problems;

- keep under periodic review the present and prospective situation regarding the development and use of water resources and water pollution control in Europe;

- keep itself informed of the relevant work done and planned by other subsidiary bodies of the Commission, by other UN bodies and other international organizations, and take appropriate steps to harmonize international efforts and avoid unnecessary duplication in this field.

In creating this Body, the ECE countries emphasized that: This Body should serve as a source of information by keeping countries informed of the progress achieved in this field of water resources development, use and quality protection not already covered by other UN and international organizations; special attention should be made on carrying out comprehensive economic studies, since such studies have not been made by other organizations.

The Committee thus serves to help the ECE Governments solve significant problems in this field - problems of policy and of a technical nature. Priority of these problems is being selected by the Committee represented by delegations of experts and responsible administrations of the ECE countries.

The main groups of studies implemented by the Committee are:

1. Improvement of methods to protect and improve the quality of water resources, as well as relevant economic methods, increasing economic effectiveness of water quality control, and abatement measures;

2. Exchange of experience and knowledge in perspective planning of water resources development and use;

3. Improvement of methods of water management (institutional and administrative) and exchange of relevant experience;

4. Exchange of experience in application of modern methods of computer techniques for water resources management, including planning of development;

5. Studies aimed at standardization of methods in water economy;

6. Improvement of methods of economic use of water in national water economies.

Thus the ECE Committee is responsible for diffusion of experience and knowledge in this field among ECE countries.

This work is being carried out by the following two and five year work program adopted by the Committee:

1. preparing studies on selected problems by groups of experts from ECE countries (or individual experts) and circulating these studies among ECE countries:

While some of the studies are being based on the advanced experience of certain countries, most of them are being prepared by reviewing and assessing the international experience and research of the ECE countries. In this case the secretariat, often with the assistance of experts, circulates questionnaires among the countries, collects the necessary information, and distributes it to rapporteurs. Some of these questionnaires are useful to ECE countries since they stimulate the raising of new questions which were important for further activity. Usually the studies, prepared on the basis of national experience and information, and based on questionnaires are discussed by the Committee and afterwards circulated among the ECE countries.

2. convening seminars and symposia on the most important problems envisaged in the work program;

3. carrying out of study tours in different countries - usually in the countries where seminars are being convened; these study tours are usually carried out after some of the Committee sessions at the invitations of the Governments of certain countries who have advanced experience in this field;

4. discussions of prepared studies and reports by participants of the Committee's session;

5. the carrying out of studies by ad hoc group of experts on the Survey of Water Resources and Needs, as a subsidiary organ of the Committee.

The studies presented by advanced experts of the ECE countries, being implemented by this group, involves more serious long-term studies, such as "The Manual for the Compilation of Balances of Water Resources and Needs" which will be completed in 1972. The reports of this group are also being circulated among the ECE countries.

Brief Discussions of the International Seminars Being Held by The Committee - Appraisal of Their Importance and Practice of Transferring Information

The Committee has convened the following seminars during recent years:

- Seminar on the Protection of Ground and Surface Waters Against Pollution by Oil and Oil Products (Geneva, December 1969)

- Seminar on River Basin Management (London, June 1970)

- Seminar on Selected Water Problems in Southern Europe (October 1971)   The Seminars and Symposia now in preparation

- Seminar on the Methodology for the Compilation of Balances of Water Resources and Needs (Budapest, 18-26 September 1972)

- Seminar on the Pollution of Waters by Agriculture and Forestry (Vienna, October 1973)

- Symposium on the Use of Computer Techniques and Automation for Water Resources Systems (26 March-4 April 1974, Washington, D.C.)

The following distinct features of the seminar on River Basin Management convened in London 1970 should be noted:

1. In planning this seminar, the Committee regarded the situation in the water economics of many ECE countries as adding special weight to the problems of improving water resources management. General recognition of the importance of improving traditional methods of water management and the importance of effective national policies and organizational arrangements for water resources development was felt essential. Therefore we felt that the problem confronting us was well worth a searching discussion. Selecting methods of optimal organization and administration on an economically sound basis had to be studied and presented to the countries.

2.   In convening the seminar the Committee recommended that a study tour, especially in a country with advanced experience in this field, would be one of the most effective ways of exchanging information, views, and experience among ECE governments and interested organizations.

3.   The seminar was convened in London in June 1970 at the invitation of the United Kingdom Government and was attended by 78 participants representing 21 ECE countries, including the USA, and 11 international organizations. Four delegates from the countries outside the ECE region, as well as observers from the host country, participated.

The main subjects of the seminar were as follow:

(a)   Present situation and major trends in management of river basins and the need for comprehensive river basin development;

(b)   Planning of integrated river basin development;

(c)   Institutional arrangements and financing;

(d)   Operational control of water flow and water quality in river basins.

The discussions on the above-mentioned subjects were based on seven reports which had been prepared by rapporteurs from six countries and by the ECE secretariat.

After extensive discussions on these topics, a set of recommendations to ECE governments were adopted. The recommendations, after their approval by the Committee, were presented to the ECE governments in 1971.

During the seminar the participants visited several water management works and river authorities in England.

Proceedings of the seminar consisting of the papers submitted, the summary of the debate, specific and general conclusions, etc., were published in 1971 by the ECE secretariat in printed form for general distribution and sale (UN document ST/ECE/WATER/3).

The following topics raised during the discussions at the ECE seminars present special interest to ECE countries:

- Quantitative and qualitative estimates of long-term water requirements by individual uses;
- Methods of long-term planning of water resources development and integration of these plans with the general planning of the economy;

- Modern techniques for water treatment, pollution control and optimal water quality management;

- Possible impact of water resources development on deterioration of environment and relevant expenses for its protection;

- Criteria and methods for the choice of investments and planning methods in water management;

- Methods of rationalizing the development and improvement in the management of water resources;

- Patterns and trends of scientific research on water problems in Southern Europe;

- Expediency, possibility and methods of using economic incentives to improve quality of water;

- Definition of scope and powers of river basin organs to provide for the comprehensive management of all ground and surface water resources, including water quality control;

- Intensification of scientific research into problems arising in integrated river basin management;

- Possibilities of assessing and forecasting water pollution as well as self-purification processes in river basins;

- Optimization of integrated water systems at the planning, designing and operative stages, using computers and appropriate mathematical methods.

One of the most interesting and instructive study-tours was conducted by the ECE in the Southern part of France in June 1971 at the invitation of the French Government. Participants were shown through the water projects and water engineering schemes in operation in that region. Participants in the study tour were mainly water engineers from ECE countries and members of national delegations at the third session of the Committee on Water Problems. In addition, there were representatives from some of the Asian, Southern American and African countries.

The tour which lasted six days included the following trips: Bassin Rhône-Méditerranee-Corse; the head office of the Compagnie Nationale du Rhone; the St. Vallier scheme on the Rhône; the Vallalirègues scheme; the headquarters and engineering works on the Canal de Provence; and a boat trip down the Rhône from Valence to Avignon. The purpose was to point out the scale of development in river basins, the quality of construction and the application of most modern techniques for management of water systems. The general conclusion of the participants was that this study tour was extremely valuable.

This method of promoting the exchange of experience among ECE countries is being implemented by a periodical (2-3 year period) comprehensive review of the experience and prospective trends in water resources management and water pollution control. This review, prepared on the basis of national reports, was issued in 1970 by the Committee on Water Problems under the title "Trends in Water Resources Use and Development in the ECE Region" (ST/ECE/WATER/1).

National monographs on recent trends, circulated among the countries by the secretariat during the spring of 1972, were discussed by the Committee in July 1972 with subsequent issuing of the latest review.

The following form of disseminating international information has also been carried out by our organization. The ECE group of experts on the Survey of Water Resources and Needs agreed that an exchange of scientific and technical information on regional water management plans and on related subjects might be arranged directly between member governments. For this purpose the secretariat circulated a detailed mailing list of national experts to whom any available documentation might be directly transmitted. Later the Committee on Water Problems included in its program of work the project which concerns "An examination of research programmes underway in ECE countries on water problems with a view to identifying areas for international co-operation." Initially this is being carried out by direct correspondence. It was suggested that such direct exchanges between governments take place on the basis of the mailing list circulated by the ECE. In addition, another useful form of information exchange has been used by our Committee. The delegates felt that it would be useful for them to be informed of the documentation already existing in ECE and in other international organizations on subjects related to projects concerning the future work program of the Committee. Thus the secretariat compiled and circulated "A list of international organizations from which documents relating to certain subjects of interest to the ECE Committee on Water Problems can be obtained" (doc. WATER/Working Paper No. 28/Rev. 1). "Documents" include reports, studies, research, etc.

In concluding, I would like to indicate that national delegations of the ECE countries consider the role of the ECE and other UN specialized organizations an important step in increasing the effectiveness of the information exchange and international cooperation in the field of water resources development.

THE ROLE OF THE INTERNATIONAL COMMISSION ON IRRIGATION AND DRAINAGE IN THE TRANSFER OF WATER RESOURCES KNOWLEDGE

By

Larry D. Stephens
Executive Secretary
U.S. Committee on Irrigation, Drainage and Flood Control
and Chief, Technical Services Branch
Bureau of Reclamation, USDI
Denver, Colorado, USA

Synopsis

The International Commission on Irrigation and Drainage provides a forum for the development of the sciences and techniques of irrigation engineering, flood control, and river training. This paper discusses the role of the Commission in transferring water resources knowledge in these areas from research to practice and from developed to developing countries. Activities of the Commission are described, and currently available publications are summarized.

Introduction

Man has long recognized that availability of water is one of nature's paradoxes - usually there is either too much or too little. Because the "right amount" of water is vital to man's well-being, great effort has been expended to develop water resources. However, much remains to be done if the world's water needs are to be met. Men of all nations must work together to solve our water problems. Thus the subject being discussed in this Conference - Transfer of Water Resources Knowledge - is most apropos.

This paper discusses the role of the International Commission on Irrigation and Drainage (ICID) in transfer of Water Resources Knowledge. The purpose and programs of ICID are outlined and described in detail, as are the activities of the U.S. National Committee of ICID.

History and Purpose of ICID

ICID was established in 1950 to provide a forum for engineers, scientists, and water users to exchange knowledge of the sciences of irrigation, drainage, flood control, and river training in the engineering, agricultural, economic, and social aspects. The specific objects of the Commission are defined as follows:

"(1) All matters relating to planning, financing, and economics of irrigation and drainage undertakings for the

132

reclamation and improvement of lands as well as the design, construction and operation of appurtenant engineering works including canals and other artificial channels for irrigation and drainage.

"(2) All matters relating to planning, financing, and economics of schemes for flood control as well as the design, construction and operation of appurtenant engineering works, except such matters as relate to the design and construction of large dams, navigation, and basic hydrology.

"(3) The study of river behavior and all matters relating to planning, financing, and economics of schemes for river training and control as well as the design, construction, and operation of appurtenant engineering works."

The transfer of knowledge has always been a basic purpose of ICID. N. D. Gulhati, the first Secretary-General of ICID, summarized the knowledge transfer role of the Commission as follows:

"...when engineers and technicians co-operate to pool their knowledge and experience, the obligations are mutual. Each benefits from the other and such co-operation represents the best contribution towards human welfare and prosperity. Knowledge knows no boundaries, political or racial, and it is a real pleasure to pass on one's knowledge and experience to another. It enriches him who gives and enriches him who receives. Concepts shared, kindred objectives and mutual confidence bind mankind more than ties of race or color. It was with such thoughts and objectives that the International Commission on Irrigation and Drainage was set up in 1950, to stimulate and promote the development and application of the science and technique of irrigation, drainage, flood control and river training."

The Commission has cooperated in many international activities. It was a founder member of the Union of International Engineering Organizations and has been given Consultative Status "B" by the Economic and Social Council of the United Nations. ICID has participated in meetings of the International Hydrologic Decade and cooperates with international water resources organizations such as International Commission on Large Dams; Latin American Commission on Irrigation and Drainage; World Meteorological Organization; Economic Commission for Europe; United Nations Educational, Scientific and Cultural Organization; and International Commission of Agricultural Engineering.

The planners of this conference have provided for two sessions - one to discuss the transfer of knowledge from research to practice and the other to examine the transfer of knowledge from developed to developing regions. The founders of ICID also recognized the importance of these two aspects of knowledge transfer. Activities of the Commission provide a number of opportunities for engineers and scientists to transfer knowledge from research to practice, and, since there are 61 member countries, transfers from developed to developing countries are accomplished as well.

ICID Activities

Congresses - ICID holds triennial congresses to discuss timely problems related to irrigation, drainage and flood control. In all, eight Congresses have been held, the latest this year in Varna, Bulgaria. About 700 engineers and scientists from 45 countries attended the Eighth Congress.

A total of 29 questions have been discussed at the eight Congresses. The questions included the following subjects:

1. Behavior of the subsoil water table under a system of irrigation and/or drainage;

2. Maintenance of irrigation and drainage channels with reference to weed control;

3. Ground water - its use for irrigation, safe yield, and artificial recharge;

4. Soil-water relationship in irrigation movement and moisture in irrigated soils;

5. Hydraulic structures on irrigation and drainage systems;

6. Interrelation between irrigation and drainage;

7. Sprinkler irrigation and comparison with other methods of irrigation;

8. Economics and financing of irrigation, drainage and flood control works;

9. Sediment in irrigation and drainage channels - methods and techniques;

10. Integrated operation of reservoirs for irrigation, flood control and other purposes;

11. Water requirements of crops;

12. Methods and economics of operation and maintenance of drainage systems in agricultural areas;

13. Development of new irrigated and drained areas - procedures and policies;

14. Field irrigation and drainage in deltaic, coastal and lowlying areas;

15. Recent and promising developments including mechanization of operations in the field of irrigation and drainage.

The Congresses also include Special Sessions and Symposia which examine in detail specialized subjects that do not meet the requirements for Questions. The following areas have been discussed in the Special Sessions and Symposia:

1. The application of computers in the analysis of various problems relating to irrigation and drainage systems;

2. Essential elements necessary for successful irrigated agricultures;

3. Essential measures for introduction and development of irrigation and drainage schemes in developing countries;

4. Water resources systems planning with special regard to irrigation, drainage and flood control.

At the Eighth Congress in Varna, more than 130 papers for the three Questions, the Symposium, and Special Session were discussed. The papers were prepared by engineers and scientists from 26 countries. Activities in developed countries constituted most of the reports, 25 of which were written by authors from the U.S.

Publications - While knowledge transfer is accomplished through exchange of ideas during the ICID Congresses, the most significant and permanent transfer comes from the publications issued by ICID. The most important of these publications is the series of Transactions of the Congresses. For example, the Transactions of the Seventh Congress, held in Mexico City in 1969, includes six volumes for the Questions along with separate volumes for the Special Session and for the Symposium. Thus, the Congress Transactions, in summarizing the contemporary thinking on a given technical area of engineers and scientists around the world, provides a significant contribution to the water resources development literature.

Following is a summary of other significant ICID
publications currently available:

1.   The Multilingual Technical Dictionary on Irrigation
and Drainage provides definitions in both English and
French of more than 10,000 words and terms related to
irrigation and drainage. Also available is an English-
German version of the Dictionary.

2.   Irrigation and Drainage in the World - A Global
Review offers a comprehensive examination of the state
of the irrigation and drainage art in 100 countries. In
1,300 pages, this 2-volume publication provides such
information as physiography, climate, water law, planned
developments, and irrigation statistics for each country
included.

3.   International Cooperation in the Development of Water
Resources for Agriculture was published in 1970 to
commemorate the 25th anniversary of the United Nations
and the 20th anniversary of ICID. Included are articles
outlining the role of many international organizations in
water resources development and others portraying the
evolution of water resources development technology.

4.   Irrigated Wheat - A World-Wide Survey is the first in
a series of surveys regarding the consumptive use of water
by crops. These surveys reflect current data and practice
in member countries. Reports on rice, cotton, and sugar
cane will follow the wheat survey.

5.   Design Practices of Irrigation Canals in the World
presents details of canal design techniques in more than
20 countries.

6.   The biannual ICID Bulletin, published in January and
July each year, is a forum for short technical articles
and news of current developments in irrigation, drainage,
and flood control. The Commission also publishes an
annual bibliography of publications and articles related
to irrigation and drainage.

7.   Now being prepared for publication are Flood Control -
A Global Survey which will provide information about flood
control needs and practice in member countries; and Small
Hydraulic Structures in Irrigation Distribution Systems,
a joint effort with the Food and Agricultural Organization
of the United Nations.

The ICID Organization

Management of ICID is vested in an International Executive Council which includes a representative of each member country and the following elected officers: president, nine vice presidents, and the secretary-general. President is E. Alekseevsky, U.S.S.R. The Vice Presidents are Wayne D. Criddle (U.S.A.), Stoyko Z. Tzanov (Bulgaria), Ibrahim Z. Kinawy (A.R.E.), A. Amaya Brondo (Mexico), H. Zolsmann (Federal Republic of Germany), S. K. Jain (India), A. Kahkashan (Iran), Sujono Sosrodarsono (Indonesia), S. Kantor (Israel). K. K. Framji of India is Secretary-General. Member countries are Algeria, Arab Republic of Egypt, Australia, Austria, Brazil, Bulgaria, Burma, Canada, Ceylon, Republic of China, Colombia, Cuba, Cyprus, Czechoslovakia, Dominican Republic, Ecuador, France, Federal Republic of Germany, Ghana, Great Britain, Greece, Guyana, Hungary, India, Indonesia, Iran, Iraq, Israel, Italy, Ivory Coast, Japan, Korea, Malawi, Malaysia, Mexico, Morocco, Netherlands, Nigeria, Pakistan, Peru, Philippines, Poland, Portugal, Rhodesia, Rumania, Senegal, Spain, Sudan, Surinam, Switzerland, Syria, Thailand, Tunisia, Turkey, Uganda, U.S.A., U.S.S.R., Venezuela, Vietnam, Yugoslavia, and Zambia.

The work of the Commission is financed from annual dues paid by the National Committees and by the sale of publications.

U.S. National Committee

The name of the U.S. National Committee of ICID is the U.S. Committee on Irrigation, Drainage, and Flood Control. The U.S. Committee is incorporated in Colorado under the Colorado Non-Profit Corporation Act.

While most ICID National Committees are government supported, the U.S. Committee is a private organization, financially supported by the dues of about 600 individual members as well as library, corporate, and institutional members.

Management of the U.S. Committee is administered by an elected Executive Committee and through it, the Executive Secretary and appointed Special Committees including Technical Activities, Research and Special Studies, Standards, Membership and Publications. Maurice N. Langley is Chairman and Harold G. Arthur, Lester W. Bartsch, J. F. Friedkin, Rolland F. Kaser, William I. Palmer, Walter G. Schulz, Henry Shipley, and Carl R. Wilder are members of the Executive Committee.

Activities of the Committee include Triennial Technical Conferences, held to preview proposed ICID Congress papers, publication of a quarterly Newsletter, and cooperation with other U.S. professional societies in the sponsorship of technical meetings. Members receive the Committee <u>Newsletter</u> and the ICID <u>Bulletin</u> and may purchase ICID publications at a discount.

Information regarding purchase of ICID publications and membership in the U.S. Committee is available from the Executive Secretary, Post Office Box 15326, Denver, Colorado 80215.

Conclusions

Engineers and scientists in nearly every nation are searching for improved methods to develop water resources. To achieve maximum benefit from this effort, to help ensure that man's need for water is met, information regarding each newly developed technique must be widely distributed. The activities of the International Commission on Irrigation and Drainage provide a vehicle for this information exchange - an exchange which hopefully will result in increased human welfare and prosperity.

DISCUSSION by V. Yevjevich*

Mr. S. N. Gupta in his paper and the general reporter in his report mentioned my name concerning an international cooperation in the transfer of knowledge and joint research efforts in flood control. Some further explanations may be useful. Mr. Gupta basically reviewed various engineering aspects related to the difficult problems of flood control, sediment transport, and channel stabilization of the large Brahmaputra River. This river has such complex problems for solution that it warrants international cooperation. The case of the Brahmaputra River exemplifies one of the most difficult worldwide problems of flood control, sediment control and channel stabilization. Any new experience gained at this river would be transferable to similar river problems throughout the world.

The flood control problems of the type found on the Brahmaputra River are related to geologically young mountains, with relatively steep river slopes in their upper and mid sections, and relatively mild slopes in their lower sections and deltas. Large mountain chains of the world, such as Himalayas, Andes, Alps, Sierras and others, represent recent geological uplifts, mostly resulting from movements of earth crust plates. Erosion activity is still very high within these mountain areas. It is very often aggravated by man's use of land and disregard for factors related to erosion. The steep slopes of the upper and mid sections, coupled with intensive soil erosion, make sediment transport one of the most difficult problems to solve. The compositions of river valleys in their mid and lower courses are such that the rivers easily undercut their banks and meander in wide ranges. The sediment deposition in what were once sea bays, lakes or oceans has resulted in very flat plains on what are now the lower river courses. The transition from mountains to sediment plains, involving a relatively sudden change of the slope, is composed of a flat deposition cone. Sediment deposition has progressed historically both longitudinally and transversely on these plains. Many islands in the world of recent volcanic origin, as well as islands with recent geological uplifts, have similar topography and flood control problems. The increases in population have resulted in an ever-increasing use of these large flat fertile sediment plains for agriculture, communities (villages, cities), industry, communications, etc., thus continuously aggravating the flood problems.

*Professor of Civil Engineering, Colorado State University.

The solution of the problem of the river's transition between the steep river slope of its upper reaches and the mild slope of its lower reaches has been mainly attempted either by flood control reservoirs in upper reaches with sediment retention, or by construction of levees along the lower reaches, or both. Solutions are only temporary, however. Neither method can work effectively on the long-range basis because: (1) the relatively steep slopes of upper reaches restrict the capacity of the flood control reservoirs; (2) the large sediment load being transported fills the reservoirs in a relatively short time; (3) the flood control levees do not prevent the raising of the channel bottom, so that some rivers become "suspended," with the bottom high above the surrounding plains (example: the River Po in Italy); and (4) the rising river bottom along the plains requires the raising of levees with larger and larger volumes of levee reinforcements. Looking from a historical point of view and considering the experience of the last two or three centuries, flood control problems, including sediment transport and channel stabilization, of rivers flowing from young mountains onto large flat plains, basically have not yet found good long-range solutions. Temporary solutions, either for soil erosion control, sediment retention, flood control, or river channel stabilization, are rather the rule than the exception.

The problem of concentrating all the transferable experiences from various parts of the world, and performing new investigations and research to find valid strategies for long-range implementation of flood control is still with us despite several centuries of various attempts. Finding the best tactical approaches for flood control, sediment control and river stabilization, using a sound long-range interdisciplinary strategy, is a pressing problem for many large rivers in the world.

An exchange of visits and letters between Mr. Gupta and myself during the last several years was an attempt to develop both a bilateral and an international cooperation for transferring valid experience and for studying the crucial flood control problems of some of the most typical Indian rivers, particularly the Brahmaputra River, with the expectation that both the presently adapted and new solutions might be of worldwide interest. It is logical to expect that the results of practical interdisciplinary investigations and research on the most complex flood control problems of particular importance to India should become a transferable source of experience and knowledge for similar conditions around the world. By coupling a vast experience, data and a large number of unsolved problems, with a modern technology of investigation involving both analysis and synthesis in an applied research approach, might lead to significant returns for the benefit not only of the cooperating countries but also of other countries. Because of the constantly changing nature of social problems and values, economical situations, human concepts and perceptions of environments, and future changes in environments, it is a very demanding task to design a long-range flood control strategy, with the inherent control of sediment transport and stabilization of river channels, which can also survive the various challenges of the future. Also, it is very difficult to design a strategy of flood control which can easily deal with temporary measures, pressures for rapid alleviations, and possible shifts in underlying technical concepts and approaches. However, nothing is more important than a sound, scientifically based, long-range strategy for finding ways to live in harmony with the vagaries of a large river.

My understanding of the paper by Mr. Gupta is that it presents an initiative to look at flood control and the associated problems of large rivers flowing from young mountains onto fertile plains from a new viewpoint. That is, from an interdisciplinary approach and from a social point of view, requiring a sound long-range strategy of flood control.

DISCUSSION by Juan Antonio Poblete*

Why, indeed, flood control in the Brahmaputra Valley? This question is not really posed. For example: another author (Prof. P. Rogers at Harvard) considers other alternatives for the same region, like small scale investments that would be consistent with a viable semi-aquatic society something that has been over centuries.

Flood control as an objective versus development objectives seems to be a question worth posing before mapping out an ambitious research program based in large scale unit expressing works for a region which must have a very serious financial resources constraint.

DISCUSSION by Peter W. Whitford**

In light of Dr. White's address, there are several vital questions which should be added to the ten posed by Mr. Gupta. These include:

(i)   Non-structural alternatives;

(ii) Non-structural measures to be used in conjunction with structural measures, to cope with the exceptional flood, exceeding the design flow;

*Universidad de Chile
**World Bank, Washington, D.C.

(iii)   Socio-economic effects of providing partial
        protection;

(iv)   Economic analysis of the proposed works.

DISCUSSION by E. F. Schulz*

I would like to indicate that additional goals or
objectives need to be emphasized. The problem of the
increased flood stages and (possibly) sediment flow downstream in the neighboring country of Bangladesh is of extreme
importance. The river must be studied all the way down the
Brahmaputra through the Mehna into the Bay of Bengal.

DISCUSION by F. H. Verhoog**

I have several comments to make. First on the
Brahmaputra; I have the impression that the studies now done
in the U.S.A. are not taking into account the work done by
Netherlands engineers in the Bangladesh for about 10 years
after the second world war.

Second, the Rapporteur seems to say in page 6 of his
general report that the UN/ECE Committee on Water Problems
consists of sociologists and economists. This is not the
case. The Committee consists of water managers on government
level and includes engineers and scientists.

Thirdly, I do not agree with Mr. Nothdurft's idea that
developing countries do not need sophisticated methods to
solve their water problems. In developing regions there is
a lack of data and a lack of experience with the hydrologic phenomena. In such a case you need to go much deeper
into the physics of the hydrologic phenomena than it is
necessary in developed regions.

DISCUSSION by Leonard Halpenny***

May I indicate that the subject of the paper relates to
the objectives of this Conference, namely transfer of hydrologic knowledge. The paper is not and was never intended
to be a report on the hydrology of an area.

---

*Colorado State University

**UNESCO, Paris, France

***Tucson, Arizona

SESSION III

TRANSFER EXPERIENCES OF REPRESENTATIVE ORGANIZATIONS

Chairman: M.L. Albertson

Rapporteur: Robert M. Hagan

● *The experience of a large number of public, private,*
or specialized agencies serves as a springboard for
the delineation of a number of suggestions concerning
faster, but more accurate communication of water re-
sources knowledge. At the same time, overviews of
services, publication, and projects are provided with
recommendations as to the maximization of information
services and effective utilization of major water
programs.

SESSION III - TRANSFER EXPERIENCES OF REPRESENTATIVE
                  ORGANIZATIONS
                Rapporteur - Robert M. Hagan
                Office of International Programs
                Utah State University

    The series of papers in this section represent a wide
variety of transfer experiences in organizations ranging from
the Bureau of Reclamation to private practice. Given the
wealth of information we need to introduce the papers briefly
and point out at the same time a few critical remarks that
seem to permeate this session.

    The work of Cohan and Simmons on "How Engineering Research
is Reduced to Practice in the Bureau of Reclamation" describes
a rather typical effort by a large agency to meet a need for
better communication by preparing reports, and memos, establishing review committees and advisory groups, and providing
for administrative review procedures. Such an approach seems
to be the principal way so far devised by administrators to
deal with such problems.

    We may want, of course, to raise with the help of the
present conference, the question of how can one generate
suggestions for new and more sensitive and at the same time
faster-acting approaches to the transfer of information in
a large, nation-wide organization. Above all, we need to
move away from the traditional approaches to transfer of
knowledge and attempt to introduce innovative schemes of
transmission, as well as more effective ways of reaching
particular audiences.

    Carter H. Harrison, in his paper, emphasizes the problem
of quick information retrieval by design engineers. He calls
particular attention to the host of problems faced, and reviews
the use of the Cumulative Index to ASCE Publications and the
Citation Index, especially underlining the usefulness of the
Water Resources Research Catalog. Of all suggestions, I find
useful the one concerning the inclusion of mailing addresses
and phone numbers, despite the fact that such information
may change rather rapidly. Anything that can facilitate
quick communication and easy access should be encouraged.

    The central issue raised in O. J. Taylor's paper,
"Technical Aid for Hydrologic Studies in Spanish-Speaking
Countries" is one that many of us find particularly relevant.
Having been involved in international programs for nearly 10
years and having carried on some activities in more than 15
countries, I fully concur with the author's conclusion that

                              145

to work effectively one must understand the language of your colleagues. Fortunately, as Dr. Taylor points out, modern science and computer activities have produced some international vocabulary, but accurate communication is often impossible without knowledge of the local language.

Donald C. Taylor, in his very informative work on "The Role of Professional Societies in the Dissemination of Water Resources Research Information" provides an exceedingly useful review of services provided by a major professional society to expedite the dissemination of water resources research information. It is doubtful that most of us realize the many communication channels provided.

However, limited consultation with reference librarians in University libraries suggests inadequate accession of some of the publications and reports referred to. Apparently reference librarians and those responsible for selecting library materials need to be better informed about the material published by ASCE and perhaps the Society needs more standardizing of its published material into series which librarians would find easier to acquire and catalog.

The work of Zweifel, Leudtke, and Kerrigan on "The Water Resources Information Program at the University of Wisconsin" provides us with a succinct case showing the dramatic rise in numbers of scientific publications. At the same time, the authors outline also the complex problem that the "information explosion" has created for information users as well as information services.

Once again several librarians consulted agree with the authors' criticism of libraries for failing to accommodate rapidly enough to the need for new and flexible forms of information services. Especially difficult and critical is the problem of information transfer and retrieval at interdisciplinary interfaces. Here budget limitations and, perhaps in some cases, lack of sufficient forward vision have constrained efforts to provide better services.

Since the authors describe the Water Resources Information Program at the University of Wisconsin, it is unfortunate that there appears to be a lack of communication with reference librarians at other libraries serving major water programs. It can be suggested here that the authors expand on steps to be taken to extend this Information Program through other libraries. Particularly useful would be further details on working relations with the Water Resources Scientific Information Center (WRSIC) of the OWRR. Such steps may make possible the ultimate combination of library resources and bring together in some manageable scheme the vast pool of information existing on water resources research and experience.

Finally, LeFeuvre and Bruce in their "Eutrophication Research Applied to Water Quality Management on the Great Lakes" point out how truly good water management programs are the end result of increased knowledge through research. The international agreement concerning research on eutrophication of the Great Lakes serves as a background for a cogent discussion of the speed with which transfer of research results took place. The authors explore in particular the ways for mobilizing scientific activity, the role of public participation, and the successful organizational structure that made possible effective meshing of research and management. At the end, a major catalyst for successful implementation has been a special coordinating body, the Environmental Quality Coordination Unit, whose sole responsibility has been the turning of research results into both proposals for public policy and into means for evaluating water quality control strategies.

This last paper brings, then, into sharp focus the necessity for appropriate organizational structure and procedures which can make possible the effective transformation and conversion of research to practice.

HOW ENGINEERING RESEARCH IS REDUCED
TO PRACTICE IN THE BUREAU OF RECLAMATION

By

Howard J. Cohan
Chief, Division of General Research

W. P. Simmons
Research Coordinator
Bureau of Reclamation
Denver, Colorado

Synopsis

This paper briefly describes the Bureau of Reclamation
and its activities. It delineates how research needs of that
agency are identified and how planning and engineering research
is organized and carried out to satisfy those needs. It
describes how research results are transferred into practice
and utilizes case histories to show successes and problems
that have occurred in this transfer. The continuing search
for improvements in ways of transferring research results into
practice and the present status of techniques being utilized
are described. The importance of 2-way communication and
feedback is stressed.

Introduction

As a preliminary step in discussing the transfer of Bureau
of Reclamation research results to practice, it will be worthwhile to briefly describe the Bureau of Reclamation and its
functions. It is a Federal agency within the Department of
Interior with the principal mission of developing the water
and water-related resources of the 17 Western States. In
carrying out its mission the Bureau has constructed many famous
structures, including Hoover, Grand Coulee, and Glen Canyon
Dams. It has also constructed hundreds of miles of major
canals and pipelines, many tunnels, a number of pumping and
powerplants, and thousands of miles of smaller distribution
canals and pipelines for transporting water to the municipalities
and farmers who need it. It is a unique Government agency in
that nearly all of the funds it expends are ultimately repaid
to the Federal treasury by the direct beneficiaries of its
projects: a uniqueness that Reclamation employees are quite
proud of.

The Bureau is organized into regional offices, a principal
Engineering and Research Center in Denver, Colorado, and
administrative offices in Washington, D.C. Regional offices
work directly with the peoples to be benefited by the water
resources development programs, and they plan and carry out

148

construction and related programs. The Engineering and
Research (E&R) Center is concerned with overall plan review,
principal design activities for all regions and projects, construction review, operation and maintenance review for all
regions, and major research programs of the Bureau. The
Washington staff is concerned with congressional liaison,
policy, general overview, funding and financial matters, and
general administrative duties.

Identification of Research Needs

In its job of developing water-related resources over a
large part of the United States, the Bureau is concerned with
conceiving, evaluating, planning, financing, constructing,
operating, and maintaining water and water resource-related
projects that maximize people-related social, environmental,
and economic benefits. Therefore, the principal objective of
Bureau research is to obtain practical answers for the many
problems that arise in connection with all aspects of achieving
the goals of these water resources development projects.

Annual research funding for the last several years has
been in the $9.5 million range. Of this, about $6.5 million
has been for Atmoshperic Water Resources Management (AWRM)
studies, and about $3.0 million has been for Water Resources
Planning and Engineering Research (WRPER). The AWRM program
is more familiarly known as Project Skywater, or as precipitation management studies. The WRPER program covers the areas
of work its name embraces and the remainder of this paper will
be devoted mainly to this portion of the program. Nonreimbursable
funds are provided by the Congress for the research activities,
which are of benefit to the entire nation rather than just to
individual projects. There are, of course, many specialized
studies for specific projects. But when such studies benefit
primarily just that one project, reimbursable funds appropriated
for that project are used.

Information about specific research needs is gained in
two ways; through formal communication within the organization,
and through well-maintained informal processes. Under the
formalized system a call is issued at least once a year to
the regional offices, all involved offices in the E&R Center,
and to the Washington Office for information on areas of
research felt to be important for the Bureau's present and
anticipated future work. These subject areas are examined by
a Research Review Committee and its companion Advisory Group.
The Committee is composed of Washington and E&R Center staff
members who represent all facets of the Bureau's major
functions of resources planning, development, and maintenance.
The Advisory Group is composed of additional E&R Center office
heads, and representatives from each of the regional offices.

The Research Review Committee and Advisory Group thus provide a very broad and practical view of all Bureau research needs and represent all segments of the organization that are users of the results of our research.

In further action the Research Review Committee, in frank and open discussions, considers the subject areas proposed through the formalized system, prepares a final listing of them, and assigns priorities to them. This priority listing then serves as the main framework upon which an E&R Center management team develops the final research programs.

Supplementing the formal channel there are well-established well-maintained informal inter-office communications which make it possible to respond quickly to new needs and changing priorities as they arise and are assessed.

Transfer of Technology to Practice

In the majority of cases the transfer of technology from researchers to users has been excellent. Typical examples include spray nozzles recently developed by the Division of General Research for the Atmospheric Water Resources Management program, which is under the direction of Dr. A. M. Kahan. These nozzles were then used, in concert with other seeding and cloud analysis techniques, for emergency drought relief activities in Texas, Oklahoma, and Arizona in 1971. Another example is a new polyurethane foam roofing system sprayed over concrete or metal roofing members and topped with selected coatings of weather-resistant, sunlight-resistant protective seal coatings. Here the need has been so great that the designers are constantly pressing our researchers so that the state of the knowledge will be adequate for roofs now being designed. A third example is in electric power. The Bureau has done considerable work on power distribution system stability because the great expanses of the Western United States and the widely-separated powerplants and markets require large and long electrical distribution systems and interties. Stability of such systems is critical and poses many problems. Here Bureau research results are put into practice as soon as possible after conclusive results are obtained. This often requires the understanding and cooperation of power system managers outside of the Bureau since our systems are intertied with other public and private systems throughout the west. The key to success has been through communication utilizing either existing organizations, such as the Western Systems Coordinating Council, or by holding special conferences prior to the introduction of newly developed devices or operating techniques. A final example is found in our Planning research studies where information obtained through a comprehensive survey on how water is actually used on irrigation projects is being put into practice through our Irrigation Management Services program. This program demonstrates to the farmers the benefits they will attain through better water management practices, trains them in evaluating when water is needed and how much is needed, and in making the proper applications.

In citing these successes we do not intend to give the impression that all has gone well in the transfer and utilization of our research results. This has not always been the case. In some instances data have been obtained, worthwhile conclusions have been drawn, and the information has been presented to potential users. But the fruits of the research were not put into use. One example is found in the development of small inlet and outlet transitions for canal structures. Here the target was to develop lower-cost, easily-precast, lower-head loss structures with less tendency to scour earth canals than did the current designs. Considerable progress was made in research projects to improve such designs and a final report was submitted. But to date little has been done toward adopting these improved designs in place of the older ones. A principal reason was that communication was not what it should have been between designers and research personnel. The new designs, while better in important respects than the older ones, have not been worth the change-over costs because nominal loss of head was not significant in most cases where our canals have been built and because the moderate scouring downstream from conventional structures could usually be handled by inexpensive gravel blankets. Research personnel did not adequately consider these practical constraints which seriously effected the usefulness of their results, nor were the designers kept adequately informed of the direction the research was taking. In the meantime a shift in emphasis has taken place and a considerable portion of our smaller waterways are now being constructed as undergound pipe systems rather than as open canals.

A dissimilar case exists in research on water wells. Our Division of Water Operation and Maintenance is concerned with among other things, designing, constructing, and maintaining water wells. Over a period of several years they have requested the assistance of the Division of General Research in working on a problem associated with such wells. Only very recently has our research group developed a real appreciation of the needs in the field of groundwater. For this reason no work has yet been done in an area that now appears to be of real importance to the Bureau. This lack of understanding of true priorities can lead to the necessity for a "crash" program to solve a problem of sudden urgency. "Crash" programs are almost always inefficient and disruptive to other work. Better communications can assure an orderly and efficient pursuit of high priority research needs.

Another kind of problem concerns differences of opinion as to whether better information is really needed in a subject area. Researchers may be inclined to feel that perfection has not yet been attained and that it is a worthy and true goal. They often tend to expend resources on a project beyond the point of diminishing returns and seek refinements in processes, procedures, and materials that the designers feel are not significant enough to justify changes. Thus there exists a searching and probing philosophy on the part of the researchers, and a practical, cost conscious approach on the part of the research users. Each has good reasons for his mode of operation, but a proper blending of the two is desirable. To achieve it, proper feedback, close communication, coordination, and understanding are required. These are constantly sought through our formal and informal communication systems.

Future Plans and Innovations

Our experience shows, perhaps not surprisingly, that research results which are quickly put into practice are those where strong needs for research are felt and expressed by the planners, designers, and O&M users of the information. On the other hand, if the needs for the results, and the benefits they will provide, lie too far down the road or are unproved in the minds of the potential users, the research results are not likely to be seriously considered, let alone used.

This poses two problems. The first concerns selection of research to be undertaken. The procedures described earlier to learn of research needs, assign priorities to them, and then develop programs based on them have been quite successful in recent years. These will be continued. We recognize, however, that through this procedure there is a tendency to emphasize only immediate problems. This is countered by the leadership and vision provided by selected members of the Research Review Committee. The result is that a balance is attained between immediate needs and visionary but still practical future needs that deserve study.

The second problem concerns maintaining adequate 2-way communication and establishing and maintaining a philosophy of continually striving for better ways to do our job. There should be no stigma attached to using tried and true methods that produce good results. The danger lies in being satisfied with what you have and not raising your eyes frequently enough to see if new approaches might be significantly better.

Our formal communication system is based largely upon conventional reports which describe and discuss the research studies, present data obtained, and present analyses and interpretations of it. These reports are listed under our

our REC-ERC numbering system and are distributed widely in the E&R Center, to the regional offices, to a mailing list of organizations with a mutual interest in the subject matter, and to the public through the National Technical Information Service. They are often supplemented by less formal internal progress reports. Our most prestigious report series is titled *Water Resources Technical Publications* and is reserved for selected research studies and for engineering monographs. There are now a number of publications in this series, including our manuals on subjects like water measurement, concrete, and soil materials. These publications receive wide distribution, are popular with the many foreign trainees who work with the Bureau, and may be purchased from the Government Printing Office.

Another means of speeding transfer of research results into practical application is by issuing brief memo-type reports as soon as reportable results are obtained. Much valuable time and much impetus may have been lost if we wait until a full final report is prepared. In cases where we feel the value of a comprehensive summary report outweighs the costs, a full final report will be issued.

We are also using an in-house, popular-press type newsletter titled "Research News." A principal function of this 4-page quarterly publication is to create a research consciousness in the minds of Bureau people - whether they be in Washington, in Denver, or in regional offices. This is done by high-lighting in an interesting way information on new research activities and research results.

This communication and reporting system does not assure that the results of our research will get into the hands of persons who need it. Nor does it assure that they will use the results even if they have them in their hand. A key to accomplishing effective research application is to involve the people who need the improvements, or who will need the improvements in the future, in the research activities. Bureau personnel concerned with planning, design, construction, or project operation and maintenance are now involved with research personnel in multidisciplinary teams established for carrying out selected research studies. This process accomplishes at least three things: first, through discussions future needs are better defined and brought to light and are included in the research program. Second, the results of the research are more likely to be put into practice immediately because the personnel working on the research are the ones who really need it. Finally, alternative ways of carrying out the research are considered.

Examples of interdisciplinary research teams are the Water Reaeration team, the Ice Problems Research team, the team assembled for developing and improving equipment and concepts for Automation of Water Delivery Systems, and our Open and Closed Conduit Systems (OCCS) team. In the latter case, representation on the group includes a liaison officer from each of the regions.

Conclusions

We recognize that there will always be some differences between the goals of research-oriented individuals and the goals of those who can use and benefit from the results of research. Based on experience, we believe that these differences can be significantly resolved by improved communications. Research personnel need to do a better job of knowing precisely what their customers really need, and of looking to the future with practical vision so that their studies will provide useful answers to real problems. The customers who utilize the results of research need to recognize the continuing need for better ways of accomplishing their work.

Effective formal and informal two-way communications between the groups is dependent upon mutual understanding, trust, respect, and appreciation of each other. From our recent experience we believe that the multidisciplinary team approach to research, in which the users of the research results are made a part of the research team, can create a situation in which the results of research are effectively reduced to useful practice.

We feel that the Bureau is making significant strides in transferring research results into practice. We do not profess that we have all the answers, or that we are doing the best job possible at this time. We are continuing to look for better ways, and are very interested in studying reports from others here at this meeting who describe different facets of the problem and alternatives for resolving it.

RESEARCH FINDINGS AND THE DESIGN ENGINEER

By

Carter H. Harrison
Assistant Professor
Auburn University

Synopsis

Design engineers in private practice often operate under
severe time constraints. In order for them to consider the
implementation of recent research findings in their designs,
a full report on the research findings must be readily available to the design engineer before the design problem arises.
At present the only method of achieving this result is for the
research findings to appear in one of the major technical
journals.

An engineer with a design problem will attempt to locate
information either by consulting a collegue or by reference
to an index. The Cumulative Index to ASCE Publications is
suggested as a good starting point. More recent research
findings can often be obtained by phoning or writing the author
of an article appearing in an ASCE journal or by contacting
a researcher listed in the Water Resources Research Catalog.
Where the Citation Index is available, more recent publications
on a given subject can be quickly located by using ASCE publications as a starting point. Abstracts alone are of little
value to a design engineer.

The design engineer's need for immediate reference
material places a large responsibility on the reviewers of
the major technical journals. These reviewers should also pay
attention to the quality of the references supplied with a
technical paper because of the increasing use of the Citation
Index.

The Present Situation

Practicing engineers, in this country at least, are sometimes criticized for failing to implement the most recent
research findings in designs. In some cases, he may know of
the research findings but be unwilling to implement them because of problems with review agencies or because of the
increasing problems of professional liability.

Unlike the researcher, the design engineer is usually a
generalist who has to bring a basic understanding of many
fields to bear on one specific problem. A practicing sanitary
engineer, for example, cannot hope to keep current in all
aspects of sanitary chemistry, biology, and process economics,

to say nothing of environmental impact, federal regulations, water law, or construction technology. The design engineer usually needs specific answers to detailed design questions, and he needs those answers in a hurry.

Abstracts are of little value to a design engineer. Most abstracts do not give the basic euqations, much less their derivation. In order to use research work as a basis of design, a practicing engineer must know not only the results of the research, but also the complications and limitations observed. The problem of product liability is a real one to the design engineer. Abstracts alone do not warn him of the problems he might encounter with a new design or method of operation.

Design engineers are usually under great time pressures. The client measures an engineer's service first by observing how well the design worked, and secondly by how fast he was able to complete the job. A design engineer must have the research findings near at hand before the problem arises. This usually means that the research findings must be presented in one of the leading technical serial publications such as the Journals of the American Society of Civil Engineers, The Journal of the American Water Works Association, or Water Resources Research. If the research findings do not appear in these journals, which are received on standing order by most practicing engineering firms, then the research will probably not even be considered, much less implemented.

Some may question why a near-by library would not be adequate. The time used by a design engineer for literature review could be equally well applied to a design job, charge-able to the client at 15 to 25 dollars per hour. When any amount of travel to and from the library is involved, the costs in terms of lost time tend to become unattractive to conserva-tively minded engineers. The research effort may result in savings that are many times greater than the costs of obtaining the information, but the uncertainty of finding the needed information is great.

Some might question the need for the engineer to do the actual literature search. My experience has been that only the design engineer or an assistant engineer who is intimately familiar with the project can effectively locate detailed information of the type needed for the basis of project design. A librarian might be able to locate information on water quality models, but when the request is for information on water quality models, excluding thermal pollution and estuary models, that are applicable to the problems in a particular location, most librarians are unable to filter out irrelevant materials. The engineer can usually screen what he has on hand faster than he can delegate and review what he has asked others to do for him.

156

For most engineers, the problem is one of locating those resources which are already at hand. Some years ago the Department of Defense conducted "Project Hindsight" in an effort to learn where design engineers working on defense projects got their information[3]. This study revealed that, at least in the defense industry, the majority of information desired was obtained by informal means such as personal notes and records or by consultation with a colleague. The most frequent demands were for specific answers to a specific question, not a collection of documents or reports. My own observations lead me to believe that the same is true with water resources engineering. In any organization, there are a few individuals who have that amazing ability to store away a collection of certain articles, then recall the approximate, if not the exact locale at the appropriate time.

When the informal approach fails to produce results, then the engineer usually turns to the more formal approaches. It must be remembered that because of time and cost constraints, real or imagined, the design engineer is interested primarily in locating information that is readily available.

A good starting place is the "Cumulative Index to ASCE Publications"[2] and the more recent ASCE Combined Index for 1970 and for 1971[1]. These indexes are based on keywords, selected from an ASCE master list by the journal authors themselves. The indexing process is now fully automated, making it possible for the ASCE to make these indexes available only a few months after the end of the time period involved.

The Journals of the ASCE do not by any means contain the results of all significant research findings, but they do provide a well indexed point of departure. The references cited at the back of these papers can often provide the basis for a revised design.

Even though the ASCE indexing process is fully automated, there is still a considerable time lag between the time an author prepares a paper and the time in which it appears in the ASCE index. In order to find the most recent research findings, the design engineer needs some method of quickly bringing himself up to date. There are now two excellent methods of locating the most recent information, both of which are somewhat more time consuming and expensive than referring to the ASCE index and the cited references in the ASCE journals.

The Institute for Scientific Information now produces a Citation Index[4]. This index consists of lists, by author, of all recent works that have included that authors work, in its list of references. The Citation Index is especially strong in the life sciences; thus engineers utilizing this index should encounter relevant publications dealing with environmental issues.

The Citation Index may be utilized, either by visiting a library that subscribes to this service, or by contacting the Institute directly. Current rates for citation searches are $25 per hour with a 2 hour minimum. For a recent engineering paper, they estimate they can supply citations to roughly five papers in one hour. For an additional charge, ISI will also furnish a copy of the complete publication.

In order to use a Citation Index, the researcher or in this case the design engineer must have previously identified the author of some book or journal article on the subject of interest. This work should be widely available and should appear in the commonly used indexes. The Journals of the ASCE provide an excellent source for such initial references because these are widely circulated and well indexed.

Source references are listed in a Citation Index along with a reference to the most recent journal articles which cited that source reference in a footnote or list of references. Listings in a Citation Index are by first author of the original reference.

Suppose a design engineer wanted the latest research findings on ways of estimating dissolved oxygen levels in a stream both before and after various improvements in waste discharge treatment. He would probably think of the work done by H. W. Streeter and E. B. Phelps back in 1925. The 1971 Citation Index lists nine journal articles appearing in that year which cited that work. The listings appear as follows:

```
STREET HW
  **146 PUBL HEALTH B
    GRANTHAM GR J SANIT ENG     97    569    71
  25 USPHS 146 PUB HEALTH
    MARTIN DC J WATER PC        43   1865    71
```

The first author, Grantham, did not provide the date of Streeter's work. His paper starts on page 569 of Volume 97 (1971) of the Journal of the Sanitary Engineering Division of the ASCE. Martin also cited the work done by Streeter (and Phelps). His paper appears in the Journal of the Water Pollution Control Federation, Volume 43 (1971), page 1865.

The 1971 Citation Index also lists seven other references to this one work as well as recent references to three other works by H. W. Streeter. By just knowing that Streeter did some of the original work in this field, an engineer can quickly locate nine of the most recent works on this subject. These may not be all of the references available, but they should be most of the ones he is interested in, that is, the ones that might already be locally available.

A Citation Index has numerous advantages over the search methods. It goes forward in time without delay for indexing or classification. The process is automated and the indexes are updated quarterly. Once a basic reference or early investigator has been identified, the job of locating recent works can then be delegated to a non-engineer.

The major limitation on the use of a Citation Index is its cost. The present price for a one year subscription is $1500. This includes the annual compilation as well as the quarterly updatings. Most engineering firms are unwilling to spend this much for such a service so the use of a Citation Index is usually limited to those who have access to a major library. As engineers become more acquainted with this type of information retrieval and more aware of the cost effectiveness of such a service, they will make more use of a Citation Index and pay more attention to the references provided in technical publications.

A less expensive alternate method of locating recent works in the area of water resources is through the use of the Water Resources Research Catalog[5] prepared by the Office of Water Resources Research. This annual two volume work contains summaries of all the water resources research currently being conducted under federal auspices. One volume contains the summary descriptions of the research projects, the other volume contains a very extensive index to the first volume. A current catalog in this series is of course convenient for locating current research projects. A slightly older catalog, say one or two years old, is quite valuable for purposes of locating reports on a given topic. A phone call or letter to the principle investigators listed in this catalog will generally bring both a finished report and suggestions on other sources on that topic. While these two approaches do not meet the "in-house" requirement previously described, they do provide a means of coming up to date on a given topic with a minimum expenditure of time.

For an example of the usefulness of the Water Resources Research Catalog, the 1970 catalog was used to locate information on water quality models for Alabama. In 17 minutes, 22 potential investigations were located. A review of the project description indicated twelve of these might warrant further investigations. Two of the works appeared so promising that the principle investigators were phoned; the other ten were contacted by mail. The letter writing was easily delegated to an assistant. If the design engineer is willing to wait for the mails on a major project, this method can bring results.

Future Improvements

The present situation, with regard to the design engineer, is only partially satisfactory. The ASCE index and Journals provides a means of quickly retrieving information from ASCE Journals. Unfortunately the other major water resources journals are not well indexed; some are not indexed at all. At the very least, those journals that are in wide circulation should strive to prepare periodic indexes based on author selected key words. It would be very desirable for all of these journals to use the same type of automated procedure so that someday it may be possible to prepare indexes devoted to water resources.

The Citation Index in its current form is too extensive and too expensive for a design engineering firm. An annual subscription costs $1500 per year. There may be a place for a special edition of this index containing only citations of works that have appeared in the major engineering journals. This limited edition might be further restricted to just references that appear in the widely circulated engineering journals.

The Citation Index concept holds much promise for the future. The preparation of the index is a fully automated process, one that does not require time consuming human interpretation and interaction. Information retrieval by use of a citation index can be easily delegated to a non-professional. The value of this method is, however, entirely dependent on the accuracy and relevancy of the references given for a particular work. Reviewers should pay careful attention to the references provided and papers with insufficient references returned for revision.

The Water Resources Research Catalog is already a very valuable source of information and available at a very modest price. The only change that might be made in it would be the inclusion of complete mailing addresses and phone numbers.

The reviewers who select manuscripts for publication in the leading journals should recognize the importance of these journals in the design area. A paper that does not contain bold new concepts or abstract formuli, may still provide much valuable information for the design engineer. The number of design engineers greatly outnumbers the researchers. They just are not as active in the publications process. Journal reviewers should recognize the value of design type information and realize that failure to publish this type of information in a serialized journal in wide circulation will greatly reduce the possibility of those findings even being considered by a design engineer.

The informal process of information dissemination by interaction with collegues will probably still be the main source of design information in the future, but there is much to be done towards helping the design engineer utilize what is readily available to him.

1. American Society of Civil Engineers, ASCE Combined Index 1970, also 1971, 345 East 47th Street, New York, N.Y. 10017, Price $2.00 each.

2. American Society of Civil Engineers, Cumulative Index to ASCE Publications, 1960-1969, 345 East 47th Street, New York, N.Y. 10017, Price $20.00.

3. Carlson, Walter M., "Engineering Information for National Defense," Engineering Societies and Their Literature Programs, Engineers Joint Council, 345 East 47th Street, New York, N.Y. 10017, April 1967, $5.00.

4. Institute for Scientific Information, Citation Index, 325 Chestnut Street, Philadelphia, Pennsylvania 19106.

5. Office of Water Resources Research, Water Resources Research Catalog, Government Printing Office, Washington, D.C. ($12.50 for the 2 volume set).

TECHNICAL AID FOR HYDROLOGIC STUDIES IN
SPANISH-SPEAKING COUNTRIES

By

O. James Taylor
Hydrologist, U.S. Geological Survey
Lakewood, Colorado, U.S.A.

Synopsis

Recent technical aid for hydrologic studies in Chile, the
Canary Islands, and Spain has emphasized the necessity for
communication in various specialties. The author assisted
hydrologists of these countries in the design and interpretation
of digital-computer simulation models for a stream-aquifer
system in central Chile and helped prepare computer programs
for the processing of chemical data from the Canary Islands.
Based on the results of studies published by the various
countries, the technical assistance was effective. The success
of the technical aid was strongly dependent on communication
between the author and the Spanish-speaking hydrologists in
language, mathematics, computer science, hydrology, and related technologies. The failure to communicate in one or
more of the mentioned specialties may easily lead to mis-
understanding problem, misleading results, or completely
erroneous results.

Introduction

The author participated in programs of technical aid to
several countries in recent years. The first program in 1970
involved aid in preparing digital simulation models of a stream-
aquifer system in central Chile for the Departamento de Recursos
Hidráulicos of the Corporación de Fomento de la Producción
(CORFO) and was sponsored by the U.S. Agency for International
Development (U.S. AID). The U.S. Geological Survey had supplied
technical assistance to the Government of Chile in previous
years, but digital models had never been used. Digital
models are needed to determine the effects of additional
irrigation wells and reservoirs on the timely delivery of
irrigation water. A second program, initiated in 1971, involved continuing assistance in computer processing of
hydrologic data for the Canary Islands, a province of Spain.
The United Nations Educational, Scientific, and Cultural
Organization (UNESCO) sponsored the program with the Canary
Islands. The author was chosen to assist in the above programs
because of his background in digital simulation models, computer programing, and familiarity with the Spanish language.

The author attempted to maintain a high degree of
communication with participants in the various programs in

order to insure that all resulting data and conclusions were meaningful. However, numerous communication problems of language, mathematical expression, computer science, and hydrology were discovered which are discussed below.

Language

Communication with Spanish-speaking hydrologists and computer scientists would have been difficult without a knowledge of Spanish. Few were able to speak English, although most were able to read scientific articles written in English. The use of a common language by the author and local scientists allowed a clear understanding of the specific hydrologic problems, the methods of solution, and interpretation of results. Following digital model studies in Santiago, Chile, the author described the results in Spanish at a seminar at the University of Chile.

The author recommends study of at least the scientific part of the language before attempting to provide technical aid in a foreign country in which English is not spoken. Any English speaker would recognize the Spanish words written "digital" or "impermeable" but few would recognize the spoken words because their pronunciation is very different from that of similar words in English. Acronyms such as sdf derived from the English words "stream depletion factor" became FAR in Chile from "factor de agotamiento del río." In Spain the name became "factor de infiltración inducida." The Spanish word "diversión" means amusement and has nothing to do with irrigation canals. Naturally the technical words vary in different Spanish-speaking countries, and the local terminology must be learned. Knowledge of the local language will also make a visit to the country more enjoyable and help avoid offending others because of cultural differences.

Mathematical Expression

Confusion in expression may arise because the decimal point and comma, normally, but not always, are used differently in Spanish-speaking countries than in the United States. For example the number written 1,600,600.88 in this country might be written 1.600.600,88 in a Spanish-speaking country. In South America, I prepared a table in English of the demand for water by month as shown below:

Demand in cubic meters

August	September	October	November
55,000	266,000	400,000	475,000

The table was typed by a secretary (who did not speak English) as shown below:

Demand in cubic meters			
August	September	October	November
55.00	266.00	400.00	475.00

The secretary presumed that all digits following the comma were decimals; she changed the commas to decimal points and dropped the unnecessary "decimals."

Apparently, the use of mathematical equations and other forms of mathematical expression are identical in the United States and the countries visited. Therefore, very complex relations in hydrology or computer mathematics can be readily expressed and understood, which is an important advantage in communication.

All hydrologic work was accomplished using the metric system of units to conform with local standards. The hydrologists were aware of our units from our literature, but expressed confusion over the actual significance of units such as acre-feet, second foot days, and gallons per minute. Consistent metric units were used to solve finite difference equations in digital models. The author acquired a healthy respect for the metric system of units and the associated efficiency in calculations.

Computer Science

In South America the digital model simulations were processed on an IBM computer in Santiago, Chile. Data processing for the Canary Islands was accomplished on a similar computer in Madrid, Spain. Both computers required programs written in the standard FORTRAN language and used the decimal point to separate integers from decimals as in the United States. The Spanish-speaking programers knew FORTRAN, but pronounced the English FORTRAN words as if they were Spanish. Hence, statements such as GO to 12; DO 10 I = 1, 5; or DEFINE FILE were not immediately recognizable. The decimal point problem was apparent in processing data for the Canary Islands. In order to print data in the Spanish style using the comma, it was necessary either to write long programs or else simplify the program to the degree that the computer was of little value. The problem could be eliminated by international standards for expression of decimals or by adjustments in computing systems designed for overseas use.

Several means were used to insure that computer programs were understandable. Comment cards with Spanish explanations of various parts of the program were used liberally. Variable names were derived from Spanish words for clarity. For example, a variable representing the change in ground-water storage was designated AGSUB to conform with the Spanish term for ground-water, agua subterránea.

In Santiago, Chile an inquiry was made concerning the availability of linear programing techniques to study the optimal conjunctive use of ground and surface water in an irrigation system. A Chilean systems engineer was contacted and informed of the type of simulation needed. The engineer was better informed on the capability and methods of linear program techniques than any other analyst the author has encountered in recent years. Hence, complex optimization studies could be undertaken with ease.

Hydrology

The author worked directly with several Chilean hydrologists in order to prepare several types of digital models of the stream-aquifer system in the Aconcagua Valley in central Chile. The models were designed to simulate the effect of aquifer recharge or discharge on streamflow and ground-water storage. The results of model studies will assist in management of the system and help to analyze the benefits and effects of proposed reservoirs and additional irrigation wells.

The preliminary results of model studies were published by the author in 1970 as an open-file report, and the results of additional model studies were published in 1971 by CORFO in Chile. Model studies were used to evaluate (1) return flow as a function of time and space, (2) the accuracy of assumed distributions of transmissivity, (3) the effect of artificial recharge, (4) various types of conjunctive use of ground and surface water, (5) the need for additional observation wells, and (6) various other interrelations in the stream-aquifer system. The preliminary report has been distributed world wide among Spanish-speaking hydrologists and water managers.

Data processing and computer analysis of hydrologic data is at a preliminary stage in the Canary Islands. The basic data and interpretive reports will be published as they are completed.

The author corresponds with administrators and hydrologists in Chile, Spain, and the Canary Islands. Reprints of published articles, technical manuals, and computer programs have been exchanged for the benefit of all participants. Anticipated problems in hydrology, modeling, or programing are discussed, and solutions are designed and communicated by mail or cable before visits. Thus, visits to other countries are productive; time is not expended on minor complex problems.

Conclusions

Complex hydrologic and electronic computer techniques may be applied successfully in foreign countries if care is taken to avoid communication problems. The author discovered differences in technical expression among various countries which could have made the results of digital simulation models misleading or completely erroneous if viewed in an inappropriate contexture. However, communication in several disciplines insured that the models were applied and interpreted correctly. The primary mode of communication is language, in the opinion of the author.

The results from digital simulation models can be used to design water-management plans and negotiate loans for construction purposes. A meaningless simulation of a water-resource system can lead to poorly designed reservoirs and well fields and result in large economic losses to a developing nation. Hence, technical aid for hydrologic studies can only be successful when good communication is achieved by all participants in all disciplines.

THE ROLE OF PROFESSIONAL SOCIETIES IN THE DISSEMINATION OF WATER RESOURCES RESEARCH INFORMATION

By

Donald C. Taylor
Manager, Research Services
American Society of Civil Engineers

Synopsis

Professional societies by virtue of their organization, membership and objectives are uniquely qualified to play a major role in the dissemination of water resources research information for its use in practice. The American Society of Civil Engineers for example has communication links in all sectors of practice. Of over 65,000 members there are 15% in research and education, 30% in local state and federal government, 30% in consulting, 15% in construction and 10% in industry and other areas.

Technical and research activities of the ASCE cover all aspects of professional practice more than one-quarter of which is related to water resources. More than 30,000 of over 65,000 total members relate themselves to the water resources field in some fashion.

Traditional methods of disseminating information by professional societies are still very effective and include conference symposia, technical magazines and journals and meetings. There also are trends toward providing easier ways for busy professionals to locate and put to use relevant information such as the use of information storage and retrieval systems and publication of state of the art studies. Research in progress surveys and research needs studies help link research as well as make it relevant to practice. New and expanding continuing education services bring new information to members faster. All possible avenues of information exchanges are needed to be continually explored to reduce log time and provide the water resources professional with the information he needs from research on a real time basis.

Professional societies, because of the nature of their membership, have a major role to play in the interpretation and dissemination, for practical use, of research information to their members. In few other ways are the members of the profession brought together so closely on technical and professional issues.

In the American Society of Civil Engineers, for example, the Society membership of over 65,000 is divided by percent approximately as follows:

15% - research and education
30% - local, state and federal government employment
30% - private consulting practice
15% - construction contracting
10% - industry and other areas

This means two things. One is that the organization is heavily composed of professionals in practice (5 out of 6 members of ASCE are registered professional engineers, not because of Society requirements, but chiefly because of personal commitments to their chosen fields) who are for the most part the ultimate users of new knowledge. The other is that the Society membership also includes, in no small number, the many other professionals who must serve those in actual practice through research, education, production of equipment and materials, and other related activities. The inter-functioning of these groups at all levels of Society activities is in itself an important means of interchange and dissemination of new information.

Technical and Research Activities

Of exceptional value to those in the water resources field are the contributions that can be made by the myriad of technical committees which form the backbone of professional society technical activities. The function of many of these committees is to provide a mechanism for expert review of work in the subject area of the committee, to interpret new information in light of expert experience, and to translate the results of research and other work into usable information for practice. Not all committees, unfortunately, carry out their missions fully. Of the 500 or more ASCE technical committees, at least 100 to 150 are somehow related to the field of water resources. These committees can have a much larger role to play in the dissemination of research information than is currently performed.

Technical Divisions and Technical Councils

There are currently three Technical Councils and 15 Technical Divisions in ASCE. For information ASCE Technical Divisions and Councils are listed in the following table. Registration figures only apply to Divisions.

Technical Divisions	Registration for 1971 - 1972	
Air Transport	1,898	
Construction	18,615	
Engineering Mechanics	6,175	
Highway	12,090	
Hydraulics	11,229	
Irrigation and Drainage	4,643	
Pipeline	1,632	
Power	2,979	
Sanitary Engineering	9,685	
Soil Mechanics and Foundations	15,239	
Structural	23,670	
Surveying and Mapping	3,652	
Urban Planning and Development	8,956	
Urban Transportation	200	(newly formed)
Waterways and Harbors	4,124	
TOTAL	124,677	

Technical Councils

Aero-Space
Ocean Engineering
Water Resources Planning and Management

Eliminating duplication, there are probably over 25,000 members of ASCE who have direct interest of some sort in water resources engineering work.

Research Councils

During the past 10 to 15 years, there have been a total of 14 Research Councils in the organizational structure of ASCE. These have been the Research Councils on:

Air Resources Engineering
Coastal Engineering
Computer Practices
Construction
Expansion Soils
Performance of Full-Scale Structures
Pipeline Crossings of Railroads and Highways
Pipeline Flotation
Reinforced Concrete
Structural Plastics
Underground Construction
Urban Water Resources
Urban Transportation
Water Quality

As will be noted, the subject areas of several of these councils are closely related to certain aspects of water resources. Research councils are as effective as their leadership, and some have produced unprecedented results.

Research Committees

In all technical divisions or technical councils except one, there is a specially designed committee that concerns itself generally with stimulation of research in the subject area of the division. In the division that does not have a research committee the division executive committee feels that this function is so important that it keeps this function to itself.

The general function of each of the technical division and technical council research activities is to initiate, organize and coordinate programs of research. Some of the ways the committee has developed these programs have been to develop and find sponsorship for research projects, determine areas of needed research, carry out conferences on special and general research types, encourage reviews to be made, make surveys of research in progress, and encourage the publication of research experiences.

Research Committees of the ASCE in the field of water resources like the Hydraulics Division Research Committee have pioneered in setting the stage for research appreciation not only in their Division but in the entire ASCE. In other water-related divisions like the Irrigation and Drainage Division, the Research Committee has led the civil engineering community to be concerned not only with solving problems of traditional methods but also with the use of new technology such as weather modification to solve the nations water problems.

Research Councils provide an unusually effective mechanism for quickly introducing the results of research into practice. They are organized when there is special need for stimulating research in new or neglected areas of interest, for raising funds for such research, and for organizing concerted efforts to initiate actual research in the field or laboratory. Membership in the councils usually consists of those in practice requiring new information, those in organizations that have the ability to support new research, and those who are capable of and interested in doing the research.

The general objectives of the research councils are "...to advance engineering knowledge and practice through stimulating and guiding research and assisting the financing thereof in the field of air pollution control; to organize research projects; in cooperation with professional committees, to interpret the findings of such research; and to make

170

available information and recommendations resulting from such research." This combination of efforts often results in direct application of research to practice of research almost as it comes off the press.

In the past few years, the Research Council on Urban Hydrology has been developing a national program of urban water resources research [1,2,3]. Many parts of this program are now being considered for major funding, and plans for implementation are already under way. Taking part in the inception of the program has been a cross section of the best creative professional talent available on urban water problems that could be found in the country. There is no doubt that the effects of new research in this area will begin to be felt in actual practice even before the formal publication of final results.

Transferring and Exchanging Information

In recent writings there has been much discussion about the statistics of the information explosion. It is not the purpose of this paper to reiterate these claims, but to comment on the ways and means professional societies have, are developing, and might develop to meet the information challenge in the field of water resources. Certainly, it should not take the 5, 10, 15 or more years now required to get useful information into practice. The means of eliminating this time lag is, of course, the development and maintenance of a variety of communication networks between those engaged in research and those engaged in practice.

Traditional Methods

Regardless of how long they have been used, a study report for OWRR [4] clearly indicates that technical magazines, professional society journals, and conferences and symposiums are well recognized and important media for the dissemination of research information. These media also make up a substantial part of most present day professional society activity. They are media that are here to stay, with the challenge, however, of how to become even more effective.

Some of the things ASCE has done in the past few years to make its programs more effective are as follows:

National Meetings - A current practice over the past several years has been for each of the ASCE National Meetings to be assigned a basic central theme, such as Water Resources Engineering, Transportation Engineering, or Structural Engineering. Such a central theme attracts particular conference members of the profession with common interest. National Meetings on Water Resources have been exceptionally well

attended over the past few years, even when they were held
in smaller conference centers. There have been Water Resources
Meetings in Omaha (1962), Milwaukee (1963), Mobile (1965),
Denver (1966), New York (1967), and New Orleans (1969),
Memphis (1970), Phoenix (1971), and Atlanta (1972). The next
one is planned for Washington, D.C. in January 1973. Research
findings are carefully integrated into all parts of these
conference programs.

Specialty Conferences - Although there is ample
opportunity for scheduling presentations of research findings
at any of the National Meetings, there is usually not enough
time to accommodate all good papers. For this reason, many
of the ASCE Technical Divisions conduct their own Specialty
Conferences to provide the additional outlets of information
needed.

Sponsorship of these conferences is one way in which
ASCE can be of greater service to the water resources field.
There is a great flexibility in the organization of the
conferences, their format, length, audience, and purpose.
Their usefulness depends on the willingness and capability
of interested groups to organize the conferences and, of
course, on their ability to attract the desired audience.

Specialty conferences can be aimed at attracting large
audiences or small. The larger ones are usually conducted
with Division-wide participation, with attendances varying
from 300 to 1,000. Smaller conferences are more oriented
toward individual discussion and direct exchange of information
from person to person.

A typical example of a very successful smaller conference of this nature was the Specialty Research Conference
on Water Quality in Reservoirs held in Portland, Oregon in
January, 1968. This conference was jointly sponsored by
the ASCE Hydraulics and the Sanitary Engineering Divisions.
It was originally intended for an audience of 100, but attracted over 180 because of the timeliness of the presentation
and the nature of the program that allowed for a maximum of
information discussion.

More conferences such as the Portland Conference, concentrating on unique and timely water resources problems,
would be welcomed by the members of ASCE and related
disciplines.

Engineering Foundation Research Conferences

A relatively new concept in research conferences has been
the Engineering Foundation Research Conferences patterned
after the Gordon Research Conferences conducted in New England

172

for several decades. Several professional engineering
societies have helped sponsor one or more of these meetings.
They are for maximum individual participation and personal
exchange of information. Several of the conferences participated in by ASCE have been related to water resources and,
specifically, urban Water Resources. Several others are
planned for this year and for the years to come.

The Engineering Foundation welcomes ideas and assistance
in developing new research conferences. They afford excellent
opportunities for high level political as well as intellectual
discussion in a relaxed atmosphere where there is time to
explore all aspects of discussion topics.

Technical Magazines - There is no substitute for a
professional society's main link to its membership - its
magazines where good editors keep the most appealing and news-
worthy information before its members. In ASCE, CIVIL
ENGINEERING goes to every member automatically. Water resources
happens to be one of the most important subject areas of the
magazine. Special issues are annually devoted to Water
Resources, Waterways and Harbors, Power, Public Works, and
Environmental Pollution Control. Information and articles
of better quality are continually needed to keep this
communication link alive.

Technical Journals - Although emphasis on type of
material changes over the years, technical journals with
carefully presented and reviewed papers provide the most
intellectual outlets or forums for information that prof-
fesional societies have to serve their members. ASCE has
several Technical Divisions which serve the water resources
field consistently. These are: Hydraulics, Irrigation and
Drainage, Power, Sanitary Engineering, and Waterways and
Harbors, and to some extent, Engineering Mechanics, and
Pipelines. Not all these Journals are overly supplied with
papers proposed for publication. There is much good material
that could be submitted for publication that is not. One
of the roles of technical societies is to ferret out this
information and encourage the presentation of it through
meetings, conferences, etc.

Current Trends in Information Exchange

Out of the traditional information activities of professional societies come many pieces of random information,
each valuable in itself, but seemingly without relevance to
the recipient - unless he has some way to put it into content and make an evaluation of its use to him. Professional
societies with extensive publication programs can be of great
help to their subscribers by assisting them in two major
ways. These are by source indexing and abstracting and by

preparation or encouragement of timely high quality state-of-the-art reviews.

Source Indexing and Abstracting - As stated in the EJC Guide for Source Indexing and Abstracting [5], "By far the major benefit of source indexing and abstracting is the reduction of duplication of the intellectual analysis of documents necessary to produce abstracts and index data. This intellectual effort is often repeated in the traditional situation, requiring recipients of documents rather than the originators to perform the indexing and abstracting operations.

"Another benefit of source indexing and abstracting is that it can provide the potential for greatly improving the currency of secondary publications as well as reducing considerably their input costs. This potential will only be realized when most technical documents are indexed and abstracted completely at the source by authors and editors."

"A further advantage to the engineering community is more subtle, but nonetheless real. As more and more editors and authors participate in improving the flow of information through source indexing and abstracting, they will become increasingly aware of the problem of the users of information resources and will achieve a fuller sense of participation in the entire communication process."

Since January 1963, all the regularly issued Society publications - the Technical Division Journals, the Journal of Professional Activities, and CIVIL ENGINEERING magazine - have included information-retrieval abstracts and key words of all major articles. The abstracts and key words appear at the beginning of each Journal and in the back of CIVIL ENGINEERING magazine.

The authors of technical papers have contributed materially to the success of this endeavor. Approximately 50% of the authors submit abstracts and key words initially. The remainder prepare them when they make the final revision of the paper prior to publication. ASCE instructions to authors for writing abstracts were published in article "ASCE Moves Towards More Efficient Information Retrieval," [6] which appeared in the August 1962 issue of CIVIL ENGINEERING.

ASCE has been careful to integrate all its information retrieval activities into the long-range, information-program goals being developed through EJC. The Engineering Index, for instance, uses ASCE abstracts for their own publications substantially as published. The benefits of the cooperation pays off not only in the long run but immediately. Other professional societies are finding similar benefits.

We should also mention the bimonthly "ASCE Publication Abstract" which lists, tabulates, and cross references all recent Society publications, along with an abstract of each. The subject indexes of these are also unique because they permute the key words for each article. The many members who receive this publication have a quick review of everything in their range of interest and can easily obtain the full publications they desire.

State-of-the-Art Trend in Publications - At this point, it may be well to mention a very significant trend developing in regard to all information activities. This is the need for consolidation of information and presentation of state-of-the-art papers that show how new information can be used in practice. As indicated in a recent report on Scientific and Technical Communications by the NAS-NAE [7] "Such consolidations of information, the preparation of which requires great intellectual creativity, have traditionally appeared in review articles, books, data compilations, and the like. But the preparation and use of such materials have not kept pace with the flood of potentially useful new information in the scientific and technical literature."

ASCE encourages the preparation of state-of-the-art studies and has recently initiated a special annual award for this purpose. "Application of Research to Practice" grants are offered periodically to encourage new work of this nature. One grant project supported and related to water resources work was an overview of "The Coagulation Process."

On a much larger scale, Research Councils of ASCE have helped develop and sponsor more extensive study, such as one on the "Use of the Soil Mantle as an Agency for Treatment," produced at the University of California at Berkeley in cooperation with the ASCE Research Council on Water Quality, and sponsored by the FWPCA. Similar studies initiated by this Research Council included the subject areas of biological treatment, physical-chemical treatment, the effects of eutrophication and the use of receiving waters as an agency for treatment.

Special Methods for Research Information Exchange

The need for maintaining overall efficiency to prevent expensive research duplication and the importance of relating research to practice in engineering dictates the need for special research information exchange activities. Two such activities which are of particular importance are 1) the provision of research in progress information, and 2) definition of research needs.

Surveys of Research in Progress - Listings of research
in progress can be valuable in many ways. One is that they
serve to help eliminate duplication of effort. Another is
that they stimulate exchange of information among researchers.
A third and very important value is that engineers in practice
can become knowledgeable about new concepts and can learn
where they are being developed well in advance of formal
publication. For this last reason, it is important that
listings appear in a form and under headings that are easy
for practicing professionals to recognize. In general, the
practicing engineer finds it difficult to take the time and
effort to search extensive subjects or other catalogings, but
he will often take careful note of material already interpreted
for his use.

In 1970, the ASCE Structural Division Research Committee
published its second "Survey of Current Structural Research."
It has nearly 2,000 entries. The entries have been carefully
cataloged under headings that are familiar to structural
engineers. If the response to the new edition is similar to
previous response, the listing will be a very popular document.
Other ASCE technical division committees have conducted
similar studies, but not on such an extensive basis. More work
of this type by professional societies has great potential
value.

Definition of Research Needs - A Reverse Process -
One of the keys to the rapid application of research to practice is to identify areas of real need and channel research
efforts into these areas. Definition of research needs is an
important service that professional societies can perform
very effectively through the use of their many technical
committees.

Over the past few years, a continuing project has been
underway in ASCE to identify major research needs and requirements in civil engineering. Each of the Technical Divisions
and Councils has taken part through its division research
committees and produced a study of research needs in its area
of interest. These studies have provided very valuable in-
sights into needs for basic as well as applied research.
They also show requirements for manpower, facilities, special
equipment and data, and last, but not least, financial support.
A listing of these study reports appears in Appendix A.

In a joint effort between Colorado State University and
ASCE, sponsored by the National Science Foundation, these
studies have been assembled into a summary resource document
called "Research Needs in Civil Engineering Relevant to the
Goals of Society" [8]. Separate reports on major areas of
civil engineering are also being made available. One of these
reports is intended to cover civil engineering research as

176

related to civil engineering. This report includes, among its other topics, a treatment of the question of the need for the technology transfer as well as research on techniques of technology transfer.

New and Expanding Continuing Education Activities

Most professional societies have extensive local activities. These local groups are more or less active, depending on their size, location, leadership and other factors. They can be excellent mechanisms through which new information is brought to members virtually at their doorstep. Much more advantage can be taken of these local groups by providing them with the right tools, devices, or other materials necessary to carry out such a function. In a coordinated study by the Engineers Council for Professional Development [9], the needs for continuing engineering studies by engineers are very carefully presented.

ASCE has recognized the major role it must play in continuing education, and in 1964, the ASCE Board of Direction adopted a "Policy Regarding Continuing Education." A copy as revised in 1971 is included as Appendix B.

Several programs have evolved over the past few years, but the two to be mentioned here are the development of local seminars, based on suggested course content and material prepared at the national level, and a new technology seminar series just being introduced.

Local Section Seminars - Rather than see several local sections of ASCE go through the pains of developing basically the same types of course materials, a survey was made of the sections to see what courses were of common interest. On the basis of the survey, several package programs have been developed and conducted with varying success throughout the country. From the start of this program, one of the major areas of general interest has been for a seminar program on water resources management. Although there is interest in the plans for development of such a series, unfortunately, no full fledged effort has been made to produce material for a course of this nature. One set of materials based on an Institute on Urban Water Systems, conducted at Colorado State University in June 1970, has been published [10]. It is hoped that in the future some of these plans will be brought into being on a continuing basis and will show positively the merits of such a program.

New Technology Seminar Series - Recognizing that the specialist talent often required to teach or introduce new technology is not always available at the local level. ASCE is experimenting with a new program in which it offers to its

177

local sections the service of arranging for competent lectures in special subject areas as they are needed. Local groups merely have to arrange for time, place, attendance, and of course, the necessary financial arrangements required to engage the speaker. Little has to be done in the way of program preparation as the experienced lecturers bring all necessary materials. This program is called the New Technology Series.

Special Education Needs on System Analysis Applications - Some of the most valuable new tools that allow the practicing professional to evaluate and apply new information quickly are those associated with the use of systems analysis and associated techniques for optimization. Many engineers in responsible managerial positions, who graduated from five to ten years ago, are either unfamiliar or only partially familiar with the potential for application of these concepts. Professional societies, through their continuing education programs and by working closely with educational institutions, can do much to help bridge this gap. Recent short courses and institutes designed for practicing engineers - such as those recently conducted by the University of California at Los Angeles and Colorado State University on optimization techniques as applied to water resources systems - are excellent examples of activities that serve this purpose. Regional and local courses of this nature would be more than enthusiastically accepted by professional groups.

Summary and Conclusions

The important role professional societies have to play in the dissemination of research information has always been recognized, but their techniques and methods require continuous reappraisal. This conclusion is well documented for ASCE in the report of the 1962 ASCE Research Conference [11] where it was recommended "That increased efforts be exerted to make the results of new research immediately available to the practicing civil engineer. This may involve changes in ASCE's publication policy and the solicitation or commissioning of specific papers for the purpose." The report of the 1971 ASCE Research Conference on the Goals of Civil Engineering Research [12] supports the same theme but re-emphasizes the urgency of the whole matter.

Real-time dissemination of research information and its application to practice depend on many diverse activities. Some of these activities that can be effectively conducted by professional societies are elaborated in this paper.

Three good principles for professional societies as well as other groups to consider in the management of scientific and technical communications are given in the SATCOM report [7]. They are: (1) The planning and management of our

178

information activities must involve constant attention to the simplification and consolidation of existing knowledge and its frequent reprocessing to adapt it to the needs of diverse users, especially those engaged primarily in the practical application of scientific and technical information; (2) the administrative entities responsible for scientific and technical information programs must be so organized and coordinated that they represent a logical and efficient division of functions, but authority over them must be sufficiently widely distributed to achieve the responsiveness we deem essential (this second principle reflects our belief); (3) the management of all scientific and technical communication activities must be as responsive as possible to the needs, desires, and innovative ideas of the scientific and technical groups they serve. These activities must be sufficiently flexible to adapt rapidly to changes in user needs and communication techniques.

The cost and demand for publication of technical information by the professional societies continues to grow at an ever increasing rate. ASCE is concerned with this problem which has led to changes in dues structure and publication charges. More studies are in progress and will be for several years to come. New ideas, new concepts and assistance by those concerned with all phases of research and practice are needed to meet the challenge of more effective and timely application of research to practice.

References

[1] Systematic Study and Development of Long Range Programs of Urban Water Resources Research, First Year Report to the Office of Water Resources Research, U.S. Department of the Interior, ASCE, New York, New York, (September 1968).

[2] An Analysis of National Basic Information Needs in Urban Hydrology, a report to Geological Survey, U.S. Department of the Interior, ASCE, New York, New York, (April 1969).

[3] Water and Metropolitan Man, a report on the Second Engineering Foundation Research Conference on Urban Water Resources Research in August 1969, ASCE, New York, New York, (1969).

[4] Research Information Exchange Systems, paper presented by Harvey O. Banks, President, Leeds, Hill and Jewett, Inc., Consulting Engineers, San Francisco, California, at the 4th Annual Water Resources Conference, Washington, D.C., (January 28, 1969).

[5] Guide for Source Indexing and Abstracting of the Engineer-
     ing Literature, edited by Frank Y. Speight, Engineers
     Joint Council, New York, New York, (February 1967).

[6] ASCE Moves Toward Efficient Information Retrieval, an
     article from CIVIL ENGINEERING, August 1962,
     ASCE, New York, New York.

[7] Scientific and Technical Communication, a Pressing
     National Problem and Recommendation for its Solution,
     Report of the Committee on Scientific and Technical
     Communication of the National Academy of Science-
     National Academy of Engineering, NAS, Washington,
     D.C. (1969).

[8] Research Needs in Civil Engineering Relevant to the Goals
     of Society, prepared jointly by Colorado State
     University and ASCE, Colorado State University,
     Fort Collins, Colorado, (1971).

[9] Continuing Engineering Studies, a report of the EPCD
     Joint Advisory Committee on Continuing Engineering
     Studies, Engineers' Council for Professional
     Development, New York, New York, (1965).

[10] Treatise on Urban Water Systems, by Albertson, Tucker
     and Taylor, Colorado State University, Fort Collins,
     Colorado, (1971).

[11] 1962 ASCE Research Conference, a report by the Committee
     on Research, ASCE Journal of Professional Practice,
     ASCE, New York, New York, (January 1963).

[12] The Goals of Civil Engineering Research - Its Responsive-
     ness to the Needs, Desires and Aspirations of Man,
     a report of the 1971 ASCE Research Conference,
     ASCE, New York, New York, (February 1972).

Appendix A - Selected Publications Related to Civil Engineering
     Research Needs

SUMMARY REPORT: Research Needs in Civil Engineering Relevant
to the Goals of Society, Prepared Jointly by Colorado State
University and ASCE, Colorado State University, Fort Collins,
Colorado, 1971 (Available also from ASCE, 345 E. 47th Street,
New York, New York 10017; $8.00 for nonmembers.

A. ASCE TECHNICAL DIVISION REPORTS AND OTHER RELATED DOCUMENTS

AERO-SPACE DIVISION

"Research Needs in Air Transportation," Report of ASCE Aero-Space Transport Division Research Committee, Transportation Engineering Journal, ASCE, Proc. Paper 7091, February 1970, pp. 45-70.

"Civil Aviation to 1970," by Robert Horonjeff and Gale Ahlborn, Journal of the Aero-Space Transport Division, ASCE, Proc. Paper 3891, pp. 1-15.

CONSTRUCTION DIVISION

"Outline of Research Requirements for Construction," Report of Committee on Research of the Construction Division, Journal of the Construction Division, ASCE, Proc. Paper 6189, October 1968, pp. 233-244.

"Research Opportunities in Construction Engineering and Management," by William H. Wisely, Constructor Magazine, Associated General Contractors of American, Inc., March 1965.

ENGINEERING MECHANICS DIVISION

Directions for Research in Engineering Mechanics, Report of Engineering Mechanics Division Research Committee, ASCE, October 1969.

HIGHWAY DIVISION

"Research Needs for Highway Transportation," Progress Report by William H. Wisely, Constructor Magazine, Associated General Contractors of American, Inc., March 1965.

HYDRAULICS DIVISION

"Research Needs in Surface-Water Hydrology," Report of the Committee on Surface-Water Hydrology, Journal of the Hydraulics Division, ASCE, Proc. Paper 4201, January 1965, pp. 75-83.

"Research Needs on Thermal and Sedimentary Pollution in Tidal Waters," Report by the Committee on Tidal Hydraulics of the Hydraulics Division, Journal of the Hydraulics Division, ASCE, Proc. Paper 7426, July 1970, pp. 1539-1548.

"Research Needs Regarding Sediment and Urbanization," by Harold P. Guy, Journal of the Hydraulics Division, ASCE, Proc. Paper 5596, November 1967, pp. 247-524.

IRRIGATION AND DRAINAGE DIVISION

1964 Irrigation and Drainage Research Conference, Report by
the Research Committee of the Irrigation and Drainage Division,
Journal of the Irrigation and Drainage Division, ASCE,
December 1964.

"Research Topics for Small Irrigation Structures," by Gaylord
V. Skogerboe, Wynn R. Walker, Brent B. Hacking and Lloyd H.
Austin, Journal of the Irrigation and Drainage Division, ASCE,
Proc. Paper 7542, September 1970, pp. 309-318.

PIPELINE DIVISION

"Research Needs in Pipeline Engineering for the Decade
1966-1975," Committee on Research of the Pipeline Division,
Journal of the Pipeline Division, ASCE, Proc. Paper 5347,
July 1967, pp. 19-50.

POWER DIVISION

"Research Needs in Civil Engineering Aspects of Power," Report
of the Research Committee of the Power Division, Journal of
the Power Division, ASCE, May 1968, Proc. Paper 5935, pp. 33-39.

"Research Needs in Civil Engineering Aspects of Power,"
Power Division Research Committee, Journal of the Power
Division, ASCE, Proc. Paper 7073, February 1970, pp. 187-276.

SANITARY ENGINEERING DIVISION

"Sanitary Engineering Research Needs," Report of the Committee
on Sanitary Engineering Research, Sanitary Engineering
Division, ASCE.

"Research Needs in Sanitary Engineering (Municipal Wastewater
and Solid Wastes)," Sanitary Engineering Division Research
Committee, Journal of the Sanitary Engineering Division, ASCE,
April 1972, Proc. Paper 8833, pp. 299-304.

SOIL MECHANICS AND FOUNDATIONS DIVISION

Ten-Year Research Needs in Soil Mechanics and Foundations
Engineering, Report by the Committee on Research of the Soil

STRUCTURAL DIVISION

"Research Needs in Structural Engineering for the Decade
1966-1975," Committee on Research of the Structural Division,
Journal of the Structural Division, ASCE, Proc. Paper 4946,
October 1966, pp. 287-311.

"Research Needed in Wood Structures," by Maurice J. Rhude, Journal of the Structural Division, ASCE, Proc. Paper 5176, April 1967, pp. 75-89.

SURVEYING AND MAPPING DIVISION

"A Research Program in Surveying and Mapping," Progress Report of the Research Committee of the Surveying and Mapping Division, Journal of the Surveying and Mapping Division, ASCE, Proc. Paper 4629, January 1966, pp. 25-41.

B. MAJOR FIELD REPORTS ON RESEARCH NEEDS IN MAJOR FIELDS OF CIVIL ENGINEERING

TRANSPORATION ENGINEERING

"Transportation Research Needs Related to Civil Engineering," by Robert F. Baker, Published by Colorado State University, June 1970.

WATER RESOURCES ENGINEERING

Symposium on Basic Research in Civil Engineering Fields Related to Water Resources, Sponsored by ASCE, U.S. Department of the Interior, Bureau of Reclamation, and Colorado State University, at Fort Collins, Colorado, June 12-15, 1961.

C. OTHER ASCE RESEARCH REPORTS

A Conference on Basic Research in Civil Engineering: A Record of Addresses and Reports, Sponsored by ASCE, The National Science Foundation, and George Washington University, at George Washington University, Washington, D.C., September 10-11, 1958.

A Conference on Research Objectives and Organization; the Second Conference on Research in Civil Engineering: A Record of Addresses and Reports, Sponsored by ASCE, The Technological Institute, and Northwestern University, at Northwestern University, Evanston, Illinois, September 10-11, 1959.

1962 ASCE Research Conference, A Report by the Committee on Research, Journal of Professional Practice, ASCE, Proc. Paper 3399, January 1963, pp. 37-91.

Advancing Civil Engineering Techniques Through Research: A Report on Research Activities, ASCE, September 1962.

D. MISCELLANEOUS OTHER REPORTS

Report of the Conference on Research Goals, Sponsored by The National Science Foundation, ASCE and fourteen other Professional Societies, at Worcester Polytechnic Institute, Worcester, Massachusetts, December 3-4, 1959.

The Nation's Engineering Research Needs 1965-1985, Subcommittee Reports of the Engineering Research Committee of the Engineers Joint Council, May 26, 1962.

The Nation's Engineering Research Needs 1965-1985, Summary Report of the Engineering Research Committee of the Engineers Joint Council, May 26, 1962.

Appendix B - ASCE Policy Regarding Continuing Education
(Approved by Board of Direction in October 1964 and revised in October 1971)

The American Society of Civil Engineers recognizes the absolute necessity of continuing education for every member of the profession. Having reviewed the various means which either are or can be made available for continuing the education of engineers, the Society encourages full participation in such programs and adopts the following as its policy:

1. Although the individual engineer has a prime responsibility for his personal development and continuing education, the employers of engineers are urged to encourage, actively support, and help plan continuing education activities of their engineer employees.

2. Schools, industrial organizations, ASCE and other professional societies should provide guidance and assistance as appropriate.

3. The Local Section is one of the most significant elements of the Society in implementing plans for continuing education.

4. The Local Section should establish a committee on continuing education to:

   a. Determine the desires and needs of individual members.

   b. Approach industry and educational institutions to develop means of meeting requirements and enlisting support for achieving them.

   c. With the assistance of Society headquarters, organize and offer courses of instruction as required by local conditions.

184

d. Consolidate plans with adjacent Local Sections and local units of other professional societies if required to meet needs.

5. Since foregoing actions of Local Sections will not meet fully the needs for individual study:

a. The Department of Technical Activities should periodically develop and make available graded bibliographies* of texts, papers and articles covering significant developments.

b. Society Headquarters should act as a source of information by:

1) Publishing significant material for use of Local Sections or individuals. Included will be a guidance statement pointing out the Society's policy and procedure for assisting in the professional development of engineers through continuing education.

2) Encouraging the development and presentation of information on source material and experience in continuing education programs.

3) Informing Local Sections of activities of other Local Sections and other agencies in this field.

---

*GRADED BIBLIOGRAPHIES - The proposed statement on continuing education refers to graded bibliographies to be developed in the Technical Activities Committee. Each Technical Division should define the subject areas for which Graded Bibliographies should be developed within its technical specialty. The graded bibliographies should be carefully selected lists of approximately ten to fifteen reference materials in a given subject area. The items should be graded as to level for the practicing engineer who: a) holds a comparatively recent bachelor's degree, b) holds a comparatively recent graduate degree, and c) though holding a degree has the occasion to bring himself up to date in a particular field.

THE WATER RESOURCES INFORMATION PROGRAM AT THE UNIVERSITY OF WISCONSIN

By

LeRoy G. Zweifel
Director of Engineering and
Physical Sciences Library/
Information System Complex

John R. Luedtke
Coordinator of Water Resources
Information Program Group

and

James E. Kerrigan
Asst. Director of Water Resources Center
University of Wisconsin-Madison

Synopsis

The rapid growth of scientific information coupled with an increasing need to correlate diverse kinds of information in specialized research has given rise to the development of directed information and technology transfer efforts. One such effort was the establishment of the Water Resources Information Program at the University of Wisconsin-Madison. The formulation and implementation of the Program was facilitated by the prior existence of several "individual" information programs typically operated at a sub-optimal level. These individual elements were consolidated to form a "critical mass" which would respond effectively to the functions of the information transfer activity, thereby expanding the potential for information resource utilization/technology transfer. The various units of the Program, the integration of their activities, and their future outlook, are described.

Introduction

The continuing accrual of scientific information coupled with the increasing need to correlate its diversity in specialized research has placed a severe burden on the information seeker. The increase in the number of journals alone is immense. It is estimated that in 1800 there were about 100 scientific journals. By 1850 there were 1000, by 1900 about 10,000, and by 1966 the figure was as high as 100,000. If this rate of growth remains constant, by the end of the century the number of journals would be in the neighborhood of 1,000,000.[1] The type of information source also is changing. The journal article is being supplemented by a complex collage of preprints, conference proceedings, private reports, ad hoc

---

[1]"The Great Journal Crush," Proceedings of the Research Institution of Great Britain, Vol. 41, Part I, 1966.

serials, and government documents.[2] A recent UNESCO report clearly states the various aspects of this problem:

> "The problem...is a complex one...unfortunately termed the 'information explosion'....Faulty distribution practices and understocked and understaffed libraries make access to these (scientific and technical articles and reports) difficult....These are the familiar characteristics of the problem. Less obvious...are the changing needs of the world scientific community for information. The interdisciplinary approach to the problems of the environment, for example, requires information drawn from a variety of sciences: chemistry, biology, sociology, to name a few. The emerging needs of applied science, technology, and engineering add complexities. The classic information services, the scientific journals, abstracting and indexing services, (and) libraries, have all demonstrated a cultural lag in accommodating rapidly to these new requirements. The achievement of new and flexible forms of information services to meet these new needs is the fundamental problem...."[3]

Numbers, multidisciplinary studies, and divergent information sources suggest the need for a strong information system that can make diverse information accessible to many different kinds of user groups. The Secretary of State's Advisory Committee on the 1972 United Nations Conference on the Human Environment acknowledged the international information problem by suggesting, as a modest beginning, an International Referral Service for sources of environmental information.[4] On the Federal level, the Committee on Scientific and Technical Information of the Federal Council for Science and Technology is developing a framework for an integrated

[2]Carl F. J. Overhage, "Science Libraries: Problems and Prospects," Science, Vol. 155, 1967.
    As a point of interest a study of physics journals carried out between 1959 and 1969 revealed a 147% increase in page growth. James M. Matarazzo, in "Scientific Journals: Page or Price Explosion?" Special Libraries, February 1972.

[3]United Nations Educational, Scientific and Cultural Organization and the International Council of Scientific Unions, UNISIST, Synopsis of the Feasibility Study on a World Science Information System, UNESCO, Paris, 1971.

[4]Stockholm and Beyond, Report of the Secretary of State's Advisory Committee on the Human Environment, May 1972.

network of information systems in science and technology.[5] In
the area of water resources, the Banks and Wolfe study, prepared for the Office of Water Resources Research, concluded
that "there is a demonstrated need to improve communications
among researchers, research administrators, and potential
users of water resources research results so that the full
benefits of the large Federal and State investments in water
resources research can be realized."[6]

Theoretical Framework

In a classic report on the interface of libraries with
information systems, Alan Rees has concluded that,

> "Information is a national resource and can be a
> powerful instrument for the betterment of mankind.
> Communication of information is an integral part of
> research, development and other forms of human
> improvement. Effective access to, and utilization
> of information requires the existence of many kinds
> of information systems involving a variety of
> institutions concerned with information transfer...."[7]

Basic concepts of information transfer must be formulated to
use this national resource and meet information needs. Information resources must be readily accessible, both in terms of
organization and available technical assistance: they must be
organized into a flexible system, responsive to changing
priorities and adaptable to current problems and opportunities
and containing a basic structure serving as a stable matrix for

---

[5]Alan M. Rees, Interface of Technical Libraries with Other
Information Systems: A Synthesis, Office of the Chief of
Engineers, Department of the Army, March 1971.

[6]Harvey D. Banks and Charles G. Wolfe, A Plan for a Comprehensive Water Resources Research Information Exchange System
(Condensed Version), Report 14-01-001-1618, Office of Water
Resources Research, U.S. Department of the Interior, August
1969.

[7]Rees, Interface...
    Robert Powell has given a similar evaluation of the crucial
role of information in coastal zone management. "Proper management of information--meaning the collection, analysis, integration, synthesis, and dissemination of information--I think,
is the key to mounting the really formidable effort needed to
resolve our continuous ocean and coastal problems." Robert
F. Powell, "Marine Technology Transfer is Dependent upon
Information Transfer," Marine Technology Society Conference,
"Tools for Coastal Zone Management," February 15, 1972,
Washington, D.C.

change. The Water Resources Information Program at the University of Wisconsin provides such a framework through the joint efforts of the Water Resources Center and Engineering and Physical Sciences Library/Information System complex.

A distinction between information transfer and technology transfer is useful. Information transfer refers to all handling of documents and materials, including acquisition, retrieval, evaluation and dissemination. Technology transfer is the application of information to individual situations and specific problem areas.

Information transfer is broken down into the following two related functions: the library function which involves the collection, acquisition, organization, processing, storage and retrieval of all forms of information, and the information function which includes the evaluation, compilation, creation, publication, and dissemination of these materials. These functions must operate together to produce efficient, comprehensive results. Together they form the "critical mass," enabling the central service unit of the Library/Information System complex to function as a focal point, and to support the information and technology transfer activities of many water-related programs.

The "critical mass" unit has two main values. First, the unit avoids costly and unnecessary duplication of expensive collections, facilities, space and services. Second, it provides an integrated information service that allows the incorporation of action programs and activities at an extremely favorable benefit/cost ratio. The individual programs gain the benefit of a total range of services.

Thus technology transfer-oriented programs can play a more active role in the transmission of research knowledge. Besides publishing research results, program units have strong information backup to utilize innovative seminars, conferences, and person-to-person contacts as transfer methods. On a broad basis, this technology-transfer role is conducted by such units as the University-Industry Research Program and University Extension Program. In specialized subject areas, a major responsibility for transferring research rests with institutions created to deal with specific areas, such as the Water Resources Center.

Information and technology transfer activities are not independent. Although the cooperating units operate autonomously within separate spheres of responsibility, continuous contact, interaction and feedback is absolutely crucial to sound information resource utilization/technology transfer. This overlapping relationship is illustrated in the figure below.

```
┌─────────────────────────────────────────────────────────────┐
│   Library           Information        Communication         │
│   Function          Function           Function              │
│ ┌───────────────────────────────────┐                        │
│ │INFORMATION TRANSFER         _____/│                        │
│ └───────────────────────────────────┘                        │
│                         ┌──────────────────────────────────┐ │
│                         │            TECHNOLOGY TRANSFER    │ │
│                         └──────────────────────────────────┘ │
└─────────────────────────────────────────────────────────────┘
```

To meet the needs of decision makers, concerned citizens,
students, faculty, industry, and government agencies, these
activities must be encompassed within the broadly developed
information resources of the University and the problem-solving
oriented programs. This is the theoretical framework within
which the joint effort of the Water Resources Center and the
Engineering and Physical Sciences Library/Information System
complex--the Water Resources Information Program-- is
evolving.

Historical Development

Traditional libraries have not been positively identified
as an information source in science and technology, as the
Rees Report indicates.[8] Failure to define shifting information needs, lack of imagination and innovation, and an unquestioning attitude toward existing services have contributed
to the assumption that libraries can serve only limited information functions. This perception of libraries has kept them
from becoming involved, or even considered, in the forefront
of management/planning activities. Recognizing these difficulties, the aim of the Engineering and Physical Sciences Library
for some twenty years has been to become an active and innovative participant in the transmission of information. Library
activities have included selectively disseminating documents
to University of Wisconsin faculty and staff, providing on-
site duplicating facilities, making available the more elusive
"report" literature, providing cooperative information services
to units within the University, such as the Sea Grant Program,
and establishing a document-procuring, literature searching
service to business and industry.

Two of these early activities are particularly important
in view of their significance to the Water Resources Information Program, the Information Services Division, and the
Federal Reports Center.

The Information Services Division (ISD) is a unit of the
Engineering Library. By providing in-depth scientific and

---

[8]Rees, Interface....

technological information that may not be locally available to business and industry, it makes secondary use of the Library's resources as well as those of other University information centers and sources of academic expertise. ISD was originally developed by the Engineering Library and the University-Industry Research Program in response to the need for a mechanism that could marshal all appropriate information and documents from campus, state, and national resources. The need for such services was later recognized by the U.S. Congress when it enacted legislation creating the State Technical Services Program in 1965. ISD played a basic role in developing and implementing the STS program in Wisconsin and, in so doing, gained valuable experience enabling it to enlarge its scope significantly.

The Information Services Division currently provides literature searches, reference and referral services, interlibrary loan services and photocopies of patents and other documents. In 1971-72, ISD answered an estimated 4000 requests for all types of information from Wisconsin businessmen, industries, programs, and interested citizens. At least 50 percent of material requested came from the Engineering Library and its Federal Reports Center collections.

The Federal Reports Center (FRC) was established with funding from the 1965 State Technical Services Act. Through FRC various federal information resources such as libraries and centers, together with their mechanized literature search capabilities, are made available to both the University and the State. The Federal Reports Center collection approaches 577,000 documents in paper and microforms. Because information of interest on water is published in many unexpected sources, FRC can concentrate on isolating these items from all publications.

Information programs were considered an essential element of the Wisconsin Water Resources Center from the unit's early development. The coordination, administration, and service responsibilities delegated to the Center by both the Federal Water Resources Research Act of 1964 and the State Accelerated Water Resources Research and Data Collection Program Act (Chapter 502 - Laws of 1965) required information backup. As a start the Center established a reference room in 1966 and made arrangements with University Extension to assign a water resources specialist to participate in their technology transfer activities.

The Reference Room's collection is essentially restricted to technical reports, committee reports, and soft-bound publications of current interest. It is located at the Center and is organized according to the categories established by the Committee on Water Resources Research/Federal Council for Science and Technology. The user orientation of the system

191

provides scanning capabilities within thirty areas. Regularly updated author and key-word indices are maintained on the more than 5000 document collection by means of the University of Wisconsin Indexing System (UWIS), a computer program developed at the University. The system is capable of single-word indexing; concept coordination is not possible.

Divisions of the Wisconsin Department of Natural Resources closely related to water resources are currently supplied with indices of the entire collection to permit search by agency staff members without visiting the Reference Room. The services are made possible by the support provided by the Department.

One of the activities of the Reference Room is the compilation and distribution of a list of newly acquired publications. The list consists of document citations organized according to subject. Numbers corresponding to subject matter are included thus providing a cross-reference for ready identification of materials. Individuals are encouraged to borrow, in person or by mail, any publication for a short period. The Acquisitions List is mailed to over 450 subscribers in Wisconsin and neighboring states.

The information role of the Water Resources Center was expanded in 1968 when it was designated a "center of competence" in the area of eutrophication by the Water Resources Scientific Information Center of the Office of Water Resources Research. The Center now identified significant literature and submitted abstracts for the OWRR's semimonthly publication, Selected Water Resources Abstracts. An expansion of the basic abstracting activity was made possible by support from the Joint Industry/Government Task Force on Eutrophication. The grant enabled the information program to broaden its literature search capabilities, increase the number of abstracts, publish specific reviews of the literature, and distribute copies of abstracts to scientists and librarians throughout the world. During the development of the Eutrophication Information Program, the Library and the Center began to see the exigency for a joint approach.

An effective abstracting program demands the selection and acquisition of articles in diverse disciplines at various campus library locations. Because of its other activities, the Library/Information System complex was able to contribute to these aspects of the program which resulted in an overall increase in efficiency, broader coverage of literature and further utilization of specialized resources. The utilization of the integrated capabilities of the Center and the Library by the program resulted in cost savings through efficient use of available resources. Through increased support from the Environmental Protection Agency, the program was also able to expand the eutrophication publications activities.

The program has three main activities. It is the "center of competence" in eutrophication, as already described. Second, the program produces literature reviews and occasional papers on water research. To date, publications treating various aspects of eutrophication, the internal mechanisms of lakes and the use of algicides have been prepared and distributed. The third activity involves publishing a bimonthly current awareness bulletin, "Eutrophication: A Bimonthly Summary of the Current Literature," which contains short summaries of all the literature judged to be pertinent to eutrophication. It is distributed gratis to over 2000 organizations and individuals throughout the world. An annual index to the bulletin enhances its usefulness as a literature search device.

The program collection consists of approximately 3200 documents, including reports, reprints, and conference proceedings. Documents are being coded to a Termatrex retrieval system to improve subject access. A copy service for articles listed in "Eutrophication: A Bimonthly Summary of the Current Literature" is also available on a fee basis. Limited information-type questions can be answered by the program; however answers to complex questions or requests for comprehensive bibliographies currently require special arrangements.

Successful cooperation in the Eutrophication Information Program led to other joint information ventures. When the Water Resources Center was designated a "center of competence" in Water Resources Economics, the Library was involved. The goals are similar to those of the Eutrophication Information Program. Published scientific literature is searched systematically for appropriate articles and reports on water resources economics, and related subjects. After the documents have been abstracted, the abstracts are published in WRSIC's Selected Water Resources Abstracts. The water resources economics collection, initiated in July 1971, is growing at the rate of 30 to 40 documents per month. A retrieval system with the capability of supplying bibliographies upon request is under development.

Another combined venture was the participation of information personnel in the management of the Center's Reference Room. As a result of these joint activities, the goals of a broadly based library/information system complex committed to information transfer, and a multi-disciplinary research unit responsible for technology transfer in water resources were mutually enhanced.

From this series of cooperative efforts, came the development of the Water Resources Information Program. This program consolidates and integrates information elements around the subject of water.

Several units are involved in the cooperative thrust of the program. One unit is the Madison Campus Library System, a confederation of five major (professional) and eight departmental libraries, supplemented by approximately 80 special literature collections which are not part of the system but which satisfy certain highly specialized information needs. This system has a two-fold mission: to provide access to the World's recorded knowledge in support of the various instructional, research, and service programs of the University of Wisconsin, and to bring together diverse resources to meet the needs of the state, national, and international community of scholars. In combination, these libraries possess extensive resources that can also be tapped for public service. Since the System is a contact point for such a large variety of users, it constitutes an ideal framework within which to develop specific information transfer programs.

The Engineering Library constitutes another of these units. Containing one of the most outstanding literature collections in the nation, the Library fulfills its traditional role by serving the faculty and students of the College of Engineering. However it has also made many efforts to go beyond this role by providing specialized information services for individuals and programs outside the College and beyond the campus boundaries.

The outreach effort is, in part, necessary to meet the challenges imposed by the enormous expansion and rapid turnover of scientific literature, by the special information needs of interdisciplinary programs, and by the information problems of planned technology transfer systems. To cope with these many-faceted changes in the nature of information needs, the Engineering Library is attempting to act as a focal point by gathering and organizing information about other engineering/scientific information resources and by promoting cooperative networks for the utilization of those resources.

The consolidation and integration of diverse sources of information has also developed on a local, and less technical, level. The information programs in the Water Resources Center and the Engineering Library are members of the Madison Area Library Council (MALC), which was formed in early 1970. MALC includes all types of local information centers--libraries of schools and newspapers, technical libraries, and information centers; it is geared to answer specific information needs by providing ready access to the specialties of individual libraries.

The principal purpose of MALC is to give the general public access to a sophisticated system which can quickly locate and accurately interpret information in specialized fields. Technical information is needed today not only by scientists; water quality, for instance, is an area of public concern, and scientific information must be available to the public if citizens are to make rational decisions.

Because information will become more and more specialized, intelligent selection and repackaging will be of increasing importance. Rees, quoting the Weinberg Report, states this succinctly: "knowledgeable scientific interpreters who can collect relevant data, review a field, and distill information in a manner that goes to the heart of a technical situation are more helpful to the overburdened specialist than is a mere pile of relevant documents. Such scientific middlemen who themselves contribute to science are the backbone of the information (analysis) center; they make an information center a technical institute rather than a technical library."[9]

The presence of subject specialists in Water Resources Information Program activities has already been specified in some program descriptions. The Eutrophication and Water Resources Economics Information Programs, for example, use them to select, classify, and abstract articles. The operation of the WRSIC computer terminal, described later, also utilizes subject expertise. The presence of these technically-oriented personnel together with the expertise provided by the Water Resources Center brings a much higher degree of quality to the entire program. Using graduate students in some of these positions has an educational benefit as well. It gives the students an opportunity to keep abreast of ongoing research identifies proposed problem solutions, and exposes the broad spectrum of resource materials available in the water field. As the Program's information/technology transfer activities develop, the services of technical expertise will become increasingly important.

The increasing specialization of knowledge combined with the continued burgeoning of specific fields increases the need for contact with a centralized computer data bank for successful information handling. In the past years the water resources information programs in Wisconsin have benefited from close cooperation with the Water Resources Scientific Information Center (WRSIC) of the OWRR. In March 1972, the Water Resources Center was invited to participate in an experimental Computer program for improving information dissemination.[10]

Early in 1971, the University of Oklahoma received a grant from OWRR to study the operation of a national network

---

[9]Rees, Interface....

[10]OWRR-WRSIC is presenting a paper at this Conference dealing exclusively with the Computer Network Program.

of computerized information retrieval centers in water resources. The budget included funds to initiate and service the first three centers, the state Water Resources Institutes at Cornell, North Carolina State University, and the University of Wisconsin. These centers are connected by remote terminal to the WRSIC computerized data bank in Oklahoma. The information bank comprises 40,000 full-text abstracts of the literature in all areas of water resources.

The network was inaugurated in Wisconsin to provide terminal services to the water resources community in a twenty-one state Western region by providing literature answers to technical and research questions. Potential users of the system include natural, physical, and social scientists, and administrators. To reclaim costs for maintaining the remote network station, a service fee is charged for information requests. As designed in the experimental program, the effectiveness of the network system will be evaluated as soon as sufficient documentation has been collected. This is expected to take several months.

Future Development

The future outlook for this program is optimistic. Growing experience, interaction, and communication channels will further improve its present activities. In addition, a number of related programs will be undertaken in 1972-73.

Enhanced cooperation among the State of Wisconsin libraries should benefit the information transfer mission of the Program. The facilitation of this cooperation will result from the establishment of the Council of Wisconsin Libraries (COWL), a statewide organization of higher education libraries. COWL is headquartered in the University of Wisconsin Memorial Library at Madison and funded by contributions from member libraries. Its goal, as it becomes operative in September, 1972, is to effect improved reciprocation between libraries, share scarce or costly resources, and utilize whatever specialties each may have. Like its local counterpart, MALC, its thrust is to build a reciprocal network of library resources.

Another function involves interaction with the State of Wisconsin Department of Natural Resources (DNR). On June 9th, the Regents approved a grant from DNR to study how the Water Resources Center and Library/Information System complex might best serve the Department's water information needs. The objectives of the program are (a) to develop procedural arrangements to interface with the Water Resources Information Program, (b) to identify and develop mechanisms to meet the informational needs of specific DNR water resources programs, and (c) to develop methodology for informing DNR of available services

196

and provide effective handling of information requests. This study should result in a model for effective information transfer to a state agency, and would open potential for direct information support to other Wisconsin government agencies.

Information transfer will likewise be enhanced by a number of related activities. The Environmental Protection agency will support an experimental program to supply selective information to two or three members of the National Eutrophication Research Program. The experimental program will be primarily an attempt to find an adequate method for tailoring information extracted from the WRSIC computer network data base to specific needs.

Selective dissemination of a different sort will also be started this coming year. This form of dissemination will be by publication of an intermittent "informational note" series. Each publication will be devoted to a specific topic of current interest and distributed selectively to those concerned. The "informational note" will consist of either a brief review of studies, key literature on the topic, or a summary of the current state of the art on a problem, written in non-technical language and oriented to technical personnel as well as laymen. It would also provide a means of announcing new developments within the water resources field with special significance to Wisconsin.

These are the immediate plans of the Program. The results they yield will play an important part in the development of future long-range activities. Whatever the specifics, however, the total outlook for the information/technology transfer mission should be greatly stimulated by the recently enacted Amendment to the Water Resources Research Act of 1964. This amendment authorizes an annual increase of up to $150,000 to each Water Resource Research Center's allotment grant to be devoted in part to "...scientific information dissemination activities, including identifying, assembling, and interpreting the results of scientific and engineering research deemed potentially significant for solution of water resource problems, providing means for improved communication regarding such research results, including prototype operations, ascertaining the existing and potential effectiveness of such for aiding in the solution of practical problems, and for training qualified persons in the performance of such scientific information dissemination." The mission espoused by the Amendment parallels the objectives of the Water Resources Information Program, and could be of immeasurable benefit to the future development of the program.

Conclusion

The transfer of knowledge from research to practice at the
University of Wisconsin is the goal of the Water Resources
Information Program, a joint activity of the Engineering and
Physical Sciences Library/Information System complex and Water
Resources Center. Accomplishment of this mission demands that
the information transfer role and the technology transfer role
continuously interact to yield efficient, comprehensive results.
As a result of applying the talents of specialists in the
discipline of water resources and in the library/information
sciences there has emerged a knowledge transfer program that
enhances both the separate and the mutual goals of the units
involved.

EUTROPHICATION RESEARCH APPLIED TO WATER QUALITY MANAGEMENT ON THE GREAT LAKES

By

A. R. LeFeuvre
Environmental Quality Coordinator
Canada Centre for Inland Waters

and

J. P. Bruce
Director, Canada Centre for Inland Waters
Burlington, Ontario

Synopsis

Wise water management programs must be the end result of increased knowledge through research. The ways in which research on eutrophication of the Great Lakes have been converted into national and international water quality management programs are described here in the hope that the example may have useful implications in other areas. An executive agreement signed by Prime Minister Trudeau and President Nixon on April 15, 1972, incorporates comprehensive commitments on the part of both countries designed to enhance and protect Great Lakes water quality. The Agreement is based on an extensive research program which covered the physical, chemical and biological processes of the lakes and spanned about six years, and on studies of the eutrophication process done in many parts of the world. The international Agreement deals with all aspects of water quality management in the lakes. However, to keep the topic of this paper to manageable size, the transfer of research results to eutrophication control programs only will be discussed here.

Identification of the Problem

The two countries recognized serious pollution problems on Lakes Erie and Ontario, and in 1964 referred the problem to the International Joint Commission asking for a report on the extent of transboundary pollution, the causes, and recommendations for cures. Early in its five-year study the IJC identified eutrophication from nutrient over-enrichment and excess biological production as one of the major problems. In Lake Erie especially this was evidenced by windrows of decaying algae along beaches, clogging of water intakes, a shift away from desirable fish species and anoxic conditions in the bottom waters of the central basin of the lake. The IJC studies were conducted by scientists from Canadian and United States government agencies and involved extensive monitoring and research on Lakes Erie and Ontario. The study also drew

199

heavily on earlier research on other lakes done elsewhere.
Perhaps the most important influence on the eutrophication
aspects was the work done by R. A. Vollenweider for the
Organization for Economic Cooperation and Development[1].

Control Factors

The role of nitrogen, phosphorus, and carbon as control
factors in eutrophication of lakes has been the subject of
scientific research in many parts of the world. Probably the
most comprehensive summary of this work is that by Vollenweider
noted above entitled "Scientific Fundamentals of the Eutrophication of Lakes and Flowing Waters with Particular Reference to
Nitrogen and Phosphorus as Factors in Eutrophication". In this
publication the trophic state of a number of lakes around the
world are related to the annual loadings of nitrogen and
phosphorus in grams per m^2 versus the mean depth of the lake.
Figure 1 is drawn from this report. It indicates in a general
way the loadings that produce oligotrophic, mesotrophic and
eutrophic states. From this diagram it can be inferred that
for a given lake morphology the trophic state can be changed
in either direction by a change in the annual loading of
phosphorus. A similar figure demonstrates the same effect for
nitrogen when that element is limiting algal growth. In some
lakes it may be necessary to control both of these nutrients,
however, in the case of Lakes Erie and Ontario the most controllable of the essential nutrients is phosphorus.

In developing a control strategy for the eutrophication
problem it is necessary not only to understand the nutrient
requirements for algal growth but also to understand the
controllability of the various nutrients. Carbon is, of course,
essential for algal growth. By far the largest source of
soluble carbon in Canadian lakes except those in precambrian
areas is due to solution of calcium carbonate and magnesium
carbonate in sediments in the drainage basins. The resulting
bicarbonate ions which arise from natural chemical processes
appear to be present in quantities much more than adequate to
meet the demands of biomass production. Carbon also enters
lakes through carbon dioxide exchange with the atmosphere.
The quantities of carbon in these forms are not readily controllable by man. As well, Goldman et al[2] in a recent review
paper concludes that "carbon will rarely, if ever, be limiting
in natural environments".

Nitrogen enters lakes from rain, snow, and dustfall
(approximately 16,000 tons per year to Lake Erie and 12,000
tons per year to Lake Ontario). Leaching from natural soils
and from soils that are artificially fertilized is another
source. In Lakes Erie and Ontario 60-70% of the nitrogen comes
from diffuse sources, including agricultural lands, which are
not readily controlled.

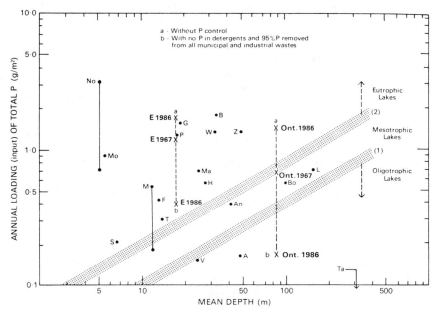

Figure 1.   State of eutrophication for a number of lakes in Europe and North America.

LEGEND

A - Aegerisee (Switzerland)
An - Lake Annecy (France)
B - Baldeggersee (Switzerland)
Bo - Lake Constance (Austria, Germany, Switzerland)
F - Lake Furesø (Denmark)
G - Greifensee (Switzerland)
H - Hallwillersee (Switzerland)
L - Lake Geneva (France, Switzerland)
M - Lake Mendota (U.S.A.)
Ma - Lake Malaren (Sweden)
Mo - Moses Lake (U.S.A.)
No - Lake Norrviken (Sweden)
P - Pfaffikersee (Switzerland)
S - Lake Sebasticook (U.S.A.)
T - Turlersee (Switzerland)
Ta - Lake Tahoe (U.S.A.)
V - Lake Vänern (Sweden)
W - Lake Washington (U.S.A.)
Z - Zurichsee (Switzerland)
E - Lake Erie
Ont.- Lake Ontario

By contrast 70% of the phosphate entering Lake Erie and nearly 60% entering Lake Ontario are from directly controllable point sources such as municipalities and industries. Throughout Europe and North America it is generally found that more phosphorus inputs to lakes are from point sources of municipal or industrial wastes than is the case of nitrogen. Thus, not only is phosphorus an essential nutrient for algal growth and frequently the controlling nutrient, but because it is introduced primarily by man's activities, it is also the most readily controlled of the three principal nutrients essential for algal growth.

The International Joint Commission study of Pollution in the Lower Great Lakes[3] identified eutrophication as a major problem requiring international action and made specific recommendations for its control. Research conducted in the Great Lakes along with results of research conducted elsewhere, such as that noted above, indicated that the most appropriate remedial program was by control of phosphorus inputs to these lakes.

The specific recommendations of IJC were that:

"The Governments of Canada and the United States enter into agreement on an integrated program of phosphorus control to include:

(a)   the immediate reduction to a minimum practicable level of the phosphorus content of detergents and the total quantities of phosphorus-based detergents discharged into the Great Lakes System with the aim of complete replacement of all phosphorus in detergents with environmentally less harmful materials by December 31, 1972;

(b)   further reduction, as a matter of urgency, of the remaining phosphorus in municipal and industrial waste effluents discharging to Lake Erie, Lake Ontario, and their tributaries and to the International Section of the St. Lawrence River, with a view to achieving at least an 80 percent reduction by 1975 and thereafter additional reduction to the maximum extent possible by economically feasible processes;

(c)   the reduction of phosphorus discharged to these waters from agricultural activities."

The extent to which phosphorus loadings to the two Lakes were to be reduced in the IJC recommendations was based on the Vollenweider graph and an attempt to return the two lakes to mesotrophic states.

Governmental Response

In response to the report of the International Joint Commission on pollution in the lower Great Lakes, Ministerial level meetings between Canada and the United States were held in Ottawa in June, 1970. These meetings established joint working groups charged with developing specific water quality management programs. Sub groups on the following subjects were formed: Water Quality Objectives and Standards; Contingency Plans; Pollutant Materials - Handling Hazards (On Water); Pollution From Watercraft; Institutional Matters; Legislation Relating to Great Lakes Pollution; Coordination of Research; Coordination of Action to Meet Special Situations; Pollution From Agricultural, Forestry and Land Drainage Sources; Pollutant Materials - Handling Hazards (On Land).

A combined report of the international working group, including a proposed water quality management program, was presented to a subsequent meeting of Ministers of the two countries at Washington, June 1971. This meeting agreed in principle to the recommended water quality management programs and established a joint negotiating team to draft in final form an Executive Agreement which was signed in Ottawa, April, 1972[4].

Eutrophication Control Programs

The IJC recommendations concerning eutrophication control included both control of phosphorus at the source (land drainage and detergent) and removal of phosphorus at sewage treatment plants. This multifaceted approach to the problem was included in the Agreement by allowing the parties to reduce phosphorus loads to agreed levels by methods most appropriate to their situation.

The Governments of Canada and of Ontario (along with other provincial governments), after a study of the interim reports of IJC, agreed that the federal government should introduce legislation to control the use of nutrients in cleaning products. The Canada Water Act[5], then under consideration in Parliament, was deemed the most appropriate vehicle for this purpose. An amendment to the Act containing a clause covering nutrient control was introduced. This clause did not itself specify any particular limitation on the chemical composition of detergents or cleaning products. It did, however, permit the Government, by Order in Council, to regulate the amounts of nutrients in cleaning products.

The Canada Water Act, incorporating the clause on nutrient control, passed the Commons and Senate in the early summer of 1970, and the first regulations under the nutrient control clause became effective August 1, 1970. The detergent industry had been informed in January 1970 of the government's intentions concerning regulations under the Act. These regulations limit the amount of phosphates in detergents, excluding dishwashing detergents, to a maximum of 20% expressed as phosphorus pentoxide (P_2O_5). Prior to the regulations most detergent powders had P_2O_5 contents ranging from 16% to 38%. This initial limitation is estimated to reduce the amount of detergent phosphates entering Canadian lakes and rivers by 25% to 30%.

Detergent Reformulation Research

However, it was clear that if reductions below 20% P_2O_5 were to be sought, major substitution of phosphates by other builders, sequestry and water softening chemicals would be needed, and that the environmental and health effects of such substitutes would have to be evaluated in crash research programs.

A number of possible replacements for phosphate have been suggested. These include carbonate-silicate combinations, borate, citrate, other synthetic organics and NTA (Nitrilotriacetic acid). Only carbonate-silicate, citrate, and NTA appear to be serious contenders for significant shares of the detergent market.

Carbonate-silicate formulations have been marketed for a considerable length of time. In fact, carbonates and silicates form part of many detergent formulations containing phosphates. However, formulations based primarily on carbonate-silicate appeared on the market in response to the publicity given to the polluting effect of phosphates. Unfortunately, some smaller producers marketed "dry mix" detergents which were very hazardous to the consumer by ingestion or eye contact due to their strongly alkaline properties. It was on the basis of this hazard that the U. S. Surgeon General advised against a detergent phosphorus control program at this time. However, it should be realized that most of the carbonate-silicate formulations present no hazards.

Citrate based detergents have had very limited distribution up until now. However, recent research[6] has shown that when formulated with the correct surfactant, citrate based laundry detergents can be as effective in cleaning as phosphate-based products. There is at present a cost disadvantage but this may be eliminated by a proposed new process for producing commercial grade citrate. Because citrate is a naturally occurring substance which biodegrades very rapidly, scientists feel confident that there will be no adverse public health or environmental effects from its widespread use in detergents.

The most promising of the potential phosphate replacements from a detergency point of view is NTA. However, evaluation of both environmental and health effects of a substance that would be used in such large quantities was essential before large scale substitution was permitted. Detergent manufacturers had undertaken, prior to 1970, considerable research on NTA as a detergent component to be used along with phosphates. It was in limited use in U.S.A., Canada and Sweden. For the governments concerned to make decisions on its more extensive use, much more extensive studies were required. Several meetings of government scientists from the three countries were convened at the Canada Centre for Inland Waters to discuss progress reports and coordinate work. Extensive studies were undertaken on health effects, particularly teratogenicity and carcinogenicity; on possible effects in complexing and transporting heavy metals; on effects on waste treatment processes; on effects on a wide range of freshwater and marine biota, and so on[7,8]. Indeed, NTA must be the best researched chemical from an environmental health viewpoint, ever considered for commercial use.

As a result of limitations on detergent phosphates in Canada and Sweden, more widespread use of NTA was made as a partial phosphate replacement in these countries. Extensive programs were undertaken in Canada and coordinated at CCIW to assess the concentrations of NTA in various parts of the water environment, lakes, oceans, rivers, harbours, sewage plant influents and effluents, groundwater and tapwater. These measurements have permitted better prediction of likely encountered concentrations of NTA should it be more widely used.

Based on Canadian assessments of the research and surveys, and on assessments of the extent and nature of eutrophication across Canada, the Canadian government has decided to seek further reductions in phosphates to 5% as P_2O_5 by the end of 1972, has encouraged detergent companies to seek a variety of possible alternative formulations rather than just NTA, and has indicated it will continue to monitor NTA and its effects on the water environment to ensure that no ill effects occur.

While the U. S. federal government is still persuing a policy of not restricting use of phosphates in detergents, and preventing the use of NTA, many states and local jurisdictions including a number in the Great Lakes Basin have in force detergent phosphate control. Such controls affect to some degree another 71% of the U. S. population in the Great Lakes basin.

Project Hypo

Subsequent to the extensive studies for the IJC Report (1970), "Project Hypo", an intensive study of the hypolimnion of the Central Basin of Lake Erie, was undertaken by a joint Canadian/United States team of scientists during the summer of 1970. The objectives of this study were to quantify the extent of oxygen depletion in the hypolimnion, to delineate the mechanisms responsible for the observed phenomenon, and to assess the effects of oxygen depletion on nutrient release rates from sediments under oxic and anoxic conditions. Although anoxic conditions were anticipated and observed during the studies of the late 1960's, nutrient release rates were not studied in detail at that time.

"Project Hypo" involved major physical, biological and chemical studies in the Central Basin. From these studies it was determined that oxygen depletion in the hypolimnion was produced by two main mechanisms[9]. Although the oxidation of reduced metallic species caused approximately 12% of the observed oxygen depletion, the vast majority, or 88%, of the depletion was, in fact, caused by the bacterial oxidation of organic material which had settled to the bottom of the basin. The primary source of this material was the massive amount of algae produced in nutrient rich surface waters.

Dobson and Gilbertson[10] showed that anoxic conditions of significant extent were probably first manifest in the Central Basin in 1960 and ten years later[9] these conditions were found to extend over 6,000 square kilometers or 40% of the whole Central Basin in late summer. The phosphorus release rate from sediments under these anoxic conditions was found to be about eleven times higher than when oxygen was present in bottom waters.

The principal conclusions from this project was that because of the vast increase in anoxic conditions in the hypolimnion "the Central Basin is now changing from being a settling basin to a production basin for phosphorus during the summer. This production of phosphorus at a critical period in the annual cycle of the Lake occurs just prior to the turnover and fall blooms, and is the result of excessive (external) phosphorus loadings earlier in the year". Phosphorus was still the one nutrient which was reduced to below detection levels during algal bloom periods, suggesting that it is still the main limiting nutrient in the extent of algal growth in central Lake Erie. In the report of "Project Hypo"[9] quantitative estimates were made of the regeneration of phosphorus from the Central Basin under oxic and anoxic conditions. These quantities regenerated were then compared with the external phosphorus loadings to the Central Basin over the same period of time. It was calculated that the regeneration of phosphorus in the whole central basin over two months under oxic conditions was approximately 670 tons[1]. It was estimated that under anoxic conditions (40% of the basin) during 1970 approximately 2590 tons of phosphorus were regenerated, and it was predicted that in 1971 this would increase to approximately 2780 tons. These figures can be compared to an estimate of the external phosphorus loading of approximately 1890 tons over the same time period. It was further pointed out that should anoxic conditions prevail over the total basin (not just the 40% observed) for a period of two months, approximately 7450 tons of phosphorus would be produced. On the basis of the above it was deduced that because of the rate of increase of anoxic conditions we can now expect an annual increase of 7.4% in the phosphorus available for fall blooms in the ensuing years if remedial measures to reduce the phosphorus loading to the lake are not taken. The authors of Project Hypo concluded that "the above findings and estimates lead to one definite conclusion: phosphorus input to Lake Erie must be reduced immediately; if this is done, a quick improvement in the condition of the lake can be expected; if it is not done the rate of deterioration of the lake will be much greater than it has been in recent years"[9].

Thus as a result of "Project Hypo" this regeneration of large quantities of nutrients from extensive anoxic conditions in the hypolimnion caused by the decay of massive quantities of algae was identified as a significant factor in the acceleration of the rate of deterioration of the water quality of Lake Erie. As a consequence, the prevention of the occurrence of anoxic conditions would be a significant initial step in the prevention of further acceleration of the rate of deterioration of the quality of the lake. Further, on the same basis, any reduction in present phosphorus inputs would thus presumably have a "multiplier effect" in reducing nuisance algal conditions.

The results of "Project Hypo" had a considerable impact during the course of negotiations of the Agreement. They were largely responsible for an acceleration of the schedule of phosphorus removal facilities on Lake Erie to complete a major portion of this program by 1973 instead of 1975 as originally planned. In particular the program in the Agreement was designed to achieve, as quickly as treatment plants could be constructed, reduction in phosphorus loadings to those which would correspond to no significant anoxic conditions in the Central Basin, as estimated from the phosphorus loading oxygen depletion rate relationships developed by Dobson, Gilbertson & Lee[11].

Transfer of Research Results

In reviewing the above account of research programs which led directly to major water quality management programs, it can be seen that there were a number of aspects of this particular situation which contributed to the speed with which the transfers took place.

A first point to note is that the International Joint Commission has developed a very effective way to mobilize scientific activity leading to solutions to problems likely to be acceptable to management agencies. It does this by forming Advisory Boards consisting of experts from the main management and research agencies concerned with the problem. While these are appointed as individual experts, they keep their agencies informed of the trend of the overall research program and the recommendations that result usually have the tacit approval of senior officers of most of the agencies that would have to implement the recommendations, if adopted. Thus IJC can muster extensive scientific expertise to attack problems, but does so in a way which ensures strong commitment to implement the recommendations on the part of the government agencies to whom the final IJC recommendations are directed.

A second strength of the situation described was the public participation in discussion of the recommendations of the Advisory Boards, through the IJC public hearings. This adds a further dimension of public and media acceptance of the recommendations going to governments.

The third significant factor affecting the rapidity of transfer of research results lies in the organizational structure of both the Canadian and Ontario Departments of the Environment. In both cases the organization is structured so that major research programs are closely meshed with the management responsibilities of the organization. For example, research on water resources is an integral part of the program of the Water Management Service of Environment Canada. There is no such thing as special Research Service. Thus senior policy makers of the Department have direct rapid access to research results such as those of "Project Hypo", on detergent phosphate replacements, etc. Several of the representatives of Canada in negotiation of the Agreement were officials with direct responsibility for major research programs. This means that research results of the government agencies were immediately fed into the system - even before the final report writing stage. Since the government scientists also have close contacts with colleagues in universities and elsewhere, the results in pertinent fields from the whole scientific community could be, and were, quickly fed into policy decisions.

Finally, a special part of the organizational structure of the Canada Centre for Inland Waters of Environment Canada is a unit, the Environmental Quality Coordination Unit, whose sole responsibility is to turn the research results from the Centre and elsewhere into proposals for public policies and to analyze proposed policies and water quality control strategies in the light of latest research results of Centre scientists and their colleagues in universities, industry and other government agencies.

In summary, the eutrophication control program and negotiation of the Great Lakes Water Quality Agreement are excellent examples of a situation in which research results were quickly and effectively used in development of public policies and had a profound impact on these policies. The ingredients of this successful and rapid transfer of research findings to action programs are (1) an effective mechanism to mobilize both scientific and management manpower, (2) a procedure for public and media involvement in formulation of recommendations, (3) governmental organizations that have research activities built into the management responsibility structure, and (4) a deliberate commitment of highly qualified manpower to help the transfer and conversion process.

References

1. Vollenweider, R. A., "Scientific Fundamentals of the Eutrophication of Lakes and Flowing Waters with Particular Reference to Nitrogen and Phosphorus as Factors in Eutrophication". Organization for Economic Co-Operation & Development, Directorate for Scientific Affairs, 1968.

2. Goldman, J. C., D. B. Parcella, E. J. Middlebrooks and D. F. Toexen, "The Effect of Carbon on Algal Growth - Its Relationship to Eutrophication". Water Research, V. 6, pp. 637-679, 1972.

3. IJC Report (1970)
   Pollution of Lake Erie, Lake Ontario and the International Section of the St. Lawrence River, Report on the International Joint Commission, Canada and United States.

4. Agreement between Canada and the United States of America on Great Lakes Water Quality, signed April 15, 1972.

5. Canada Water Act - Bill C-144, House of Commons, Canada, 1970.

6. Report of Gillette Corporation under contract to the U.S. Environmental Protection Agency re Citrate.

7. Internal document - "Detergent Phosphate Control Alternative Formulations and their Potential Environmental Impact" - Report to the Interim Interdepartmental Committee on Water, March 1972.

8. Assessment of the Potential of Nitrilotriacetate (NTA) to Compromise Human Health - Report to the Assistant Secretary's AD Hoc Group on NTA, Department of Health, Education and Welfare, Washington, April 1972, by Virginia Commonwealth University.

9. Project Hypo Report - 1971
    Project Hypo-An Intensive Study of the Lake Erie
    Central Basin Hypolimnion and Related Surface Water
    Phenomena", CCIW Paper No. 6, U. S. EPA Technical
    Report TS-05-71-208-24.

10. Dobson, H. & M. Gilbertson, 1971.
    "A History of Phosphorus Loadings and Hypolimnial
    Dissolved Oxygen in Lake Erie" in "Project Hypo",
    CCIW Paper No. 6, U.S. EPA Technical Report TS-05-71-
    208-24.

11. Dobson, H., M. Gilbertson & T. Lee, 1971.
    "A History of Phosphorus Loadings and Hypolimnial
    Dissolved Oxygen in Lake Erie" in "Project Hypo",
    CCIW Paper No. 6, U.S. EPA Technical Report
    TS-05-71-208-24.

SESSION III - COMMENTS

DISCUSSION by John F. Miller*

The methods advanced by Messrs Cohan and Simmons and Taylor of involving the practicing engineers in research teams are certainly useful. They need to be expanded with more people in operational positions working for periods of one or two years. Equally important, however, but not mentioned by the authors or the general reporter is the transfer of research workers into operational positions. This would provide those who work in research an opportunity to see the problems involved in applying new methods. This transfer would have the secondary advantage of keeping the researcher informed on problems which need to be solved by research and enable those in operational positions to be aware of new methods and thus be more receptive in applying them.

DISCUSSION by J. A. Cunge**

Speaking of transfer of knowledge from the researcher to designer (which often means from the University to the consultant engineer), I would like to say that very often the theory is applied (and sometimes developed further) by consulting engineers but the results of these applications are never known. They are property of the client, of the consultant and disappear - unless their owner, the client, publishes what he thinks is important. Thus, when the researcher is looking for "study cases" on the application of his theory, he finds scarcely any of them. This is the information which lost and which is making further research even more difficult.

DISCUSSION by Nathan Buras***

In transforming research generated knowledge into planning and design tools useful to practicing engineers, two more methods might be used:

1. Researchers and university staff members might spend their sabbatical leave with engineering consulting organizations.

2. Setting up specially designed workshops for senior planners and designing engineers in which specific problems

---

*Office of Hydrology, National Weather Service

**Colorado State University

***Technion, Haifa 32000, Israel

are analyzed and their possible solution indicated by the application of knowledge generated by research activities.

DISCUSSION by Sie Ling Chiang*

In discussing the transfer of knowledge and the communication within and across the nations, I believe we have overlooked an important element - that is of the individual's responsibility.

The major transfer mechanism so far, is either by writing or by verbal presentation. Although technical writing courses have been offered in almost all colleges, they are not sufficient. Even worse is the speech. Most Americans can drive cars, yet find it difficult to place a slide right side up. Most of the people do not know the volume of their voice, and, cannot talk effectively within a limited time allowed. Obviously, there is a strong, basic need in education to emphasize the ability of verbal communication, if a more effective transfer of communication is to be achieved.

DISCUSSION by W. W. Doyel**

Although the title of the conference is Transfer of Water Resources Knowledge and this session relates to transfer experiences of representative organizations, the stress somehow seems to have shifted from the broad to the narrow-- from knowledge to research results. Does this mean that knowledge is equal with research and that conference is concerned with translating research results into action? Actually, the study and development of water resources is a function of management and while research may be a contributor, it isn't always needed. The need is to transfer information, know-how and the results of experiences. Nor should research be confused with the investigations that are part of every water resources project.

DISCUSSION by Lester A. Herr***

I suppose some of you wonder why the Federal Highway Administration is interested in water resources. First, it gives me a good feeling to hear that others have problems too, and secondly, for the last few years there has been expenditure of over $8 billion for highway construction in the U.S., including interstate and rural highways and city

---

*Bureau of Engineering, Pa. Dept. of Environmental Resources

**U. S. Geological Survey, Washington, D. C.

***Federal Highway Administration, Washington, D. C.

212

streets. Of this total, we spend 20 to 30 percent for drainage
structures in some areas, including bridges, culverts, storm
sewers, roadside channels and other miscellaneous drainage
facilities. The national average spent on highway drainage is
about 15 percent.

The Federal-aid highway program is rather unique, in that
several eschelors of state and federal engineers are involved
in preparing and approving most designs, especially the larger
projects. In these various reviews, alternate designs are
examined with one of the objectives being to find the most
economical and efficient design, including the incorporation
of the latest research. I might mention that an example
of hydraulic research and how we "preach the message" of its
results can be seen in a movie called "Spur Dikes" available
from the Federal Highway Administration, 400 7th St., S.W.,
Washington, D.C. 20591 (A 15 minute, 16 mm. colored film,
free* except for return postage).

The question always arises, however, as to "How much time
and money should be spent on research and studying alternatives in designing a project?" Some administrators and
managers, especially those strong in accounting and what
the figures show believe design costs should be minimum and often
assigning percentage costs of 2 to 10 percent of this phase
of the project. Most engineers know that some projects are
more difficult to design and construct than others so the point
of design time and costs is a very smart question. We, as
engineers, must through our personal and professional integrity
be the judge of what is required for the job to be done.

DISCUSSION by Howard J. Cohan** and William P. Simmons***

We were disappointed with the synopses of papers prepared
by the rapporteur for Session III. Our comments are intended
to supplement the synopsis of our paper on reduction of research
to practice, or to serve as information useful in a revision
and correction of the synopsis. Considerable solid and useful
information is contained in the paper in addition to "reports,
and memos, establishing review committees and advisory groups,"
references mentioned by the Rapporteur.

Being closely organized, concerned with practical problems
in water resources development, and beneficiary to many years
of experience, the Bureau of Reclamation has learned important

---

*FREE - indicates FOR LOAN-RETURN POSTAGE REQUIRED

**United States Bureau of Reclamation, Denver, Colorado

***United States Bueau of Reclamation, Denver, Colorado

213

lessons for reducing research to practice. As stated in the paper, one of the basic points is to be sure the research is directed toward real problems. To help insure this we involve our planning, design, construction, and O&M people in defining and outlining Bureau research needs. Then, to help insure that the research stays on track we maintain involvement of the same groups while the research is carried out. Finally, as soon as research results are available for use, the very people who outlined a need for it and helped develop it are in a position to and are anxious to put them into use.

Effective communication, both formal and informal, with the public at large as well as within the organization, is another key element. Bureau procedures for accomplishing this are also described in the paper.

Finally, examples are given of instances, where, for various reasons, research results have not been used as expected. These examples illustrate typical transfer problems that can be guarded against by other organizations.

DISCUSSION by J. A. Kay*

In lieu of general comment, I would like to submit the following paper exemplifying experience of a multi-national consulting firm.

TRANSFER OF KNOWLEDGE
THE VIEW OF A MULTI-NATIONAL CONSULTING ENGINEERING FIRM

Introduction

The following remarks apply to the transfer of general engineering knowledge (rather than specifically water resources knowledge) because the firm's professional experience includes a wide range of engineering and environmental disciplines, and because the techniques of knowledge transfer are much the same.

Brief History

Perhaps a short resume of the firm would put the following remarks in better perspective. The partnership of Dames & Moore was founded in Los Angeles, California, in 1938. After more than three decades of growth the firm now has 33 operating offices, of which 13 are outside the United States. Over the years there has been a corresponding expansion in its fields of engineering practice. Originally specializing in soil mechanics and foundation investigation, the firm now offers a wide range of hydrological, geotechnical, oceanographical, meteorological, ecological, and environmental services.

*Hydrologist, Dames & Moore, London, United Kingdom

Overseas offices were initially opened and staffed by
U. S. personnel until local professionals could be recruited
and trained. Recent office openings, however, have signalled a
new phase of overseas development. New offices in Nigeria and
South Korea were opened and are managed by a national of the
country concerned, both of whom are experienced employees
of the firm. In other overseas offices the trend is much
the same; Americans are less involved in day-to-day operations
and are gradually being replaced by local employees. The
two Australian offices, for example, are entirely Australian.
Americans are also being withdrawn from the firm's office in
Spain as Spanish professionals are trained to replace them.
In other offices, too, this hand-over is making steady
progress.

Today the firm regards itself as multi-national, with
partners from Spain and Australia as well as the United
States. Presently some 60 employees are citizens of other
countries, and it is to be expected that a number of these
professionals will be admitted to partnership in the future.
New partners will also include professionals drawn from a
wider range of technical and scientific disciplines.

Knowledge Transfer - The Problems

In a firm whose range of services is rapidly expanding,
a "knowledge transfer deficit" could easily exist, even if
the organization were concentrated in only one or two offices.
In a firm like Dames & Moore--with some 400 professional staff,
including 53 partners, spread among 33 offices worldwide--this
problem could be even more acute unless positive steps were
taken to overcome it.

Within Dames & Moore, as in other consulting engineering
firms, engineers and specialists on the staff vary in the degree of their professional development. The inexperienced
need more exposure to a varied range of "real-world" problems
within their specialities to temper their theoretical knowledge
with practical experience and to help them develop administrative and managerial skills needed for progressive advancement.
By the same token, veterans of many difficult engineering
projects should maintain reasonably close ties with the
universities to ensure that their "standard practices" are
well founded in up-to-date engineering principles.

When a firm's professionals are scattered around the
world, usually subject to extensive travel and extended tours
of duty in foreign countries, problems of knowledge transfer
are compounded by a number of other factors, many of which
are little related to the transfer of knowledge.

The foremost is perhaps the language barrier; it can
present difficulties even between engineers from
different countries speaking the same "mother" tongue.

215

Differences in engineering units, too, can cause mis-
understanding for the careless or unwary (e.g., metric
vs. imperial systems).

Standards of engineering practice often vary from
country to country and are also responsible for a
measure of "static" in the transmission of knowledge.

Travel itself can be a significant hindrance to the
transfer of knowledge, to the extent that it makes the
communicators less alert (the "jet time-lag" effect),
or otherwise disrupts their attention to professional
matters (differing social customs, requirements for visas
and innoculations, etc. and the general unfamiliarity
of the surroundings which may turn engineers into
tourists).

Given the necessity of practicing one's profession in
foreign countries, anything that inhibits the familiar
conduct of business--such as licensing, or currency
exchange and control problems--can be considered a
detriment to the transfer of knowledge.

In many foreign countries the entry and exit requirements
and currency restrictions combine to form a major barrier to
the easy and rapid transfer of knowledge and experiences.
Ironically, these barriers are highest in the developing nations
of the "third world"--the very nations that would most benefit
from knowledge transfer.

Admittedly, we have painted the problems of knowledge
transfer on an international scale with a rather broad brush;
our list is by no means complete, but it should at least
outline the magnitude of the problem.

Approaches to, and Partial Solutions of, the Problems

We cannot claim to have come up with completely satisfactory answers in attempting to solve these and other problems
of the transfer of knowledge, but perhaps our approaches may
be of interest to others facing similar difficulties.

Professional Development Program - Career advancement of
every professional employee is an important aspect of the firm's
manpower planning operations. In an effort to increase the
amount and quality of professional communication within the
firm, Dames & Moore has recently organized its engineers and
specialists into "Technical Service Groups" and has instituted
a Professional Development Program to find, train, and utilize
the best professional talent during the planning and accomplishment of projects for clients.

The Technical Service Groups correspond with the firm's general areas of professional practice:

1) Land Planning and Development Services

2) Environmental Services

3) Foundation Engineering Services

Each of these service groups are further divided into a number of technical subgroups, roughly corresponding with an engineering specialty (e.g., Geotechnical Engineering, Mining Engineering, Soil Dynamics and Earthquake Engineering, Meteorology, Applied Life Sciences,...etc.).

Each service group functions in five basic areas essential to the successful operation of the firm:

A. Professional Development

B. Quality Surveillance

C. Staffing and Recruiting

D. Management Activities (to a limited extent)

E. Sales Support Activities (as required)

The primary function of these groups is in the area of professional development. The groups provide for advice and guidance of each professional by more experienced persons with similar interests. A desired sequence of assignments for each professional is outlined annually, and outside education and independent study are encouraged. The managers of each group coordinate members' professional society activities to enable each employee to enhance his professional status (thereby, of course, enhancing the firm's). Though now in the organizational phases, it is hoped that the Technical Service Groups will provide a convenient vehicle for exchanging technical information during the course of projects worldwide, and will facilitate internal seminars and training programs.

Quality surveillance, too, is an important area of activity. Technical Service Groups provide readily identifiable pools of talent for reviewing major proposals (i.e., is the project or approach technically sound? is the scope feasible? is the time schedule reasonable? etc.) and for serving on internal technical review boards. Reports to clients are also scheduled to be reviewed for accuracy and professionalism where a specific discipline was a key element.

Each service group will be expected to determine future needs of the firm for trained professionals in its area and

to predict unique or special talents likely to be required
in the future. As part of the recruiting function, each
Technical Service Group manager coordinates all contacts
with key universities and professors (to be used as outside
consultants, or for special training assignments within the
firm).

Management activities for which the service groups are
responsible include an annual review of each individual's
professional performance, and an analysis of manpower
utilization by technical specialty.

It is anticipated that the service groups will assist
in the preparation of brochures and other sales literature
related to their specialties, and will provide technical
input on major proposed efforts.

Dames & Moore's Technical Service Groups are designed
to facilitate the transfer of knowledge within the firm; the
new Professional Development Program should make it easier
for the firm's engineers to communicate with those outside
the organization, and vice versa. Pertinent portions of the
plan include:

1) Sponsorship and support for continuing education,
   training, and other self-improvement activities.

2) Encouragement of individual research and development
   activities.

3) Payment of all professional society dues.

4) Increased support for the preparation of technical
   papers and increased financial support for attendance
   at professional meetings and conferences, especially
   by junior personnel.

5) The development of internal technical seminars.

Most of these professional development activities are
not new; they are extensions of present activities or those
that have been tried, with varying degrees of success, at other
times during the history of the firm. What is new is the
decision to expand and coordinate them on a firmwide basis.

The firm has developed contacts with universities in
several countries and professors regularly work with Dames &
Moore engineers on specific projects, or for longer periods.
It is felt these arrangements are of major benefit to both
sides: the firm is made more closely aware of current research;
and university personnel receive valuable practical experience.

Computerized Uniterm Search System (CUSS) - Through a cross-referenced key-word system every job is classified and listed on a firm-wide basis. The system is available in every office and means that any engineer in any office can rapidly:

1) identify each and every job which deals with a particular problem.

2) identify all work done in a particular geographical area.

3) identify all work done for a particular client.

4) identify the controlling consultant for a particular job.

In addition, the date of completion and costs involved can be identified. Both current and all past jobs are indexed on microfiche, for ease of distribution and storage.

In every case a copy of both the report and the job file can be obtained; previous analyses made can be obtained for reference. It is our experience that this system is an invaluable tool, facilitating rapid identification of work done in the speciality or region and providing access to all the analytic, laboratory and reference data previously gathered.

Inter-Office Transfers - Dames & Moore has always operated as though it had a large pool of professional talent (albeit spread rather evenly through the firm's 33 offices on five continents) which could be made available to work on projects obtained by any firm's offices. This has eliminated the need for duplicating special talent unnecessarily at several locations and has permitted the firm to staff relatively large projects any where in the world on fairly short notice. Professional employees, both senior and junior, have thus had the opportunity to acquire practical knowledge and experience on a worldwide basis.

These temporary transfers have exposed junior professionals to a wider range of technical problems and standards of engineering practice than they might have otherwise acquired in a single office. This normally results in greatly accelerating their professional growth and speeds the transfer of knowledge throughout the firm. Inevitably, in the close working relationships developed on these projects, greater awareness of and experience with special engineering techniques is gained by all the personnel involved.

It is recognized full well that this policy also tends to impede the transfer of knowledge to a certain extent, by

219

accentuating the problems associated with travel previously enumerated. The firm feels, however, that the benfits far outweigh the disadvantages, and has acted to reduce the negative impact of worldwide travel on the transfer of knowledge. Dames & Moore insists on formal language study, for example, for long-term assignments where any language difference is involved.

The transfer of professional staff between offices in different countries is made more complex by visa regulations of some of the home countries, but the United States has recently (1970) introduced a new visa status, L-1 (for intracompany transferees), which has eased the problem considerably. Problems still remain, however, in several countries where the time scale for obtaining a visa or work permit compares unfavorably with the time needed to complete the actual assignment. In these instances, of course, Dames & Moore attempts to solve the problem by avoiding it if at all possible.

The entire area of legal and financial constraints to knowledge transfer on an international scale, in fact, is one that no single company, or government, can do much to alleviate. Such difficulties have always been with us, and are likely to be until the millennium. When viewed from a historical standpoint, however, these barriers are generally lower today than they have been in many years.

Transfer of Knowledge - A Practical Example

Perhaps an account of how the author and two colleagues recently fulfilled their duties in Korea would serve to illustrate the Dames & Moore approach to the transfer of knowledge.

The project involved work in the fields of soil and rock mechanics, geology and hydrology as part of a major highway study. Project offices were made available by the Korean Government, and counterpart Korean engineers assigned to each expatriate.

For the counterpart engineers it was often their first experience of a highway study, their previous experience being largely on construction control. However, this was also an advantage, as they had experience of the techniques currently employed in Korea.

Working with individual counterparts through the stages of data collection, data analysis, development of recommendations and report preparation allowed each to follow a particular technical specialty of the project through to completion. This type of assignment places extra responsibilities on the

expatriate, especially when the schedule makes little
allowance for the instruction and tuition which should be
an important part of the working relationship.

The Future

For the individual employee, the firm will place increasing
emphasis on continuing education, whether by formal university
matriculation, attendance at short courses or seminars, or
through membership in professional societies. A large annual
sum has been earmarked to encourage individual advancement
through these channels on a firmwide basis as part of the
new Professional Development Program. Dames & Moore's
recently instituted Technical Service Groups should provide
for the wider transfer of professional engineering knowledge
within the firm at an accelerating rate as they become more
firmly established. Short- and medium-term transfers, too,
will continue to provide wider project exposure for each
individual.

The organization is expected to continue its expansion
within and outside the U. S. New offices are being planned
and existing ones are expanding both their physical facilities
and personnel. Over the next decade the firm anticipates a
substantial increase in the number of partners, of which a
significant portion is likely to be foreign nationals. This
trend toward becoming more truly multi-national in character
will continue to provide additional opportunities for the
transfer of knowledge, but it is recognized that many attendant
problems will require solutions before the optimum state of
knowledge transfer will be achieved.

We believe we have made a start and that our policies
and practices tend to surmount the many present barriers
to the transfer of knowledge. As projects grow both in size
and multi-disciplinary participation, transfer of knowledge
within project teams will demand increasing attention. Future
expansion of the frontiers of knowledge will pose new problems
and re-emphasize existing ones. A continuing awareness of the
difficulties, coupled with sound management practices, will
be essential in overcoming each and every one.

Given the firm's increasingly multi-national character,
we look forward to playing a significant role in the development
of the human environment throughout the world, and to participating in the continual process of knowledge transfer which
is demanded by, and should be involved in, all stages of
engineering work.

THE PHILOSOPHY OF WATER RESOURCES UTILIZATION

Chairman: Khalid Mahmood

Rapporteur: Evan Vlachos

● *The papers in this session raise some larger
questions as to the general context within which
transfer of knowledge takes place, and its role
for national development.   The authors explore
the assumptions of traditional training, the
difficulties of applied research and the educational requirements for diversified cultural
systems.   More than anything else the underlying theme is that of the role of technology and
knowledge as a force in development.*

Rapporteur: Evan Vlachos
Associate Professor of Sociology and Anthropology
Colorado State University
Fort Collins, Colorado

The ambitious title of this section does not necessarily
indicate that there is a comprehensive analysis of all major
issues involved in water resources utilization. There is,
however, in all papers a common concern on the general premises
of transfer of knowledge, a discussion about the major considerations in water resources development policies, the presentation of central issues in transfer methodology, and, last
but not least, the common concern as to the role of water
resources in the context of national development. In reading
these papers one is struck with the common preoccupation with
such major issues as the holistic approach, the need for
interdisciplinary integration (especially the gratifying
concern with the vital role of social sciences), the awareness
of cultural relativism, and the concern for systematic planning
with general goals rather than the traditional preoccupation
with simple, small projects.

Aaron Wiener is the proper authority to set up the
discussion about water resources development policies and
transfer of knowledge from developed to developing countries.
His earlier work, The Role of Water in Development, is an
outstanding example of introducing not only a cogent framework
but also succinct principles of planning for national development. In his present paper, Wiener immediately hits the major
themes of our concern by pointing out that water should not
be conceived only as a means (either in terms of infrastructure
or as a production output) but also as truly an important
and vital part of larger goals of social-economic development.
At the same time, in the distinction between developed and
underdeveloped nations the author makes a point that repeatedly
will appear in his paper, namely that underdevelopment does
not primarily mean lack of structural changes, but more
important lack of a capacity to adapt to new environments.
The last implies that in addition to physical infrastructures
we need also rural organization, attitudes, and information in
order to complete the transition towards a developed nation.

The key problem that Wiener attacks is the fact that
although technological information is easily transferable
the same is not true about decision making ability. Decision
making becomes, then, a keystone for being able to maximize
the opportunities of a changing production environment. In
developed countries experience provides the answer of how
technology is incorporated in the mainstream of the country.
In developing nations, however, inexperienced professionals are

225

ill-prepared to provide major decision making. This inexperience is not only a result of usually junior people in key or high positions of decision making, but also of what the author indicates as a result of "insufficient personality" to respond to the forces of development.

Wiener, then, proceeds in analyzing three major fallacies in "transplanting" water knowledge in developing nations. The first has to do with the transferring patterns of professional specialization. The problem here is that the discipline-by-discipline approach is inadequate because underdevelopment means a much larger transformation of a constellation of socio-economic conditions rather than a single approach. This of course implies that we need an interdisciplinary planning methodology and orientation and, at the same time, a more sensitive recognition of intermediate stages of transformation.

While the first fallacy attacks the narrow specialization the second concerns the fallacy of transferring problem-solving models which are usually more responsive to conditions in developed countries. Thus, while such an approach may be appropriate to developed nations, it should be remembered that in less-developed countries the strong emphasis on public intervention and transformation, as well as interventions of medium or long-range commitment, needs a multiplanning dimension rather than a simple, one-sided problem solving approach characterizing water projects in developed nations.

Finally, a last fallacy involves transferring problem solving routines. The technological reflex, engineering responses usually found in developed nations are not particularly suited for the unusual situations in many developing nations. Here we need a new set of tools much more sensitive to Third World situations.

The author concentrates his attention in discussing five categories of information transfer. These five categories, technology, agrotechniques, psychological space of the farmer, rural and regional institutions, and considerations relating to the capacity of development agencies, can be perhaps classified into two major clusters, namely "hard" and "soft" information. For "hard" information the process of transfer is smooth, provided that consideration has been given to timing or phasing of the transfer of information. The transmission of "soft" information, however, lags either because data are not available or proper data cannot be generated. Thus, the preoccupation with engineering infrastructures so far has avoided the critical problems involved in the transmission of "softer" data. As a result of this lack of total transfer and project design, we have had higher preponderance of lopsided and unsatisfactory projects, as well as forms of "pseudo-adaptation," from institutions devised and of socio-political processes which are not responsive to the real situation and which tend not to provide insightful information and therefore perpetuate patterns of underdevelopment.

In recognizing these major fallacies and difficulties involved in a total transfer of knowledge from developed to developing countries, Wiener proceeds, then, with a number of suggestions. Essentially his suggestions revolve around a basic reorientation of efforts on the transfer of knowledge, particularly:

(a) pilot projects to generate essential parametric information and trained local working teams;

(b) prototype projects for continuous retraining and remotivation of professional personnel; and

(c) planning of resources use within a sectorial framework in such a way as to select projects that lead truly to the achievement of explicit development objectives, rather than political expediency or tradition or even sheer mimicry of impressive engineering feats in developing in developed nations.

The work of Wiener sets up a theme that it is followed by many of the authors of the following papers. In particular, the work of Franceschi can be used as an example of the need for holistic planning. The author starts his theme by indicating that water as a natural resource involves a series of characteristics of variability:

(a) Varying supplies in both time and space

(b) Diversity of water uses and water requirements.

These conditions of variability and diversity create a complex situation leading to confusion and uncertainty affecting decision-making processes. As contrasted to Wiener, however, Franceschi emphasizes structural conditions of underdevelopment such as climate, per capita income, facilities, etc. Yet, both authors seem to emphasize "future-orientation" and the type of responses to challenging circumstances. Future-orientation, indeed, becomes the common thread for many of the authors of the papers in trying to untangle the key element or response to changing environment that may lead to development.

Concentrating on water projects, Franceschi emphasizes two conditions which seem to be particularly important in the transfer of knowledge: lack of sufficient available funds, and lack of reliable basic information. More important, however, than these is the need for long-range planning and the integration of water uses within a larger context of development.

What, then, do such integrated water plans entail in
incorporating foresight for decision-making, delineation of
priorities, and understanding of the interrelatedness of water
problems? The author proceeds in delineating the conditions
and stages of such a master plan by describing both the
characteristics of the master plan (scope, timing, disciplinary
input, extent, etc.) and the process of formulating a master
plan (including data acquisition, determination of demand and
availability, assessment of water problems, and questions of
policy options).

In describing the conditions of the master plan, Franceschi
seems to place particular emphasis on the formulative stage
and on the adaptability of the system to effectively meet
demands (even under conditions of population growth) if "users
are given sufficient time for technological adaptation and
motivation." This, of course, is a questionable argument
since in the development literature, questions repeatedly
have been raised concerning the response of users or consumers
without many other conditions, particularly larger socio-
economic changes.

While the discussion of Franceschi is general, the paper
of Hewapathirane and White offers specific cases illuminating
the arguments raised previously. Their paper underlines many
of the points raised, especially by Wiener, in that it traces
the failures of planning agencies to give consideration to
alternatives to conventional engineering techniques. The
authors use the cases of Ceylon and the Lower Mekong in order
to show how traditional approaches, and almost reflex, single
engineering solutions to water resources management with
little consideration to other alternatives, including major
socio-economic changes, have been producing immense difficulties in the planning of natural resources in developing nations.

In the case of Ceylon the historical analysis of water
development through the centuries leads to an exposition of
current schemes of water source utilization largely dominated
by engineering techniques involving large capital investment.
This is particularly true in the Dry Zone Irrigation schemes
where large costly reservoirs have increased devastating
floods. The authors point out that although certain level or
river regulation is necessary, in the case of Ceylon, the
sense of protection increased population occupation of the
flood plain. At the same time, increased dependence upon
engineering devices made the whole area much more vulnerable
to even minor floods with disastrous consequences to a fragile
socio-ecological area. What the authors, then, recommend is
that rather than simply reacting in the traditional engineering
way, a broader approach should have been followed involving
not only technological considerations but also wider conditions
such as land use regulation, relocation schemes, flood warnings,
etc.

In the case of the Lower Mekong the problems of water resource utilization center around the emphasis that should be given between large multi-purpose structures or gigantic main-stem control structures as contrasted to auxiliary measures and the design of pilot agricultural programs. The United States, as the largest single financial contributor, preferred concentration on one technique (a power-flood control-irrigation structure) rather than comprehensive rural development or other flexible types of investigation. By narrowing alternatives, the authors maintain, that the success of the project is very much in doubt.

Given these characteristic examples of simple transfers of engineering capabilities to rather complex situations in developing nations the question must be raised: Why do planning groups resort to traditional approaches or to narrow ranges of alternatives? The answers have to be found among others in:

First, the professional training of those involved, that is those who are highly skilled in hydrology or engineering, but are rather insensitive to questions of policy and strategy.

Second, the restricted definition of mission for administrative agencies especially through legislative restrictions, by the definition of engineering task, etc.

Third, the tendency of administrators to prefer large and visible structures (what I would label the "Pharaoh syndrome") associated usually with large-scale public projects.

Knowing these limitations and the heavy hand tradition, we need to ask ourselves, as the authors properly raise the point: What is to be done? Two major recommendations are offered to us by Hewapathirane and White: first, organization of special short-term training workshops for individuals responsible for planning water management in developing countries; second, revisions in the review criteria employed by multi-lateral and bilateral funding agencies in considering allocations of funds for planning and construction of water projects.

At this point, we should also emphasize something that the authors do not underline, namely, that there is a lot to be learned from failures and at the same time there is urgent need for increasing the multi-disciplinary character of teams involved in water planning. Perhaps we need much more basic changes in the training of the professionals. Even more, although, this may be an expensive proposition, we also need to introduce at least some rudimentary efforts for environmental impact studies, trying to anticipate long-range consequences of such important public projects.

While the previous authors have outlined both some
general considerations on water resources development policies
and have underlined both the need for comprehensive planning,
as well as increased consideration of a wider spectrum of
alternatives, the papers of Hotes and the following of Anderson,
concentrate primarily on more specific aspects of transfer
methodology.

Hotes in narrating personal experiences in water resources
and agricultural development all over the world re-emphasize
the general theme of this section: for developing nations,
specialized mechanical skills are not enough. Broader physical
and social sciences are needed in order to create an active,
permanent reservoir of water resources knowledge.

The author then provides a cogent discussion of what
transfer of water resources knowledge entails by discussing:
the definition of the term, the diversified methods in transfer
of methods, the appropriate space and locale where transfer
takes place, and, frequent problems involved in efforts of
transfer.

The methods of transfer can be grouped into three major
categories: a) purely informal methods; b) more formal
methods; and c) formalized methods. Each of these groups of
methods requires different degrees of formalized training as
well as diversified approaches for reaching various segments
of persons involved in water use and utilization.

According to Hotes, the most crucial problem in terms of
location of transfer is that such a process, so far, takes
place rarely within developing countries. The point should
reinforce the general argument of Wiener, in calling attention
to the thorough knowledge of the specific local socio-economic
conditions, rather than the blind transfusion of overly
sophisticated, if not irrelevant, highly complex water resources
procedures from the laboratory or the dissimilar conditions of
developed nations.

The author is explicit in emphasizing the most frequent
problems involved in transfer efforts, such as the narrow
and unimaginative mentality of foreign experts which leads
either to a retreat to more complex reasoning, or to over-
simplification of the situation and application of procedures
usually formulated in developed countries. The attitudes of
developing countries nationals vis-a-vis a given project are
also a central problem. Hotes notes here the disdain by
young professionals of any work that may involve "nuts and
bolts" operations, avoidance of assignment in places other
than the national capital, and impatience with the long and
many times arduous process of becoming "Chief Engineer."
The last point is very important, since as reiterated by other

authors, too, given the scarcity of professionals in developing nations, many young professionals find themselves in vital positions of formulating and implementing macro-level policies. To be a "Young Turk" is important for motivation, but no good substitute for experience and for judicious decisions as to what is necessary knowledge.

Hotes is also outright critical of the practices of bringing developing countries' nationals for quick grand tours of organizations and projects in developed countries. Other than perhaps goodwill, the time, effort, and money would be more profitably spent in demonstration projects within their own countries. Finally, in discussing problems, Hotes emphasizes that transfer of over-sophisticated methods is as deadly as complete lack of information. While basic data is lacking and elementary knowledge of local circumstances is just about absent, it is ironic to introduce complex stochastic hydrologic models.

Hotes builds in summary form a number of guidelines for the transfer of knowledge. His essential argument is that there is no simple, single method of knowledge transfer. While nothing is fundamentally wrong with past efforts, the crucial catalyst in future attempts will once again be the active, permanent reservoir of receptive and flexible professionals within developing nations.

Anderson addresses himself to a more specific issue on knowledge transfer, namely the role and significance of U.S. universities in the education of foreign students.

The author proceeds from the general premise that technological advances and differential rates of their application have created an ever widening gap between nations. There is an immense challenge in closing this gap and to provide more equitable distribution through both increased knowledge and information, and by an understanding of how to apply the knowledge so as to reach from abstraction to the practical level of production.

Anderson then concentrates his attention in discussing the problems involved in transfer of knowledge to the academic community and to the professionally trained sector of society. While he introduces quite an array of methods, his emphasis is on higher education associated techniques.

University and College Level Training

The accusations against the over-sophisticated training of a foreign Ph.D. are well-known. But beyond that, Anderson provides a much longer list of a host of problems involved in the training of foreign students. Language handicaps, differences in background both in terms of country and school, disassociation from home problems, lowering of standards, etc. are all parts of a complex and difficult situation in responding to the special demands of the foreign student.

The solutions that the author offers include staff orientation and preparation (including travel abroad), facilities for field problems applicable to a diversified number of countries, some teaching in a foreign language.

Short Courses, Seminars, Workshops, Conferences and Institutes

These are specialized mechanisms for knowledge transfer. They have the characteristics of flexibility, successful application of case studies, site benefits and generally the aspects of an educational means adaptable to very specific situations.

Whatever their character, scope, or duration, however, the key to their success is proper planning. This calls for sufficient time, money, and administrative help. At the same time, Anderson points out that new, exciting possibilities exist in extending the usefulness of such mechanisms in a technetronic age through use of video tape, telestart relay, and all aspects of modern technology extending communication The most important suggestions for the success of these flexible mechanisms include: a) involvement of local people; b) intense preparation of professional staff; and c) emphasis on the "practical aspects," field experiences, or demonstration techniques.

A last critical point in the transfer of knowledge according to Anderson is the perception and definition of roles and responsibilities of the multitude of agencies and organizations involved in this process. Indeed, overlapping jurisdictions, inflexible administrative infrastructures, and unresponsive programs create additional confusion and situations where often goals and subgoals of various units are incompatible and insensitive in bringing theory and practice together.

The author proposes among other things the possibility of establishing an international university and the need for more direct contact between institutions. Yet, when all is said, there still remains an immense challenge for the U.S. higher educational system to respond to the new forces of change by providing a more meaningful mechanism for enlarging the impact of knowledge transfer.

While Anderson postulates some general principles for knowledge dissemination and indicates the diversified problems involved in training foreign students in U.S. universities,

Poblete and Harboe describe experiences from the receiving end. The authors delineate not only transfer of knowledge between countries, but also the transmittal process from research to practice. Using as a central example the work of the Centro de Planeamiento (CEPLA) in Chile, they discuss two major educational innovations and also attempts toward practical application of knowledge.

University Research and Graduate Training

The joint research program of CEPLA with both MIT and UCLA served as crucial catalysts for introducing not only concepts and principles of systems analysis in comprehensive multi-unit, multi-purpose water resources research, but also specific specialized training and promising research regarding applications of systems analysis. The emphasis on methodology and on model building provided a solid basis for a core of professionals in Chile, who although not large in number seem to have a very strong intellectual presence in the country.

Yet during their presentation, the authors do not fail to bring forward their dissatisfaction with the lack of grass-roots research. Excluding some problem of training (such as, in particular, the perennial issue of training on problems of the host country rather than acquiring experience on relevant issues in the native country), the authors point out the following reasons for the lack of concerted, practical research:

(a) lack of effective demand for applied research in the field;

(b) splitting of groups for training purposes, with result scatterization of precious personnel, fragmentation, and lowering of intensity of group commitment;

(c) lack of adequate or competitive salaries and adequate research environment.

Anyone familiar with the professional scene in many developing countries would agree with the authors' list, especially on the lack of the surrounding research environment which provides not only the immediate supportive working mechanism, but, more important, contributes to the motivation for continuous professional growth and development.

Professional Working Seminar

While university training and education in institutions abroad provide the basis for extensive professional training, the authors also narrate how in the case of Chile the effort to implement a successful university extension activity led to

233

the establishment of a prolonged Professional Werling Seminar. Although this seminar (mostly in the form of periodic meetings) seems to be a purely internal affair of exchange and communication of forces within Chile, emphasis has been placed on analysis of relevant developments in other countries. Papers of foreign specialists and the general eclectic tone of such a seminar have accentuated a problem oriented atmosphere, a continuous forum for sharing experiences about applied research projects and for discussing methodological breakthroughs.

The emphasis of CEPLA on systems analysis has become the central axis around which revolve efforts for applied research and contribution to national plans of water resources development. The examples offered by the authors underline the faith towards a holistic, systems approach as means for meeting the challenge of planning complex, multi-purpose projects. In concluding their paper, however, the authors seem to place a rather undue stress on the importance of intensive graduate training of young researchers abroad. Other authors in this group of papers would question such a strong faith without the cautions that Anderson succinctly brought forward.

Poblete and Harboe extend their conclusions by underlining a number of concerns for a successful transfer of knowledge both between countries and from research to practice. Their remarks emphasize not only the need for strong financial support, continuous leadership, and careful planning, but also the necessity for long-range commitment in an atmosphere of real problem solving. Relevance, planning, and scholastic approach become also here the necessary ingredients for the successful transplantation of generalized knowledge to the specific problematic situation of a given country.

The last paper by Albertson and Chaudhry projects a number of previous comments into a broader discussion of research and education for development. Thus, we have come a full circle from the general guidelines of Wiener to the questions raised in the last paper as to what national development entails and what programs and institutions can carry it out. The authors' paper only indirectly refers to water knowledge transfer, since they tackle the larger question as to what is the more general concern with development and efforts for planned change.

Their definition of development reiterates a common preoccupation of all authors in this group, namely the multi-dimensionality of the process in that it involves integrated aspects of physical and human resources. The term "resources" becomes the key element for discussing a whole variety of conditions such as manpower, information, natural, socio-political, cultural, institutional, etc., impinging upon development. There is, however, difficulty for understanding the emphasis of the authors on what they call "right values and right attitudes" for motivating development (behavioral component) without an equal emphasis on structural changes of the social system that would provide the springboard for the emergence of these proper values and attitudes.

In describing their development model the authors emphasize the following central components:

1. Manpower resources, as expressed especially in the skill, dexterity and judgment of individuals (perhaps analogous to what Wiener describes as the capacity to spontaneously adapt to improved environments).

2. Values and attitudes, especially with reference to future-oriented thinking. As contrasted, however, to previous authors who underlined the need for understanding cultural relativism, Albertson and Chaudhry proceed with a rather diffuse discussion of universal values, pluralistically beautiful, but semantically highly ambiguous.

3. Information resources, their acquisition and circulation, are also important ingredients and dynamic elements for mobilizing or completing the developmental process. The authors, importantly enough, emphasize here the role of the reverse flow of information not only in the traditional direction from developed to developing, but also from historically and culturally reached nations to technologically advanced.

4. Finally, the institutional resources call attention to the need for developing a "democratic" participatory system where individuals can realize their potentials.

If we agree that such general remarks are important ingredients for the achievement of true development, what mechanisms or processes do exist for maximizing resources in developing nations? The authors continue with a broad discussion of such conditions and means as:

1. Systems approach, as a tool for understanding the holistic nature of problems, the integrated environment and the systematic linkages of a multitude of environment, resources, dimensions, disciplines, factory and variables.

2. Education for the creation of enlightened colleagues and associates, rather than dependance to traditional elites or emerging over-sophisticated professionals (one may again observe the common thread of distrust towards specialization and the incipient dictatorial

power in the hands of professionals or other national elites.

3. Much more difficult is the proposal of the authors for the creation of democratic institutions. Not that anyone disagrees with such a lofty goal. But exactly because of its loftiness and because of the widespread misuse of the term "democracy" (including the authors' diffuse definition as having "its seeds in the inner soul of the masses"), it is difficult to see what exactly research and education can do for the creation of grass-roots institutions. This transformation of "heart" is the crux of the problem in all developmental literature and simple exorcising will not suffice to chase the ghosts of underdevelopment. Intermediate solutions, realism, hard work and structural as well as behavioral changes are all parts of the necessary equation.

The authors do not address themselves to the question of knowledge transfer. But at the end offer suggestions for action very much in line with a number of arguments forwarded by the previous authors of this group of papers. Yet, they leave us with the same lingering doubt as to how indeed research and eventually education will help us replace authoritative structures with well-meaning democratic institutions. There is strong debate at this point centering around the catch phrase "evolution vs. revolution," between contending schools of thought as to how change can come about, and as to the role of knowledge and technology as a force in development.

WATER RESOURCES DEVELOPMENT POLICIES
AND TRANSFER OF KNOWLEDGE FROM DEVELOPED
TO DEVELOPING COUNTRIES

by

Aaron Wiener
President, Tahal Consulting Engineers Ltd.
Tel Aviv, Israel

Synopsis

A kind of homology appears to exist between the comprehensiveness of policies and the bureaucratic structure of the underlying decision process: fragmented decision processes cannot be expected to produce integrated policies, and vice versa. Furthermore, the systems boundaries to which development policies refer ought to reflect the scope of public interventions that have to be interpolated into ongoing processes in order to achieve the desired change: in developed countries, the scope could be confined to basic infrastructural features (engineering facilities), while in the developing countries a much broader transformation will usually be a precondition for success.

In both aspects, developed countries greatly differ from underdeveloped ones, and uncritical transfer of models (implicit or explicit) and methodology will therefore prove abortive. Technological information is, of course, directly related to relevant policies; scope and depth of information collection programs and the very nature of these programs in developed and developing countries will therefore also differ.

Scope of Water Projects

A meaningful study of the transfer from developed to developing countries of information, know-how, and technology relating to water resources will have to consider not merely water as an isolated resource, but the whole complementary complex that is relevant to its use. Water is either an infrastructural feature-as it is in community and many industrial water supplies, or a production input-as it is in irrigation or in the "wet" industries. In both modes of water use the transfer of information ought not be confined to the resources aspects alone, but should also include economic, social, institutional, and political aspects.

Information is but one of the inputs of an objective-oriented project. The type, scope, and depth of information that has to be transmitted will, to a great extent, depend on the type and scope of the project for which it is intended. This consideration is of special importance in the transfer of knowledge to Third World countries concerning water resources projects, since-and this is one of the basic theses of this paper-for reasons to be gone into later, the scope of water resources projects in both modes of water use in developing countries will greatly differ from that in developed countries.

Infrastructural Information Insufficient

To elaborate this point in greater detail, one must remember that underdevelopment is characterized primarily not so much by lack of capital and other resources, as by the community's lack of capacity to spontaneously adapt itself to improved production environments, such as irrigation facilities. For example, a generation ago, when the U.S.B.R. built the Columbia River Project, its contribution to the project could be confined almost exclusively to the construction of the basic infrastructural features of the project: dams, hydro-electric and pumping installations, irrigation and drainage canals. Transformation of the area into an intensively irrigated and cultivated region was almost exclusively the result of the adaptation of a selected farmer population to an improved production environment created by the physical features of the project. The provision of similar infrastructural features in a developing country will have very different results: left to itself, the farmer population within the project area, conditioned to traditional production methods, will neither be capable of spontaneously adopting new production methods, nor will it be capable of generating the institutional structures that are needed for modern agricultural production, processing, and marketing. The project will either remain unused or partially used for long periods, or, where the farmer population is familiar with irrigation, it will be used for the production of traditional crops by inefficient traditional production methods. In neither case will the investment have been justified.

Complementary Elements to Overcome Underdevelopment Inadequacy

For projects to be effective in developing countries, they would have to include not only the physical infrastructural features from projects in developed countries, but also the elements connected with overcoming the inadequacy of underdevelopment, such as the lack of capacity to spontaneously produce the necessary transformation relating to rural organization, motivation, and information transfer down to the production level.

It thus appears that the achievement of the same objective (i.e. major production increase as a response to the provision of irrigation) in developing countries will require projects of a scope radically different from those in developed countries.

The scope of the former type of project will be much wider and much more complex. As a corollary, projects in the developed countries will require a much more limited body of information than those in the Third World. Information relating to the former type of projects will comprise mainly items of a technological nature; information referring to projects in the Third World will have to include also information on agro-technique, rural institutions, farmers' motivation, i.e. site-specific information. Thus, the body of additional information needed for Third World countries can only be gathered within these countries themselves.

Knowledge transmitted to the Third World in relation to irrigation projects will therefore have to comprise the methodology of collecting, in these countries themselves, the pertinent parametric information on all such aspects of water development that distinguishes Third World projects from their counterparts in developed countries. A quandary will here arise, due to the fact that professionals of developed countries, who have received their professional training in their own countries, rarely have sufficient knowledge or even awareness of the specific additional information needed for Third World projects.

Farmers' Response Indispensable

The reasons for the differences in the conceptual approach to projects between developed and underdeveloped countries is obvious. Farmer populations in developed countries possess sufficient adaptive capacity to spontaneously take up appropriate production methods in response to an improved production environment (such as a new irrigation project) and to spontaneously set up the necessary rural institutional framework: in short, they are development-minded, and if they need some technological information, they will know how to look for it themselves. Such rural societies are, to a great extent, self-regulative; a new challenge will elicit an appropriate response. By definition, this is not the case in Third World countries; farmers are governed by traditional methods and will resist sudden change. No spontaneous adaptation to new production environments will occur. Project interventions will therefore have to comprise all those activities that relate to the transformation and upgrading of the psychological space of the farmer, with a view to motivating him to appropriately respond to new production environments.

Professional Training Aided by Outsiders

As a matter of course, that part of the information that refers to the technological features of water resources projects will not substantially differ between developed and Third World countries-although here, too specific considerations of phasing, avoiding complexity, etc., might apply to the latter type of countries.

There ought to be no major difficulties in the transfer of information of a technological nature. Engineers, in both types of countries, dispose of the same body of knowledge, normally taught to trained professionals in relation to technological issues. However, the main problem here will be transforming Third World professionals into professional decision makers. In the developed countries such a transformation process normally takes place by junior professionals working for years under the supervision of experienced senior professionals. In many Third World countries such an opportunity does not exist; young professionals are often called upon to perform responsible technological-executive duties for which they are insufficiently prepared. To achieve the desired training in professional decision making, the professional group in Third World countries ought to include a limited number of outside professionals possessing the necessary experience and insight.

Personality Aspects

Another aspect of information transfer that applies to all types of water resources development is the fallacy of assuming parallelism of personality characteristics and motivation between the developed and the Third World countries. This assumption will result in the working postulation that professionals in the Third World will be motivated in a way similar to the development consultant's own motivation; that the promotional system is similar; and that social status is also gained in a similar way. Because of this assumption, the development consultant will spend little effort on personality formation of the professionals with whom he is working. Insufficiencies in motivation, in the promotional systems, etc., are, however, among the principal weaknesses of underdevelopment that have to be overcome when trying to initiate a sustained growth process. Neglect of this all-important factor will, therefore, not do. The consultant who wishes to free himself from the said fallacious assumption will have to devote part of his effort and part of the available development resources to identify in the development agencies such weaknesses in personality formation, and to implement the measures necessary to gradually overcome them.

The Three Basic Fallacies of Transfer

The real difficulties in the transfer of knowledge will be encountered in irrigation projects in which the transformation of producer populations and of their institutions constitutes the most important project target. Here one

240

encounters in the attempts of information transfer three more basic fallacies involved in the belief that it is possible to transplant bodily the following features of present-day practice from the developed countries: (i) patterns of professional specialization, (ii) problem-solving models, (iii) problem-solving routines.

Patterns of Specialization

The fallacy of transferring patterns of professional specialization from developed to developing countries will induce the development consultant to transfer the discipline-by-discipline approach which might have proved reasonably successful in his own country. However, this approach will not be effective in developing countries. A country which is underdeveloped mainly because its socio-economic system, including its role occupants, is lacking growth-orientation; therefore, the paramount aspect of development in the Third World is transformation of the socio-economic system and its role occupants. This transformation is a complex task in-volving the application of a number of technical (including agricultural), economic, behavioural, and socio-political disciplines and their interaction. Since the consultant is operating on a living system in operation, the planning of such a transformation cannot be confined to defining an initial status quo and a target status: in addition, he must define the intermediate stages of transformation and ensure that the process, in all its phases, will result in viable transients. This difficult task can be achieved only by the application of an interdisciplinary planning methodology; if such a methodology does not yet exist, the development consultant will have to make use of makeshifts which will approximate a desirable more rigorous approach.

Problem-Solving Models

The fallacy of transferring problem-solving models is probably the one that has most heavily vitiated the effective-ness of development consultants in the Third World. As pointed out before, development planning in mature economies relies on spontaneous response of the socio-economic system, as opposed to the application of diversified public intervention in developing economies: the allocation of resources for short-term production, as against interventions aimed at medium or long-term transformation.

In the Third World, the emphasis will be on public inter-vention and transformation. The less developed a country, the more strategies will differ from those of mature economies. A planning approach embracing this new emphasis will introduce all those planning dimensions of development and combinations

of disciplines that may usually be neglected in economically
mature countries.

Problem-Solving Routines

The fallacy of transferring problem-solving routines relates to the transfer of routines acquired and proven over
years of professional work in the developed countries. This
fallacy might prove the most difficult to eradicate; it is the
direct result of the prevalence of the first two fallacies.
A great conscious effort on behalf of the development consultant
will be needed to recognize that an important part of his professional stock-in-trade does not fit problems encountered in
developing countries, and that a new set of tools is needed for
easing Third World problems. Such a retooling process presupposes the availability of an appropriate substitute planning
and evaluation methodology.

After having reviewed the general difficulties relating
to the transfer of knowledge, the more specific problems that
bear on water supply and irrigation projects can be discussed.

Water Supply Projects

Since the essential information in water supply projects is
of a technical nature, the transfer of knowledge from developed
to developing countries will usually be relatively smooth.
Difficulties will arise only where differences in the socio-
political modes may greatly affect the success of projects, or
where, for socio-economic reasons, different planning approaches
are indicated.

The first type of difficulty may arise in connection with
water rates and collection of dues. Considerations as to the
height of water rates and ways of collection will differ greatly
between rich and poor countries; therefore, the blind transfer
of principles in connection with the rate structure should be
avoided. Potable water in poor communities will be a highly
political issue; the real cost of water may be burdensome or
even beyond the payment capability of the poorer population.
Thus a more flexible attitude towards repayment of full project
costs ought to be adopted.

Differences of the second category may refer mainly to the
fact that in developing countries funds allocated, over a
planning period of four to five years, to community water
supplies are strictly rationed and only take care of a
relatively small part of the communities that lack adequate
water supplies. This would be in contrast to the developed
countries, where funds can usually be raised to provide adequate
supplies to all communities that need them. The question of
raising cost effectiveness of investments to the highest

possible level and maximizing the aggregate of the services resulting from the capital allocated to the planning period ought to rank paramount among allocation considerations. This will greatly affect the extent of pre-building capacity to take care of future demand, the standard of construction used, the extent of sophistication adopted, etc. Some of these considerations ought to be adopted also for other reasons; for example, sophisticated automatization equipment ought to be avoided in the Third World countries because of the lack of adequately trained personnel and maintenance facilities, etc.

Irrigation Projects

The types of information that will have to be transmitted comprises five main categories: (i) Technology, (ii) Agro-techniques, (iii) The psychological space of the farmer, (iv) Rural and regional institutions, (v) Considerations relating to the capacity of development agencies.

Information on technology and, to a limited extent, on agrotechniques, are the most straightforward categories of all. Since there is little difference in engineering design between developed and underdeveloped countries and some of the agrotechniques are identical, the transfer is usually smooth, and project implementation, as far as these modes are concerned, successful. However, one aspect should be given special consideration-that of phasing: in the Third World, absorption of the improved production environments constituted by irrigation facilities will, as a rule, be relatively slow; therefore, where possible phasing of investments will be indicated.

Regarding transmittal of information relating to the three latter categories and to the adaptive aspect of agro-techniques, there arise two major difficulties: the necessary information is, as a rule, not available in the developed countries and cannot be generated. It can only be generated within pilot operations in the Third World. Because of these difficulties, little information-related to these categories-has in fact been transferred to the Third World. Therefore, the majority of irrigation projects have only been completed as far as engineering infrastructural features are concerned, while the at least equally important transformation aspects have only been approached half-heartedly and with little success.

Although the facts are well known, they have led to little re-thinking and re-consideration in the various aid agencies and consulting firms. Program approaches practically lacking the three latter categories have proved eminently successful in the developed countries; this has led to the assumption that they should also lead to satisfactory results in the

Third World: If they do not, the blame is put on the politicians, on the lack of capability, or on insufficient perseverance of the local development agencies, etc. In brief, the under-developed are being accused because projects in their countries have shown unsatisfactory progress.

Numerous notable exceptions, of course, exist. But a closer analysis of success stories will show that, where agricultural projects have succeeded in the Third World, the success is mostly attributable to the fact that the projects are being operated by agricultural entrepreneurs who could spontaneously (i.e. without dependence on public institutions) create the necessary rural transformation. Irrigation projects in Mexico's North-West and North-East are perhaps the best known examples of such successes. Yet, in the same country other projects, not blessed with similar entrepreneural talent, have a rather unsatisfactory record.

The activities of the transfer of knowledge over three decades on the above lines have had three major negative effects: (i) they have obviously led to a high percentage of lopsided unsatisfactory projects. (ii) they have been instrumental in setting up institutions and political processes for such lopsided projects, and these institutions will resist change. (iii) they have failed to create the essential information in relation to the four latter categories of information enumerated above.

Re-Oriented Approach Needed

To improve the situation, it will be necessary to adopt a basic re-orientation of efforts on the transfer of knowledge. It would be beyond the scope of this paper to go into the details of such an effort, but a rough outline can be sketched out.

First pilot projects will have to be established to generate the necessary parametric information required for the design of large-scale projects within the framework of Third World development agencies. Such pilot projects could within one or two seasons generate sufficient information for activities to be conducted on a much wider scale. They would, at the same time, serve to train local working teams and trans-mit to them the requisite information and the necessary skills of professional decision-making. Once the basic parametric information is available, one could proceed to the establish-ment of full-scale prototype projects whose objective would be to create prototypes for further operations that could be under-taken on a truly national scale. In such prototype projects, re-training and re-motivation of professional personnel could be continued and greatly expanded.

A further and possibly more important aspect of the transfer of knowledge is in the field of planning of resources use within a sectorial framework. In most countries irrigation projects are undertaken not because they promise to provide the maximum or even a satisfactory achievement of objectives, but because they are similar to (usually unsuccessful) projects constructed in the past, or because of local political pressures. To improve the situation, transfer of planning methodologies ought to be encouraged that would facilitate the selection of such project categories and projects that would lead to the achievement of explicit development objectives-making due allowance for the political framework within which one has to operate.

Lately, the international and the principal multinational and bilateral development agencies have become aware of the necessity of re-orientation of information transfer in relation to irrigation projects. The president of the IBRD (World Bank) stressed this point at the annual meeting of the Board of Governors. It is to be hoped that the awareness of the necessity of re-orientation of these most influential institutions will make a revision of procedures, scope and contents of information transfer a much easier task in the future.

WATER RESOURCES UTILIZATION IN DEVELOPING COUNTRIES

By

Prof. Luis E. Franceschi
Universidad Central de Venezuela
Caracas, Venezuela

Preface

Life would not be possible without water. In the annals of the human race man has been remarkably successful in solving the problem of using water resources for his own development. However, water uses have not escaped the complication of contemporary life; the utilization of water resources has become one of the most intricate of man's activities, especially in a country facing urgent development problems.

Characteristics of Water as a Natural Resource

The use of water as a natural resource involves a number of varied characteristics; all of which lead one way or another to confusion and uncertainty. The hydrologic cycle which implies continuous movement and change, shows a picture of varying supplies both in time and space. Thus the availability of water depends on a natural process as yet not controlled by man; but man can intervene to control pollution and irrational withdrawals.

Water uses are as varied as human endeavors: Municipal water supply, irrigation, power generation, and waste disposal. These are all consumptive uses because some form of consumption is involved: volume, quality, energy. Together, the three forms would become conflicting; simultaneously the demands could also become conflicting in a relatively short period of time creating extremely complex problems. On the other hand, the situation may be the frustrating result of economic growth unaccompanied by progress, and necessarily leading to an uncertain future. The diversity of requirements are so extreme that for some uses, like domestic consumption, water is essential; and for others, like some individual uses, water is only another factor to be considered in a benefit-cost evaluation.

Uncertainty is always present when the decision-making process is not accompanied by the necessary data that is used to forecast results. However, when water utilization is involved, the problem is aggravated by the fact that water could be both beneficial and harmful; however, if improperly used by man, it can be spoiled and rendered useless beyond restoration at any reasonable cost.

Characteristics of a Developing Country

The notion of underdeveloped, developing, and advanced nations is an over-simplication that serves to show many of the characteristics common to all. Notwithstanding the sharp historical, cultural, and geographical differences, most of the underdeveloped nations share many interdependent characteristics. Climate is usually tropical, per capita income is low and unevenly distributed, a large percentage of the active work force is engaged in farming and mining, sanitary and educational facilities are poor, and, in general, man's efforts are dedicated to the solution of present problems with never a thought to the future. It would seem that development is a question of changing human attitudes from a passive acceptance of traditional events to an active struggle against challenging circumstances.

A nation cannot enter the stage of successful self-sustained development unless it manages to do away with the tendency toward individualism and routine, arouses a desire for self-improvement and better conditions in general, and work with energy for improvement.

Thus, it is important to bear in mind that in a developing country human attitudes have to change radically, from the acceptance of traditional ways to a desire to attain a more brilliant future, regardless of risks and frustrations.

A problem common to developing countries is the insufficiency of available funds. These nations never have enough money to meet the requirements of their violent growth. As a result, potential users of capital contend with each other for the available funds; and while simultaneously needing foreign investments, overseas capital is not always willing to cooperate in meeting the goals and objectives of developing countries. The scope of this paper does not permit an extensive discussion of a socioeconomic development.

Another aspect having an important bearing on the use of water resources, is the lack of reliable basic information. The reliability of national statistics, the precision and impartiality of previous analyses and studies, the lack of regularly kept reliable records are contributing factors to the state of disorder previously mentioned. Under these circumstances, decisions are improvised to solve apparent, but insufficiently defined problems.

The Need for Planning

In a country whose future should depend primarily on the will to attain higher stages of development, water uses should never become a factor limiting growth. The uncertainty of the

future and the confusion of the present are obstacles to be
eliminated with due consideration to the best solution of such
problems. There may have been a time when the consequences
of the decisions made did not affect the destiny of future
generations. This is no longer true. The problems attending
industrialization, population growth, increased demands for
agricultural products, and pollution, call for clear guide
lines leading to the ultimate goals, and conscientious programming of present efforts.

Water Plan for a Developing Country

Basically, a water plan for a developing country should
provide the necessary foresight to the decision-making process, so that decisions are made with an awareness of their
consequences, under priority preferences for solving the
multiple, interrelated problems to be encountered.

Considering the characteristics of water as a natural
resource and of the developing countries, a water plan should
be regarded as an instrument designed to eliminate uncertainty
and confusion. This calls for identifying the problem areas
associated with water; assessing water problems, water availability and related land use conflicts; and preparing a plan
that considers several planning stages differing in detail
and precision, but within the same orientation scope.

The first stage is the preparation of a Master Plan. It
should identify and assess water problems and give clear
orientations for establishing priorities. The second stage
is the implementation of the preceding stage through detailed
plans designed comprehensively as indicated by the original
assessment. Control and budgeting of the detailed plans make
up the third state. The three are closely related and therefore dependent one on the other.

The Water Plan which is part of the national development
policy, should provide for:

a) Gaining more information on the location, availability,
   and quality of the nation's water resources;

b) Meeting both consumptive and non-consumptive demands
   at the right time;

c) Protecting lives and property against the damaging
   effects of water;

d) Protecting water and related land resources against
   irrational human action;

e) Assigning priorities to projects and works;

f) Indicating needs for financial resources;

g) Providing measures for controlling the implementation
of the Plan itself.

The Master Plan

Planning the use of a scarce resource is a permanent and
continuous process in which the Master Plan encompassing the
other stages is the most important instrument for any developing country.

Characteristics of the Master Plan

National in scope with no regional preferences.

Transversal insofar as it allocates the available amounts
of a scarce resource among competitive bidders, and in the
process has to go through the various sectors of the
economy.

Unique because one of its aims is to promote cooperation
and eliminate individualism.

Integral since it has to consider the various water uses.
Prospective because it has to base decisions on future
targets and not on the future that is simply a projection
of the past.

Long-term since all action involving water resources
development can be properly assessed only after a long
period of time.

Dynamic, to keep in tune with technological advances
that cause rapid changes of political, social and economic
consequences.

Formulation of the Master Plan

The formulation process of the Master Plan comprises
five phases:

> Compilation of basic data;
>
> Determination of water demands;
>
> Determination of water availability;
>
> Assessment of water problems;
>
> Policy formulation.

The compilation of basic data could become a frustrating
experience when the objectives of the Plan are forgotten and

the compilation work itself turns out to be another objective. Data on availability, demands, uses, and related problems is usually scarce. However, for a long-range plan in a developing country, the magnitude of the present problems is negligible when compared with possible future conflicts that could arise if water utilization is not properly planned.

The determination of water availability could be influenced by unforeseen technological advances. Climatic changes, ground-water exploitation techniques, pollution abatement in sources rendered useless, and surface water utilization are some of the fields where major changes might occur in the near future. Thus, surface and groundwater volumes, quality, location, and variability can be determined with conventional methods, bearing in mind that the characteristics of the problems to be assessed require thorough but not too precise treatment.

Water demands in a developing country will increase at a rate that will depend more on the attainable and desirable future than on the immediate past or on traditional growth. A threefold increase in unit demands for municipal use can readily take place in a matter of years in a rapidly indus-trializing community; the same increase in population will take at least three decades at a very high rate of population growth. Here again technological advances could bring about substantial changes; however, it is just a question of time for the estimated demands to materialize. Large agricultural demands could be postponed by implementing water saving tech-niques if users are given sufficient time for technological adaptation and motivation. Industrial demands can be increased or reduced depending on cost considerations.

After water demands and availability have been determined, the problem areas associated with water can be identified and classified according to importance. In a developing country where industrialization and agricultural innovations must go hand in hand with population growth, the major problems of the future probably will bear little resemblance to those of the present. Moreover, many problems, including damaging floods, erosion, and pollution, arise as water and related land resources are utilized.

To assess water associated problems and formulate the Plan, the most important tool is the water balance which is used to make logical allocation of the available water among potential users of a hydrographic unit in which several basins may be grouped. Generally, the most significant problems are the result of water shortages; nevertheless, in some instances pollution abatement could be so costly that quality becomes the most important factor to be considered.

The formulation of the Plan has to take into consideration
the basic elements mentioned in preceding paragraphs, but above
all it has to consider that water utilization should not hamper
the socioeconomic development of the country. Thus, the
national development policy is a guide for formulating the Plan.

The Master Plan is an aggregation of strategies for using
previously analyzed water sources considered available. The
strategies will define the content of the subsequent planning
stages and should be precise in orienting all action since
their purpose is to reduce future uncertainty by anticipating
problems before they become critical.

While it is true that each country will have its own
problems and solutions with water utilization, the advantages
of a plan thoroughly treating water problems instead of a
list of projects to be constructed, have been quite evident
in Venezuela's case. Important water planning aspects, such
as appropriate laws, erosion control, pollution abatement and
flood plain regulation are often ignored because of short
sighted solutions of minor conflicts today.

OBSTACLES TO CONSIDERATION OF
RESOURCES MANAGEMENT ALTERNATIVES:
SOUTH ASIAN EXPERIENCE

By

Daya U. Hewapathirane
University of Sri Lanka
Nugegoda, Sri Lanka (Ceylon)

and

Gilbert F. White
University of Colorado
Boulder, Colorado, USA

Synopsis

One of the principal reasons for ineffective water management measures in developing countries is the failure of planning agencies -- both consulting firms and government offices -- to give consideration to alternatives to conventional techniques. As a result, some works fail to meet their social goals or have the opposite effects, and the less conventional techniques are neglected. Experience with river management programs in Sri Lanka (Ceylon) and the Lower Mekong Basin illustrate these points. This failure stems in large part from the method of training professional personnel and from the rigid definition of administrative missions for government agencies. Neither of these conditions is susceptible to early or easy correction. However, we think it likely that partial remedy could be obtained rather readily at low cost by a combination of two activities: 1) adoption of a criterion that examination of alternatives should be an integral part of review of project proposals by multilateral and bilateral financial agencies, and 2) short-term training for principal technical personnel.

Sri Lanka and the Lower Mekong have a somewhat similar range of environmental conditions but differ markedly in their size and in the scale and intensity of water management. Similar obstacles seem to arise in both areas.

Stages of Water Development in Sri Lanka

On the basis of distribution of rainfall, the island is divided into a wet and a dry zone. Two distinct water problems are encountered in these two zones -- drought in the Dry Zone and floods in the Wet Zone.

Construction of an extensive network of tanks and canals began 2,000 years ago for the purpose of irrigating paddy land

252

(S. Arumugam, 1969). This was confined exclusively to the Dry Zone, then widely inhabited. The Wet Zone where most rivers of the island find their sources, was largely forested and uninhabited.

Beginning in the early part of the 13th century, population drifted to the Wet Zone. Among the reasons given are the desiccation and impoverishment of soil in the Dry Zone.

The advent of European colonial powers to the island after the 15th century and their interest in Wet Zone resources enhanced the development of settlements there and led to the neglect and consequent decay of a large part of the ancient irrigation system. Peasant agriculture in the Wet Zone was almost entirely rainfed and largely confined to flood plains.

During the four and one-half centuries of foreign domination the subsistence economy of ancient Sri Lanka was transformed to an export-oriented commercial economy. Coffee and later tea and rubber plantations were opened up in the Wet Zone hill country. Low lying areas attracted large populations. Urban centers, including Colombo, grew in the flood plains. Before long floods emerged as a problem. There is a popular belief that the clearing of forested, highly sloping upper catchments of rivers for plantation purposes, and the little attention paid in these areas to soil erosion control aggravated flood conditions (R. Maclagan Gorrie, 1954; United Nations, 1955).

The Dutch rulers (1698 to 1796) were the first to take measures against floods, constructing a flood protection levee and several canals. They also repaired some ancient tanks in the Dry Zone. The British rulers (1796 to 1948) improved these works and built levees to protect settled coastal areas of West and South Sri Lanka (Sessional Paper V, 1949).

Arumugam, S., Water Resources of Ceylon: Its Utilisation and Development, Water Resources Board: Colombo, Ceylon, 1969, pp. 16-20.

Gorrie, R. Maclagan, Report on Kotmale Landslips and Adjoining River Catchments, Sessional Paper XVII, 1954, Government Press: Ceylon, September 1954, pp. 5-6, 38.

United Nations, Multiple-Purpose River Basin Development, Part 2A: Water Resources Development in Ceylon, China: Taiwan, Japan, and the Philippines, Flood Control Series No. 8, Economic Commission for Asia and the Far East, United Nations: New York, December 1955, pp. 15-16.

Sessional Paper V, 1949, Flood Protection Schemes, Government Printer: Colombo, Ceylon, 1949.

However, floods continued to threaten the activities and occupants of the flood plains, because the protection measures were largely meant to curb minor floods (International Engineering Company Inc., 1948; Ferguson's Ceylon Directory -- 1934; Irrigation Department, Ceylon, 1963). In the Kelani and Kalu flood plains, in particular, flood-protection works increased the occupation of areas behind levees, thereby greatly enhancing potential damage. The number of people displaced in the city of Colombo alone by the 1940 floods was 59,000 and by the 1947 floods 135,250 (International Engineering Company, Inc., 1948).

During the past twenty-four years of independent Sri Lanka, emphasis again shifted to the Dry Zone in order to develop new land for food production as a substitute for food imports necessitated by a steadily growing population. Several of the ancient irrigation works were repaired and new schemes were undertaken. Until the construction of the Gal Oya project, such development was limited to single-purpose projects (S. Arumugam, 1969), for irrigation, hydro-power or water supply. The Uda-Walawe and Mahaweli Diversion projects were also subsequently conceived as multi-purpose schemes.

Several development plans were drawn up for other river basins. The Irrigation Department of Sri Lanka as well as foreign agencies were involved in this planning.* The Department had come into existence during the British period and continued to function as the foremost governmental agency dealing with water resources management.

All except one of these schemes adopt the conventional approach with emphasis on engineering techniques involving large capital investment. The scarcity of financial resources

International Engineering Company, Inc., Report on Flood Control for Kelani River, International Engineering Company Inc.: California, USA, October 1948, pp. 25-33, 12.

Ferguson's Ceylon Directory - 1934, Ceylon Observer Press: Lake House, Colombo, Ceylon, 1934, pp. 36, 43, 61, 76.

Irrigation Department, Proposals for Development of the Gin Ganga Basin, Irrigation Department: Colombo, Ceylon, 1963.

Irrigation Department, Proposals for Development of the Nilwala Ganga Basin, Irrigation Department: Colombo, Ceylon, 1963.

Arumugam, S., Water Resources of Ceylon: Its Utilisation and Development, Water Resources Board: Colombo, Ceylon, 1969.

*Cotton, John, Report on the Control of the Kelani Ganga, John Cotton, Consulting Engineer, USA, 1948.

and an acute foreign exchange problem caused delay in initiating water management in several basins. Among policy makers as well as professionals it is evident that in the selection of projects, Dry Zone irrigation schemes assume greater importance compared to Wet Zone schemes where flood loss reduction is the dominant consideration. This attitude may be attributed to: 1) a failure to comprehend the seriousness of the flood and related problems of the Wet Zone as a result of the inadequate methodology adopted in the assessment of flood losses; 2) overestimation of costs as a result of the sole dependence on engineering devices as solutions to water problems; 3) underestimation of possible benefits from a comprehensive scheme of flood loss reduction; and 4) overestimation of benefits and underestimation of costs of Dry Zone irrigation projects.

A mission from the International Bank for Reconstruction and Development prepared a scheme for the Kelani Ganga in 1952, proposing resettlement of flood victims in higher localities in preference to constructing costly reservoirs to control floods. This is the only instance where the conventional structural approach was modified.

Increased Vulnerability to Flood Losses

Low returns on investment were the result in many of the major development projects (V. N. Rajaratnam, 1971; P. H.

International Engineering Company Inc., Report on Flood Control for Kelani River, International Engineering Company Inc.: California, USA, October 1948.

International Bank for Reconstruction and Development, Report on Kelani Flood Scheme, International Bank for Reconstruction and Development, 1952.

Technopromexport, Kelani Ganga Basin Scheme for Flood Control and Utilization of Water Potential of the Basin with a View to Flood Protection, Development of Power and Irrigation, Technopromexport: Moscow, USSR, 1961.

Engineering Consultants Inc., Feasibility Report on Multi-Purpose Development of the Nilwala Ganga, Gin Ganga and Kalu Ganga Basins, Engineering Consultants Inc.: Colorado, USA, 1968.

Hydrotechnic Corporation and Engineering Consultants Inc., Report on Samanalawewa Irrigation and Hydroelectric Project, Ceylon, Hydrotechnic Corporation, New York, USA, and Engineering Consultants Inc., Colorado, USA, 1960.

Department of Irrigation, Proposals of the Department of Irrigation, Ceylon, for the Development of Kalu Ganga, Nilwala Ganga, Gin Ganga, Kelani Ganga, Deduru Oya, Malwatu Oya, 1960-1963.

Perera, 1971). An approach which neglected social considerations was followed by failure to achieve the desired goals.

The Mahaweli Diversion Scheme which was planned in association with a team of specialists supported by the United Nations Development Programme shows a sharp deviation in the planning approach. For the first time a multidisciplinary team was established. However, engineering devices dominate the final plan which is now under construction (FAO, 1969).

An evaluation of the Gal Oya project was made in 1966 after fifteen years of its operation (Report of the Gal Oya Project Evaluation Committee, 1970). This exposed the colossal waste of resources as a result of faulty planning and poor management. To quote the report, "...the effects of the construction of the Gal Oya reservoir have been complex: drainage water from the newly-irrigated and colonized lands has so affected certain of the purana lands* that they have become waterlogged and have, wholly or in part, gone out of cultivation." The significance of this effect is better understood when it is realized that "...the concept of the Gal Oya Reservoir Scheme originated largely, if not entirely, from a desire to protect some at least of those purana lands (especially those in the Pattipola Aar Scheme) from the devastating floods that swept down the Gal Oya valley...."

Possible post-reservoir flood damage received little consideration in the construction of the Gal Oya reservoir (P. H. Perera, 1971). A notion of complete protection encouraged greater occupation and investment on the flood plain. Thus, when the 1957 floods occurred, the damages that resulted were unprecedented in the history of the area (Report

Rajaratnam, V. N., Scope and Prospects for Planning of Water Resources Development in Ceylon, Institution of Engineers: Colombo, Ceylon, 1971.

Perera, P. H., Planning for the Full Realization of the Potential Benefits from Irrigation Projects, Proceedings of the Twenty-sixth Annual Session of the Ceylon Association for Advancement of Science, Part II, Colombo, Ceylon, 1971.

FAO, Mahaweli Ganga, Final Report, Rome, 1969.

Report of the Gal Oya Project Evaluation Committee, Sessional Paper No. 1, 1970, Government Printer: Colombo, Ceylon, 1970.

*Purana lands are large extents of mainly alluvial and almost entirely under paddy, that were cultivated before the inception of the project.

Perera, P. H., 1971, op. cit., p. 205.

of the Gal Oya Project Evaluation Committee, 1970). A similar disaster occurred in the newly constructed Uda-Walawe project during the 1969 December floods. Strong criticisms have been made on the defects in the design of this reservoir (D. L. O. Mendis, 1968).

A leakage in the Castlereagth reservoir of the upper Kelani has been detected.* In the event of a failure of this dam, a vast extent of developed land and settlements as well as the city of Colombo are bound to face disaster.

Increased vulnerability as a result of exclusive dependence upon engineering devices are seen in the series of flood protection levee schemes along the rivers of the most densely settled and intensively used Western and Southern areas. Levees of Kalu, Gin and Nilwala basins serve little purpose as protection (H. O. T. Scharenguivel, 1962; Engineering Consultants Inc., 1968; Implementation Program, Matara District, 1970). They are easily overtopped during average floods. During minor floods local rainfall in the so-called "protected areas" and the ingress of runoff from the upper reaches result in the accumulation behind levees of water which cannot be drained until the river level subsides. Long stretches of previously productive agricultural land has been totally abandoned as a result. Land values have been considerably reduced. In the nonagricultural areas around the levees of lower Kelani, damage potential is increasing due to unrestricted invasion by buildings of areas behind levees. Indeed, large-scale government industrial enterprises are located in the lower Kelani flood plain, as well as several private establishments. Flood loss potential is increased by the poor state of repair of the old levees.

Report of the Gal Oya Project Evaluation Committee, Sessional Paper No. 1, 1970. Government Printer: Colombo, Ceylon, 1970, pp. 10-11.

Mendis, D. L. O., Design of Uda-Walawe Reservoir, Institution of Engineers, Colombo, Ceylon, October 1968.

*Water Resources Board, Colombo, Ceylon, investigation in May, 1969.

Scharenguivel, H. O. T., Development of Multi-Purpose Reservoir Projects in Ceylon, Institution of Engineers, Colombo, Ceylon transactions for 1962, p. 29.

Engineering Consultants, Inc., Feasibility Report on Multi-Purpose Development of the Niwala Ganga, Gin Ganga and Kalu Ganga Basins, Engineering Consultants, Inc.: Colorado, USA, 1968, pp. IX-IV to IX-VI.

Implementation Program, 1970, Matara District Agricultural Development Proposals 1966-1970, Ceylon, 1970, pp. xi-xii.

There is no doubt that a certain level of regulation is called for in several rivers of Sri Lanka. But it is important that consequences of such regulation should receive greater attention in the planning process. A broader approach incorporating devices such as land use regulation, watershed management, flood warnings, flood proofing and insurance which are not purely engineering in nature, would enable more optimal management of water resources and flood plains.

The Lower Mekong -- Concentration on One Technique

In contrast to Sri Lanka with its long history and distinct stages of water management, the Lower Mekong Basin constitutes a largely blank tablet on which major water management was first written in 1957 with initiation of an extensive program of data collection and planning on the part of the four countries of Cambodia, Laos, South Vietnam, and Thailand.* In brief, the history of the collaborative investigations in the Lower Mekong is one of initial emphasis upon hydrologic and physical data, preliminary planning of a number of tributary and main-stem water regulation projects on the river, auxiliary social and economic investigations, and the initiation of construction on a few of the tributary projects, culminating in an indicative basin plan which was reviewed in 1970 and finally published in 1971 (Lower Mekong Committee, 1971).

---

*Experience in water planning in the Lower Mekong is thoroughly reported in the annual progress reports of the Committee for the Coordination of Investigations of the Lower Mekong Basin (annual reports to 1971), and in a number of other documents (Schaff, 1963; Sewell, and White, 1966; and Huddle, 1972).

Committee for Coordination of Investigations of the Lower Mekong Basin, Annual Reports, Committee for Coordination of Investigations of the Lower Mekong Basin, 1958-1971.

Schaaf, C. Hart and Russell H. Fifield, The Lower Mekong: Challenge to Cooperation in Southeast Asia, Princeton, New Jersey: D. Van Nostrand, 1963.

Sewell, W. R. Derrick, and Gilbert F. White, The Lower Mekong, International Conciliation, Carnegie Endowment for International Peace, May 1966.

Huddle, Franklin, P., The Mekong Project: Opportunities and Problems of Regionalism, prepared for the Subcommittee on National Security Policy and Scientific Developments of the Committee on Foreign Affairs, U.S. House of Representatives, U.S. Government Printing Office: Washington, D.C., 1972.

The Lower Mekong planning effort, persisting in the face of the deepening tragedy of war in South Vietnam, Laos, and Cambodia, put together programs for improvement in the welfare of the peasants and scattered townsfolk in the area. The indicative basin plan of 1971 states vividly a problem which has plagued the planners in the four nations and in 20 collaborating donor countries since the beginning. This is the problem of what emphasis should be given to large multi-purpose structures in contrast to auxiliary measures and to smaller, more complex sets of activities having a similar aim. In most acute form the choice may be seen in the contrast between priority on design of a series of gigantic main-stem control structures and the design of pilot agricultural development programs. In 1963 the U.S. Bureau of Reclamation proposed a thorough investigation of a power-flood control-irrigation structure at Pa Mong on the Laotian-Thai-reach of the river. More recent estimates show that the project at an optimum design for river regulation would involve storage of 107 billion m^3 of water, the production of 4.8 million kilowatts of electric power, and a cost for the structure of approximately 1.2 billion dollars.

In contrast, a comprehensive rural development was seen as involving intensive land use and land-use capability study, investigations of farmer adaptations to present conditions, soil studies, observations on horizontal and vertical movement of water and accompanying research on crops, fertilizers, water management, and all related social and economic measures needed to carry out genuine rural development. An area of 3,000-5,000 cultivated acres was proposed as an initial demonstration project.

The investigations at Pa Mong have cost to date approximately $14 million. A comprehensive rural demonstration project was anticipated in 1962 to cost $2,500,000 (White et al., 1962). A more recent venture along the same line, now being undertaken with IBRD help, was outlined in the amplified basin plan. Pa Mong occupied the largest single item in the study budget and embraced thorough dam site, soil, and water distribution surveys by the Bureau of Reclamation with AID support as an integral part of the Lower Mekong planning.

Committee for the Coordination of Investigations of the Lower Mekong Basin, Report on Indicative Basin Plan, a Proposed Framework for the Development of Water and Related Resources of the Lower Mekong Basin - 1970, Publication No. e/CN.11/WRD/MKG/L.340, 1971.

White, Gilbert F., Egbert de Vries, Harold B. Dunkerley, John V. Krutilla, Economic and Social Aspects of Lower Mekong Development, January 1962, reprinted with revisions July 1962.

In effect, the United States as the largest single financial contributor to Lower Mekong planning concentrated its financial resources upon the investigation of one large structure, thereby reducing the possibility of making funds available for other types of investigation, and it focused the interest of many administrators and investigators upon the single project. We doubt very much that it advanced the welfare of the people of the basin. Although it gave some critical attention to the problems of relocation of population and to development experience (Ingersoll, 1969).

Why the Narrow Range of Alternatives

Why did planning groups assisting in planning water management in these Southeast Asian areas concentrate upon a narrow range of alternatives?

One cause is the professional training of the individuals offe·ing advice. Highly skilled in matters of hydrology or engineering, they find it difficult to deal with broader questions of technique or public strategy. Properly cautious as to fields for which they were not trained, and sensitive to the views of professional engineering and scientific organizations, they not only restrict their efforts but fail to ask others to supplement their restricted competence. We may applaud this prudence while lamenting the reluctance to canvass other lines of action.

A second contributing factor is the restrictive definition of mission for the administrative agencies. Both the Irrigation Department in Sri Lanka and the Bureau of Reclamation in the United States operate under legislative instructions which they interpret to deal primarily with design, construction, operation and maintenance of certain types of engineering works.

In addition to professional training and restricted mission orientation, other factors are the tendency of many administrators to prefer large and visible structures to less dramatic activities and the weight of experience with major engineering works.

Early Action

Perhaps two lines of action might help remedy the situation in the near future. One would be the organization of special short-term training workshops for individuals responsible for planning water management in developing countries. An

Ingersoll, Jasper, The Social Feasibility of Pa Mong Irrigation Requirements and Realities, July 1969, a report to the U.S. Bureau of Reclamation, U.S. Department of the Interior and the U.S. Agency for International Development, U.S. Department of State.

example is the United Nations Seminar on Flood Loss Reduction held in Tiblisi in October 1969, in which representatives from more than 27 developing countries met with a group of UN and USSR consultants to canvass possible improvements in methods of flood loss reduction. FAO has had an influential role in fostering such training for workers in the field of agricultural water use. It would be important to include personnel of consulting firms who from positions in Paris, London, Delft, Rome, Tokyo, or New York exercise a profound influence on the character of water planning throughout the world.

A second action would be revision in the review criteria employed by bilateral and multi-lateral funding agencies in considering allocations of funds for planning and construction of water management. Explicit statement as to the need for canvassing the whole range of practical alternatives for achieving particular social needs could be included in the checklist of items which regularly are considered by IBRD, UNDP, AID, and similar agencies. It will be a slow job to shift from the more narrow to the broader approach. It must come in time.

Meanwhile, we must candidly expect that with the present professional and agency orientation in managing water in developing countries we are likely to expand careful programs which ignore important alternatives and which are self-defeating in seeking the public aims they are intended to serve.

TRANSFER OF WATER RESOURCES KNOWLEDGE FROM DEVELOPED TO DEVELOPING REGIONS OF THE WORLD

By

Frederick L. Hotes
Principal Staff Consultant
International Division
Enviro-Engineers, Inc.
Berkeley, California and Washington, D.C., USA

Synopsis

This paper reflects the experience of the author in work-ing in 29 different countries of the world, primarily in water resources and agricultural development. Emphasis is on prin-ciples, problems, deficiencies, and successes, rather than on specific techniques, although a list of the many various methods available is presented. Knowledge of specialized mechanical skills, as well as that of the physical and social sciences, must be transferred. The transfer process is not complete until the developing nation has, within the country, an active, permanent reservoir of water resources knowledge. More transfer activities should take place within the develop-ing countries. Examples are given of problems stemming from the attitudes and traditions of both expatriate experts and developing country nationals. Oversophisticated methods inapplicable in most developing countries should not be taught intensively. Practically all of the methods used in the past can be used in the future successfully. However, they can be improved if formulated with the specific physical condi-tions and limitations of the particular developing nation in mind. If they are conceived with the aid of people in such countries, and executed in the developing world as frequently as possible, they should produce better results.

Introduction

"One of the unfortunate facts of life is that very few of us live long enough to profit from our own experiences." This paraphrase of a statement made at a university engineering student honorary society banquet, by a distinguished engineer retired from a major U.S.-government agency, while perhaps an overstatement, contains a considerable amount of truth.

Recognizing that our own experiences are limited when viewed in the context of the total range of international activities in almost any field, most of us appreciate opportuni-ties to learn the experiences of others working in similar spheres of interests. Conferences such as the one for which this paper is prepared certainly can provide such opportunities, especially when the experiences presented can be questioned, explained further, and discussed by knowledgeable people, as well as newcomers to the field.

This paper reflects the experience of the author in working to-date in 29 different countries of the world, primarily in water resources and agricultural development. Emphasis is on principles, problems, deficiencies, and successes, rather than on specific techniques, although a list of the many various methods available is presented.

Definition

The term "transfer of water resources knowledge" is comprehensive; thus it includes anything which involves water or its use. For example, it could include training of bull-dozer operators for land-levelling and the excavation of irrigation canals, since good operators are essential elements in efficient application of resources in many developing countries. It could include training of farmers in irrigation practices. Indeed, the transfer of these types of knowledge can pay much greater dividends in many instances than the transfer of knowledge on systems analysis and computer techniques.

However, for the purposes of this paper discussion will be directed primarily to water resources knowledge normally utilized by persons trained in the physical and social sciences.

"Transfer" also means more than simply offering the technical material, either verbally or in writing. The baton is not fully transferred until the next runner has it firmly in his grasp and is proceeding on his own toward the finish line. The water resources knowledge transfer process is not complete until there exists within a country an active reservoir of knowledge which is permanent. It need not be large, but it must be permanent, it must be available as reasonably needed, it must be useable, and it should be active. Activity is a good parameter with which to judge success. When nationals of the country are providing substantial inputs to their water resources technological work, the transfer process has been effective, at least to some degree.

Methods of Transfer of Knowledge

A systematic grouping of the various available methods of transferring water resources knowledge appears to be both difficult and unecessary. However, an attempt at a general listing of methods is as follows:

Purely Informal Methods	More Formal Methods

On-the-Job Learning (Experience)
Informal association and
  conversations
Incidental Cinema and TV programs
	Technical Journals and
	  Magazines
	Books
	Letters
	Special Cinema & TV programs
	Research
	Pilot Projects

Formalized Methods

On-the-Job Training
Technical Trade Schools
Universities
Short Courses
Workshops
Symposia, Seminars & Institutes
Lectures, by individuals or Teams of Experts
International Conference
Tours
Field Demonstration Programs

All of these methods have contributed to the transfer of water resources knowledge in the past and can be used successfully in the future, when applied appropriately.

Location of Transfer

The initial transfer of knowledge can take place inside or outside of the developing country. One of the greatest deficiencies of past transfer activities in the field of water resources knowledge is that too little takes place within the developing countries. This is the greatest single criticism of transfer methods which the author has heard from developing country nationals.

It can be argued that the place of transfer should make no difference. This may be correct theoretically, but too little knowledge applicable to their conditions is being transmitted, and too much knowledge which is inapplicable is being disseminated. They suggest that if more of the transfer activities were to take place within the developing countries, and if they were to be directed specifically towards the local conditions and problems, not only could this knowledge be translated into action more rapidly and efficiently, but also the transfer process itself would be much more meaningful, stimulating, and challenging to those being trained or educated. The author concurs in that belief, while cautioning that the attitudes of the transferors and the transferees and the general atmosphere of the transfer process are also important factors.

The teaching of interesting but irrelevant and sophisticated but inapplicable procedures within a developing country is an even greater sin than doing so outside such an area. One perhaps can be excused for not knowing a particular physical situation in Africa when one is lecturing in California, but it would be inexcusable to ignore local conditions when making the same presentation in Africa.

Problems of Expatriate Attitudes

Some developing country nationals carry their criticism another step further. They say that too many foreign experts come to their countries with narrow and unimaginative minds. They may be recognized international authorities in a particular field, but when encountering a new and complex combination of variables in a foreign land, they react by emphasizing the complexities and the problems, rather than by trying to apply their expertise to simplify, analyze, and resolve the problems. They want to study the situation for months or years before proposing any solutions. Developing countries often cannot wait years; needs must be satisfied in the immediate future.

Another type of expert sees no complexities, but quickly prescribes solutions similar to successful procedures he has seen or used elsewhere. This type of action is commendable when appropriate for the local conditions. However, if important physical or social differences are not taken into consideration the proposed solution may not work, and additional time and money may be required to correct oversights. Review and analysis of important basic facts should precede design.

The planning and design period is one of the best to transfer knowledge from the experienced to the inexperienced. Unfortunately, not enough attention has been given to formalizing on-the-job training during this time, or to supplementing such training by seminars, lectures, and workshops. Here the pressure of immediate production deadlines works contrary to the longer-term goal of transferring water resources knowledge. Compromise is the inevitable and unavoidable result.

Twenty years ago most developing nations were willing to accept our educational and training methods and the instructional content of the methods used. They did not feel justified in questioning the methods of successful people. Now many of these nations have acquired considerable experience with us and our methods and recognize that the pace of knowledge transfer can be accelerated. The developed nations must respond by doing more of the transfer work in the developing countries with experts who are qualified.

In-depth articles have been written on the necessary personal qualifications for work in developing countries. Even
the expert's family situation and their attitude must be
considered. This is not the principal topic of this paper or
of the Conference, but, since it is a vital essential for the
successful transfer of water resources knowledge, it is proper
to state again some of the principal qualifications for experts
on assignment in developing countries.

> They should be:
>> Competent in their specialties.
>> Cognizant, and appreciative, of the contributions
>> of other experts.
>> Willing to exert the energies required to attain
>> the goal, even under difficult conditions.
>> Patient, and sensitive to the desires and objectives
>> of the host country peoples, and to their regional
>> and national goals.
>> Experienced.
>> Imaginative.

Problems of National Attitudes

Problems and attitudes of the developing country nationals
who must acquire the knowledge to be transferred also deserve
attention. Not all of the problems which will be mentioned are
present in every developing country.

On occasion the professional must "get his hands dirty."
While there may be no intrinsic virtue in working with the
hands, there are many important pieces of information which
can be obtained best by a young professional actually performing a certain task. When he is unwilling to do so, he must
depend upon the statements and reactions of men unqualified
or less-qualified than himself, and in some cases they simply
can not convey the correct information. More commonly, however,
the loss is one of time. If the developing nation is impatient
with present knowledge transfer rates, then they should be
willing, at least occasionally, to break with custom and
tradition to speed progress. This is not always easy; however,
it has been done successfully in many countries.

Another problem for the developing country is the "National
Capitol Syndrome." Many young technical personnel believe that
they will not receive recognition or promotions unless they
are headquartered in the Capitol City. Unfortunately there
is much truth in this belief. Still, unless competent
personnel direct and execute field work at some time in their
careers, they will never fully acquire the knowledge needed
for a profound understanding of water resources technology.

How is a developing nation going to have personnel fully-competent to serve as a "Chief Engineer" some day? It is the author's contention that no method exists by which a nation can transfer within a period of a few years, all of the knowledge and experience needed by a Chief Engineer. This job requires more than pure technical knowledge and management techniques. It requires a knowledge of the detailed processes by which designs are brought from the idea stage to construction. He must know not only that a drawing must be made, but how many and what kind of man-hours are needed to produce the drawing, and he must be able to know when the drawing is correct and complete. Normally 20 to 25 years of design experience are required before a man is ready to discharge the responsibilities of a Chief Engineer. Under the best of circumstances 10 years would be too short a time, 15 years---maybe, for a very competent individual.

The shortage of technical personnel is so great in some countries that young engineers only two or three years out of university find themselves in charge of a national program in their specialty. They must supervise and evaluate the efforts of foreign consultants who may have had years of experience and decide on the merits of competing claims of competence. This is unfair, but there seems to be no avoiding such situations, for the young man in charge quite probably is the best qualified man in the nation to do the job. He can have and frequently does have independent expatriates, who can help him in his difficult task.

Both he and his government should not be too impatient nor too hasty in minimizing foreign assistance. They must recognize that many years are required to build up the experienced reservoir of knowledge which, when truly established, can carry the nation on for succeeding decades. Several nations have achieved highly commendable progress in this way.

The differences in background, training, and experience between nationals of developing countries and those of developed countries should be noted carefully when preparing specific educational or training programs. For example, a great many university students majoring in agricultural sciences in the U.S.A. have had experience as farm laborers and mechanics; whereas in many developing nations the agricultural science student has never worked as a laborer or mechanic. Some of them may be the scions of parents who own farm lands, a position which often involves the making of farm management decisions. Thus since the degree of practical experiences differs from one student to another, the educational process must be different if both are to achieve the same level of necessary knowledge. The challenge for those in charge of such transfer processes is to recognize what is necessary and to tailor the instruction accordingly.

Boondoggle

Probably the greatest boondoggle and least efficient method of transferring knowledge is that of bringing developing country nationals to a developed nation, and giving them a grand tour of organizations and projects. These really can be justified only on other "fall-out" benefits, such as goodwill. The same time and money spent in taking the same people to projects within their own countries or as near their homelands as possible, and with advance instruction on what to see, how it operates, etc, would be far more effective.

Over-Sophistication

Over-sophisticated methods already have been mentioned as a waste of time. A good example may be found in the topic being discussed in the Symposium immediately preceding this Conference, on "Decision Making with Inadequate Hydrologic Data". When streams have no data, or little data, it is extraneous to intensively teach the complex methodology of stochastic hydrology. Instead, emphasis and examples should be directed towards determining how hydrologic data deficiencies can be remedied in the shortest possible time, and how basic principles can be applied to obtain data upon which some reasonable action can be taken.

For example, if a large valley having several villages and perhaps a city or two is subject to flooding, it is possible, using basic hydraulic principles and common sense, to estimate annual flood damages and river stage-damage curves even though no or few streamflow data have been recorded. Any university graduate in civil engineering has the basic tools to do this job, but how many know how to do it?

Combination of Methods Needed

While it may be an obvious conclusion, it is necessary for the sake of completeness to state that no single method of knowledge transfer is sufficient to do the job by itself. All of the methods mentioned should be used to some degree to accomplish the greatest results in the minimum time with the least cost.

Summary

Some of the principal guidelines and conclusions set forth in this paper are summarized as follows:

1. "Water Resources Knowledge" in its broadest sense includes specialized know-how required of farmers, laborers, and mechanics, as well as the training

and education of professional and sub-professional
personnel in the physical and social sciences.

2. There are many different methods of transferring water
   resources knowledge. All of these have been used
   successfully at times in the past, and can be used
   again with positive results in the future, when
   applied appropriately.

3. The transfer process is not complete until there
   exists within the developing country an active,
   permanent, reservoir of water resources knowledge.

4. One of the greatest deficiencies of past transfer
   activities in the field of water resources knowledge
   is, that too little takes place within the developing
   countries.

5. There are important problems stemming from certain
   attitudes and traditions of both expatriate experts
   and developing country nationals which must be
   avoided or overcome.

6. One of the least effective methods is that of
   bringing developing country nationals to a developed
   nation and giving them a grand tour of organizations
   and projects.

7. Less time should be spent in presenting sophisticated
   water resources techniques which are inapplicable
   presently in developing nations.

8. There is nothing fundamentally wrong with any of the
   knowledge transfer methods used in the past. They
   can be used more effectively in the future, if
   formulated in each case with the specific physical
   conditions and limitations of the particular developing nation in mind. If they are conceived with the
   aid of people in such countries and executed in the
   developing world, they should produce better results.

KNOWLEDGE TRANSFER

By

Bruce H. Anderson
Director, International Programs
Utah State University
Logan, Utah, USA

Synopsis

This paper postulates that United States' universities
and colleges will be involved in the education of foreign
students for sometime. Thus the mechanisms or techniques of
knowledge transfer and the kinds of problems that impede the
process are discussed. Also for universities wanting to
accommodate the real needs of foreign students ideas and
innovations in training are considered. At the present time
budget limitations hamper the kinds of programs that need
consideration. Emphasis was given to special short courses
which can provide excellent opportunities for practical
training programs. Properly planned courses can provide
excellent knowledge transfer opportunities. However, this
raises the question of the role to be played by various
agencies and suggests that a new mechanism be found allowing
a more direct approach between institutions involved in knowledge transfer.

Introduction

The transfer of knowledge between peoples and between
countries has been in progress since time began. The past
twenty to thirty years, however, have seen a marked acceleration of the process of transfer in an attempt to share in
the vast accumulation of modern-day knowledge and technology.
The exchange has been deliberate and organized. It involves
many governments and governmental agencies seeking to improve
their own operation; international organizations such as the
United Nations, Organization of American States, private
foundations such as Ford, Rockefeller, Kellog, private industry
interested in developing their capability to do business
abroad; bi-lateral governmental programs operating under
direct government to government agreements such as AID (Agency
for International Development); and the many individuals
seeking to upgrade their own expertise who participate
entirely of their own volition.

It is difficult, to obtain a realistic appraisal of the
impact such programs have had on the world scene. But, there
is evidence to support the fact that giant strides have been
taken by many countries of the world. There is evidence also
to the contrary, where the constraints that exist in given

270

situations have limited the impact and the progress that had been expected from knowledge transfer and technical assistance programs containing emphasis on increasing competence of local technical and professional peoples. The developments of science and the increases in knowledge and understanding in many disciplines or subject matter areas in recent years in many countries have reached new heights of achievements. Thus, the technological advances through the application of this knowledge and the discoveries of science have created an ever increasing disparity between nations of the world. How to close the gap and to create an atmosphere wherein greater uniformity, opportunity and mutual progress can occur becomes the challenge to those engaged in the process of knowledge transfer. In the final analysis, however, it must be in the application of this knowledge and its benefit to man, and not alone in its gathering that we judge achievement.

This discussion will emphasize knowledge and technology transfer in the area of land and water resource development in the agricultural sector. Although many of the points considered may be applicable to other sectors, the experience and background of the paper draws mainly from problems associated with the production of food and fiber. One of the problems that continues to plague many countries is the inability to apply known knowledge at the production level. Generally there is knowledge available at some levels of society in the country, but this knowledge has not reached the level of the farmer, the producer, the man on the land who is the key link in the chain of production for increasing the food supply. Until ways and means are found to implement programs which accelerate knowledge transfer to this level of society, very little can be achieved in increasing food production.

It is recognized that there are many other problems that impinge directly on this production process, such as credit, markets, transportation, processing, incentives, etc., but again, these are inextricably linked to knowledge and to an understanding of how to apply the knowledge. The process of education must be a continuous one and must be considered at all levels in the society. To omit any of these levels may set up constraints that will weaken the chain of events that leads to the solution of production problems.

Transfer Mechanisms

There are methods of knowledge transfer that have been in use for many years. The ones discussed here will be those used to transfer knowledge to the academic community and the professionally trained sector of society. It is the hope that this sector would then continue the transfer process in their own country and throughout their society at all levels.

The commonly accepted methods of direct knowledge dissemination include:

A. University and college level training
   i. for degree programs
   ii. for non-degree programs
B. Short courses of various kinds
   i. in-country courses oriented to specific needs
   ii. international and regional courses
C. Seminars
D. Conferences and institutes
E. Study tours
F. Workshops
G. Technical assistance programs
H. On the job training such as is provided by technical assistance programs specifically designed to provide this experience.

Not all of the above mechanisms will be discussed in the paper, but enough will be said to highlight some key ideas and innovations.

University and College Level Courses - There has been some criticism directed toward the scholarship programs which fund students for university degree training. The Ph.D. level programs have been criticized because so many graduates have returned to their countries with an expertise that they couldn't apply at the level of development existing in their country; Their studies were oriented to problems at a higher level of sophistication. Consequently, many were misfits and sought employment elsewhere. Those who did stay usually migrated to administrative type jobs, and their technical competence was never effectively used. It can be argued, of course, that the education received "paid off" in other types of work.

There is now a growing awareness within the colleges and universities who accept foreign students of the vast differences in training needs of these students. Changes have been made and more are, perhaps, needed. It is difficult, however, to provide the kind of experience needed by the foreign student in some fields without additional financial support to institutions to offset the added costs. In many situations, the kind of training needed is that which was prevalent on campuses twenty or twenty five years ago. To reconstruct programs and set up the facilities which existed then takes additional support. The result is that while some progress has been made, present programs are still a compromise between what should and could be done.

Students with differences in language are under additional handicaps. They need to acquire the basic language to communicate in a new culture, and the "jargon" attributable to their

272

particular field of study. This "jargon" must be mastered to enable the easy flow of knowledge within the discipline. This is further complicated if inter-disciplinary programs are followed, since each discipline requires continued effort to learn and understand the points of view expressed by specialists in the field.

The background of students varies substantially from country to country, and from school to school. This complicates the time scale of their scholarship programs, because often students are required to take a number of prerequisite courses to develop the proper background for the study program undertaken. This requires time, and thus, additional funds. If this is not done, the student will not be able to take full advantage of his training experience. Many scholarship funding groups do not take into consideration the lack of background and falsely equate training in-country as comparable to training in universities of the United States, where carefully prepared prerequisite programs build a good foundation for the student. Many programs are predetermined in time before the student arrives at a university and undergoes diagnostic analysis for his program. It is quite difficult to make up deficiencies and the student is the one who suffers.

In order to make university training more applicable to the student, some effort has been made to encourage the student to do his thesis or dissertation on a back home problem. This may be done in his own country. Results are variable and unless a cooperative atmosphere exists in the home country to support the program, considerable time is lost in completing the research and getting the degree. Obviously, if good work is required, supervision by the major professor or committee members is essential. This approach requires additional financial support to allow travel for the student, committee members, and other costs associated with completing the thesis and satisfying the committee requirements.

Unfortunately the many problems that plague the foreign student may elicit a certain empathy from a professor or a committee to the extent that academic standards are relaxed. This works to the disadvantage of the student by not requiring him to develop the proper background or knowledge based upon which he can build expertise. On the other hand, undue pressure can be brought to bear on the student, and a lack of understanding of his problems may elicit a negative attitude from faculty and place an unfair burden on the student. Both of the above situations should be avoided and every effort made to establish an acceptable learning atmosphere for the student.

Non-degree programs are usually easier to administer, but many of these programs do not put any pressure on the student to learn. Unless the participant is highly motivated, he does not put forth much effort to absorb and retain the information and knowledge made available to him. Unfortunately, some just "go along for the ride." The challenge, then, is in the selection of participants, and in matching their interests to the material offered. If the course can provide a case study problem applicable to his back-home situation, then interest will usually be higher. This approach may require that the professor have previous experience in the country and an understanding of specific country problems.

Problems Facing United States Universities

It seems logical to anticipate that many foreign students will continue to come to countries like the United States to attend school. Although considerable emphasis is being placed on institutional development in many countries, it is unlikely that they can proceed at a fast enough pace to develop courses, staff, and facilities to offset the need for some training abroad. Also, the rapid expansion of knowledge through programs of research and development is centered primarily in a few countries, and these, undoubtedly, will continue in the forefront, necessitating that students from other countries look to them as an information source. Also, the experience gained in the application of knowledge will normally occur in the countries where the information is generated so that, again, this experience should be examined as adaptation is considered for other areas.

If universities plan to adopt programs that will more adequately meet the needs of foreign students, then changes are needed. Staff will require some orientation and preparation, and in some cases, new staff should be added. The staff needs opportunity to travel and work in projects abroad. More than a one-time travel program is needed so continuity can be maintained even during the inevitable periods of staff changes. Indiscriminate travel should not occur, but travel should be tied to some specific effort or proposed development of competency at the institution concerned.

A university may need to develop facilities to consider field problems applicable to many countries. Present facilities reflect the needs of the United States and local situations and may not apply to the problems of other countries. Funds from state sources cannot be justified to readjust to the requirements of other countries and must be found from other sources.

The possibility of doing some teaching in a foreign language should be considered in special cases. The language barrier is still a formidable one, and every effort possible needs to be made to help alleviate the difficulties of communication. There are bilingual competencies available in the professional field, and some schools are now teaching technical courses in a foreign language. However, this should not be done at the exclusion of learning English. Students need a language which will provide them a ready contact with current research findings, and English certainly provides a great deal of literature for the professional workers.

An alternative to considering the types of changes indicated above is to pay no attention to foreign student needs, and take the approach that what we do now is good enough. This may be the approach many will have to take since funds for change are limited, but there are degrees of change possible that would span the spectrum between change and no change. Each university must adopt its own policy in this regard. Realistically, the present policy of accommodation within present limitations will continue.

Short Courses

The mechanism of short courses has been used extensively throughout the world as a professional improvement tool. It provides flexibility as to time or date, length of course, number of participants, quality of staff available, time away from work for the participant, credit or non-credit courses, administrative burden, and backstopping required, including classroom and field facilities. A short course combined with a case study problem associated with a development project offers an excellent vehicle for knowledge transfer. The addition of the case study component brings the course to the application stage, thus, dealing with real problems. A successful use of the case study technique requires more time on the part of the staff. Staff must be prepared to visit the project area to discuss the problems of the project, and to advise and consult with participants who may be looking for solutions to problems they have encountered on the project.

Courses can be designed for a particular country or a region. They can be sight specific which may limit their appeal to students from other areas. Generally, however, students react favorably if the subject matter is properly presented and a good learning atmosphere created. If participants are selected from areas with comparable problems, there is usually no problem of relevancy if a case study is used. If, however, persons from a tropical area are brought in to consider the problems of arid agriculture, then you have a more difficult time.

The other mechanisms mentioned, such as seminars, workshops, conferences and institutes, study tours, and on the job training, each have their place in knowledge transfer. One important aspect in all of these mechanisms is to provide for proper planning. Usually budgets are restrictive, and travel funds, planning time, and sufficient administrative help is hard to get. The process of knowledge transfer is important enough that programs should be properly funded and provision made for adequate planning, and evaluation.

We are now entering a new era in our ability to reach people. Now we can use techniques such as video tape and prepare materials which can be used far from the site of the teacher or professor. The possibilities of television usage and the telestar relay system are in infancy, but their usage may well revolutionize present day classroom teaching. The use of modern technology should improve our ability to reach the many levels of society involved in a more efficient use of the land and water resources. Again, adequate planning and preparation, of course, are essential elements to successful programs.

The need for basic information, in the native language is usually a limiting factor in most training programs. There is no doubt that a few countries predominate in research data and information availability. The production of printed material in these countries proceeds at a rapid rate and requires great effort on the part of professors to keep current. This increases the burden on other countries to provide even a selected summary of material in their native language. Some countries require their professionals to be bilingual with the second language selected from one of the countries in the forefront of research and development in the given field. No easy solution is available, and although high speed duplication processes are available, these are only as valuable as a county's ability to translate, interpret, and prepare material for duplication. Budget is always a limiting factor.

Elements of Short Course Planning - In the planning of programs, such as those mentioned above, several important factors must be considered. Foremost among these is the involvement of the local people with the course. They should provide inputs as to course objectives, course content, nature of participants, time availability, case study data, accessibility of project site, contacts with project management to help explain the project for study, local arrangements, classrooms and other facilities, availability of qualified local staff to participate in course material presentation, and the coordination of the course at all required levels. Attention to these details requires time, and entails a commitment on the part of the local people where the course is to be held. If the course involves an international group, the planning should include, wherever possible, visits to each country and a dialogue with proposed participants.

The preparation for such courses by the professional staff must also be intense. Data from the project area, if a case study is to be used, should be available to staff in sufficient time for them to familiarize themselves with it. They should arrive ahead of the beginning date of the course and visit the area and see problems first hand. Only then can they react to the needs of the local people. Great care must be exercised to teach the course at the level of the participants. A presentation that is beyond the level of the students is of no avail and only indicates the inadequacy of planning. The same is true of teaching below the level of the participants. A wise and knowledgeable staff will check this factor carefully.

Emphasis on the Practical - There is growing concern in many countries for emphasis on the "practical aspects." Many development projects and technical assistance projects have not been as successful as administrators had hoped. One apparent reason for this is the failure to achieve results at the "pay off" level. This "pay off" level may include production and marketing of crops, and these in turn will have a number of variables affecting them. How is knowledge transfer affected by the concern for the lack of success in some countries in their development programs? Can a heavy emphasis on the "practical aspects" help to solve the problem?

It is evident in the agricultural sector, that many of the professionals involved have had only a minimal contact with problems of producing food and fiber. The producer is reticent to accept advice or change his practice unless he has confidence that the advice will benefit him-increase his share of the production and bring increased returns once the crop is sold. The problem then becomes one of how to develop the know how and the skill at the appropriate level to accomplish this task.

Over the years, it has been adequately demonstrated that experience is necessary to establish a knowledge base, to provide the confidence required of professional people to do their job. Thus, some courses should contain components that will give sufficient field experience so participants can see, understand, and learn how to do certain tasks. By evidencing their ability to do, plus an adequate knowledge base, their contacts with the producer level will be acceptable and fruitful. This kind of program requires adequate time, proper field facilities, and a qualified staff. The rewards, however, from such a program will be great indeed. It provides one way of introducing realistically the "practical aspects."

Another tried and true way of introducing the "practical aspect" is still the demonstration technique. In the agricultural sector, producers will modify their practice if they see success or benefits that can be gained from a change.

Unfortunately, lack of field experience has resulted in many failures with the demonstration approach. But when it is handled and directed by qualified personnel, the results are usually successful. Prerequisites to success include sufficient funds, facilities, and back-up support to handle the problem realistically.

"Role" Problems

As indicated earlier, there are many international agencies, governments, foundations, universities, colleges, private industries and organizations of many kinds involved in the process and business of knowledge transfer. The definition of roles and responsibilities of those involved may constitute an impediment to accelerating the process and achieving a high degree of success. In the academic community of colleges and universities, there are usually two parties concerned with the process other than the people or institutions directly concerned. These are the local government, and perhaps, a funding agency which acts as a go-between and administrator for the program. Many decisions are made about training programs and the participant before the training institution and the professors become involved. The scholarship mechanism often falls short of providing the funding required by the institution and the participant. Perhaps a more direct relationship would be advantageous and less costly.

Currently, some thought is being given to establishing an international university. But, it is difficult to see how this type of program could meet the needs of countries in many areas. At best, it could serve the needs of only a few disciplines or subject matter fields. Future needs may identify a role for such an institution but it appears to be limited in meeting the needs of training in land and water development and in agriculture.

Often, funding agency goals are not entirely compatible with educational goals. There is a tendency to train or develop people to fit snugly into preconceived slots. Scholarships are for particular areas, and students may move into programs because a scholarship is available.

To accomplish the task of knowledge transfer, there is good reason to suggest that the educational institutions of respective countries exercise more direct contact with each other. Their role is one of knowledge generation, accumulati 1, and dissemination, and every effort should be made to let them assume full responsibility to discharge their obligations. It is essential that some outside funding be available for programs which take them into other countries. Perhaps, it is time to think in terms of some mechanism that will allow the universities to fund programs between institutions. A grant mechanism administered by a council from the academic community to screen applicants for assistance would be worth considering. Such an arrangement would help to remove the politics from the program and, hopefully, allow a more meaningful cooperation between institutions. Inter-change of professors and students could be handled easily; cooperative research may become a reality in many countries, and there would be less administrative problem from intermediary organizations.

The above does not close out or preclude the need to cooperate with organizations concerned with various aspects of knowledge transfer. It is anticipated that these would continue, but in addition, a certain autonomy and responsibility would be taken by universities to work directly - institution to institution - in developing viable programs for knowledge transfer. Thus, a unique role fitted to the capabilities of the interested schools would begin. The two types of programs would compliment each other.

The university and college system has been a vital link in carrying out the charge to educate the youth of the country. The results of research and development over the past number of years speak for themselves. The system is oriented toward change, for change is inevitable in modern society. The United States system can join hands with systems in other countries to enlarge the impact of knowledge transfer.

A CASE ON TRANSFER OF KNOWLEDGE IN WATER RESOURCES
SYSTEMS PLANNING FROM A DEVELOPED REGION TO A
DEVELOPING ONE, AND FROM RESEARCH TO APPLICATION

By

Juan Antonio Poblete

and

Ricardo Harboe
Centro de Planeamiento (CEPLA)
Facultad de Ciencias Físicas y Mátematicas
Universidad de Chile (UCH)
Casilla 2777 - Santiago, Chile

Synopsis

In this paper a brief description of a process of transfer of knowledge, from one region to another and from research to application, in the area of Water Resources Systems Planning is given. This description is based on the experience gained by the Centro de Planeamiento (CEPLA), a center of applied research and teaching in Planning and Economics at the School of Engineering of the Universidad de Chile (UCh), over a period of approximately ten years.

In the first section as an example of transfer of knowledge between regions, two inter-university programs, one between the Department of Civil Engineering of the Massachusetts Institute of Technology (MIT) and CEPLA, and the other one from the Water Resources Planning Group at the University of California, Los Angeles (UCLA) and CEPLA, and the results obtained are described. In the second section a prolonged Professional Working Seminar and two applied research projects, both in their beginnings, are sketched out. These activities have been designed by CEPLA as a means of transfer of knowledge from research to application. In the third section some general conclusions are drawn.

University Research and Graduate Training as a Means of Transfer of Knowledge Between Regions

During 1962 CEPLA decided to undertake research and to train a teaching staff in Water Resources Systems Planning, taking into account the importance that this subject would have for the country and for its engineering profession.

A MIT - CEPLA Program - In 1963, a joint research program in Water Resources Systems Planning was initiated between the

The authors acknowledge the comments of their colleagues: Patricio Barros, Fernán Ibáñez, and Miguel L. Leonvendagar. Remaining shortages, major or minor, are the sole responsibility of the authors.

Department of Civil Engineering of MIT and CEPLA. The program
was started under the following major objectives:

i)   Analysis of existing planning methods for multi-unit,
     multi-purpose water resources systems;

ii) Research in those areas that seemed most promising
     regarding the application of Systems Analysis concepts;

iii) Specialized training for a group of professionals
     in the field.

An additional interest of CEPLA was to begin comprehensive
planning of the water resources in Chile, a relevant, yet an
untouched problem area. For accomplishing this task, there
was a clear need for reaching out for knowledge which was not
available in the country and which was being developed in
foreign universities.

Thus, from the beginning the application of the forthcoming
analyses and methodologies to a real world case was given
special emphasis. The Maule River Basin, located in Chile,
was chosen as a case study. It represented a multi-unit,
multi-purpose water resources system with relatively large
civil engineering works (hydro-power plants, reservoirs, and
irrigation developments) that were either operating or under
construction. Interesting technical alternatives were present,
within the framework of a developing nation.

Financial support for the research program was provided
by MIT's Inter-American Program in Civil Engineering, which
had as a major sponsor the Ford Foundation, and by the UCh.

In 1963 Eng. Fernan Ibáñez (at that time Director of the
Water Resources Project of CEPLA) spent a period of time at
MIT and had the opportunity to work out with Dr. Ronald T.
McLaughlin (at that time Assistant Professor at MIT) the
framework for the forthcoming program. At MIT as well as at
CEPLA two research teams, composed of students and headed by
Dr. McLaughlin and Eng. Ibáñez respectively, developed.

Up to mid 1964, both the MIT and CEPLA research teams
worked in parallel, without having any relevant direct contact. At the beginning the main tasks were those of gathering
information on the Maule River Basin (1), and of setting up
preliminary planning models, that were later to be developed
at length.

During July and August of 1964, an intensive course on
Water Resources Development (2) was given by Dr. McLaughlin to
practicing engineers and advanced students of the School of
Engineering at the UCh. He and the MIT research team came to

Santiago, and thus a real opportunity was given to both groups to learn from each other and to work out future research.

The next year and a half was a period of elaboration of the preliminary planning models set up by each team separately, yet discussed jointly. Models which made use of Linear Programming, Simulation and Dynamic Programming approaches were developed (4, 9, 11, 12, 13, 17, and 18). Most of these studies were aimed at a) analyzing from the technical and economic point of view the system (or part of the system) selected, and b) the testing of the usefulness of the various Systems Analysis approaches when applied to "real world" planning issues.

Each study would start with the available information and whenever possible update it. The improvement of the data from stage to stage, typical of preliminary engineering studies, became a major preoccupation throughout the studies. In two cases a short exchange of researchers of both teams was necessary: One for a field research in Chile (13), and the other one (17) for processing a mathematical programming model at MIT, taking advantage of its adequate computer facilities which at the time did not exist in Chile.

Several special purpose studies and papers were also published in this initial period of the MIT-CEPLA program described (3, 5, 6, 7, 8, 10, and 16). One of the studies, worked out at MIT in the early beginnings of the program (6), had the purpose of identifying relevant technical problems in the development of water resources in Latin American as well as identifying suitable topics for university research. Another study (7) was worked out by CEPLA on request of the UN Latin American Institute for Economic and Social Planning, and Resources for the Future Inc. This study was used, later on, by Prof. Nathanial Wollman for his book, The Water Resources of Chile (John Hopkins Press, Baltimore, Md., U.S.A. 1968). A third study (8), done by CEPLA on request of the Government of Chile, later became critical in the decision which stopped the on going construction of a low net benefit three purpose reservoir.

The final period of this research program 1965-1969 was characterized, first, by studies which emphasized more the methodological aspects of the models developed and second by the acquisition of advanced training of the participating Chilean research engineers (14, 15, 22, and 23), through post graduate work at MIT. It was both a period of joint research and teaching at MIT and of research and teaching at CEPLA. Intense post graduate training at MIT, in Systems Analysis and Economics, allowed three of the members of the Chilean team to acquire full command of the knowledge available on the subject at MIT.

An UCLA-CEPLA Program - In 1966, in an effort to increase
the transfer of knowledge towards CEPLA, a joint research
and study program with the University of California (UC) was
prepared and submitted to the Universidad de Chile - University
of California Convenio in order to obtain financial support.
No action was taken by the Convenio at that time. Nevertheless
a limited joint program with the Water Resources Planning
Group of Profs. Warren A. Hall and John A. Dracup at UCLA
was started.

A Chilean research engineer, who had three years
experience in the field was sent to work on research and to
enroll in a graduate program at UCLA. This program was suc-
cesful both in the research done and in the training acquired
by the participating research engineer. Research activities
were a fundamental part of it and dealt with problems that
the Water Resources Group at UCLA was facing rather than with
relevant problems of Chile. As a result, several studies
were published (19, 20, 21, 24, 25, and 26).

Within these three years a new proposal on a more extensive program on Water Resources Systems Analysis was submitted
to the Convenio. This time the program was approved as a part
of the existing one on Water Science and Engineering. It
allows UCLA and CEPLA to have faculty and student exchange
as well as to finance specific technical assistance.

Results Obtained for CEPLA - The results obtained from
this inter-university effort (MIT-CEPLA; UCLA-CEPLA) were
for CEPLA qualitatively extremely valuable, yet quantitatively
rather limited.

Quantitatively: one senior and two junior researchers
started out in this buildup of a specialized team that should
later on carry out research and do the teaching in the field
of Water Resources Systems Planning at the UCh. After one
year the group grew to one senior and five junior researchers.
Five of them reached a desired level of training*, with
different emphases, according to personal preferences and
opportunities available. Only one of them ended up working
specifically in the field; another works partly in the field.
Three ended up working in different fields within the country.
The latter contribute to the university as part time professors
in Engineering-Economics.

---

* In terms of the degrees obtained by the five Chilean participants the results were the following: 4 Civil Engineering
  degrees, 5 Masters degrees, 1 Ph.D. degree, and 2 Ph.D.
  candidates (all but dissertation). One Master degree and the
  two remaining Ph.D. degrees are not wholly specific to the
  Water Resources Systems Planning field.

Qualitatively: the training acquired by the participating research engineers was of the highest quality available, and of general applicability: Engineering, Systems Analysis, and Economics in varying proportions made up the curricula of all of them. Those that remained at CEPLA, even though they are not working directly in the Water Resources Systems Planning Field, have contributed greatly in a reorientation of the institution, in several different research projects, and in its teaching. Thus, they have been transferring their acquired know-how to an extensive student body of the main School of Engineering of the country. A separate paper would be needed to focus on this particular transfer process, which characterizes CEPLA in general.

Several major reasons can be stated as an explanation for the mentioned outcome about the few researchers of the original water resources team who ended working in the specific field.

First, the absence of an understanding (confidence?) of the potentialities of new approaches for solving problems at higher echelons within the water resources agencies combined with a poor extension activity on the part of the university resulted in a lack of effective demand for applied research in the field. This demand, as will be mentioned in the next section, has been increasing over the last few years, that is to say, eight years later.

Second, a more concentrated financial support for CEPLA's research program in the last, more advanced stage would have prevented the Chilean group from splitting to make the training abroad possible. It would have made possible a more intense working out of the Maule River Basin case study, contributing to a closer and more continuous teamwork. Due to the splitting, the case study had to be pursued at a lower level of intensity and separately by those at MIT and those at CEPLA. Thus the methodology became the only link between the participants at some points in time. All these facts contributed strongly to a partial falling apart of the original Chilean group, which took place after the first trainees returned.

Third, the lack of competitive salaries and adequate research environment within the UCh made it impossible to keep all of the trained researchers once they had reached an advanced standing.

University Extension and Applied Research as a Means of Transfer of Knowledge from Research to Application

So far, no substantial development of a multi-purpose water resources project has been undertaken in Chile, nor has there been any successful effort in the working out of a unified policy to favor the planning, the development and the administration of multi-unit, multi-purpose water resources systems.

The allocation of financial resources and the development of projects has primarily followed the plans of the different sectors. These plans are based on the particular technology required by the sector involved and at best the economics associated with that sector. Complementarities (or substitutions) between projects of different sectors and/or regional implications of alternative projects have not found a place in this planning process. Yet, the situation is beginning to reach a stage in which these issues are becoming ever more apparent. Interference at the river basin and at the national level, especially among irrigation, hydroelectric, and municipal water supply projects is beginning to increase. An anachronic institutional setup has not favored the coordination necessary among the agencies related to the planning, distribution and/or use of the water resources, even though most of the agencies involved are government agencies.

A Professional Working Seminar - The situation in the Chilean water resources field presents weaknesses that have become apparent to almost everyone involved, especially to those engineers who have been working for some years in this field. CEPLA, in an effort to contribute to an objective analysis of this situation, and with the hope to implement a successful university extension activity in this matter organized a prolonged Professional Working Seminar. This seminar is taking place in three one week meetings spread over a period of approximately one and a half years. The objectives of this seminar were stated as follows:

i) Analysis and discussion, at a specialized professional level, of the past, present, and probable future of the Planning and the Use of the Water Resources of Chile. The emphasis was to be placed upon the multi-purpose use of these resources (surface, underground, and desalted water) focusing particularly on irrigation, generation of hydroelectric energy, municipal use and quality control activities.

ii) Analysis of relevant development in the Planning of the Water Resources in other countries so as to extract from these experiences those features that could be relevant for Chile.

iii) The working out of a set of recommendations for action regarding priorities for research, and guidelines for the government, which would ultimately contribute to further development and the conservation of the water resources of the country.

So far, two meetings of the three planned by the seminar have taken place. The first one took place in September 1971 and the second one, in May 1972. The third meeting will take place before 1973.

The first stage was devoted to a) the characterization of the general Chilean water resources problem focusing on the hydrologic, geologic and climatic aspects of it (27, 28, 29, and 30) and, b) the presentation of basic social, economic and political concepts related to the stating of objectives and the "state of the art" of the Systems Analysis methodology related to comprehensive Water Resources Planning (31 and 32).

The second stage centered on several applications of Systems Analysis to Water Resources Systems Planning in Chile and particularly elsewhere (33, 34, 35, and 36).

The third stage will be devoted to a) the major sectoral plans that guide the water resources investments in Chile and the incidence of these plans on the use of the resource and, b) the present institutional problems. The intention is to survey the past and present experience and to analyze the relevant changes that are necessary for having a future more efficient institutional setup, which should favor better planning and administration in the use, and conservation of the resource.

The Professional Working Seminar has been far more successful than envisioned at its beginning. The participation has been fairly numerous and enthusiastic: approximately one hundred professionals, mainly engineers who are government officials of the major agencies involved. The seminar has had the official backing of all of these institutions, and it benefited from their financing. Approximately fifteen papers, specially prepared for the seminar, will have been presented altogether and will make up the major part of the proceedings to be published as a book during 1973. Several of these papers were presented by foreign specialists who made most valuable contributions to this university extension activity.

So far two outstanding conclusions of this seminar can be stated.

First, it was a neutral meeting place where professionals had the rare opporunity of presenting problem oriented papers to an audience very much interested in complementing their knowledge about the general problem area. Although this audience was made up of specialists working in the field, they often do not have access to the studies done in other government offices for they are rarely published. The prolonged time span over which the seminar took place turned out to be very useful for the working out of the presentations and for spreading the impact of the whole effort.

Second, it was a meeting place where professionals had the opportunity of hearing about some applied research projects, especially on the application of new planning methodologies, done in various universities and foreign countries.

Two Efforts of Applied Research - Two years ago CEPLA decided not getting involved in any major research effort in Water Resources Systems Planning unless this research had a counterpart (e.g., the government) interested in and financing the application. That is, there has been the strong feeling that the problem to be faced in this area is rather the application and extension, at a high enough planning level, of the existing Systems Analysis approach and methodologies, than the development of new methodologies. Two research activities, which point toward this mentioned direction, are sketched below. They are both in their beginnings.

The first research activity refers to a "Project for the Development of the Water Resources in Northern Chile." This project is sponsored by the Chilean Government and the United Nations Development Programme (UNDP). CEPLA has been asked to participate in the development of a mathematical decision-making model which should become an aid in making specific recommendations to the government regarding future investments for the development of the extremely scarce water resources of the desertic Antofagasta Region.

The major copper and nitrate mines of the country, agriculture, and the municipal supply for the city of Antofagasta are the main water users. There are several water sources such as small amounts of ground and surface waters, and the possibility of desalination of sea water, requiring the former some degree of treatment due to their low quality. There have been about fifteen projects proposed so far. The degree of elaboration of these proposals range from some technical analyses to just preliminary ideas. The Government of Chile-UNDP Project, which is supposed to last four years, is at this moment concerned with a) gathering of basic data, and estimating future needs for water, and b) analyzing the most promising Systems Analysis approaches that would allow a comprehensive study of the problem. CEPLA's contribution is supposed to be in this latter part.

The second research activity mentioned here refers to a probable participation of the CEPLA group as such in a nation wide planning study, already started by the government. This study has as the ultimate objective the working out of a long-run national plan for the use and conservation of the water resources of the nation. The interconnection of the major river basins, by means of transferring water from the southern basins, where the resource is a relatively abundant one, to the water needy northern regions of the country is to be evaluated. So far the group of professionals who are looking into this problem have been primarily concerned with the broad technical questions involved. The next stage consists in generating alternatives and studying the regional and/or sectoral implications of such a plan. Then a comprehensive evaluation of the alternative paths that could be followed will be studied. CEPLA's participation in this latter part of the program has been foreseen.

It is still too early to pass any judgement on the development of such a complex study. Nevertheless, it should be pointed out that a multi-river basin approach to Chile's water resources problems, especially for the central part of the country, does look promising for most specialists who have dealt with the development of the agriculture and hydroelectric energy projects of the country. Only detailed future studies will tell how decomposable such a system is, be it for technical, economical, administrative or other reasons.

CEPLA, in both projects described, is supposed to help in the solution of the specific planning problem posed, as well as to contribute in the training of professionals who participate as technical staff in these projects.

As a final word it should be added that CEPLA's present research activities in the field of Water Resources Systems Planning have the support of the UCh, a grant of the FORD Foundation, and resources that are provided by the institutions interested in its applied research.

Some General Concluding Remarks

The process of transfer of knowledge among regions through universities is a promising one for the receiving region, since it has the long term effect of creating an autonomous research capability. Intensive graduate training abroad of young researchers, in the best--worldwide-- university centers, is possibly the best answer for a future successful transfer of technology and technical assistance among countries. This conclusion is a fair description of the experience which CEPLA has accumulated in different fields such as Industrial Planning, Regional and Urban Planning, Transportation Systems Planning, Science and Technology, and in Water Resources Systems Planning, approximately over a period of ten years.

The following aspects should be of prime concern to the parties involved in such a transfer of knowledge among regions:

   i) Specific inter-university research programs will help
       in this process of transfer of knowledge, yet one

might very well run into an over optimistic start and find that universities, even the most resourceful ones, do not have access to the necessary means for implementing ambitious joint case studies, such as those one would like to have in an inter-disciplinary area like Water Resources Systems Planning. The writing of individual theses on topics which relate to the specific problem area of the receiving country might well be a more realistic and thus successful approach, especially developed partly on site and partly in the transferring center.

ii) Financial support for faculty and students during and after a transfer program is a basic prerequisite. Extra university assistance will usually be required during the program. Universities of the receiving region must provide adequate funds once the program has been finished, and an adequate research environment to prevent newly formed researchers from migrating. This migration tends to increase once an advanced standing has been reached.

iii) Continuous leadership and careful planning throughout the fulfillment of the program is crucial. If it is not provided the whole effort might be jeopardized.

The process of transferring knowledge from research to application is a difficult one, particularly in the tradition oriented field of water resources. This process in this field is a recent one, even in developed countries.

The following aspects should be of prime concern for those research groups interested in this transfer.

i) The transfer process from research to application should be started early, considering the long time it takes to create an effective demand for applied research in the field.

ii) A working seminar for professionals, extended over a prolonged period of time, and organized at a university proves to be a successful media and a neutral ground for discussion among specialists of the conflicting aspects which characterize the water resources problems. It also provides an opportunity to present to professionals some of the relevant applied research projects that are being developed at universities and foreign countries.

iii) Real world problem solving, that is, applied research projects with a counterpart interested in and financing the application, and the training of

professionals and students, who participate as
technical staff in those projects, looks like a
promising vehicle of transfer from research to
application. Nevertheless, it is not easy to get
such an activity under way!

List of Publications

1. CEPLA, La Hoya del Río Maule, (Informes Nos. 1 & 2), 1964.

2. McLaughlin, Ronald T., Water Resources Development, (Class
   Notes), CEPLA, August 1964.

3. McLaughlin, Ronald T. and Ibáñez Fernán, "Systems Analysis
   in Water Resources Engineering," Proceedings 2nd IAHR
   International Congress, Porto Alegre, Brazil, August 1954.

4. Males, Richard M., A Dynamic Programming Model for
   Reservoir Simulation, (S.M. Thesis 1964), Department of
   Civil Engineering, MIT, August 1964.

5. Ibáñez, Fernán, and Leonvendager, Miguel L., Métodos de
   Planificación y Desarrollo de los Recursos Hidráulicos,
   CEPLA, Publication No. 67/7/A, Augusut 1965.

6. Bulkley, Jonathan W., Ibáñez, Fernán, and McLaughlin,
   Ronald T., On the Water Resource Problems of Latin America,
   Department of Civil Engineering, MIT, Hydrodynamics
   Laboratory, Report No. 87, October 1965.

7. Ibáñez, Fernán, Harboe, Ricardo, and Poblete, Juan Antonio,
   Estudio de la Disponibilidad de Recursos Hidráulicos en
   Chile, CEPLA, Publication No. 65/5/B, July 1965.

8. Leonvendagar, Miguel L., Córdova, Julio, and Neut, Alfredo,
   Evaluación de Proyectos Alternativos en la Gardanta del
   Río Malleco en Collipulli (Chile), CEPLA, Publication
   No. 65/11/B, July 1965.

9. Poblete, Juan Antonio, Programación Matemática Aplicada
   al Estudio del Aprovechamiento de Recursos Hidráulicos,
   (Civ. Eng. Thesis 1966), Escuela de Ingeniería, Universidad de Chile, CEPLA, Publication No. 66/2/B, January 1966.

10. Ibáñez, Fernán, and McLaughlin, Ronald T., "Operating
    Policy in the Simulation of River-Basin Development,"
    Proceedings ASCE Conference, Miami, Florida U.S.A.,
    February 1966.

11. Wallace, James R., Linear Programming Analysis of River
    Basin Development, (Sc. D. Thesis 1966), Department of
    Civil Engineering, MIT, May 1966.

12. Assereto, Oreste, and Barros, Patricio, Asignación Optima del Agua en un Embalse de Uso Múltiple Mediante Simulación, (Civ. Eng. Thesis 1966), Escuela de Ingeniería, Universidad de Chile, CEPLA, Publication No. 67/5/C, October 1966.

13. Bulkey, Jonathan, and McLaughlin, Ronald T., Simulation of Political Interaction in Multiple-Purpose River-Basin Development, (Ph.D. Thesis 1966), Department of Civil Engineering, MIT, Hydrodynamics Laboratory, Report No. 100, October 1966.

14. Ibáñez, Fernán, Operating Policies in the Simulation of River Basin Development, (S.M. Thesis 1966), Department of Civil Engineering, MIT, November 1966.

15. Leonvendagar, Miguel L., and McLaughlin, Ronald T., A Simulation Model of the Upper Maule River-Basin, (Unpublished Report), Department of Civil Engineering, MIT, November 1966, (CEPLA, ed., 1972).

16. McLaughlin, Ronald T., "Experience with Preliminary Systems Analysis for River Basins," Proceedings International Conference on Water for Peace, Washington, D.C., USA, May 1967.

17. Poblete, Juan Antonio, Assereto, Oreste, Ibáñez, Fernán, Harboe, Ricardo, and Leonvendagar, Miguel L., Un Modelo Simplificado de Programación Matemática del Sistema de Recursos Hidráulicos de la Hoya del Río Maule, CEPLA, Publication No. 67/3/C.

18. Harboe, Ricardo, Aplicación de Programación Dinámica al Diseño y Operación de un Embalse de Uso Múltiple, (Civ. Eng. Thesis 1967), Escuela de Ingeniería, Universidad de Chile, CEPLA, Publication No. 67/4/C, July 1967.

19. Harboe, Ricardo, Optimum Firm Power Output From a Single Reservoir System by Dynamic Programming, (M.S. Thesis 1968), Department of Engineering, UCLA, December 1968.

20. Hall, Warren A., and Harboe, Ricardo, Optimum Firm Power Output From a Two Reservoir System by Incremental Dynamic Programming, Water Resources Center, University of California, Contribution No. 130, 1969.

21. Mobasheri, Fereidoun, and Harboe, Ricardo, "A Two-Stage Optimization Model for Design of a Multipurpose Reservoir," Water Resources Research, A.G.U., Vol. 6, No. 1, February 1970.

22. Poblete, Juan Antonio, and McLaughlin, Ronald T., Time Periods and Parameters in Mathematical Programming for River Basins, (S.M. Thesis 1969), Department of Civil Engineering and Department of Ecnomics, MIT, Ralph M. Parsons Laboratory for Water Resources and Hydrodynamics, Report No. 128, September 1970.

23. Males, Richard M, and McLaughlin, Ronald T., Optimal Operating Rules for Multi-Reservoir Systems, (Ph.D. Thesis 1969), Department of Civil Engineering, MIT, Ralph M. Parsons Laboratory for Water Resources and Hydrodynamics, Report No. 129, September 1970.

24. Harboe, Ricardo, Optimization Models for the Analysis of Water Resources Systems, (Ph.D. Thesis 1970), School of Engineering and Applied Science, UCLA, September 1970.

25. Harboe, Ricardo, Mobasheri, Fereidoun, and Yeh, William, "Optimal Policy for Reservoir Operation," Journal of the Hydraulics Division, ASCE, Vol. 96, No. HY11, November 1970.

26. Mobasheri, Fereidoun, and Harboe, Ricardo, "Optimum Conjunctive Use of a Dual-Purpose Desalting Plant and a Surface Water Reservoir," Desalination, No. 9, Elsevier Publishing Co., Amsterdam 1971.

27. Fouquet, Héctor (Director Dirección General de Aguas, Ministro de Obras Públicas y Transportes de Chile), Política Nacional de Aguas, CEPLA, Publication No. 71/16/C, September 1971.

28. Court, Luis, et. al., El Problema de Aguas en Chile, CEPLA, Publication No. 71/11/C, September 1971

29. Alamos, Fernando, et. al., Necesidad de una Evaluación Integral de los Recursos y Consumos de Agua en Chile, CEPLA, Publication No. 71/12/C, September 1971.

30. Karzulovic, Juan, Características Geomorfológicas y Geológicas de Chile y su Aplicación a la Evaluación y Approvechamiento de Recursos de Agua, CEPLA, Publication No. 71/13/C, September 1971.

31. Hall, Warren A., The Objective Functions of Water Resources Systems Analysis, CEPLA, Publication No. 71/15/C, September 1971.

32. Dracup, John A., The State of the Art in Optimal Conjunctive Use of Ground and Surface Water Systems, CEPLA, Publication No. 71/14/C, September 1971

33. Poblete, Juan Antonio, and Leonvendagar, Miguel L., Programación Matemática y Simulación en la Planificación de un Sistema de Recursos Hidráulicos: Una Experiencia de Investigacion, CEPLA, Publication No. 72/11/C, May 1972.

34. Harboe, Ricardo, Experiencia con Modelos de Programación Dinámica Aplicados a Sistemas de Recursos Hidráulicos en Chile, CEPLA, Publication No. 72/12/C, May 1972.

35. Rogers, Peter, Gavan, James, and Smith Douglas, Sectoral Planning for Water and Agriculture in Bangladesh (Preliminary Draft), CEPLA, Publication No. 72/13/C, May 1972.

36. Loucks, Daniel P., Some Applications of Systems Analysis to Water Resources Planning, CEPLA, Publication No. 72/14/C, May 1972.

RESEARCH AND EDUCATION FOR DEVELOPMENT

By

Maurice L. Albertson
Centennial Professor, Civil Engineering Department
Colorado State University
Fort Collins, Colorado

and

M. T. Chaudhry
Colorado State University
Fort Collins, Colorado

Synopsis

Development is an ideal which has taken on the quality of
a universal value. Most people agree that development in a
country is desirable, but each person has his own concept of
what features are desirable. In many of the developing
countries, development has for many decades meant modernization,
implying westernization -- usually in styles of dressing,
eating, and living but seldom in styles of thinking and working.
During the last few decades the increase in the GNP and per
capita income has become synonymous with development. However,
more recently, development specialists are questioning this
approach by saying it is fallacious "to assume that more
capital is better than less capital, that more roads are
better than fewer roads, and that rapid economic development
is better than slow economic development" (Letwin, 1964 [1]).
Generally speaking, the purpose of development is to "improve
the quality of life" (Albertson, 1972 [2]), or to "promote the
general welfare" (Constitution of the United States of America).

To accomplish the foregoing purpose requires plans and
programs and manpower and institutional resources. Manpower
and resources, in turn, are the result of education, training,
and experience, while the basic informational resources for
plans and programs come from research and study.

This paper discusses the process of development and the
way in which education and research can contribute to development.

Development -- A Process

Development is a complicated process. It involves all
resources in one way or another. Not only is it necessary to
develop these resources, but it is necessary to understand
their inter-relationships and the significance of each part.

The development process can be explained by the development
wheel, see Fig. 1. This wheel shows development as a sequential
process involving both physical resources and human resources.
It is called a wheel not because it is shown in a circular
geometric form -- it could have been in a square, a rectangle,
or some other shape. It is called a wheel because the development process has a cyclic nature. It can even be a "viscious
circle" when the wheel turns backward. The intent is to have
it as a beneficial circle, turning forward and faster (Albertson, 1972 [2]).

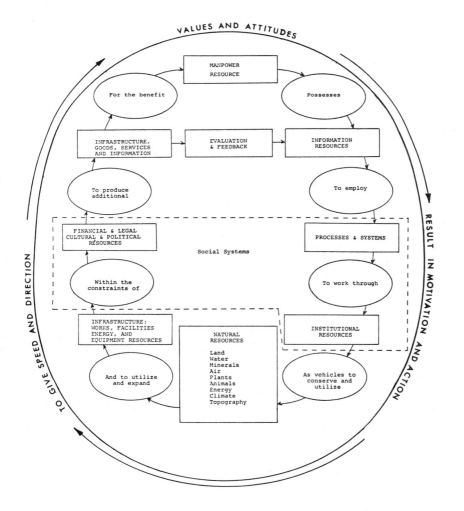

Figure 1.   The development wheel, illustrating the development
             process. (Adapted from Albertson, 1972).

295

The manpower resource is the live resource which activates the developmental wheel. Man, of which the manpower resource is composed, is both an actor and a spectator in the development process. He creates other resources and becomes the vital energy for them. Development begins with the manpower resource, is accomplished by the manpower resource, and eventually inures to the benefit of the manpower resource. Potentially, this resource is limitless, but only a small part of it is actually used. Natural resources are the only resources in the development process which exist independent of man. Their potential is virtually unlimited, but their realization is a function of the developed potentialities of the manpower resource.

Man acquires information resources through observation, research, study, and education. To employ the information resources, he develops processes, models, and systems which are part of the body of knowledge, the organized information, and the rules through which it is organized. Equipped with information and knowledge, the manpower resources creates institutional resources, which he uses as vehicles to conserve and utilize the natural resources. The institutional resources, are important to realize man's potentialities and to utilize his skills and capabilities.

Man employs his information, knowledge, and institutional resources to exploit the natural resources in order to create and use works, facilities, energy, and equipment which can be called economic infrastructure. This he does within the constraints of financial, legal, political, and cultural resources which he created to regulate himself and his institutions. As an end product he receives goods and services to benefit himself and receives additional information to start the cycle anew.

An important part of the development wheel is the values and the attitudes. Right values and right attitudes result in right motivation and right action to impart speed and direction to the development process, see Fig. 1.

The relationships between the component parts of the development process are complicated. For example, man is the creator of most of the resources for development, and he himself is the most important of these, i.e., the manpower resource. Man is the actuating force which turns the development wheel, yet he is not free from his own institutions. This and many other relationships must be included in educational programs and are subject to further research.

Manpower Resources

The greatest resource of a society is its people, the men and women who do the accumulating, discover, investing, and consuming. The actions which a society takes to nurture, develop, and utilize its manpower potential are a primary determinant of its wealth and welfare. The skill, dexterity and judgment of individuals is the heart and soul of the development process. The manpower resource is a resource with unlimited potential and it creates other resources, yet this is the resource which is squandered most easily through unemployment, underemployment, inadequate training, and arbitrary barriers to employment (Ginzbert, 1958 [3], Grant, 1971 [3]). A society which lacks understanding and respect for its manpower resources, particularly the poor people, is doomed to poverty and misery. "The scanty maintenance of the laboring poor,..., is the natural symptom that things are at a standstill, and their starving condition that they are going fast backwards" (Adam Smith, 1965 [5]). A wise society invests liberally in its people and helps each citizen to realize his maximum potentialities. They are its wealth, strength, and security (Ginzbert, 1958 [3]).

For these reasons it is imperative that extensive education and training programs be established to provide this all-important manpower resource.

Values and Attitudes

Needs, goals, and values are the major determinants of an individual's preference system. All human beings share the same fundamental needs which result from deficiencies and potentialities (Drews and Lipson, 1971 [6]). Whatever meets a deficiency or a potentiality appears good to the person involved. There are many ways of meeting these and the preference attached to a particular way reflects the values held by that person. Related to needs and values is a time dimension. Rapidly developing societies have strong hope and vision of the future; they invest heavily in the future. People who have no hope or vision of the future are often overindulgent in the present gratifications or simply lazy and indifferent. Such persons are caught up in a vicious circle of degradation. Values and attitudes are the determinants of motivation and action in this and many other ways, see Fig. 1.

Mankind needs to develop a sense of brotherhood and a common destiny just to continue as human beings or to exist as a species. They need a base of universal values for proper motivation in the right direction. Here again research and education must play a major role.

Truth, beauty, and love are the most fundamental universal values "through which we relate ourselves to our environment and communicate with our fellow man." Liberty, equality, justice, and democracy are other fundamental universal values. They strike at the very roots of elitism, a phenomenon in most countries which has strangled a vast human potential and has inhibited or prevented development.

The value of work (physical labor) is another fundamental universal value. In many countries, work is generally avoided. Work is considered menial -- the role of the poor and the lowly. To work is to lower your position, particularly when it happens to be physical labor. Examples of the United States and China, however, whose people have adopted physical work as a basic value and a way of life, show that the ultimate status lies in work.

Information Resources

Information or "know-how" is an accumulated heritage of humanity. For rapid development, capital information and money circulation are important -- otherwise the economy will become stagnant. Information acquisition and its circulation are even more important for otherwise the developmental wheel will come to a halt or may even go in reverse. Creation of knowledge needs enormous effort in manpower, money, and materials. Fortunately, the more developed countries have accumulated a storehouse of technological knowledge and information which the less developed countries can draw upon. Education and research are the necessary media through which this "accumulated wisdom" can be transferred from country to country.

Establishment of world-wide communication links between universities and development agencies is important. Radio, television, and libraries are developing tremendous capabilities to transfer knowledge. Televised education programs, of which "Surge" and "Co-Tie" at Colorado State University are examples, offer great potentials to make instructors available to students at any time or place, (Baldwin, et. al., 1972 [7]). There is also a potential for "experience making". Alvin Toffler (1970) [8] describes experiential industries, with simulated and live environments. A person need not wait until he is 50 years of age to become "experienced". Experience workshops can impart the social, psychological, technological experience at a younger age -- not just by vicarious learning, but by actual participation. There is already a proposal at Colorado State University to start action-oriented workshops. (Albertson and Birky, 1972 [9]).

Institutional Resources

Institutions are the vehicles through which human beings channel their energies and realize their potentials. In many of the less developed countries, the existing institutions are "rule oriented". They tend to work through "slave driving" in their internal relationship, in their relationships with the common people and their propensities for receiving orders from above. This has greatly impaired their potential for performance. The causes for this are in part related to pre-independence days of many countries, during which most institutions represented and exercised the political power of foreign rule. After independence, because of weak political structure, these institutions obtained more political power. Later some of these institutions lost power, but instead of deriving their support from people and their representatives they became dependent on those organizations which retained political power. This made matters worse, resulting inefficiency, corruption, graft, and frustration (Manteiro, 1970 [10]; Abbas, 1970 [11]; Mydral, 1968 [12]).

Some efforts have been made to create new and better institutions in the past, but most have failed because of social environmental factors. There is a need for research into creating democratic, "work-oriented" institutions which are so essential for development.

Processes and Systems

Possession of analytical and working tools, which may be called mechanics of technology, are important. Ability to use them with understanding is even more important for development. Nothing can be accomplished haphazardly. Processes and systems of all kinds need to be established and continually improved upon for adequate performance, (Vlachos, 1971 [13]). This is expanded further in the next section.

Systems Approach

Systems engineering has been defined by Hall and Dracup (1970) [14] as follows:

"Systems engineering may be defined as the art and science of selecting from a large number of feasible alternatives, involving substantial engineering content, that particular set of actions which will best accomplish the overall objectives of the decision makers, within the constraints of law, morality, economics, resources, political and social pressures, and laws governing the physical, life and other natural sciences".

The concept of a system is described graphically by Hall and Dracup in Fig. 2, as involving inputs and outputs, the environment and feedback. The "black box" which converts the inputs to outputs is the system itself.

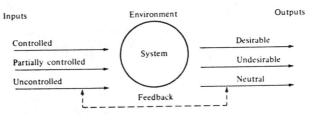

Figure 2. The concept of a system (from Hall and Dracup, 1970).

Systems engineering applied to water resources is useful in helping to analyze problems which would otherwise require much greater expenditures of time and energy, and it provides the engineer with important information regarding alternatives which should be considered in planning and design. In this connection, Hall and Dracup (1970) [14] state:

"Systems analysis is a very powerful tool, capable of dealing with large-scale problems involving millions of people and billions of dollars. It can lead to decisions which (for better or for worse) may prove to be quite irreversible in an economic and social sense. As such, systems analysis is a very dangerous tool in the hands of those lacking full understanding of the water resources systems and the multiplicity of objectives. It is equally dangerous when utilized by those who lack a reasonable appreciation of both the power and the limitations of the methods of systems analysis, however well they may be versed in the details and idiosyncrasies of the system".

The systems approach permits a view and an analysis of the larger picture involving many disciplines, factors, and variables. This is a way of combining the inputs of specialists from many different fields of development especially in water resources development.

Specialization is essential for development. It improves dexterity and skill, it saves time, and it invents new machinery and analytical tools. But when taken too far it tends to narrow the vision. This is usually due to lack of general education with which all specialists must be equipped to sharpen their vision of the whole. The technologists and specialists, therefore, must have a broad education, including the humanities and social sciences.

300

Recently specialization has created problems in integration. According to Smelser (Hoselitz and Moore, 1970 [15]) differentiation which results in specialization, is a natural consequence of developmental change. The differentiation in turn imbalances the system, and it needs adjustment or integration, or it creates disturbances. To avoid serious disturbances in the social system as a result of developmental change, it is necessary to understand both the society and the change process. This demonstrates the fact that those concerned with development must have at least some education in sociology, political science, economics, and philosophy of development in addition to their technical training and specialization.

Thinking of the whole is also important from the viewpoint of balanced development. A bottleneck anywhere in the development wheel will slow down the circulatory process and may create serious surpluses at some points and serious shortages at others. For example, in many less developed countries, the trained and educated manpower, although a trickle, happens to be "surplus". Being a surplus to the existing system, most often it is squandered away, somewhat thoughtlessly by unemployment, underemployment, frustration, and other means. Curtailment of training and educational opportunities has been considered in some countries as a measure to overcome the problem of the "educated" surplus. This is a sure way to make the development wheel turn backward. Reasons for a surplus of educated and trained personnel, which none need more than the less developed countries, may well lie in the bottlenecks created by institutional deficiencies and attitudes and values they practice. (The declared values are often different and better!) Most less developed countries cannot afford to pay adequate salaries to a large number of educated and trained people, but the payment and reward system is not limited to money. Social appreciation, social status, privileges and power, responsibility, participation, pride of performance, satisfaction of work and goal attainment are some of the other equally or even more important components of the payment and reward system, (Macarov, 1972 [16]). Thus much education and research needs to be devoted to understanding the development process if the development wheel is to turn faster.

For an excellent treatment of water management systems and the social processes involved, See Vlachos (1971), [13].

Colleagues and Not Elites

The goal of education and much of research should be to produce enlightened associates in development and not development elites. Elitism is extremely detrimental to the development process. It breeds dictatorship and hinders democracy. Strangling popular aspirations produces bloody revolutions and hinders healthy evolution of development. Elitism obscures the vision of those who think themselves to be elites. Despite an overall label of democracy, it creates innumerable centers of oppression and dictatorship at local, sub-regional, regional, provincial, and federal levels, which form a pyramid of dictatorship. Even if a minaret of democracy is erected on top of this pyramid, the democracy stands in a very precarious state, always in danger of collapse. The three C's of elitism: group consciousness, coherence, and conspiracy, combined with their rationale to rule, provides ready-made structures to invite, to establish, and to maintain super-dictators. In crude form their rationale to rule is that the few should rule because they are especially able or simply because they are in fact ruling or that since only a few can rule, the many do not and never will (Meisch, 1962 [17]).

The self-styled, self-centered, and self-perpetuating, so called elites to whom the suffix has been attached have done very little for the common man in the less developed countries. They are incapable of doing much good. The structures or institutions through which they work have a strong "detrimental" or "zero-sum" character, which means that "the gains of one are at the loss of the other".

Much research is needed to inquire into the psychology and sociology of the educated elites. In the past, much research has been directed at the poor, which is of little use. How the educated people can eliminate elitism and become an integral part of the masses, to be one of them and not the one above them, is a problem yet to be solved. The educated must be friends of humanity and not their masters. These concepts of democracy and the elimination of elitism must be an important part of all educational programs.

Democratic Institutions for Development

Development requires the collective effort and the genious of the masses; it requires democracy. Democracy, in turn, requires democratic institutions at all levels of society.

Democracy, to be effective, must first exist in the minds of the people as a value (Drews and Lipson, 1971 [6]). It must have its seeds in the inner soul of the masses. It must grow from within to be stable and durable. For this the common man must experience democracy in his day to day life. He must have a say in all affairs affecting him; in fact, he must have control over the affairs of his day to day life. The student activities and government in schools, colleges, and universities in the United States provide an excellent base for this, as does the city, county, and state governments. These and many other such grass-root institutions make it difficult to form a dictatorial government at the federal level -- although some would have liked to try, had they the slightest hope for success. Initially, a dictatorship appears to work wonders-- assuming a development motivated, benevolent dictator; the best of the species, but in time the entire social organization becomes sluggish, indifferent, and even fatalistic. It refuses to do anything except under force. It refuses to cooperate, to act, and to understand. Then the functionaries of the dictatorial system, the elite of the elites, complain about the uneducated, their sociology and their way of life, and to shift the blame of inefficiency onto them.

Through research and education, democratic institutions can be created for development. They are necessary to liberate and use the vast human potential available. These must be institutions headed and controlled by peoples' representatives, in all fields and in all levels of human activity, from water distribution to general administration with the exception of judiciary which needs to be independent and high level. The government employees will then have the chance to work creatively in association with the people as their enlightened and respected colleagues. The entire environment will then change from rule by fear and disassociation (keep away from the people, the civil servants have always been taught) to rule by understanding and association. Such a change would create a self-respecting, self-supporting, self-disciplining and self-motivating society. Once this is done the development wheel will turn faster and faster to eliminate hunger, disease, squalor, and misery. Eventually, there will be no poor to be called "the wretched of the earth". This is a vision, based on belief in the limitlessness of human potential. Realization of this vision, however, requires a vast investment in research and education.

Finally, it may be emphasized that democracy is the basis for all meaningful development, and to endure, it must exist in the minds of all individuals as a "value", cultivated and strengthened by day to day observation and practice.

Advancement Versus Diffusion

Development means change, it means creation and introduction of new knowledge, new institutions, new attitudes and higher values, new objects of culture and therefore cultural patterns and much more. But the rate at which this can be done is limited to the people's capacity to assimilate and adopt. The faster the innovation can be routinized, the faster can be the rate of introducing new innovation, and the faster the development wheel will turn. If the introduction of innovation is considered to be advancement and its adaptation as diffusion, then the ratio of advancement and diffusion, and the resultant development, can be qualitatively represented as in Fig. 3 (Chaudhry, 1971 [18]).

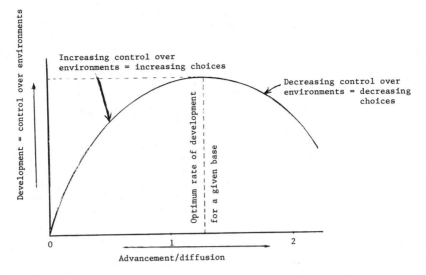

Figure 3. A conceptual relationship between rates of advancement, diffusion and development. (Chaudhry, 1971).

This means that for a given rate of advancement, a certain
value of the advancement/diffusion ratio is needed to obtain
the optimum rate of development. For larger advancement/
diffusion ratios the development rate may even be negative.

This brings out another important aspect of democracy and
popular participation -- it facilitates diffusion and, therefore, the transfer and flow of knowledge.

A Program for Action

One can dwell on theoretical ramblings without much real
achievement. The theoretical constructions or models are
not of much value unless they are put to the test of practice.
This requires a blue print or a program of action in specific
terms. In this regard, the following are suggested:

1. Literature on development should be expanded and made
available to the people.

2. Participation of people from the less developed
countries should be increased. This means more students, and
participants in seminars and discussion groups.

3. Documentary films of lectures of the outstanding
professors on various topics related to development should
be prepared and made available to students and working people.

304

In suitable cases the entire series of courses could be filmed or taped and then transferred from one university to another. The same can be done on TV and radio. The knowledge and teaching of famous professors can thus be made available in the four corners of the world.

4. Stronger and more extensive links should be established between universities and development agencies.

5. Programs of research should be initiated to study the sociology of the educated, to determine their values, attitudes, and difficulties as they reflect on the development process.

6. Research should be carried out to promote the participation of local people in development efforts not just as followers of orders but as identifiers of the problems, as analyzers, as decision-makers, and then as actors.

7. A research program should be started, and education should be spread on establishing democratic developmental institutions, which should replace the existing authoritative structures. This should be possible, in most cases, within the value systems of the people -- not always those values which people practice but those which they advocate and consider to be the highest most positive values.

References

[1] Letwin, William, "Four Fallacies about Economic Development," in Development and Society: The Dynamics of Economic Change, eds. David E. Novack and Robert Lekachman, New York: St. Martins Press, (1964).

[2] Albertson, Maurice L., The Development Process, Honolulu, Hawaii: East West Centre (in Press).

[3] Ginzberg, Eli, "Human Resources," in The Wealth of a Nation, New York: Simon and Schuster, (1958).

[4] Grant, J. P., "Marginal Men: The Global Unemployment Crisis," Foreign Affairs, (October 1971).

[5] Smith, Adam, The Wealth of Nations (1776), New York: The Modern Library, (1965).

[6] Drews, E. M., and L. Lipson, Values and Humanity, New York: St. Martin Press, (1971).

[7] Baldwin, Lionel V., Preston Davis, and Lee M. Maxwell, "Innovative, Off-campus Educational Programs of Colorado State University," Special report to the

President's Science Advisory Committee, panel on Educational Research and Development, (1972).

[8] Toffler, Alvin, Future Shock, New York: Bantam Books, (1970).

[9] Albertson, Maurice L., and Pauline E. Birky, Blueprint for Change: The University -- Relevancy for the Future, Fort Collins: Colorado State University, (1972).

[10] Manteiro, J. B., "The dimensions of corruption in India," in Political corruption, ed. A. J. Heidenheimer, Holt, Rinehart and Winston, Inc., (1970).

[11] Abbas, M. B. A., Public administration training in Pakistan: A retrospect and outlook for the future, Honolulu, Hawaii: East West Centre, (1970).

[12] Myrdal, Gunar, Asian drama, New York: The Twentieth Century Fund, (1968).

[13] Vlachos, Evan C., "Social Processes in Water Management Systems," in Treatise on Urban Water Systems, eds., M. L. Albertson, L. S. Tucker, and D. C. Taylor, Fort Collins: Colorado State University, (1971).

[14] Hall, Warren A., and John A. Dracup, Water Resources Systems Engineering, New York: McGraw Hill Book Co., (1970).

[15] Hoselitz, B. F., and W. E. Moore, "Industrialization and Society," UNESCO - Mouton, (1970).

[16] Macarov, D., "A test of the two-factor theory of work motivation in an Israeli kibbutz," In Industrial Relations Research Association (IRRA) Proceedings of the Twenty-fourth winter meeting, New Orleans, 1971, ed. Somers, G. G., (1972).

[17] Meisch, J. H., The Myth of the Ruling Class, Ann Arbor: University of Michigan Press, (1962).

[18] Chaudhry, M. T., "Is overdevelopment possible?" Unpublished Paper, Colorado State University, (1971).

SESSION IV - COMMENTS

DISCUSSION by J. A. Rodier*

I have much appreciated the double sense of the connection
between developed and developing countries. I shall give an
example. In Senegal our pedologists have established a
classification with 6 or 7 types of soil. The farmers of
Senegal know 12 types of soils.

We have experienced in West Africa the same difficulties
with the projects of big structures. After some experiences,
the general policy has been the policy of small structures.
But this is not enough; the most difficult thing is the cultivation of land and finally we find the sociological problems
which are often the key of the projects. If the purpose is
to produce cotton, it is impossible to obtain this work from
people who are working traditionally with cattle.

I would mention a type of transfer of knowledge we use
sometimes in France. Hydrologists of developing countries
are working together with our hydrologists on practical
problems related to their country exactly in the same way.
It is assumed that the French hydrologists working with this
hydrologist of Africa, for instance, know perfectly well the
country of this individual, particularly for what concerns the
practical aspects of water management. From time to time, it
is the contrary, the French hydrologists, working in Africa
with his African colleagues. The same way is used for cooperation between a developed country and another developed
country. I use these words of developed and developing in
order to be short, in fact, I recognize that this is not so
simple and it would be better to speak about developing regions.

DISCUSSION by D. R. Sikka**

In India, water resources projects are meant primarily
for irrigation and flood control, and utilization is more
than 85% in general. There are no such problems as highlighted in various papers. The engineering projects are
approved at highest level, in consultation with administrators
and all social, political and regional aspects are taken into
consideration during project formulation from field level
to sanction level. Of course, in certain projects due to
local problems, such as non-availability of adequate infrastructure development, undulating topography, drainage and
size of land holdings, utilization problems exist, but these
are not due to any transfer of knowledge. Practical

---

*19 Rue Eugene, Carriere, Paris 18

**Control Board for Major Projects, West Pakistan Government

307

considerations if attended to at the finalization stage with efficient institutional structure and finance, would help considerably in utilization in such cases.

DISCUSSION by Dijon Robert*

To start with, in developing countries water resources development is not carried out primarily for increasing the G.N.P. but for fighting against thirst, hunger, poor sanitary conditions and overall worsening living conditions, due to population explosion. It is therefore a priority with some exceptions of "luxury projects" which ended in failure. Speaking of "Young Turks" the first step is to have nationals as partners in development, who can be the advocates of water resources development with their government. With time they will become sometime very soon responsible development planners if the necessary opportunities are provided to them.

DISCUSSION by Peter W. Whitford**

I would like to make two comments concerning the paper of Albertson and Chaudhry.

1. The paper is crowded with vague ascertations and generalizations. In most cases, these are not backed up by any evidence or even an illustration. While many of the ideas are intuitively attractive, they are out of place in a scientific paper.

2. The word "democracy" is used often in the paper but without definition. The impression is left that nations may be classified as "democracies" or "dictatorships." In fact, there are dozens of political systems in the world which differ widely along such dimensions as personal liberty, participation in the political process, freedom of the press, etc. Countries which have been relatively successful in the development process do not fall easily into any neat classification along these lines.

DISCUSSION by R. G. Thomas***

Within many nations professional organizations are also powerful means to transfer technical knowledge within the country and should be encouraged. Specifically, for interdisciplinary transfer of ideas the Society of International Development can provide a very useful forum on a professional basis and independent of organizations.

*United Nations

**World Bank, Washington, D.C.

***F.A.O.

DISCUSSION by Sarfraz Khan Malik*

The excellent presentation by the general reporter who is
a sociologist for a gathering of engineers brings home to
engineers the need for an effective communication by engineers
and non-engineering groups and the decision makers.

The first step in the philosophy of water utilization is
to transfer knowledge from research to practice. This can
be done effectively if research work done in developed and
developing countries is goal oriented and research is not done
for the sake of research. In his speech, Mr. Butcher
observes that even in the U.S. research in water resources
so far was not specifically goal oriented. Therefore, goal
oriented research should be aimed to quickly transfer the
research knowledge to practice. The practical action programs are hampered further because often such proposals do
not take into account the capacities of the beneficiaries/
founders to pay cost and involve considerably subsidies from
the Government. All action programs for water utilization
should therefore recognize this limitation.

DISCUSSION by F. L. Hotes**

I should like to indicate that I made a recent addition
on my paper by inserting "Libraries, Fixed and Mobile" in the
"More Formal Methods."

This addition was suggested by a young Indian national,
now an industrial economist with an international organization,
who received his Master's degree from UCLA and his Doctorate
from a Dutch university. He advises that it was the traveling
library which stopped periodically in his village, that provided him the information on the outside world and stimulated
his thinking (i.e., made him become "future oriented"),
and eventually led to his departure from the village, his
higher education, and taking his place as a trice international expert in a highly technical and important field.

---

*Chief of Water Resources, National Planning Commission,
Government of Pakistan, Islamabad, Pakistan.

** Enviro-Engineers, Inc., 600 Bancroft Way, Berkeley,
California 94710.

SESSION V

NATIONAL TRANSFER EXPERIENCES

Chairman: Khalid Mahmood

Rapporteur: David B. McWhorter

● *Another series of specialized experience
shed additional light to problems of water
resources knowledge from developed to developing countries. Among the perenial
problems underlined here are the role of
foreign advisors (including an interesting
typology) and the various stages involved
between diffusion and adoption of knowledge.*

SESSION V: NATIONAL TRANSFER EXPERIENCES

Rapporteur: David B. McWhorter
Assistant Professor of Agricultural Engineering
Colorado State University
Fort Collins, Colorado

Venezuelan Experience on Transfer of Knowledge in Water
Resources Engineering - Julio Aceituno and J. I. Sanabria

The authors justify a study of the mechanisms of knowledge
transfer upon the thesis that benefits to be derived from
scientific achievement are directly dependent upon knowledge
transfer. A source of information is identified, distinct
from the user of the information, and the transfer of knowledge
is divided into two "phases": 1) the "previous phase" and
2) the "subsequent phase". Apparently, the previous phase
consists of transfer from the source to the user, and the
subsequent phase involves the processing of the information
by the user.

The authors contend that the mechanism involved in the
previous phase is that of transfer via journals, publications,
books, proceedings, seminars, and personal contact. The users
may·be in various fields ranging from research to operation
and maintenance.

The processing of the information by the user is carried
out in the subsequent phase and apparently involves, as a
principle function, the identification of information that can
be directly applied, applied with modification or unusable for
a variety of reasons. Information is identified as "not
applicable" for the following reasons:

1) not clearly explained,
2) poor background of user,
3) no evidence of application in previous cases,
4) language barriers,
5) data required for application is not available.

A feedback loop is indicated by which the users can
communicate with the source which completes the transfer
process.

The framework for knowledge transfer, outlined above, is
conceptual, and the authors report the results of a survey
which was based on this conceptualization of the transfer
process. The conclusions are summarized as follows: The
principle source of information for engineers involved in
project activities is experience from developed areas, whereas
local experiences are used chiefly by planning people. Information is generally obtained through books and journals and

313

is, for the most part, applicable with modification. It was
indicated that publications from the developed areas trend
away from the applied aspects and are, therefore, of limited
use to the developing regions.

Achievements of India in the Field of Water Resources Development - S. K. Jain

This paper consists chiefly of a summary of the importance
of water management and development in India and the
accomplishments toward a fully developed water resource. The
author points out that in 1947, the year of Indian independence, the government of India identified two high priority
problems which would require the development of the countries
water resources. The two problems were "totally inadequate"
irrigation facilities and an inadequate capacity for electrical
power generation. It is noted that, by 1974, the irrigation
potential will have been increased by a factor of two and the
power generation capacity will have been multiplied nine
times.

The increase in water resource development over the past
two decades has resulted in expertise on the design and construction of barrages, the technology of large concrete and
earth dams, and the construction of large canals. Absent in
the paper, however, are any comments on how this expertise
was gained and diffused. The author states that the expertise
now resides in the Central Water and Power Commission and in
various irrigation departments. The author concludes with
"knowledge gained in the country can be made available to the
developing countries for the development of their water
resources, which is one of the best means of transferring
technical knowledge on the subject".

Experience of the U. S. Geological Survey in Transfer of Hydrologic Knowledge to the Developing Countries - George C. Taylor, Jr.

This paper contains numerous statistics documenting the
substantial participation of the U. S. Geological Survey in
foreign technical assistance in the last three decades.
Between 1940 and 1970, USGS personnel from the Water Resources
Division, representing a variety of background disciplines,
completed 347 overseas assignments in 80 host countries.
During the same period more than 426 foreign personnel from 61
countries have received training through USGS/WRD facilities.

The objective of the USGS participation is to develop or
strengthen administration personnel, technical staff, and
operational functions of water-resources agencies in the host
countries in the interest of advancing the economy of the host
nation. These objectives have been pursued by on-the-job
training of foreign water scientists and engineers, by

providing experts to participate at various levels in international symposia, by exchanging research specialists, by sharing knowledge in applied and scientific hydrology, by providing advisory services, by participating in projects undertaken as joint efforts, and by assisting in the development of institutions dedicated to programs of hydrologic education and research.

Education and training is accomplished through on-the-job learning under the guidance of USGS specialists, in-service assignments in the United States and assistance in curricula and university selection for foreign participants.

Most USGS (Water Resources Division) long-term overseas projects and assignments are accomplished by means of a bilateral program sponsored by United States AID and by direct agreement arranged through the U. S. Department of State.

The author identifies several factors essential to a successful technical assistance program. These include 1) sincere, competent, highly motivated specialists, 2) energetic back up and support by the parent agency, 3) an ability to instill a desire for scientific and engineering excellence, 4) host country willingness to provide highly qualified counterpart personnel, and 5) host country willingness to provide essential administrative machinery.

It is also important that the specialist be genuinely interested in the problems of the host country and cognizant of constraints imposed by the religions, cultures, politics and national economy of the host country. Continuity of contact is another important ingredient of success; especially in institution building.

Some Problems Associated with the Use of Expatriate Advisors in Developing Countries - Willis W. Shaner

In this paper nine specific problems related to the use of foreign specialists by a developing country are identified. The author suggests that these problems are relevant to many developing nations, even though they are drawn from his experiences in a particular country. It is explained that the developing country must first focus on a set of national goals and priorities from which a plan of development is drawn up. In the particular country referred to (country name was not disclosed) the planning stage resulted in 3 5-year development plans. The second of the plans was prepared with the assistance of a group of advisors from a single country and reflected this fact. The third was prepared with the cooperation of specialists from several countries and a plan evolved which more nearly reflected the aspirations and traditions of the host country.

Problems of institution building are discussed briefly.
These include the nonexistence of the rudiments of an organization, limited qualified personnel, and contradictory advice
and teaching from foreign specialists from diverse countries.

Once a country has "geared up" for development any or
all of the following nine problems may be experienced.

The Promoters - These are people who present themselves
as seasoned investors who sell grandiose projects to the
government through contacts at high official levels. These
schemes usually result in low returns or outright losses which
are often borne entirely by the government. The solution
offered is to "know your investors"; admittedly a difficult
task.

The Biased - Misallocation of resources may result
because of biases in the experts appraisal of investments.
This problem can be solved by insuring that a careful economic
feasibility study be carried out.

The Vacationers - This problem refers to foreign specialists whose professional interest is dominated by their desire
to see the world. The nationals are often very sensitive to
the degree of sincerity of the advisor and their attitudes
and cooperation are influenced accordingly. Careful screening
of candidates for foreign assignment is required to circumvent
this problem.

The Impossible - This problem occurs when the advisor has
been charged with a task that is too difficult to accomplish
effectively, given the constraints under which he must perform.
Recognition that the advisor does not possess all knowledge,
especially as concerns intimate details of the country, and
cooperation of resident specialists can alleviate this
problem.

The Irrelevant - Donor countries may offer financial and
technical assistance for a particular project that would be a
misallocation of effort for the developing country. Development, in most cases, should be confined to country's more
obvious and immediate needs.

The Confusion - Too many advisors on the same project can
cause confusion and result in inappropriate actions. The
solution offered is for the developing country to be more
selective and able in the use of foreign specialists.

The Out of Place - Technology of an advanced nation
cannot be imposed upon the developing country unless it has
been appropriately adapted to local conditions.

<u>The Sophisticates</u> - This problem arises when highly
refined techniques of analysis or application are used when
simpler procedures are in order. This is a special case of
the previous problem category. A clear understanding of
local issues and conditions will greatly aid the selection
of appropriate techniques and procedures.

<u>The Old Timers</u> - After long tours of duty, some advisors
may become out of date, complacent, and non-progressive, and,
therefore, unaffective in accomplishing the objectives. These
characteristics do not apply to all "old timers" of course.

The author chose to describe some of the negative
aspects of the use of foreign advisors because they need to
be understood and corrected so that the transfer of knowledge
can take place more efficiently.

<u>Transfer of Knowledge in Water Resources From Developed to
Developing Regions with Special Reference to the Conditions of
West Pakistan - S. K. Malik</u>

Shortly after independence in 1947, Pakistan was faced
with two critical water resource problems. The first involved
a settlement with India on the distribution of water in the
Indus River system. The second problem concerned the rapid
spread of water logging and salinity as a result of a large
network of irrigation canals.

Under the Indus Waters Treaty, Pakistan was required to
construct a system of link canals to the western rivers which
would provide water for the canals previously supplied from
the eastern rivers given over to India in the treaty. This
project became known as the Indus Basin Project.

To implement the Indus Basin Project and a water
logging - salinity control program, the West Pakistan Water
and Power Development Authority was created. Resolution of
the problems in these two large undertakings was approached
by seeking assistance from outside sources. The employment
of consultants was prompted by necessity in some cases and
by conditions attendant to foreign aid in others.

The results of a survey show that the performance of
foreign consultants and contractors has been satisfactory as
regards work acceleration and quality, although there is a
question as to whether or not the work could have been
accomplished more economically by using local talent. It is
unlikely that the Indus Basin works could have been completed
on schedule without foreign assistance, however. Some of the
factors which prevented greater local participation in the
Indus Basin project and the water logging-salinity control
program are the "time factor, tight conditions of foreign

financial assistance, and the import requirements of certain equipment".

The conclusions are summarized in the following. Most of the work was completed on schedule and according to specifications. A major share of the foreign assistance returned to the donor countries in the form of payments to contractors and consultants. Partial failures in design and construction occurred when the foreign advisors were not qualified. Unqualified advisors resulted because of improper selection procedures or because of conditions imposed by the donor country. Project costs were higher than if the construction had been accomplished through local effort. Participation and training of local engineers and technicians was inadequate. In some cases, the advice offered by foreign experts proved to be less valuable than that of local experts.

In addition to the above conclusions, the author comments that the donor countries often make only half-hearted attempts to transfer knowledge and skills. A better understanding of the aspirations and needs of the people in developing countries is an essential feature in effective knowledge transfer.

Project failures involving foreign advisors are due to "limited intellectual equipment" of advisors, inadequate knowledge of problems associated with developing countries, and lack of proper control by the local government. It is pointed out the reason for incompetent people in an advisory role is the limited number of people in the donor countries willing to accept foreign assignments. Thus, the positions are filled with less than competent personnel.

The problems of acquainting the foreign expert with local conditions and insuring solutions which reflect these conditions can be solved to some degree by long-term contracts. The sociological and economic aspects of technology transfer should be carefully examined before recommending automation and mechanization. These solutions may not be appropriate.

General Summary, D. B. McWhorter

The authors of "Venezuelan Experience On the Transfer of Knowledge In Water Resources Engineering" define the transfer of knowledge as the means by which knowledge is transmitted from its source to the user. Subsequent discussion and their conceptualization of the transfer process indicate that the transfer process is much more than a mechanical function, however. Transfer of knowledge, information or ideas is not complete until these items are adopted or applied by the user. This seems to be the basis for the "subsequent phase" discussed by Aceituno and Sanabria. The "previous phase" as used by these authors, apparently, is similar to what has been

318

called the diffusion process by social scientists and the "subsequent phase" corresponds to the adoption process.

It is entirely proper to distinguish between the two phases of transfer because the diffusion phase and the adoption phase involve two different processes. The diffusion of knowledge is the process of spreading of knowledge from the source to the user and involves many persons and groups of persons. On the other hand, adoption is a much more individual matter. Although diffusion of knowledge is undoubtedly constrained by many factors including physical limitations of access to information, cultural norms etc., adoption is probably the larger bottleneck to effective knowledge transfer.

The process of adoption includes the sub-processes of learning and decision making and much can be learned about adoption by studying the science of these two sub-processes. The author of these comments is not qualified to discuss the pertinent aspects of these sciences in significant depth, but a simplistic breakdown of the process of adoption into stages will help to bring out some important points. Adoption of knowledge, ideas, information or innovations is a continuous process that has been discretized into the stages of 1) awareness, 2) interest, 3) evaluation, 4) trial, and 5) adoption.

Awareness is the stage in which the user first becomes aware of the new knowledge. It is the diffusion phase that provides for the exposure which is a requisite of awareness. Exposure, however, is probably not sufficient in itself to cause awareness. Apparently there is considerable evidence that awareness is accomplished only if the user has identified a present or future need for the knowledge or information to which he is exposed. For example, researchers should not be too surprised when their work is not readily adopted if they have provided answers to questions which the user has not yet asked.

Taken at face value, the conclusion that the user must identify a need or use for the new knowledge before knowledge transfer can be completed, means that new knowledge or ideas beyond the imagination of the user cannot be transfered. It is quite possible, however, for the person or group of persons at the source of the information to point out to the user the need or possible applications which he would not have recognized otherwise. In other words, the researcher, by some means, should cause the user to ask the question for which the researcher has the answer. I believe that the experience of the extension service in the United States has been that extension personnel, often, must generate a request by the individuals of a community for knowledge or information in order to create a genuine awareness of the knowledge, even though these individuals may have been previously exposed to it. Possibly we have something to learn from Madison Avenue in this regard.

The second stage of the adoption process is interest. At this stage the user actively seeks more knowledge or information, after which he proceeds to make an evaluation of the knowledge. Again, the people at the source of the knowledge or information can decrease the chances that the new knowledge will be discarded at the evaluation stage by providing a pertinent evaluation themselves.

If the user has not already discarded the new knowledge at a previous stage, he makes a trial in the situation of interest to him. If the results of the trial are favorable he will adopt the new knowledge and the transfer has been completed. The chances of adoption are increased if the people at the source assist in the trial. They can guard against the knowledge being discarded if the trial fails because of inappropriate use or for reasons having nothing to do with the knowledge itself.

All of the reasons for discarding knowledge listed by Aceituno and Sanabria fit within the above concept of the adoption process. In addition several of the problems of transferring knowledge from developed to developing countries discussed by Shaner appear to fall within this framework. The problems identified as "the irrelevant", "the out of place", and the sophisticates are examples of problems at the adoption phase. Some of the problems discussed by Malik also seem to stem from one or more of the adoption stages.

It has been indicated in this discussion that knowledge may be discarded at various stages of the adoption phase unless the people at the source of the knowledge take an active part in seeing the knowledge safely through each stage. The method by which this is accomplished certainly must depend upon a wide variety of factors including the relationship between the source and the user. A researcher interested in insuring that other researchers use his work would approach the problem of adoption differently than if he wanted his work to be used by a farmer, and insuring adoption of knowledge from a developed country in a developing country requires still different techniques. In any case, recognition and anticipation of the stages at which the adoption process is apt to fail can provide a basis for appropriate action which will increase the efficiency of knowledge transfer.

VENEZUELAN EXPERIENCE ON THE TRANSFER OF
KNOWLEDGE IN WATER RESOUCES ENGINEERING

By

Julio N. Aceituno
Associate Professor
Universidad Central de Venezuela
Caracas, Venezuela

and

Jose I. Sanabria
Assistant Professor
Universidad Central de Venezuela
Caracas, Venezuela

Synopsis

The purpose of this paper is the determination of the
mechanics of the transfer of knowledge in Water Resources
Engineering. Owing to the lack of local information on this
topic, conclusions have been drawn from a recent survey performed by the authors. Since other developing regions show
similar problems in the transfer of knowledge, it is believed
that the results obtained herein may be of considerable value
to these areas.

Introduction

The benefits of a scientific achievement are closely
related to the effectiveness with which the obtained knowledge
is transmitted.

The above is self explanatory and shows the importance
of optimization of transfer of knowledge. It is obvious that
the greater the possibility of information to be analyzed
and discussed, the greater the significance of the contribution
and the more use is given to it, the better it will be known
and applied. Many examples can affirm such an assertion;
results of individual experiences without initial theoretical
bases (in its original publication) find this theoretical
support later on because of the diffusion they have afterwards.

The purpose of the present paper is the determination
of the mechanics of transfer of knowledge and the path followed
in Venezuela, in order to bring out the difficulties of the
actual system and search for recommendations which permit the
increase of efficiency of such transfer. Because, to the
writer's knowledge, there are no previous local publications
relating to this study, no bibliography is indicated, and
reference is made only to a survey performed by the authors.

Mechanics of Transfer of Knowledge

Transfer of knowledge may be defined as the means through which any scientific or general information produced by investigations or experiences of any kind, travels, from the source where it is generated to the user.

Since the sources of information, as well as the users, are of many types, this definition is mainly applied to the knowledge related to the development of water resources.

The mechanics of transmission may be divided in two phases: A previous phase corresponding to the transmission of knowledge from the source of information to the user and a subsequent phase involving the mechanics of transfer itself; finally, there exists a connection closing a loop, whereby the processed information becomes a new source of knowledge. The previous phase may be represented by the first part of diagram 1 where the most common paths of transmission, may be observed. The subsequent phase, represented in the same diagram, shows a general view of the processing of the information, as well as the possibility of producing new sources of knowledge.

From the Source of Information to the User

Sources of information can be divided accordingly:

1. Experiences from developed areas
2. Experiences from developing areas
3. Local experiences

According to the way of transmission to the user, it can follow the following paths:

4. Journals of professional societies
5. Publications
6. Books
7. Proceedings of Congresses
8. Seminars
9. Personal contacts with members of research institutes, universities, or consultants.

The user receiving the knowledge may be included in any of the following fields:

10. Research
11. Planning
12. Projects
13. Constructions
14. Operation and Maintainance

From the User to the Applications

The information received by the user can be:

1. Applied with some modifications; this information follows the path to the storage for further use as a source of information;

2. Directly applied and stored in order to be used again as a source of information;

3. Not applicable for some of the following reasons:

    a. Because it is not clearly explained;

    b. Because there is not evidence of its application in similar cases;

    c. Because of a poor basic background;

    d. Because of language barriers;

    e. Because of data required for its application.

This information, even if not used, is stored for further application after supplementary research. In this way the complete cycle of transference is closed. There exists a dead end point, where some information leaves the path of the closed cycle by any of the following reasons:

A. Because of its character of specific use;

B. Because it is unpublished;

C. Because it is published in journals of limited diffusion;

D. Because it is not clearly explained when published;

E. Because of its obsolescence.

    1. National experience in transfer of knowledge
    2. Local survey

In order to infer the local mechanics of transfer of knowledge in the field of Hydraulic Resources, a survey based on the possibilities discussed above has been performed.

Subjects surveyed are engineers dedicated to some of the fields of Hydraulic Resources Engineering and only specific differences in their professional activities are established; in other words, they are classified as engineers involved in research, planning, project, construction or operating, and maintenance. The pattern used for the survey follows points

4 and 5 indicated in this paper, and its results are shown on diagram N° 1.

Results - Data solicited is indicated in table N° 1 and in order to present an easy interpretation, the percentage of affirmatives are calculated, thus permitting a weighted evaluation of the various paths followed in Venezuela.

From observation of diagram N° 1, the following conclusions can be drawn:

1. Experience from developed areas are the main source of information of engineers involved in project activities.

2. Experiences from developing areas are sometimes used, but they constitute a secondary source of information.

3. Local experiences are mainly used by engineers working on planning of water resources.

4. Information is generally obtained by means of books and journals of professional societies.

5. The lowest-percentage path followed by the knowledge corresponds to a personal contact with members of research institutions and universities.

6. Information obtained is sometimes modified, leaving unpublished its applications, creating therefore, a new individual source of information.

7. Engineers involved in planning activities reported the non-application of some experiences, because of the quality and range of data required.

8. Language barriers are also reported as a cause of non-application of experiences from developed areas.

9. Location of sources of information is the first problem commonly faced by users. Experiences related in Journals are easily available in libraries, however, many valuable individual experiences are lost.

10. There is logical trend among publications from developed areas to be more scientific than practical. Thus publications are becoming a limited source of information for developing areas, due to the character of their specialized problems. A typical example is research in the fields of scour; many laboratory studies have been realized, but few fields measurements are reported.

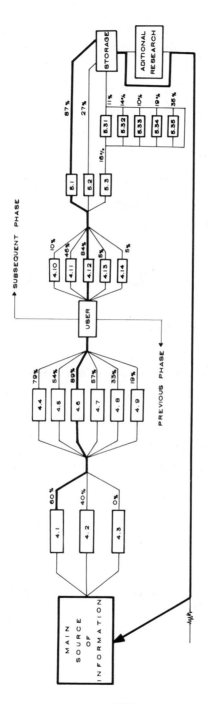

Diagram N° 1

325

1. You work in planning (46)* project (84) construction (5) of Hydraulic Engineering.

2. The main sources of information

    a. Local experiences (40)

    b. Experiences from developed areas (60)

    c. Experiences from developing areas (0)

3. Location of this information (if you have answered b)

    a. Journals of societies (79)

    b. Publications (54)

    c. Personal contacts (19)

    d. Books (89)

    e. Proceedings of Congresses (57)

    f. Seminars (33)

4. Applicability of Material

    a. Directly applicable (27)

    b. Applicable with some modifications (87)

    c. Not applicable (16)

5. Reasons Why Information Cannot be Used

    a. Is not clearly explained (11)

    b. Not being evidence of application in similar cases (14)

    c. A poor basic background (0)

    d. Language barriers (19)

    e. Lack of data (35)

6. General Comments

    *Figures in parentheses indicate percentage number of affirmative answers.

11. The difficulty of obtaining information from developing areas because of lack of publications in water resources engineering is clearly pointed out.

12. Some of the people surveyed consider that personal contacts with members of institutes and universities are the best way of obtaining information.

13. Final comments indicated that, periodical meetings, seminars and short courses are good means of making personal contacts and effecting interchange of knowledge.

ACHIEVEMENTS OF INDIA IN THE FIELD OF
WATER RESOURCES DEVELOPMENT

By

S. K. Jain
Chairman, Central Water & Power Commission,
New Delhi

Synopsis

The paper outlines in general terms India's recent progress
in the development of her water resources. In assessing water
resources and the efforts for planning, emphasis is placed not
only on structures and design, but also on the management and
operation of various projects. Knowledge gained through such
organizations as the Water and Power Development Consultancy
Services as well as a multitude of other state agencies can be
made available to other developing nations and, thus, contribute to the needed continuous transferal of experience.

Introduction

India is predominantly an agricultural country with a
culturable area of over 55% of its total geographical area
extending over 3.28 million sq. km. Nearly 70% of its population depends on agriculture for their livelihood. Agriculture
accounts for about half the national income, in addition to
supplying raw materials for a number of important industries.
The development of water resources, both to augment food
production and to sustain industrial growth is, therefore,
of utmost importance as the success of agriculture entirely
depends on the occurrence of adequate and timely rainfall which
is very irregular in most of the years.

The water has positive as well as negative values. The
former lies in its use for irrigation, industries, rural and
urban water supplies, hydro and thermal power generation, water
transport, pisciculture, and recreation. The negative values
are the damages caused by floods, waterlogging, pollution, etc.
Optimum utilization of the available water resources for
maximizing the positive values and minimizing the negative
values of water is a vital necessity in the development of
the country.

Assessment of Water Resources

The vastness of the country presents considerable variations in topography, geology, climate, water resources, soil,
vegetal cover, and population from region to region. India
has a network of rivers well spread-out over its entire
territory except for the desert tracts of Rajasthan in the

328

north-west. The rivers generally fall under two categories namely the snow-fed perennial rivers of northern and north-eastern India and the monsoon-fed seasonal streams of Central and Southern India. There is a wide degree of variation in the rainfall in various regions, from 12 cm in the arid areas of Rajasthan to 1200 cm in some parts of Assam in the East. In about 1/3rd of the entire area, rainfall is less than 75 cm and in another 1/3rd, less than 113 cm.

Assessment of water resources, its current utilization, and future requirements is basically required in planning for optimum utilization. Since the Independence of the Country, considerable attention has been paid to the collection of this data.

The number of reporting raingauges existing in the country to the end of last year were 4599. There are about 1200 discharge stations maintained and operated by the State Governments. In addition, the Central Water & Power Commission under the Union Government maintains 140 gauge discharge stations in the Ganga basin in the north, 64 stations in the Godavari and Krishna basins in the South, and 64 key hydrological sites in Southern, Eastern, and Western regions of the country.

The various river systems in India are estimated to yield an average annual runoff of 168 million hectare metres. This figure includes the surface as well as ground water resources of the country. On a broad basis, because of topographical and other considerations, half of this quantity can be utilized for various purposes.

Planning for Development

The Independence of India in 1947 brought in a new era of development, particularly in the field of utilization of water resources for irrigation, hydro-power generation, and domestic and industrial water supply. Prior to Independence, irrigation facilities were available for an area of 22 million ha which were totally inadequate as 83% of the cultivated area had still to depend on the vagaries of monsoon.

With regard to electrical power, the total installed capacity was less than 2.3 million kw, extremely inadequate to meet the domestic and industrial demands. Therefore, in 1951 the Government of India attached a high priority to the harnessing of the vast water resources in the planned development of the country.

During the two decades 1951-71, 560 major (each costing over $6.7 million) and medium (each costing more than $0.34 million but less than $6.7 million) irrigation projects were

329

undertaken. Of these, 345 have been completed, and the remaining are in different stages of construction. The development of irrigation potential in the country since the inception of the Plans is indicated in Table I.

TABLE - I

	Irrigation potential in million hectares			
	1951	1961	1969	1974 (anticipated)
1. Surface Water	16.1	21.0	26.6	32.0
i) Major & Medium Schemes	9.7	14.4	18.5	23.3
ii) Minor Schemes*	6.4	6.6	8.1	8.7
2. Ground Water	6.5	8.2	10.9	13.5
3. Total	22.6	29.2	37.5	45.5

* Schemes costing less than $0.34 million

The installed power generation capacity is likely to be 23.15 million kw by the end of the Fourth Plan, i.e. 1974, indicating the phenomenal rise of 900% over that in the Pre-Plan period.

India's Achievement in the Field of Construction and Designs

Diversion weirs across rivers were the earliest structures for utilization of river waters for irrigation. Because of their higher pond levels and flexibility in operation and control of river regime, the latest structures across large rivers have been gated barrages. Kosi (1150 metres), Gandak (740 metres), and Sone (1405 metres) are examples of latest design practices of barrages on alluvium. The solution of problems of design, construction, and operation of these barrages, has been made possible by extensive hydraulic model tests. These tests are carried out at the Central Water & Power Research Station, Poona, which is recognized as the Regional Research Station by the Economic Commission for Asia and The Far East.

During the last two decades, more than 25 dams over 60 metres high have been undertaken. The 226-metre high Bhakra dam ranks among the highest concrete dams in the world. Tungabhadra (3700 m.cu.m.) on the Tungabhadra, Hirakud (8150 m.cu. m.) on the Mahanadi, Gandhisagar (7750 m.cu.m.) on the Chambal, Nagarjunasagar dam (11580 m.cu.m.) on the Krishna, are some of the completed large storage reservoirs. Ukai (8500 m.cu.m.) on the Tapi, Ramganga (2200 m.cu.m.) on the Ramganga, a tributary of the Ganga, and Beas dam (8150 m.cu.m.) on the Beas, a tributary of the Indus, are a few more reservoirs nearing completion.

The damsites are becoming more and more complex in their geological features requiring very special and intricate foundation treatments, for which considerable technical know-how has been developed in the country.

In the construction of large canals, India is a leading country having constructed such large size canals as Nangal Hydel Channel (340 cumecs), Nagarjunasagar Left Bank Canal (595 cumecs) Rajasthan Canal (524 cumecs). The last one extending over 400 km, will irrigate about 1.1 million ha of desert areas of Rajasthan.

With the rising labor costs, the Indian Engineers are facing the challenge of keeping the cost of engineering works at a more or less constant level by improved technology.

Operation of Inter-State Projects

India is a Union of 21 federative states and 9 Centrally Administered Union Territories. Most of the major rivers of the country flow through more than one State. The projects aiming to provide benefits in any particular state are planned, investigated, constructed, and operated by the concerned organizations in each State. For the optimum development of water resources, the projects cannot be confined to State boundaries and have to be planned on basin-wise basis including transfer from one basin to another. According to the Indian Constitution, the Union Government has the exclusive power to make laws with respect to control and development of inter-state rivers and river valleys by a suitable legislation of the Parliament.

The construction and operation of inter-state projects is done through Special Corporations or Control Boards comprising representatives of the concerned States. The development of the Damodar Valley in the East for irrigation, hydel power generation, flood control, etc. is done by the Damodar Valley Corporation set up in 1948. The operation of the Bhakra Project benefiting the States of Haryana, Himachal Pradesh, Punjab and Rajasthan, has been assigned to the Bhakra Management Board. A number of such boards has been set-up for the construction and operation of projects on inter-state rivers and even on uni-states rivers, in some cases, depending upon the size of the project.

Water Management

It has been recognized that in India, water is relatively scarce and must, therefore, be utilized most economically. In the field of irrigation, new concepts of farm management such as pre-irrigation soil surveys for establishing suitable cropping pattern, and water requirements, integrated development of surface and sub-surface water, shaping of land for irrigation, construction of water courses and field channels and provision of field drainage are advocated and adopted on irrigation projects.

Training Facilities

With the planned development of the water resources, the Indian Engineers have the expertise in planning, investigating, designing, and constructing the various types of river valley structures such as earth and concrete & masonry dams, barrages, canals and canal structures, and in the operation and maintenance of such projects. Such expertise is built up in the Central Water & Power Commission under the Union Goverment and in the Irrigation Departments of the States. The technical know-how on the subject is being imparted to in-service engineers of some of the developing countries of the region, such as Afghanistan, Indonesia, Thailand, etc.

The University of Roorkee is organizing a Training Course of one year's duration in Water Resources Development for the serving engineers of the country and other countries of Asia, Africa and the Far East. The course covers advanced and broad-based integrated training in all aspects of water resources.

India is also rendering assistance to neighboring countries like Afghanistan, Nepal, etc. in planning, designing, and construction of projects for water resources development.

Role of Water and Power Development Consultancy Services

Water & Power Development Consultancy Services (India) Ltd. (WAPCOS) provide and perform engineering and related technical consultancy services for development of water resources, irrigation and drainage, electrical power, flood control and water supply projects; and procurement, installation, management of construction and related services in connection with the construction of resources development projects like dams, barrages, canals, hydro-power and thermal power stations and transmission and distribution systems. WAPCOS offer services for pre-investment surveys and investigations, including topographical surveys, aerial photography, geological surveys, material surveys, and foundation investigations. The coordinated facilities of the Central Water &

Power Commission, the Geological Survey of India, the Survey of India and the India Meteorological Department are made available by WAPCOS for the investigation, planning, design, and construction of projects in this country as well as in other countries.

Some of the projects investigated, designed, and executed outside the country, by the constituents of WAPCOS, are as follows:

1) Trisuli Hydro-Electric Project in Nepal,
2) Tonle Sap Barrage Project in Cambodia.

Conclusions

Organizations like WAPCOS, Central Water & Power Commission, Geological Survey of India, Survey of India, India Meteorological Department, Central Water & Power Research Station, Department of Agriculture, etc. are very well equipped to deal with all aspects of water resources planning and development. The knowledge gained in the country can be made available to the developing countries for the development of their water resources, which is one of the best means of transferring technical knowledge on the subject.

EXPERIENCE OF THE U.S. GEOLOGICAL SURVEY IN TRANSFER
OF HYDROLOGIC KNOWLEDGE TO THE DEVELOPING COUNTRIES

By

George C. Taylor, Jr.
Chief, Office of International Activities
Water Resources Division
U.S. Geological Survey
Washington, D.C.

Synopsis

The U.S. Geological Survey (USGS) has participated in
overseas technical assistance programs of bilateral and multilateral agencies for more than 30 years. Between 1940 and
1970 USGS water scientists and engineers completed 347 project-
oriented assignments in 80 host countries. During the same
period 426 water scientists, engineers and technicians from 61
countries received academic and in-service training through USGS
facilities in the United States. Experience from these activities has demonstrated that training is a basic ingredient of
the institution-building process. Technical competence,
adaptability to host-country constraints, and personal sympathy
with host-country needs and aims are important qualities in
the USGS specialist on foreign assignment. Most important to
successful technical assistance is the willingness of the host-
country to provide qualified individuals for training as well
as leadership and administrative support for designated project
activities. Continuity of relationship between the USGS and its
host-country counterpart has been found to be the single most
important factor contributing to the growth of a viable water-
resources organization over a period of years.

Introduction

Under the aegis of the United States Agency for International Development (USAID) and its predecessors, the agencies
of the United Nations (UN) family, regional intergovernmental
agencies, and direct government-to-government agreements, the
U.S. Geological Survey (USGS) has actively participated through
the years in overseas technical assistance related to water-
resources appraisal, development, and management as well as
scientific exchange in hydrological research, not only in the
developing countries but in the developed countries as well.
Between 1940 and 1970 geologists, chemists, engineers, and
hydrologists from the USGS Water Resources Division (WRD)
completed 347 short and long-term project-oriented overseas
assignments in 80 host countries. These water scientists and
engineers have worked with a wide variety of host-government
organizations including geological surveys, hydrological

334

investigative and research services and institutes, hydropower and flood-control agencies, agricultural and irrigation departments, water-development and land-reclamation authorities, and health and sanitation or public water-supply agencies. During the same time more than 426 water scientists, engineers, and technicians from 61 countries have received in-service and academic training through USGS/WRD facilities in the United States. Many of these former participants have assumed positions of leadership within their own governmental organizations. Others have gone into private enterprises for water-resources appraisal, development and management or university programs of hydrological research, education, and training. Virtually all have continued professional contacts with the USGS as well as with related resources-oriented public and private organizations in the United States.

General Objectives

During the past 30 years the central objectives of USGS/WRD work in the developing nations have been (1) to strengthen administration, staff, and operational functions of counterpart governmental hydrological and water-resources agencies; and (2) to improve the skills and capabilities of host-country scientific, engineering, and technical personnel so that they may better direct and guide the investigation, development, and management of water resources--all in support of advancing national economies. With the developed nations as well as with many developing nations, USGS/WRD objectives have been largely directed toward (1) exchange of research specialists and publications in the sharing of advances in hydrological knowledge and methodology; and (2) participation in mutually beneficial international organizations, symposia, conferences, seminars, and special programs dedicated to various aspects of scientific and applied hydrology.

In the furtherance of these objectives the USGS/WRD (1) has trained foreign water scientists, engineers, and technicians either in USGS/WRD domestic field offices and laboratories or by on-the-job training from USGS/WRD scientists and engineers on overseas assignment; (2) has provided hydrologic experts to guide, conduct, and participate in international symposia and seminars in scientific and applied hydrology; (3) has exchanged research specialists and shared knowledge in scientific and applied hydrology; (4) has provided direct advisory services through overseas assignments of USGS/WRD personnel for the establishment or improvement of operating host-country hydrological and water-resources organizations and institutions; (5) has participated jointly with host-country water scientists and engineers in field and laboratory projects designed to appraise, explore, and evaluate indigenous water resources and water problems; and finally (6) has advised,

supported, encouraged, and instructed in institutions and professional societies dedicated to programs of hydrologic
education and research.

Education and Training

During the last 30 years, the supply of well-trained and
experienced scientists, engineers, and technicians in the
developing countries has been inadequate; consequently, the
education and training of such personnel is an essential
ingredient of any effort to help these countries attain higher
levels of economic and social viability. As the principal
agency in the U.S. Government concerned with geologic, hydrologic, and cartographic surveys and research, the USGS has
recognized its responsibility to help train scientific and
technical personnel and encourage the growth of agencies with
comparable functions in the developing countries. During the
past three decades the USGS has provided or arranged for the
training and education in the United States of some 1,100
participants from 79 countries in geology, geophysics, geo-
chemistry, hydrology, hydrogeology, cartography, scientific and
technical publication, administration, and related fields. The
bulk (perhaps 90 percent) of the participant training has been
sponsored and financed by the U.S. Agency for International
Development (US AID) or its predecessor agencies. The USGS,
however, has also provided training for a substantial number
of participants sponsored by agencies of the UN family as well
as regional intergovernmental agencies and also by direct
government-to-government arrangements through the U.S. Department of State.

USGS assistance in the education and training of foreign
nationals has been carried out in three ways: (1) on-the-job
training under the guidance of USGS specialists assigned to
technical assistance projects in other countries; (2) in-service
(intern) training of individual participants assigned to headquarters, field projects or laboratories in the USGS domestic
program; and (3) guidance or assistance by the USGS foreign
participant program staff in selecting appropriate curricula
and universities for academic studies in science and engineering
by participants. Depending on the needs of the participant,
individual programs have been designed either for intern training
or for academic studies; however, many programs in recent years
have been combinations of both. Also intern training available at USGS domestic facilities has been commonly coordinated
or augmented with training at other U. S. Federal agency
facilities and from time to time with private companies, so as
to give the participant a spectrum appropriate to his individual
needs.

The USGS/WRD has been involved in foreign participant
training since the early 1940s, but the level of activity

was relatively low during the 1940s and early 1950s. Beginning in 1956, however, a sharp increase in activity occurred that built up to a high in 1962. The number of participants trained per year during 1956-70 ranged from 26 in 1956 to 57 in 1962. The average number trained during the 1960s was 47 per year at a relatively constant rate.

The numbers of foreign participants provided intern and academic training and education programs through USGS/WRD domestic facilities and their countries of origin are shown for 1950-70 in Table 1. As of the end of 1970 and since 1940 the USGS/WRD has provided training in the United States for 428 formally scheduled and funded participants from 60 different countries. The duration of individual programs ranged from a few days to as much as a year but most of the programs were in the range of 2 to 6 months. In addition, informal scientific and technical consultation has been provided by USGS/WRD specialists in the United States to an even greater number of unscheduled or casual foreign visitors. It is interesting to note from Table 1 that the countries providing the largest number of participants correspond to those where the USGS/WRD has had intensive involvements in U.S. bilateral technical assistance projects--notably Brazil and Chile in Latin America; Egypt and Sudan in Africa; and Afghanistan, India, Jordan, Nepal, Pakistan, Philippines, Thailand and Turkey in Asia.

Most of the in-service training in USGS/WRD facilities during the past 30 years has been directed to the scientific and technical requirements of foreign geologists, engineers, chemists, and professionals in various aspects of the basic disciplines of general hydrology, surface-water hydrology, groundwater hydrology, and hydro-chemistry. From time to time, however, training has been provided for participants of supervisory grade in administration, management, programming, and planning techniques necessary to the operation of water-resources and hydrological organizations that function at national, regional, or provincial levels. The USGS/WRD has also provided group training in hydrology for foreign participants on several occasions during the past 10 years, chiefly through its Water Resources Training Course in Denver, Colorado.

Overseas Activities

Owing to the diversity of requirements of the sponsoring agencies, through which the USGS must operate, the USGS overseas activities do not constitute and cannot be a tightly integrated program. These activities can be grouped as follows: bilateral program; multilateral agency activities; governmental scientific and technical exchange and cooperation; non-governmental international organizations; and investigations and

337

Table 1. Countries for which Participant Education and
          Training has been provided in the United States
          through USGS/WRD Domestic Facilities with Numbers
          of Participants from each Country, 1950-70.

North and South America	Europe	Africa	Asia
Argentina - 6	France - 1	Congo	Afghanistan - 13
Bolivia - 2	Germany - 1	(Kinshasa) - 4	Burma - 1
Brazil - 37	Great Britain - 1	Egypt (UAR) - 17	Ceylon - 1
Canada - 1	Greece - 7	Ethiopia - 3	India - 29
Chile - 15	Iceland - 2	Ghana - 3	Indonesia - 7
Colombia - 3	Poland - 2	Kenya - 2	Iran - 5
Costa Rica - 2	Spain - 5	Liberia - 11	Iraq - 4
Cuba - 1	Yugoslavia - 2	Sudan - 11	Israel - 9
Guatemala - 1		Tanzania - 1	Japan - 7
Guyana - 5	Total -- 21	Togo - 1	Jordan - 19
Haiti - 2		Uganda - 1	Korea - 8
Jamaica - 2	Australia - 1	Union of	Lebanon - 1
Mexico - 3		South Africa - 1	Libya - 4
Panama - 1			Nepal - 16
Peru - 2			Pakistan - 46
St. Lucia,		Total --- 45	Philippines - 28
W.I. - 1			China
Uruguay - 1			(Taiwan) - 16
Venezuela - 8			Saudi Arabia - 1
			Syria - 1
			Thailand - 13
Total -- 93			Turkey - 38
			Vietnam - 1
			Total--- 268

research abroad in extension of domestic projects. However,
technical assistance under the U. S. bilateral program and
related foreign participant training still constitutes the
bulk of USGS/WRD overseas-oriented activity, but during the
past 10 years, there has been a marked increase in the level
of USGS/WRD activity with multilateral agencies and non-
governmental international organizations. In other categories
listed above, USGS/WRD activity also has been highly significant, scientifically and technically, but not large in terms
of funding or intensity of involvement.

Most USGS/WRD long-term overseas projects and individual
assignments can be grouped in the U. S. bilateral program,
sponsored by US AID and its predecessors and also by direct
arrangements through the U.S. Department of State with foreign
governments. USGS/WRD overseas activities in this category are
authorized under terms of Public Law 80-402 and 87-195.

Between 1940 and 1970 some 260 individual assignments,
ranging from a few days to several years duration, were

completed on short and long-term projects in 48 countries
(Table 2) in the bilateral program. Regionally, the bulk of
USGS/WRD activity in the U. S. bilateral program has been
concentrated in the countries of the Near East and South Asia,
where high priority has been given during the past 20 years
to water-resources development and related institutional
building. Generally, a somewhat lower level of activity has
prevailed in Africa with the notable exceptions of the United
Arab Republic (Egypt), Libya and Nigeria. In Latin America,
USGS/WRD activities in the U. S. bilateral program have been
concentrated very largely in Brazil and somewhat less in
Chile (Table 2). Many recipient countries in Latin America
and elsewhere currently prefer technical assistance under terms
of multilateral programs.

Table 2. Countries to which USGS/WRD Personnel have been
assigned under the U.S. bilateral program with
numbers of assignments in and years during which
projects were active in each country, 1940-70.

Latin America and the Antilles

Argentina - 3--1959; 1962
Bahama Islands - 5--1953; 1954-55
Brazil - 26-1953; 1960; 1961-75*
Costa Rica - 1--1964
Chile - 8--1945-48; 1950; 1955-62;
        1969; 1970
El Salvador - 2--1943-44
Guyana - 1--1957
Haiti - 2-1948-49; 1959
Nicaragua - 3--1943; 1956
Panama - 4--1949; 1962; 1964-65
Peru - 1--1955-59

        Total Number of
        Assignments-------63

Europe

Belgium - 1--1960-62
Greece - 2--1948-50; 1966
Netherlands - 1--1958-59
Portugal (Azores) - 1--1950

        Total Number of
        Assignments-----5

*For currently active projects final year indicated is that
of planned project termination.

Africa

Chad - 1--1962
Congo (Kinshasa) - 1--1968
Egypt - 26--1953-56; 1959-67
Ethiopia - 4--1966; 1968-74*
Ghana - 1--1964
Kenya - 5--1967; 1968-74*
Libya - 13--1952-64; 1967;
        1969; 1970

Asia

Afghanistan - 10--1952-69;
        1971
Cambodia - 3--1958; 1959;
        1963
India - 10--1950; 1951-57;
        1966; 1968; 1970;
        1971-73*
Iran - 6--1952; 1953-63; 1968

Table 2 - Continued

Africa

Nigeria - 14--1961; 1962-1968   Iraq - 1--1958
Rhodesia - 1--1959   Israel - 1--1962
Senagal - 1--1965   Japan - 2--1951; 1964
Sudan - 2--1955; 1961-63   Jordan - 4--1958; 1959-60;
Tunisia - 3--1958; 1959-65   1962; 1966
Zambia - 1--1968-1970   Korea - 5--1963; 1964; 1965;
                                                   1966-71
    Total Number of   Kuwait - 2--1947; 1965
    Assignments------74   Nepal - 9--1961; 1962-74*
                                       Pakistan - 27--1953-72*
Australia -7--1963; 1966;   Philippines - 5--1955; 1957-61;
            1967; 1969   1967
                                       Saudi Arabia - 2--1945-46;
                                                   1952-53
                                       Thailand - 8--1954; 1961; 1970
                                       Turkey - 8--1957; 1958-62;
                                                   1963-65; 1966; 1967
                                       Vietnam - 9--1964-66; 1968-70

                                           Total Number of
                                           Assignments-----112
*For currently active projects final year indicated is that of
planned project termination.

Comparatively, the USGS/WRD participation in multilateral
activities of the United Nations and regional intergovernmental
agencies during 1950-70 was extensive in terms of subject
matter and geographic coverage but less intensive in terms of
manpower, training, and commodity inputs than in the U. S.
bilateral program. Overseas activities of the USGS/WRD in this
category are authorized under Public Laws 85-795, 87-626, and
most recently 91-175.

USGS/WRD scientists and engineers completed 87 assignments,
most of less than 90 days duration, in project-oriented activities of international and regional intergovernmental agencies
(table 3) in 70 countries during 1950-70 (Table 4). Some 29
of these assignments were undertaken for projects under the
aegis of the United Nations Educational, Scientific, and
Cultural Organization (UNESCO), chiefly since 1965, in support
of the program of the International Hydrological Decade (IHD).
Another 17 assignments were undertaken in behalf of projects of
the Food and Agricultural Organization of the United Nations
(FAO), 16 assignments on projects of the United Nations (UN)
itself and the rest scattered among some 8 international and
regional intergovernmental agencies. In addition USGS/WRD
scientists and engineers have been deeply involved in numerous

symposia, seminars, working groups, hydrologic research panels, and training activities sponsored by these agencies, most particularly since 1965 in the International Hydrological Decade (IHD).

Table 3. United Nations and Regional Intergovernmental Agencies to which USGS/WRD Personnel have been assigned, 1950-70

United Nations Agencies

Economic Commission for Africa (ECA)
Economic Commission for Asia and the Far East (ECAFE)
Food and Agricultural Organization of the United Nations (FAO)
International Atomic Energy Agency (IAEA)
International Bank for Reconstruction and Development
  (IBRD or World Bank)
United Nations Development Program (UNDP)
United Nations Educational, Scientific and Cultural
  Organization (UNESCO), including the International
  Hydrological Decade (IHD)
United Nations (UN)
World Meteorological Organization (WMO)

Regional Intergovernmental Agencies

Central Treaty Organization (CENTO)
North Atlantic Treaty Organization (NATO)
Organization for Economic Cooperation and Development (OECD)
Organization of American States (OAS)
Organization of African Unity (OAU)
Pan-American Health Organization (PAHO)
Pan-American Institute of Geography and History (PAIGH)

Experience in the Developing Countries

USGS/WRD personnel working overseas have provided technical assistance for water-resources projects in the developing countries for almost three decades. Projects oriented toward specific and tangible goals, such as design, construction, and operation of hydrologic networks on river systems; of water-quality laboratories; of exploration and pilot development of ground water; or of technical evaluation of other hydrologic problems, have generally achieved a high measure of success. In the more intangible goals of building hydrologic and water-resources institutions, which generally accompany specific project activity, progress is difficult to measure over spans of a few months or even several years. Yet viable scientific and technical institutions, including those directed toward water problems, are vital components of political stability and economic growth in the developing countries, or for that matter any country that pretends to be current with the 20th century.

Training is, of course, all-important in the institution-building process. To the extent feasible, the USGS has encouraged the transfer of knowledge and methodology in the host country through a day-to-day relationship in the field and laboratory between the USGS/WRD specialist and local counterparts. The USGS, however, also has provided training or arranged for study in the United States for participants from abroad. Such training and study has been most effective when coordinated with on-going USGS/WRD overseas technical assistance projects.

Table 4. Countries to which USGS/WRD Personnal have been assigned in projects of United Nations and Regional Intergovernmental Agencies, 1950-70

North and South America	Europe	Africa	Asia and Oceania
Argentina	Austria	Algeria	Aden
Brazil	France	Angola	Afghanistan
Barbados	Germany	Burundi	Cambodia
Bolivia	Hungary	Cameroon	India
Canada	Greece	Canary Is.	Iran
Chile	Iceland	Chad	Iraq
Colombia	Italy	Egypt (UAR)	Israel
Costa Rica	Norway	Kenya	Jordan
El Salvador	Poland	Libya	Korea
Ecuador	Spain	Morocco	Kuwait
Guatemala	Switzerland	Mali	Laos
Honduras		Mauritius	Lebanon
Jamaica		Mauritania	Nepal
Mexico	Australia	Niger	Pakistan
Nicaragua		Nigeria	Philippines
Panama		Sudan	Saudi Arabia
Paraguay		Tunisia	Thailand
Peru		Uganda	Turkey
Trinidad		Upper Volta	Vietnam
Venezuela			

Although there are many factors involved in successful technical assistance, the USGS has learned that some are relatively more important than others. These include the following: (1) the USGS specialist assigned overseas must be highly motivated, technically qualified, genuinely interested in the problems of his host country, sympathetic with the needs and aims of his counterparts, and sensitive to the cultural, political, and economic constraints of his host country; (2) the USGS specialist needs to receive optimum logistic support and technical backstopping from his parent agency at the proper times and places; (3) the USGS specialist needs to have the capability for inculcating desire for

scientific excellence in his counterparts to insure viability
of the institution, of which they are a part; (4) the host-
country receiving institution must be willing to provide the
best counterpart personnel available for training as well
as continuity of leadership and administrative support for
designated project activities; and (5) the host-country must
be willing to modify or to create new and appropriate administrative machinery to accomodate technical assistance inputs in
institution building.

However, progress in technical assistance, is often
hampered by unstable governments, internecine and international
wars, military coups, and Communist insurgency. All too often
the efforts of years of institution building can be set back
or totally thwarted by adverse political events. Typical
examples of such events that have affected, directly or indirectly, USGS/WRD overseas projects during the past two
decades include: the Suez incident of November 1956; the
military coup in Iraq in July 1958; the Indo-Pakistani war of
August-September 1965; the Arab-Israeli war of June 1967; the
civil war in Nigeria during 1966-70; more recently, the
military combat and civil conflict in East Pakistan (now
Bangladesh) during 1971; and the Vietnam conflict in which
the U.S. has been continuously involved since 1963. Then
again, there are age-old social and cultural constraints which
still exist in the Arab World, Black Africa, South Asia, and
the Far East. These constraints place bonds on goals of
institution building that are sometimes more restrictive than
short-term political events.

In spite of obstacles and set-backs the USGS/WRD has left
a notable record of achievement and has contributed substantially to the economic advancement of many developing countries.
Examples that might be cited are: hydrologic investigations
and research for salinity control and reclamation in the Indus
Plains of West Pakistan; groundwater appraisal and development
of the Nubian aquifer in the Western desert of Egypt; country-
wide goundwater investigations and pilot development in Chile,
Peru, India, and Libya; country-wide surface-water investigations in Turkey, Iran, Brazil, Afghanistan and Nepal; and
regional surface-water and/or groundwater investigations in
Korea, Sudan, Tunisia, the Philippines and Nigeria.

Projects in all these countries have also been accompanied
by efforts in institutional development. Perhaps the highest
levels of success, have been achieved in Pakistan, India,
Turkey, the Philippines, Chile, Iran, Egypt, and more recently
Brazil and Korea. Modest success can perhaps be claimed for
efforts in Afghanistan, Sudan, Tunisia, and Nepal. On the
other hand, the seeds of institutional development which have
been sown in Peru, Libya, Nigeria and a number of other countries
have yet to germinate. If there is any lesson to be learned

from past experience, it is the importance of continuity in the institution-building process. The USGS/WRD has sought to maintain continuity of scientific and informational contact with counterpart organizations in the developing countries, in spite of adverse political events and termination of direct technical assistance support. Such contacts are maintained through correspondence, exchange of publications, occasional official details, or personal visits.

Since 1963, involvement in Southeast Asia has engaged much of the U.S. foreign aid resources. In addition, annual Congressional appropriations for aid to developing countries elsewhere have declined and in 1970 reached their lowest level since 1948. The compelling need for continuing technical and economic aid in the developing countries still exists, however. Hopefully, with reorganization of the foreign aid program as recommended by President Nixon's Task Force on Foreign Aid, it may be possible to redirect and revitalize past efforts toward more fruitful goals in the future. Scientific and applied hydrology as well as more basic water-resources investigations and institution building will play a vital and important role in these efforts.

SOME PROBLEMS ASSOCIATED WITH THE USE OF
FOREIGN ADVISORS IN DEVELOPING COUNTRIES

By

Willis W. Shaner
Associate Professor
Department of Mechanical Engineering
Colorado State University
Fort Collins, Colorado

Synopsis

This paper explains how one country in the early stages of
economic development and planning has had to rely on foreign
organizations and advisors. This reliance is likely to continue
until sufficient time has elapsed to permit the country to
develop its institutions and train its own specialists and
administrators. However, making good use of foreign technology
involves a number of problems, many of which are only discovered through living and working in such countries. These
problems center on the promoters, the biased, the vacationers,
the impossible, the irrelevant, the confusion, the out of
place, the sophisticates, and the old timers. Better knowledge
of these problems followed by appropriate action should lead
to an easier and more efficient transfer of technology between
the developed and the developing countries.

Introduction

The account that follows draws on the experiences of the
author in a country that is in the early stages of economic
development and planning. The country was relatively isolated
from development trends until the Second World War. Since
then changes have occurred. However, the base for development
is low, and the annual per capita income is still under
U.S. $100.

Through discussions with economic advisors who have worked
in this country, the author is led to believe that his experiences
there are relevant to a number of low income countries. Such
countries would be those that are striving to improve their
economic positions, but are limited by the lack of experienced
local staff.

The experiences of the author were obtained while holding
the position of senior economic advisor to the project wing
of the country's central planning organization. This project
wing specializes in project identification, preparation,
evaluation, and implementation. However, only part of this
work is actually carried out by the group's own staff; the rest
is undertaken by visiting consultants and other experts.
Working with local and foreign experts has made it possible

345

to observe the transfer of technology through studies covering a range of subjects, such as agriculture, industry, infrastructure, and water resources. The approach to the review, analysis, and implementation of the various proposals applies more or less uniformly to all of them. For this reason it seems justified to report on this work at a conference on the transfer of technology in water resources.

This report describes the country's drive for development and its reasons for heavy reliance on foreign advisors. In addition the body of the report contains a rather lengthy discussion of the problems encountered by the advisors along with brief suggestions for overcoming these problems.

Gearing Up for Development

As noted above, the country's drive for development began after World War II. Since then the country has outlined its national goals. Given the many claims on the central government, this selection of goals has not been easy. Decisions were required on such issues as taxation, land reform, employment, and division of authority between central and regional governments.

Three five-year development plans have been prepared to help formulate the policies, investments, and other actions needed to achieve these goals. The second five-year plan was prepared with the assistance of a small group of foreign economic advisors and bore the influence of a single country. The third plan, now being implemented, was prepared with the cooperation and assistance of the United Nations. In this case the advisors came from several countries. This, together with the greater participation of the host country, has led to a plan that is more conventional in the economic development sense. Moreover, it has incorporated more of the country's aspirations while maintaining some of the country's cultural traditions. The third plan has its defects, but progress in the planning process is being made.

Institutions require building in some cases and major restructuring in others. False starts were made followed by new approaches to accomplish similar ends. Often organizations have lacked such rudiments as clearly defined objectives, a set of job descriptions, properly functioning filing systems, or capable secretarial and filing staff. These difficulties obviously reduce the efficiency of the organization. The first priority of the government, therefore, has frequently been to overcome these restraints. Later, efforts can be devoted to the operating tasks of the institutions which, taken as a whole, are to raise income and employment, and to spread more widely the overall benefits of development.

346

Adding to the institutional problem is the limited number of well-trained and experienced staff. Those who are mature in judgment are often of the traditional school. The younger ones may be well trained, but they usually lack experience. Top positions in the newer and more technical organizations may be filled by appropriately qualified officials; but immediately below them could be a layer of officials with only a few years experience in their particular line of work. Training programs and graduate education abroad will eventually produce the required staff. In the meantime, organizations are disrupted due to the officials' absence from their regular positions.

During this stage of institution building, the need for foreign technical assistance is especially great. Advisors not only help in on-the-job training, they frequently carry out major tasks themselves. Occasionally, they assume important administrative posts. Although, the latter is generally not considered satisfactory, except as a fill in until a national can be properly prepared to take his place. In selecting the advisors, the host country may wish to guard its neutrality by seeking help from a variety of sources and countries. This dispersion of influence may accomplish its purpose, but it can also lead to confusion when the approaches followed by the advisors are contradictory.

Some Problems in the Transferral of Knowledge

The foregoing problems would generally exist even with excellent staff working under favorable conditions. The problems exist because the development process itself is fraught with obstructions. Other problems exist that are more of a human nature.

Some individuals and organizations have excellent records of accomplishment and the human problems, to be described below, normally do not apply to them. On the other hand, others have a poor record. Also, not all organizations are good for all countries. It is part of a country's development tasks to learn which of these groups and individuals best suit their national goals and temperaments. Fortunately, the list of possible sources is large: e.g., United Nations organizations like the World Bank, UNIDO and FAO, bilateral donors, private and public consultants, universities, foundations, research organizations, investors, and private companies.

The problems to be described below arise from many sources. Some are recognized and discussed in the standard literature on economic development; others are only understood after living and working in the developing world. The problems have been categorized as follows: the promoters, the biased, the vacationers, the impossible, the irrelevant, the confusion, the out of place, the sophisticates, and the old timers.

The Promoters - Perhaps the most serious of the problems
encountered by the author were the promoters. Many of them
are masters of deceit. They appear on the local scene as
serious and seasoned investors who offer grandiose schemes
for carrying out projects that would appeal to the government.
Typically, they make their initial points of contact at high
official levels. If this access is blocked, they try to work
through their embassies. After these preliminaries, they are
usually turned over to the relevant technical departments of
the government for detailed negotiations. There they may offer
to carry out a feasibility study of the venture, participate
in its preparation, or get some preselected organization to do
it. Some have even dared to suggest that such a study is
unnecessary. Quick action is necessary, they say, otherwise the
opportunity for profitable investment may be lost. Since they
are putting up the money, why delay?

But for this type of arrangement, the promoters seldom
risk very much of their own money. Proposed debt to equity
ratios may be four or more to one. Of the equity portion, they
may offer to put up something less than fifty percent. Their
portion of total investment could thus be only ten percent.
This small amount can be covered easily by inflated equipment
prices and commissions. High fixed management fees, not related to profits, further guarantee their financial success,
regardless of the profitability of the project itself. The
government and local investors are the ones who stand to lose.
As loans falling due often cannot be covered by the cash
generated by the project, loan payments are converted into
equity stock. The government not infrequently ends up as the
principal owner of a bad investment. After a few years, sometimes less, the promoters will have left the scene, and the
government owns a business that it often knows little
about.

In one extreme case the promoters put up only the few
thousand dollars required by law to establish a corporation.
The Government subsequently guaranteed loans amounting to
about fifteen million dollars for the purchase of equipment.
In its six years of operation the company has accumulated
losses of about six million dollars. The promoters even
succeeded in persuading the Government to buy out the promoter's
original shares so that the Government is now virtually the
sole owner. There is no conclusive proof, but it is almost
certain that these promoters shared in the profits from the
sale of the equipment.

Low returns and sometimes outright losses of capital are
serious to a developing country. Perhaps equally serious is
the heavy drain on the time of local and foreign advisory
staff. In the country of the author's experience the lack of
management and advisory capacity is commonly accepted as the

prime bottleneck to the country's more rapid growth. Capital, especially from foreign sources, is claimed to be available if the country can produce well prepared investment schemes.

The solution to the problem of promoters is simple: know your investors. But in the rush for development, this simple and obvious advice often goes unheeded.

The Biased - Another misallocation of resources comes from the experts' biases in their appraisal of investments. This is frequently the engineers' bias where the tendency is to show how to build the facilities instead of determining if they should be built. Of course, those engineering consultants with strong economic capabilities in project planning will not make such mistakes. However, frequently they are insufficiently alert to the need for economic expertise.

An example of a project that was stopped at the outset involved the offer of a foreign government to prepare a feasibility study for the supply of equipment for a new shipbuilding and repair yard. Of all possible investments open to the country, this one would rank near the bottom. Advisors were able to sidetrack this offer by requesting that a marketing study be done by a professionally disinterested consultant. The results of this study will almost certainly show that the type of facilities originally proposed cannot be economically justified and that the country cannot support a shipbuilding industry.

Another example involved the construction of a tannery to produce finished leather for export. This was another case of assistance from a friendly country. Unfortunately, a contract was signed before an adequate economic feasibility study could be undertaken. Equipment was selected and construction started without firm knowledge of the sources of demand for the plant's output. Results of a marketing study, belatedly undertaken, are expected to reveal that demand will be for semi-finished leather instead of finished leather. Had the plant been designed after the marketing study, investment could have been drastically reduced because of the high cost of finishing equipment.

Here again the solution to the problem is relatively simple. Carry out an economic feasibility study before proceeding to the design stage. Moreover, be certain that those doing the study have the requisite economic capabilities, or acquire them as needed. Consulting firms may think they have the staff to adequately perform such economic studies; however, often they do not.

The Vacationers - The appeal of living and working in some far-off land attracts a number of advisors to accept a tour of duty in a developing country. Some of these become seriously interested in their assignments and perform well, but others, unfortunately, are dominated by their interests in seeing the world. Plans are made for vacations and excursions before, during, and after their stay in the country. Some of the more seasoned and gifted can carry off this duality of interest without seriously affecting their work; the rest usually cannot.

Living and working in a foreign environment can be a demanding task until one becomes acquainted with the people and their customs. It takes time to learn the country's geography, economy, politics, and other relevant factors. Accomplishments may come slowly simply because of the inefficiency of customary services such as stenography, telecommunications, reproduction of documents, and so on.

Furthermore, the nationals of the country are frequently sensitive to the degree of interest shown by an advisor in their country. Should they sense that the advisor is only on a junket around the world, he may find himself without influence. This, of course, can destroy the advisor's effectiveness, for not only should his advice be technically correct, it also must be accepted. Undue diversions for whatever reason make the foregoing difficult to accomplish, and the transfer of knowledge can be diminished to a surprising degree.

To guard against this problem requires careful screening of candidates, especially those new to this work. To some extent there is an informal society of professionals dedicated to development where one's reputation is known. These normally would not suffer from disinterest. But the size of this group seems to fall short of demand. When reasonable doubt arises about the professional motives of an individual applying for an overseas assignment, it may be preferable to go without his services altogether. The costs of frustrated advisors can be high to all parties concerned--to the developing country, to the donor if there is one, and to the individual himself.

The Impossible - The origin of this problem rests more with the developing countries and the donors than with the advisor. The advisor is given tasks that can be too difficult for him to carry out effectively in the time allotted. Such a situation can arise when he is expected to make a general appraisal of a problem that calls for intimate knowledge of the country, but he is given only a few months--perhaps less--to do this and to finalize his recommendations.

For example a foreign consultant is expected to review some sector of the economy, identify its problems and opportunities, and offer recommendations on policies and specific investments. Although the consultant may know his specialty, he will hardly be able to familiarize himself sufficiently with local conditions, gather and evaluate data, and propose constructive solutions to problems within the sector. In the past, some consultants who found themselves with such assignments were fortunate if they were able to identify the problems commonly recognized by those resident in the country.

Far better use can be made of a foreign consultant's capabilities if the host country adequately prepares itself for his arrival and recognizes that the advisor's expertise seldom extends to areas requiring comprehensive knowledge of the country and its sectors of activity. This is the domain of the resident specialists--nationals and foreign advisors. A better division of tasks is for the resident specialists to gather data, study the issues, propose alternative solutions and possibly draw preliminary conclusions. Such work can be expected to sharpen many of the issues. This not only aids in the choice of the advisor but also focuses his attention on specific issues that are within his field of competence. Even for studies lasting for one or two years, the advisor may still be in an inferior position to the older residents when it comes to questions involving thorough knowledge of conditions in the country. The plea here is twofold: 1) the advisor should not be considered as a font of all knowledge in the sector being studied, and 2) resident specialists should actively participate in the study along with the advisor.

The Irrelevant - At one time the country of the author's experience was considering technical assistance from four donor countries in the study of its water resources potential. The donor countries had each offered to carry out a comprehensive river basin survey in an area to be agreed upon. Emphasis in the surveys would be on original data collection, covering such things as rainfall, stream flows, soils classification, population, and land use. The receiving country at one point in time was seriously considering which areas to select and the amount of local costs in money and manpower entailed. Even though the donor countries would pay for most foreign exchange expenditures, local costs were also sizeable. They would be for counterparts, local transport and supplies, administrative staff, etc.

The country was urged to accept these offers of assistance as the donors might take their aid elsewhere. But in this instance, the comprehensive surveys could have led to a serious misallocation of effort. First, the most likely areas of agricultural development had already been identified. Their development awaited appraisal of specific investment opportunities. Attention given to other areas would likely have diverted the efforts of the limited staff away from projects of known potential for which feasibility studies were in the process of being prepared. Evaluation of the other basins was not expected to uncover agricultural opportunities significantly

better than those known to exist. Second, national power
requirements were expanding at only a modest rate and future
power sites were considered adequate. Finally, more immediate
problems of community water supply, livestock ponds, and small-
scale supplemental irrigation could be solved by studies of
more limited scope.

In this instance, the preferred approach to the development of the country's water resources potential was to confine
the areas of study to the country's more obvious and immediate
requirements. Given the country's limited ability to implement
projects in areas of known potential, opportunities to be un-
covered from further basin studies were considered to be
largely irrelevant. Study findings might not have been of
serious practical use for perhaps ten to fifteen years. Within
this span of years other more relevant studies could be undertaken with available local and foreign funds.

The Confusion - Too many advisors on the same project can
confuse the issue. Government officials of the country have
been in the habit of circulating a report to ten or more
advisors for their review and comments. This would not be a
problem if the issues were many calling for breadth of experience, and if each expert were given individual assignments.
Usually, however, this has not been the case. All advisors
have been asked to consider a report in its entirety. With
advisors' time in short supply, this has been a serious diversion of efforts. Also, it only takes one vocal, persistent,
and ill-informed advisor to waste hours of time by asking
questions not in his field of specialty. Since individual
advisors may represent different ministries, it is not always
prudent for the chairman to halt the discussions. Meanwhile,
advisors sit idle and confusion reigns as those not particularly
knowledgeable in an area give their views.

This will remain a problem until government officials
in these countries learn to be more selective in their use of
experts. Efficient chairing of meetings, for example, can be
learned through experience. On the other hand, having large
numbers of reviewers may originate in the culture where undue
stigma is attached to erroneous decisions. Dispersion of
responsibility lessens the risk of individual condemnation.
Dispersion is accomplished by involving large numbers of
advisors in group discussions and decisions. There are
encouraging signs that this cultural bottleneck can be overcome
by the more capable and courageous nationals.

The Out Of Place - The literature of development often
contains admonitions about attempting to impose the technology
of an advanced economy on a developing one, unless it is adequately adapted to local conditions. Although this problem has
been clearly identified, it still exists. A few of the author's

experiences in this respect follow. A steel mill was proposed for the country even though industrialization there is in its infancy, demand is accordingly small, and coal and iron ore are absent. A large-scale cattle-feeding venture was proposed based on an example from the United States. Yet, the meat of fattened cattle is not in significant demand in the local market, nor can it be profitably exported because of disease problems. Subsurface water was assumed to be easily tapped by drilling in the alluvial fan at the base of a high plateau. Test wells drilled in the fan turned up dry. Water was eventually found in the tilted sandstone and limestone blocks. More careful study of locally available data on the geological formations of the area led to the successful tests. Finally, management, marketing, and planning techniques applicable to large, modern corporations in the advanced economies were suggested for local organizations with limited staff, experience, and resources.

Attempts to transfer successes from one situation to another are natural and sometimes desirable. What is not desirable is to make such transfers without having taken the time to adequately learn the uniqueness of local conditions and how to adjust for them. Perhaps a healthy measure of skepticism to "easy" solutions is in order, provided this approach is not used as an excuse to stiffle creative search for new ideas. Many quick and easy solutions proposed by short-term advisors have been considered but rejected by those more familiar with local conditions.

The Sophisticates - The problem of the sophisticates is a special condition of the foregoing: the application of highly refined techniques of analysis to situations where more simple procedures are in order. This applies to the use of certain complicated models and statistical projections when base data are lacking or significantly in error. Data on the growth of the country's gross national product, for example, have been employed for progressively more elaborate and refined projections without the realization by some that the original estimates of the national product were based on crude guesses about population, calorie consumption per capita, crop yields per hectare, and so on. Obviously, the advice for this type of error is simply to know the quality of one's data. Recent arrivals are perhaps justifiably mislead by thinking that at least the more rudimentary of national statistics would be reasonably accurate; but in this case they are not.

In another instance, the author had hoped to apply shadow pricing and consideration of indirect benefits and costs in the economic evaluation of projects. But upon closer inspection it was found that the most fruitful area of concentration would be on improving such fundamentals as market projections, selection of technology, comparison of alternatives, and costs of investment. Refinements in methodology using shadow prices have

altered the rates of return of some projects by no more than
a few percentage points, whereas failure to accurately forecast
the size and character of demand has led to several rather
serious financial failures.

As stated earlier, clear understanding of the issues and
the relevance of ones techniques of analysis can help in the
proper choice of procedures. Through experience in analyzing a
variety of projects according to different approaches, one can
eventually judge the returns gained from applying progressively
more refined techniques. But with the limited time that is
customarily available for such studies, experience has shown
that more will be gained by focusing on fundamentals.

The Old Timers - A final type of problem to be described
in this report originates with the foreign advisors who have
become "old timers" in the country. Their years of service in
a single country are many. Some have grown old there. One
advisor known to the author was well into his seventies. Many
of this type can be quite useful. They know the country, its
people, their history, their idiocyncrasies, their aspirations,
and most significant of all, the country knows them. The
result is that they have access to high government officials
and can influence important decisions.

The problem arises when these advisors have grown professionally soft; they may have become out of date in their
specialty. They may rest because their positions seem secure,
or they may become overconfident through their frequent contact
with those less well educated. In one case, an advisor predicted famines in specific parts of the world resulting from sun
spots and urged the government to alter its agricultural program
to meet these export opportunities. Another suggested building
a thousand-mile canal beginning at sea level and extending
through valleys that rise to over 3,000 feet. As astounding as
such schemes may appear, high government officials often take
them seriously because of their personal affection and general
respect for these advisors.

Naturally, the above deficiencies do not apply to all old
timers. Those who do remain alert and up-to-date in their
profession are among the most constructive individuals in the
country. The others are the ones who may lead the country
astray. Fortunately, these old timers are usually easy to
spot and due caution can be exercised when dealing with them.

Conclusions

A variety of practical problems associated with making
good use of foreign advisors has been described and illustrated.
This problem is just one of many involving the transfer of
technology from the developed to the developing countries.

Overall, these shortcomings tend to diminish the flow of knowledge rather than block it completely.

The author has dwelt on the negative aspects of advisory assistance because they need to be better understood and corrected. They are problems not often mentioned in the literature of economic development. Despite this emphasis, the author remains firm in his belief that foreign advisors play a strategic role in the growth of many developing countries. The intent of the report has been to suggest that more could have been accomplished had the advisors been better prepared for their work and been better employed by their host countries.

TRANSFER OF KNOWLEDGE IN WATER RESOURCES FROM DEVELOPED TO DEVELOPING REGIONS WITH SPECIAL REFERENCE TO THE CONDITIONS OF WEST PAKISTAN

By

Sarfraz Khan Malik
Chief of Water Resources
Ministry of Finance, Planning & Development
Government of Pakistan
Islamabad

Synopsis

The paper explores the main problems of water resources development in West Pakistan, especially the major works undertaken in the Indus River Basin. In the context of these works the role of foreign advisers, consultants and contractors from developed countries is discussed, and the successes and failures of such a cooperation are juxtaposed. From past experience, proposals for the future include the acquainting of foreign experts with local circumstances, raising of the level of technical expertise, and a broader understanding of the socioeconomic million within which development takes place.

The Main Problems of Water Resources Development in West Pakistan

Soon after its creation as an Independent Nation in 1947 Pakistan was faced with two major problems in the field of water resources development - (a) to find a settlement with India on the distribution of waters of the Indus River system along with its tributaries like the Jhelum, Chenab, Ravi, Bias and Sutlej and (b) to combat the menace of waterlogging and salinity which had started spreading in alarming proportions as a result of the vast network of irrigation canals constructed in the Indus basin towards the end of the nineteenth and during the first half of the twentieth century.

When the Indus Waters Treaty was signed in 1960 between the Governments of Pakistan and India, with the World Bank performing the coordinating role, the three eastern rivers, namely, Ravi, Bias and Sutlej were given over to India, while the flows of the three western rivers, namely, Indus, Jhelum, and Chenab came to the share of Pakistan. Pakistan was required to construct within a period of ten years a system of replacement works which would connect the canal systems previously fed from the eastern rivers given over to India under the Treaty, from an alternate source on the western rivers. This necessitated the implementation of a gigantic

356

system of replacement works under an Indus Basin Replacement
Plan which would permit the transfer of stored or flood flows
from the western rivers on to the canals of eastern rivers. It
was in the preparation and execution of this plan that the
Pakistani Engineers were assisted by the Irrigation Engineers
and other water resource experts from the developed nations.
The works to be constructed included the construction of two
large storage dams, viz, an earth fill dam on the Jhelum river
at Mangla and an earth cum rock fill dam on the Indus river at
Tarbela. Seven barrages and eight link canals, apart from a
host of complementary works were needed to remodel some of the
existing irrigation structures. This whole venture which came
to be known as the "Indus Basin Project" according to last
estimates is expected to cost over 2400 million US dollars. The
Indus Basin Project is a unique example of integrated river
basin development. The various components of this project have
since been completed except the Tarbela Dam which is scheduled
for completion in 1975. The Indus Basin Project provided a
great opportunity for the transfer of knowledge and skills in
water resources development from the friendly developed nations
to a developing country like Pakistan.

While a settlement was found on the allocations of Indus
waters, the other problem which still faces West Pakistan today is the one relating to Waterlogging and Salinity Control.
Of the total area of West Pakistan, 198.4 million acres, about
39 million acres are cropped annually to some degree. The
area within the command of irrigation systems is about 33
million acres, of which upwards of 24 million acres are cropped
annually. Notwithstanding that West Pakistan is a predominantly
agricultural country and that a larger proportion of its lands
are irrigated than in any other country of the world, it
presently does not produce sufficient food to supply the needs
of its people.

The low crop yields are attributable to a number of
factors. Farming methods for the most part are comparatively
primitive, and the small farmers still do not make use of
adequate fertilizers. Apart from these factors, the manner
in which irrigation supplies have been utilized has resulted
in low crop yields per acre. The fact that under most canal
systems there is more arable land than can be adequately
irrigated with the available supplies has led to the practice
of applying too little water over too large an area of land.
For instance, while one cusec of water is supplied for 333
acres in West Pakistan, a cusec is used for only one hundred
acres or less in the western part of the United States and in
other countries under similar climatic conditions. The water
applied is less than the evapotranspiration requirements of
crops; hence, the water does not wash down much beneath the
root zone, and salts are left behind in the upper surface of
the soil. Because of the low salt content of the canal waters,

this practice does not do much harm in a few years; however, over many decades it leads to damaging salt accumulation. More serious is the capillary rise and evaporation of the underground water that occurs when the water table comes to within about ten feet of the ground surface. The salts left behind by evaporation are deposited on the fields, and within a few years the salt content of the soil builds up to a level that retards and ultimately prevents crop growth.

An idea of the severity and extent of waterlogging and salinity can be gained from the results of the studies made by M/s. Tipton & Kalmbach for the Northern Indus Plain of the Punjab and Bahawalpur and by Hunting Technical Services for the Lower Indus Plain of Sind, as given below:

Extent of Waterlogging & Salinity

(a) Sind

		(1,000 acres)	
Gross Commanded Area (GCA)	Culturable Commanded Area (CCA)	Area (CCA) Moderately Affected by Salts	Area Severely Affected by Salts (CCA)
14,917	13,196	8,353	4,843

Depth of Water Table*

0 - 12'	:	10,520	(70.5% of GCA)
12 - 16'	:	1,715	(11.5% " ")
Over 16'	:	2,685	(18.0% " ")

(b) Punjab and Bahawalpur

Gross Commanded Area (GCA)	Culturable Commanded Area (CCA)	Normal Soil	Area Moderately Affected by Salts (Saline & Saline-Alkali Conditions)	Area Severely Affected by Salts (Alkali Conditions Requiring Chemical Amendment)
23,489	19,650	13,873 (51% of GCA)	6,714 (28.6% of GCA)	2,902 (12.4% of GCA)

Depth of Water Table*

0 - 10'	:	9,440	(40% of GCA)
10 - 20'	:	8,420	(35% " ")
Over 20'	:	6,050	(25% " ")

*Water table fluctuates during the year; it is the lowest during April and highest during August. Average figures have been indicated above.

The Major Works Undertaken in the Indus River Basin

To implement the Indus Basin Project, to combat the problems of waterlogging and salinity, and to further develop water resources for increasing agricultural and industrial production, Pakistan created the "West Pakistan Water and Power Development Authority" known as "West Pakistan WAPDA" to survey, investigate, prepare, and execute water resources projects. Subsequently, the Government created an Indus Basin Development Board to study the problems arising from the implementation of the Indus Basin Replacement Works.

The National Planning Commission was charged with the overall responsibility of preparing national Water Resource plans and integrating them with the national economic plans for development at periodic intervals, and to progress the implementation of approved development projects, particularly aided projects. It was also required to measure performance against promise, especially by comparing the actual with the estimated cost of projects, and to identify the causes of delays and difficulties, and to promote specific solutions. In addition it was to examine and recommend large development projects to the Executive Committee of the National Economic Council, headed by the Central Minister for Finance, Planning & Development.

The particular skills involved in the planning, preparation, and implementation of the water development program were:

(1) To prepare a comprehensive master plan for the development of water and power resources of West Pakistan,

(2) To prepare a plan of action for immediate implementation to match the available financial resources,

(3) To identify the areas where technical skills and know-how would have to be imported to complete certain projects,

(4) To identify the areas where local experts were competent to handle jobs,

(5) To identify competent international agencies for the transfer of skills and knowledge in water resources development that would be readily forthcoming to implement the sophisticated works in Pakistan.

For executing the Indus Basin Project the technical skills involved surveys, investigations, planning, designing and executing of (a) large earth and earth-cum-rock fill dams, (b) link canals both lined and unlined with discharges varying from 10,000 to 21,700 cusecs and (c) barrages (gated weirs) across the Indus River and its major tributaries with a discharging capacity in most cases of over a million cusecs and (d) remodelling of existing hydraulic structures.

For the control of Waterlogging and Salinity and Reclamation of the affected lands, a comprehensive plan was prepared in May 1961, drawing upon the extensive studies which had been going on for many years with the assistance of foreign firms of consultants. This plan called for the construction of 31,500 tubewells, 7500 miles of major drainage channels, and 25,000 supplementary drains at a total cost of Rs.5900 million ($540 million). The entire irrigated area of West Pakistan was to be divided approximately into 26 project areas of different sizes for Waterlogging and Salinity Control. However, later only 8 Salinity Control and Reclamation Projects commonly known as "SCARPs" could be approved. A list of these projects along with the areas that they will benefit is given below:

Status of Project Completed Ongoing or Planned	Name of Project	Area to be Benefited in Million Acres	Cost of the Project in crore Rs. 1 crore = 10 million
Completed	SCARP I	1.21	16.05
Ongoing	SCARP II	2.43	50.81
Ongoing	SCARP III	1.28	22.44
Ongoing	SCARP IV	0.56	14.98
Completed	SCARP Khairpur	0.36	15.28
Completed	Larkana Shikarpur Surface Drainage Stage I.	0.58	2.62
Ongoing	Rohri North	0.79	18.02
Ongoing	Surface and Sub-surface Drainage in G.M. Barrage.	2.3	15.24

The first project, SCARP I, was completed by installing about 2067 tubewells in the sweet ground water zone of the Punjab in the central part of the area lying between the rivers Ravi and Chenab. The remaining projects are nearing completion.

The Role Played by Foreign Advisers, Consultants and Contractors From Developed Countries in Transferring Knowledge in Water Resources to Pakistan

Transfer of foreign capital from an advanced to a less developed country is generally combined with the transmission of technical expertise. The inflow of foreign technicians and experts tends to increase with the increase in foreign aid. In many cases the project assistance is subjected to the condition that the entire technical work relating to the project (ranging from surveys and investigation to designing, construction and initial operation) would either be done by the technicians imported from the donor country or by the agencies which are considered competent by the concerned aiding agency.

In the field of water resources, large programs such as the Indus Basin Project and the "SCARPs" could hardly be implemented without seeking assistance from outside sources. In regard to the employment of consultants for undertaking the various stages of the projects receiving foreign assistance, it has sometimes been done out of sheer necessity and sometimes out of underlying conditions of the foreign aid. These factors led to an active participation of foreign advisers, consultants and contractors from developed countries in transferring knowledge and skills for completing the gigantic water development programmes in West Pakistan. The association of the foreign experts with the local water resources engineers began with the preparation of detailed reports for the development of the lower Indus Basin and the northern regions of the Indus Plain. The services of international experts such as Dr. Roger Revelle who produced a report on "Land and Water Development on the Indus Plain", were made available at the highest level. Thereafter, as a result of mutual cooperation between the President of Pakistan and the President of the International Bank for Reconstruction and Development, a World Bank Study Group headed by Dr. Peter Lieftinck produced (in a set of volumes) a comprehensive plan of Water and Power Resources of West Pakistan in which an Action Plan was recommended for implementation keeping in view the costs and benefits of the proposed projects and the financial resource projections for Pakistan assessed by the Bank Study Group. Although it was not possible to implement the Action Plan of the Bank in its totality, it provided a sound basis for going ahead with some of the projects recommended in the Plan.

However, the important question is whether the transfer of knowledge from developed regions through foreign advisers, consultants, and contractors has achieved more successful results than the local engineers in the Government or the private consulting and contracting agencies could have achieved. The results of a survey show that the performance of the Foreign

Consultants and Contractors has in general been conducive to
acceleration of work and improvement in quality. There are,
no doubt, examples where the performance of foreign consultants
despite continued support from the aiding agencies has been
unsatisfactory and too expensive for the country, However, it
would be denying the fact, if it is claimed that we could
reach the present level of development in such a short period
of time with the limited technical and financial resources
available in the country. It may be true that a large part
of the Indus Basin Works could be constructed more economically
by local talents and resources, but it is doubtful if the
targets could be accomplished within the stipulated period of
time. For instance, it would have been possible to construct
the link canals and barrages through local effort and expertise
because this is a field in which century old experience is
available within the country, but it would not have been
possible to undertake construction of Tarbela and Mangla Dams
without importing foreign skills and knowledge, since this
experience is relatively new for Pakistan. Similarly, after
the experience of the Salinity Control and Reclamation Project
No. I, it was probably possible to construct the remaining
SCARPs through local effort. However, the time factor involved
in completion of the projects, the tight conditions of the
foreign financial assistance, and the import requirements of
certain equipment are some of the factors which prevented a
greater participation of the local engineers and contractors
in the water resources development program.

Successes and Failures of Such a Cooperation Between Developed and The Developing Countries

The story of transfer of knowledge and resources from the
developed to the developing regions is one of partial successes
and partial failures. An impartial analysis of the matter
showed the following:

1. Most of the works were completed on schedule or even
ahead of schedule and according to the prescribed specifications.

2. A major share of the foreign assistance was syphoned
back to the donor countries in the form of payments to foreign
consultants and contractors and other experts.

3. Partial failures in design and construction occurred,
in cases where proper selection procedures had not been adopted
or the foreign consultants had been imposed by the aiding
agency. The recipient country, on the other hand, was forced
to accept without protestation even inferior services in the
interest of attracting foreign capital.

4. The project costs rose tremendously higher than if
some of the components of these projects were constructed

through local effort. This would have been possible due to much lower labor and supervisory costs and a significant reduction in the foreign exchange costs. It may be mentioned that the real cost of a foreign expert ranges from 5 to 10 times the remuneration paid to a local expert of equal qualifications and experience.

5. The participation of the local engineers and technicians in the preparation and execution of water resources projects, particularly those completed under the Indus Basin Replacement Plan, was not available to the desired extent, and those who were actually deployed to work with the foreign consultants and contractors were not given a chance to acquire experience of the sophisticated skills involved in the project construction. This deprived them of a sense of fuller participation in the implementation of the project.

6. In some cases, the advice tendered by the foreign experts, contrary to the opinion of the local experts, later proved to be erroneous which led the Government to a revision of their policy at some loss to the national exchequer.

7. Because of the standards prescribed by the aid-giving agencies many of the local contractors were eliminated during the pre-qualification process due to their limited financial resources. However, many items of works awarded to the foreign contractors under the main contract were actually done by the local contractors, taking sub-contracts from the main contractors. This created some heart burning among the local contractors.

Proposals for the Future

1. Although the basic objective of the financial or technical assistance and the transfer of knowledge is said to be to meet the short range demands of the recipient countries and to make them capable of undertaking the responsibility of development independently in the long range, the donor countries rarely consider this philosophy to be the guiding principle in the provision of financial and technical assistance. It has been noticed in a number of cases that the services provided by the aiding country have been mediocre and the attempt to transfer knowledge and know-how to developing nations has been half-hearted. The local technical personnel, who under pressure of circumstances, have been deprived of acquiring knowledge and skills in the various scientific subjects feel frustrated when they find that foreign specialists carry out the job and leave without imparting proper training to successfully run the project. A better understanding of the aspirations and requirements of the people of the developing regions by the developed nations is, therefore, most

essential to ensure that transfer of knowledge in water resources and other fields produces a healthy effect and develops a full appreciation of the contribution of knowledge and technical know-how made by the developed to the developing regions.

2. An analysis of the projects which have failed to be completed successfully and economically, despite foreign services, would reveal that the factors chiefly responsible for such failures have been the limited intellectual equipment of the experts arriving in the country, their superficial understanding of the problems of developing regions and lack of proper control by the local Government. The technical incompetence of the visiting experts stems from the limited supply of competent people to work in an underdeveloped country like Pakistan. A large percentage of the foreign assignments sponsored by the Governments of the advanced countries remain unfilled for want of properly qualified persons. In order to overcome these shortages, many of the program directors resort to providing anything which is available. This results in expensive mistakes at the cost of the underdeveloped countries. There is a justifiable feeling that the funds received in the country should be straight-forward loans or qualified and experienced expatriates be provided to undertake jobs and train local personnel. The recipient country should not be forced to spend valuable foreign exchange on incompetence.

3. The problem of acquainting the foreign experts, consultants, and contractors with the conditions in the country is much easier to solve if the short-term contracts are discouraged. A comparatively long stay in Pakistan, would allow foreigners to become conversant with the general conditions in the country and also the tendency to judge problems and to suggest solutions on the basis of the techniques which are more suited to their own country would be reduced.

4. There is a general trend among the foreign experts to recommend automation and mechanization for achieving efficiency. This may be true in countries where labor is extremely expensive, but in thickly populated countries where labor is abundantly available, there is a need to combine the machine with the human resources in a most economical manner. This can only be done if the sociological and economical facets of the country are carefully examined and studied before undertaking the works.

5. The Government generally imposes conditions on foreign enterprises working in the public sector to associate local personnel with them throughout the process to properly train them in the design, construction, and operation of the projects. Unfortunately, in many cases it has been reported that the

Pakistani counterparts attached to the foreigners have not
been adequately trained and have rarely been associated in the
decision-making process or in getting designs prepared. It is
necessary that Pakistani counterparts are properly trained by
the foreign enterprises to maintain and operate the projects
after their completion and to undertake similar new ventures
on their own in the future.

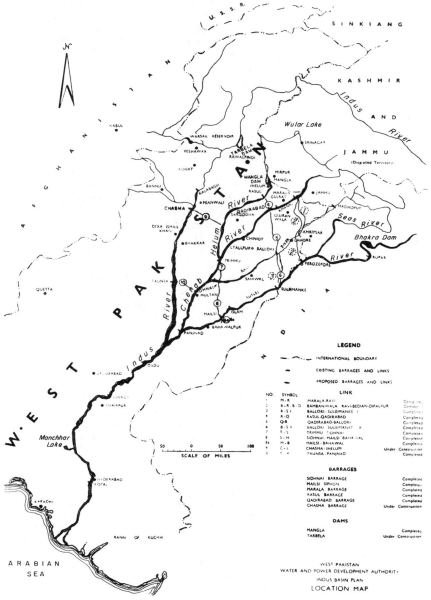

WEST PAKISTAN
WATER AND POWER DEVELOPMENT AUTHORITY
INDUS BASIN PLAN
LOCATION MAP

DISCUSSION by Dijon Robert*

Many criticisms were addressed during this session against international experts. It cannot be denied that engineers of construction firms engaged in a major operation overseas do not feel in general personally involved in the transfer of knowledge. What can be expected from them is efficiency in their work. Experts of firms carrying out surveys and prospective operations are often requested or committed to train counterparts. International experts recruited by multinational organizations such as those of the U.N. system are much more involved in the transfer of knowledge. It has to be kept in mind that the requirements for such experts are multiple. Age: not too young (mature enough), not too old (active enough). They must be proficient in their field of speciality and in addition they should be able to work in remote areas without discomfort, submitted to health hazards for themselves and their families and without opportunity for a career with the organization. They must be aware of the sociological, political and economical factors of the country in which they work. They have to be good report writers, diplomats, flexible with the host government without yielding too much. They must be able to train counterparts and to work in international teams. In addition, they must be able to communicate with the nationals in vernacular languages. They must also carry responsibility without detaining real authority. With all those various and sometimes contradictory requirements it is astonishing that there should even be a vast majority of experts who bring their projects in to a more or less satisfactory completion.

DISCUSSION by E. M. Laurenson**

Expatriate engineers working on water resources development schemes in developing countries take a couple of years to become knowledgeable about the physical, psychological, and sociological conditions of the country and only then can their work be fully effective. When the expatriates leave, not only is their expertise lost but also their hardly won local knowledge. It is, therefore, very important that local engineers should be trained to carry out the works in their own countries.

However, the problem of training faces the same difficulty as the applied engineering problem, namely that expatriate teachers usually return to their own countries soon after they gain sufficient local knowledge to be fully effective in their

*United Nations

**P.O. Box 793, Papua, New Guinea

work. In particular, western engineering academies tend to teach principles and techniques and <u>assume</u> that graduates will be able to <u>apply</u> these to practical problems. While this assumption is not valid in any country, it is particularly damaging in a country where all or most of the graduates will go into practice rather than research, teaching or post graduate study. It is especially important in developing countries that engineering courses should include a great deal of experience in the practical application of engineering principles and techniques.

<u>DISCUSSION</u> by Carlos Gois*

The international cooperation for the joint utilization of the water resources, discussed in various papers, has been established and given fruits in Southern Africa where an agreement was signed between Portugal, South Africa, Botswana, Swaziland establishing the steps to be followed at a technical level to discuss and obtain the best joint utilization of the international rivers in the area.

In these discussions the technical experts of the several countries concerned are free to discuss and study general plans for the joint use of the water resources not considering the political boundaries aiming to recommend to their governments specific lines on which a diplomatic agreement based on solid technical basis can be signed.

At the present, four international rivers are under common study at technical level and a diplomatic agreement was already signed between Portugal and South Africa for the joint use of the water resources of EUNENE BASIN. In this agreement the share of expenses and benefits was established for the best joint use of the available resources.

One of the steps at the technical level is the free interchange of hydrologic data and experience so that a better and cheaper understanding of the hydrological characteristics of the basin of international rivers can be achieved.

<u>DISCUSSION</u> by M. T. Chaudry**

There are two important aspects of knowledge transfer:

1. The overall environment in which the knowledge transfer takes place.

2. The mechanism of transfer.

---

*Cabinete do Cunene-Ministerio do Ultramar, Restelo - Lisboa - Portugal

**Colorado State University

This second aspect is strongly contained and limited by the first, if that is not favorable. The mode of transfer is also determined by this environment.

One wonders what mechanism has been used by the Chinese in order to obtain the knowledge and skill they have used in their rapid developments.

DISCUSSION by R. G. Thomas*

The problem of competancy of advisors is a management problem common to any organization and can only be improved by management. As a matter of fact, a survey in FAO of individuals who had received training indicated very clearly that the nearer the environment of training is to the home country, the more effectively can the training be used.

Today, there are over 50 countries with population of less than 1 million. A serious problem exists here in the training of individuals within these smaller countries and efforts should be increased for regional training facilities to be shared by them.

DISCUSSION by Eduardo Basso**

I would like to refer to a matter which has not been aired up to now. It refers to the study of Water Resources problems in small countries, much as the ones in Central America.

The population of these countries range from 1.5 to a little over 4 million inhabitants; so the isolated treatment of their problems should be clearly uneconomic. Therefore, I would like to refer to our experience in this area.

The Central American countries (Costa Rica, El Salvador, Guatemala, Hondurus, Nicaragua, and Panama) agreed in 1966 in the creation of the Regional Committee for Water Resources. This Committee meets once or twice a year and is composed by the top technical officers of each country in the field of water resources.

In spite of the different characteristics and individualities of each country, the Committee has been quite successful in coordinating and planning the hydrological and meteorological activities of the six countries, mainly related with the central American Hydrometeorological Project.

---

*F.A.O., Rome, Italy

**Apartedo 5583, San Jose, Costa Rica

Taking into account that a quite large proportion of Central America is drained by international rivers, the Committee will also coordinate the general hydraulic policy of these countries seeing as an advising body to the governments in matters related with Water Resources.

Therefore, my feeling is that this successful approach could be used in other regions of the world.

DISCUSSION by Lester A. Herr*

From the implications expressed at this meeting one gets the impression that the developed countries are perfect in transfer of knowledge. I have worked conscientiously for the past 25 years in one of these developing countries in the development of hydraulic engineering in the field of highway engineering--right here in the U.S.A. I can tell you today that within 50 km of this spot we should not have any difficulty finding a highway engineer who still believes that Talbot's formula is the only way to size a culvert or a bridge. Also, I might relate that within the same distance you can find some outdated practices in irrigation. We still have a job to do here.

To illustrate the slowness of progress, Mr. Carl Izzard, whom some of you have met over the years and recently retired, has promoted highway hydraulics for the past 30 years. It was only two years ago that the American Association of State Highway Officials established a Task Force on Hydrology and Hydraulics for the purpose of preparing guidelines related to this subject. After preparing the first three guidelines we have now run into trouble in getting them pointed and distributed--which leads me to the main point of my comment.

Yesterday we had some discussion on the cost of publications. This is a problem which concerns me greatly. Paper is cheap and I believe its general use as far as worthwhile publications are concerned is an acceptable expense to be included as a part of the cost of preparing its contents. Publications of small cost can involve more charges in clerical help in arranging for payment than to give them out on a discretionary basis. We do our best to satisfy requests made from public agencies or institutions involved in highway work. Because of this approach or policy many of our publications are not only used here in the States, but internationally and one has been translated into several languages.

---

*Federal Highway Administration, 400 7th St., S.W., Washington, D.C. 20591

DISCUSSION by Peter W. Whitford*

Concerning the paper of Mr. Malik, on page 5, Section IV, what was the "impartial analysis" referred to and by when was it performed? Does the study refer to the whole India Project or to the SCARP's?

In point IV (3) it is stated that "partial failures in design and construction occurred" and "the recipiant country was forced to accept inferior services." What is the evidence for this, to what extent did it occur and what effect did it have on the overall project?

In point IV (4) it is stated that costs rose much higher than if some components had been constructed through local effort. Again, what is the evidence for this and what was the effect on the overall project.

In point IV (6) evidence again is needed.

In point IV (7), what is wrong with local contractors being awarded sub-contracts when they were judged to be unqualified to hand complete contracts?

In point V, para 2, the impression is left that the whole program has been an utter failure. Is that the impression the author wanted to leave?

Point V, para 4, relating to one-mechanization is an excellent point and deserves greater prominence. The comments of others present were on the use of labor or capital-intensive technology would be appreciated.

DISCUSSION by Sarfraz Khan Malik**

In elaboration of the points brought out from my paper by the general reporter, I have the following suggestions to make for furthering the Processes of Transferring Water Resources Knowledge from developed to developing countries.

1. Tendencies on the parts of Foreign Consultants to contractors in doing the job in the developing countries and pulling out without imparting proper training to local personnel and engineers should be discontinued, otherwise the purpose of transferring knowledge from the developed to the developing regions is defeated.

*World Bank, Washington, D.C.

**Chief Water Resources Planning Commission, Government of Pakistan, Islamabad

2. Only developed and competent firms should be deputized to impart and transfer knowledge to the relatively advanced developing countries.

3. Local talents should be encouraged and afforded fuller and greater participation in contributions, planning and designing of Water Resources projects by than those foreign agencies which secure contracts under foreign financing arrangements to carry out jobs in developing countries. If this is not done it will defeat the underlying purpose of sharing knowledge.

4. Instead of laying stress on automation and mechanization, emphasis should be placed on labor intensive projects and efforts.

5. The local counterparts attached with foreign advisors, and consultants by the local Governments should be fully and thoroughly associated in the various stages of project planning design and construction rather than treating them as onlookers.

● *An interesting extension in water resources transfer of knowledge is the effort to integrate water systems transcending national boundaries. The complex social and political problems involved affect not only countries of similar technological levels, but are particularly vexing when technologies must be adapted to local conditions and special constraints. The general lack of knowledge concerning transfers across borders makes it both difficult to generalize, and imperative that guidelines for such multifaceted problems be established.*

Rapporteur: Jaromír Němec
Chief, Department of Hydrology and Water Resources
World Meteorological Organization*
Geneva, Switzerland

Introduction

Intensive transfer of knowledge across national boundaries, generally speaking, is a science, art and business backed by diplomacy. It is a science, as without some basic scientific principles it results in a haphazard exercise without any durable effect. It is a behavioural art because it involves contacts between human beings, and without talented people the effect may be the reverse of that desired. Finally, it is most often based on economic considerations, either as a private, commercial investment-benefit operation or as a component of economic activities of nation-wide significance.

Thus the analysis and development of a successful trans-national transfer of knowledge is not an easy task, even if every additional consideration is neglected such as those of ethics, including man's concern for the environment, allegedly the antithesis of technological and economic growth, the latter being in the last resort the immediate impetus for transfer of knowledge across State boundaries.

The transfer of knowledge in water resources activities, in addition to this general character, has the peculiarity of specific climatic and physiographic conditions in different countries and thus further barriers may exist against its successful operation.

Transfer of Knowledge in Countries at Similar Technological Levels

It should be noted that, while the flow of scientific and technological knowledge from industrially developed to developing countries is of paramount concern to this meeting and to international activities in general, the trans-national transfer of knowledge is also important between countries at more or less similar levels of development and scientific technological character.

While in a large number of industrial fields, such a flow is very active and is fostered by commercial exchange (for example, the European Common Market) in water resources research

*The views expressed in this paper are those of the author as an individual and should not in any way be interpreted as the official views of the World Meteorological Organization.

and technology such trans-national flow of knowledge is far
from being satisfactory.

Although very general and perhaps not the best, a fairly
significant index of this flow is the number of references in
papers presented at international symposia, to works of authors
of a nationality other than that of the author of the paper.

We have ascertained this index for a large international
symposia organized in the past seven years within the framework
of the International Hydrological Decade, namely those held in
Quebec, (1965), Leningrad, (1967) and Reading, (1970). It
has an irregular and rather slow tendency throughout this period,
which would indicate that transfer of knowledge in research has
not increased significantly over a period of about 6 years.

TABLE 1

Year of Symposium	1965	1967	1970
$K = \dfrac{\text{number of trans-national references}}{\text{number of papers}}$	0.86	1.53	1.23
Growth in % (1965 = 100%)	100	178	143

Of course a more detailed examination would be necessary,
namely along different national lines. By far the largest
number of papers are presented by authors from the North American
continent who, as a rule, most often confine their references
to research within the continental boundary of North America.

The result of the above exercise may not be generalized.
Furthermore, there is a certain difference between transfer of
research results through symposia and transfer of operational
or routine, although advanced and modern, practices. These
last are transferred more easily and readily. An example of
such transfer is presented to this Symposium in the paper by
G.T. Orlob, I.P. King and D.F. Kibler, "Development of Mathematical Modeling Capabilities for the Vistula River Project,
Poland".

This United Nations Development Programme (UNDP) financed
project, executed by the UN Headquarters, was a special type
of technical assistance project aimed at the transfer of
modern technology to Poland, a country which, at least in the
field of water resources and hydrology, can be qualified as a
highly developed one. The primary objective of the project
was the development of a comprehensive plan for the orderly
and operational utilization of the water resources of the
Vistula River Basin, with many competing demands. Many planning
variants, numbering in hundreds, were envisaged.

The transfer of the knowledge technique selected here was to employ on the project an experienced contractor (Water Resources Engineers - WRE - Inc., California, USA), who supported a highly-qualified Polish team of specialists in devising a set of mathematical models whereby alternative strategies could be computer-simulated. The phases of the project comprised: training, model implementation in Poland and model improvement.

The transfer of knowledge was most significant in the first and second phases, the first consisting in: 1. formal classroom lectures on selected topics in the field of water resources systems analysis; 2. discussion of case studies of actual projects in which system analysis and mathematical modeling have been sucessfully employed; 3. individual study and model development by the Polish/WRE team; 4. evaluation of the Vistula Project and scoping of "on-site" work in Poland; 5. field trips to selected projects, laboratories, and other locations of water resources planning interest in the United States.

The co-operation of the American and Polish specialists resulted to a degree in a two-way traffic in the second phase, during which the actual technique of the water resources planning strategy in the Vistula Basin was mapped (see Fig. 1).

The difficulties encountered in this knowledge transfer project partly consisted, according to the authors, in the Polish team's lack of familiarity with third generation computers, and some relevant programming skills, but mainly in difficult access to high-speed computer hardware.

In our opinion, the use of one single contractor and one school of thought, while having many advantages, bears with it inescapable drawbacks, including, for example, the insistence on the use of a hardware not currently available in the receiving country. Other inconveniences of this method of knowledge transfer will be mentioned later.

Transfer of Knowledge to Developing Countries

The barriers of national boundaries, including the linquistic, technological, economic, social, cultural and political elements, in addition to the difference in climate, physiography and demography, are most marked in water resources knowledge transfer to developing countries. The process in its general aspect, is also receiving most attention from many international and national institutions.

By far the largest single international contribution to this process is within the United Nations family of Organizations. It is, however, somewhat surprising that among different

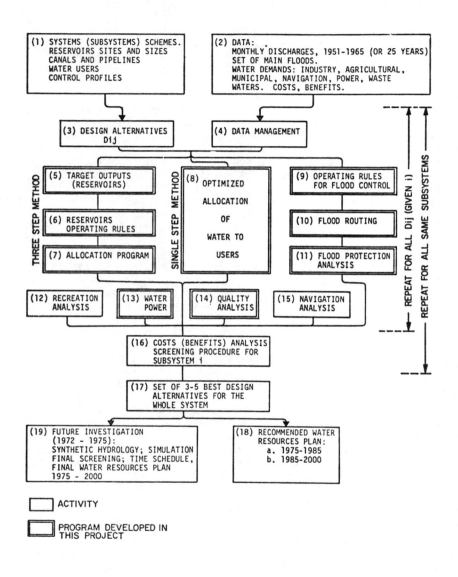

Figure 1. General water resource planning strategy in Vistula basin.

studies made of the structure and capacity of the United Nations
Economic Aid and Development System, very few relate to the
specific problem of knowledge transfer. Thus, in the some 300
odd references quoted in an exhaustive study of the structure
of UN economic aid by Kirdar (1969), only three marginally
touch the substance of the problem of transfer of knowledge,
the rest being devoted to the institutional, legal and economic
aspects. The well known Jackson report, while devoting considerable attention to the transfer of knowledge by way of
experts and sub-contracting of projects, does not indicate a
single reference to a study of the substance of the problem.

From our own personal experience in Africa, Latin America
and Asia, the greatest barrier to this transfer is the limited
capacity of absorption of the developing countries. The
causes of this limitation are complex but are mainly economic
and political and certainly beyond the scope of this report,
as well as the field of water resources.

An aspect of this limitation has been expressed by Dr.
Omer J. Kelley of the U.S. Agency for International Development
(AID) in his paper "Methods of transfer of water resources
knowledge from developed to developing regions with special
emphasis to on-farm water management." He rightly points out
that the focus in transfer of modern technology to the developing countries is in the selection of the technologies that can
be adapted to the local conditions within their constraints.
There is no direct step in the transfer process. These conclusions of the author are illustrated in two parts of the
paper, resulting from the vast experience acquired by AID.
In the first after a definition of the on-farm water management,
the scope of the physical and manpower problems is outlined.
The on-farm water management is described in the high and low
rainfall areas and irrigated lands. The manpower problems
include lack of trained scientists and institutions, and
administrators who understand the problem and lack of education.

The second part of the paper elaborates on methods of
transfer of water resources knowledge in general and in the
field of "on the farm" water management in particular. These
methods are:
1. Educational systems;
2. Demonstration and pilot projects;
3. Adaptive research;
4. Training of counterparts and gifted individuals;
5. Publications;
6. Seminars;
7. Short courses;
8. Field observations (study trips);
9. Consultants and experts;
10. Legislation;

379

11. Development of institutions; and
12. Development of incentives and improving markets.

Over the years, AID has been involved in all these methods and the author illustrates briefly each of them by AID experience. While no particular conclusions are drawn on the suitability of the above methods of transfer, an interesting comment is indicated with respect to demonstration and pilot projects, which are considered as "mildly successful, but not entirely so." While we would be inclined to agree wholeheartedly with this comment we have certain reservations on the comment on publications. The author considers that "the printed page ... is probably more of a convenience in recording knowledge transfer eyeball-to-eyeball than a transfer mechanism. Most books, technical papers and similar publications are used by the author to record his ideas and findings and for reference to the knowledge transfers that take place on an individual basis."

This may be correct for publications prepared without any special regard to transfer of knowledge to developing countries; it is certainly not so for guidance material prepared specifically for this purpose. Indeed the printed page is not only "a recognized method of information transfer," but also the most accessible, most economic, and probably the most effective way to provide the largest possible transfer of knowledge. The experience of the World Meteorological Organization with its Guides and Manuals prepared with a specific bias to developing countries is most encouraging in this respect. Experts in the field projects are literally pressed by their counterparts to record their knowledge on the "printed page," which in some instances results in an almost undesirable proliferation of heterogeneous transfer of individual views, not always of a sufficient technical and scientific level.

An integrated international experience recorded in guides and manuals of international organizations remains thus the basic source of knowledge for operational and practical activities in developing countries. It may even be said that in certain cases it is a pity that tradition and deeply-rooted national practices in some developed countries prevent them from benefiting from transfer of new knowledge by such internationally prepared "printed pages."

The AID experience is of course most valuable and may no doubt serve as an example for an organized effort of transfer of knowledge in water resources.

The AID activities, being quite naturally and understandably strongly biased to US practices, developed under substantially different social and economic conditions to those of developing countries, may not always yield the impact to commensurate with the expenditures involved. Often a technically well-prepared and even better implemented "crash" project, has simply no follow-up in the recipient country due to a lack of adequate social, educational and institutional background of the local conditions. The paper of Mr. Kelly therefore rightly points out that "the best success is obtained when the introduced technology is adapted and modified to suit the local conditions rather than attempting to change the local conditions to match the introduced technology." It is sometimes difficult to impress the above point on consultants and experts who for their entire life had access only to the sophisticated and most advanced U.S. technology.

The methods of transfer of knowledge, enumerated in the paper of Mr. Kelly, may be summarized in three groups:
1. "Printed page" transfer;
2. Trans-national contractual projects;
3. Consultants and experts.

While in all the above activities the training and education component must be present institutionalized education and training on short-term (seminars, courses) or long-term bases (training and research centers, departments in universities, education and training in institutions of developed countries) belongs in a long-term perspective to the most effective method of transfer of knowledge.

Some aspects of the above methods will be discussed briefly and illustrated by papers submitted at this symposium.

A special type of "printed page" transfer of knowledge is the establishment of internationally valid standards. The WMO has a long experience dating back a century in preparation and use of such standards included in the WMO "Technical Regulations." The third volume of these Regulations, adopted in 1971 concerns "Operational Hydrology," important for water resources inventories, since it includes standards of hydrological observing networks and stations, hydrological observations and hydrological warnings and forecasts. Standardization is of course needed also for other water resources practices. The paper by Mr. D. R. Sikka entitled "Guidelines for Transfer of Practices to Applications for Optimum in Planning of Key Items of Water Resources Projects" emphasizes the need for an internationally standardized classification of components of water resources projects, primarily in irrigation and dam construction, with the aim of making available in an orderly classified form knowledge and experience gained in different projects. Documentation and communication systems, involving only a minimum fraction of investment costs, may lead to more economic and productive design and construction. The time factor is of utmost importance here and represents, in the author's view, the key factor for transfer and availability of knowledge. "Supposing a dam is completed in a country in

381

1972 and its case history report is documented and published in 1978, it is not of much use to dams under construction between 1972-1978, while after 1978 construction requirements would have changed considerably." Along with documentation transfer the author considers it necessary to encourage standardization in designs of components of hydraulic structures looking to the proposed requirements of benefits, methods of construction based on the type of equipment and labor employment methods. "The basic difficulty," continues the author, "in achievement of some of the above objectives is the lack of effective organization, finance and the required initiative. It would therefore be essential to provide a micro-percentage, say 0.001 of the investment cost for this work ... with a Central Information or Control Room of the Organization in charge." After discussing several other barriers to a free flow of knowledge across borders, and between private and public sectors the author gives examples of the Control Board for Major Projects in Madhya Pradesh State (India) and of his personal experience in grouting of foundations of the Hasdeo Barrage. From his personal experience Mr. Sikka calls for international standardization and classification of foundation rocks, based on data from all sizable dams constructed all over the world.

While several reservations may be made on the feasibility of an international information flow institutionalized according to the author's views, the urgent need of technicians working under operational conditions for international standards in the field of water resources is evident. Indeed a recent survey of the International Standard Organization, conducted jointly with WMO, indicated that a very limited number of national standards exists in the field of water resources, even in developed countries. Thus the call for guidance publications and international standards in water resources appears as quite justified.

An example of international contractual projects was given in the first part of this report. A separate and much larger report could be written on this subject based on cases which were encountered during the five-odd years of our activities in an international organization and other, more competent people, would probably be able to write a book about it. We should not, however, like to let pass the opportunity of saying a word in favor of the international and multilateral approach within the projects of the UN Development Programme. Indeed, this is the only approach which, providing it is correctly technically guided, ensures the integration of knowledge transfer from different schools of thought and the desirable corrective of possible national biases. The already mentioned Jackson report provides an insight into the efforts of this approach to solve many problems that are inherent in it. These problems are connected also to the transfer of

knowledge by consultants and experts. One of them is apparent
from the paper by Mr. Mohiuddin Khan, "New Frontiers in
Drainage and Reclamation Engineering in the Indus Plains."
No less than eight groups of experts of different national
and international agencies in turn gave advice on the solution
of the water logging and salinity problem of the fertile
irrigated Indus Plain in Pakistan during a 22-year period. It
is not surprising that the advice given was often contradictory,
pilot projects were suggested, but later condemned. The author
notes that "by actually undertaking large projects that transfer
of knowledge has been possible in Pakistan." Tubewells and
surface drainage were used and the controversy regarding
horizontal versus vertical drainage continued. Finally the
problem was discussed at an FAO Seminar and large-scale private
initiative of tubewell building was adopted with the assistance
of the World Bank. The author concludes that the transfer of
knowledge in his country resulted in a two-way traffic - not
only to developing countries but also from them to the general
pool of knowledge. "Mistakes have been made, but Pakistan
and the world would be wiser for it." And the author concludes: "Greater success in transfer of knowledge would have
been facilitated by adopting the following methods: (a) intimate
association with local experts who know the area and problems
and proper check on consultants of foreign aided projects;
(b) restriction on large-scale transfer of sophisticated
techniques of developed countries to developing countries without thorough analysis of all technical and socio-economic
aspects; (c) seminars and symposia at different stages of
investigation planning, project preparation, operation and
maintenance; (d) a more thorough post project monitoring and
evaluation of the projects."

Obviously these conclusions are concurrent with those
indicated earlier in this report.

Conclusions

The experiences with transfer of knowledge in water
resources across state borders are not lacking. Nevertheless
a unique methodology or a best method are not available and
will probably never be, since such multifaceted problems
require multifaceted solutions. There are many barriers to
this knowledge flow, and they are often not inherent in the
recipient, but rather in the originator. A two-way traffic
is also not unusual, both between developed and developing
countries. However, some general principles must be followed,
of which the most important is that conditions should not be
adapted to the technology but rather the opposite is desirable
if the transfer of knowledge is to be reasonably successful.
Finally it is suggested that the field of water resources is
relatively lagging behind the trend and intensity of trans-
national knowledge transfer in many other industrial fields
and that studies of ways to increase it, while scarce, could
prove as useful.

DEVELOPMENT OF MATHEMATICAL MODELING
CAPABILITIES FOR THE VISTULA RIVER PROJECT, POLAND

By

G.T. Orlob   I.P. King
Water Resources Engineers, Inc.   Water Resources Engineers, Inc.
Walnut Creek, California   Walnut Creek, California

and

D.F. Kibler
Water Resources Engineers, Inc.
Walnut Creek, California

Synopsis

Under sponsorship of the United Nations Development Program the People's Republic of Poland performed a study of alternative plans for the optimal utilization of the Vistula River System, the country's primary water resource. An important element of the study involved training of Polish engineers in mathematical modeling techniques already in use in the United States and the transfer of this knowledge through a working team to facilitate development and application of models in Poland. This paper describes the participation of Water Resources Engineers, Inc. in the project, the training program that was implemented, and the accomplishments of the Polish-U.S. team. A critique is presented to guide similar efforts of international cooperation.

Introduction

The Vistula River Project was initiated in October 1968 under the United Nations Development Program (UNDP) with joint participation of the UN and the People's Republic of Poland. Its primary objective is the development of a comprehensive plan for the orderly and optimal utilization of the water resources of the Vistula Basin, Poland's largest and one of the major river basins of Europe. It was realized at the outset that to achieve this objective many alternative plans would have to be evaluated and that traditional planning techniques, whereby only a few select alternatives could be assessed, would not be adequate. The means would have to be found for satisfying in a near optimal fashion many competing demands for water--municipal, industrial, agricultural, power, navigation, water quality control, recreation, etc. over a future planning horizon extending at least to the year 2000. Many planning variants, numbering in the hundreds, were envisioned and enormous quantities of data would have to be assembled, organized, and analyzed to describe the behavior of all the viable possibilities. Truly, the task of developing the best possible plan for the Vistula was herculean in proportions.

To cope with this problem in an orderly fashion and to achieve the objective of a comprehensive plan within the project period of approximately two years, it was proposed to employ a set of mathematical models whereby alternative strategies could be simulated on the computer. Moreover, because this approach is relatively new in the field of water resource planning, it was proposed to employ on the project an experienced contractor who could support a qualified Polish team in the modeling work.

As a result of the visit to Poland of Dr. Daniel P. Loucks, a special UN consultant on mathematical modeling, it was determined that the modeling work should be conducted in two phases, an initial phase of about three months' duration involving training of selected Polish specialists in the home office of the contractor, including some initial model development, and a second phase of about six months on-site in Poland to complete development of models and to adapt the programs to the locally available computer hardware. Water Resources Engineers, Inc. of Walnut Creek, California, was selected as contractor and initiated work on Phase I in July 1970. Phase II commenced in November 1970 and work was completed under the initial contract in June 1971. Subsequently the contract was extended to include a third phase concentrating on planning methodology and model application; this was completed in June 1972.

Each of the principal phases of work on the project is described below and, where appropriate, attention is directed to specific problems encountered. The experiences of the contractor and his counterpart in solving these problems are highlighted.

Phase I. Training

In its proposal to the UN, WRE outlined a schedule consisting of five major activities:
1. Formal classroom lectures on selected topics in the field of water resources systems analysis.
2. Discussion of case studies of actual projects in which system analysis and mathematical modeling have been successfully employed.
3. Individual study and model development by the Polish/ WRE.
4. Evaluation of the Vistula Project and scoping of "on-site" work in Poland.
5. Field trips to selected projects, laboratories, and other locations of water resources planning interest in the United States.

Shortly after notification of its selection as the contractor WRE was advised of the membership of the Polish team and of the individual backgrounds in the field of water resources

planning and particular skills in computer application. The
general level of expertise and experience of the team was
exceptionally high. All members were experienced in water
resources planning, with backgrounds in applied hydrology
especially notable. Educational preparation was at the M.S.
level or higher, 6 of the 11 team members held doctor's
degrees. The team was headed by Professor Zdzislaw Kaczmarek[1],
Director of the Institute for Environmental Sciences of the
Polytechnic University of Warsaw, an internationally renowned
hydrologist and statistician. Four other members hold
appointments at Polish Universities in addition to affiliations
with government water and economic planning agencies. All have
a working knowledge of the English language.

Several of the team were experienced in computer applications, although background in third generation electronic
computers, such as the Univac 1108 employed by WRE, was
generally lacking. Experience in model development, per se,
was limited to only a few team members. In all cases mathematics backgrounds relevant to computer applications in hydrology
and hydromechanics was considered excellent, and in several
instances skills were demonstrably outstanding.

After a brief review of backgrounds, interest, and needs
of the Polish team, it was determined to divide the three-
month work period in Walnut Creek to give about equal weight
to lectures, case studies, and model development. As it turned
out, lecture hours totaled 147, case study hours, 118, and
individual study and model development totaled 152 hours. One
work-week was allocated to Phase I planning and one-half week
to field trips. A total of 10 weeks was devoted to Phase I.

Classroom lectures were tuned to the backgrounds of the
Polish members with special emphasis given to the following
topical areas:
    (1) Water quality concepts and modeling techniques;
    (2) Linear and non-linear programming;
    (3) Dynamic programming;
    (4) Computer programming (Fortran IV) and numerical methods;
    (5) Economic concepts and modeling techniques;
    (6) Deterministic hydrology;
    (7) Statistical and stochastic hydrology; and
    (8) Search techniques and decomposition theory.

---

[1]Presently Vice Minister for Higher Education, Science and
Technology, People's Republic of Poland and Director, Institute
for Environmental Sciences, Polytechnical University of Warsaw.

Lecturers were drawn from the WRE staff and selected consultants including:

Daniel P. Loucks, Ph.D. - Cornell University
    (Dynamic Programming, Stochastic Processes)
Rolf Deininger, Ph.D. - University of Michigan
    (Linear and Non-linear Programming)
Wilbur L. Meier, Jr., Ph.D. - Texas A & M University
    (Dynamic Programming)
Leonard Merewitz, Ph.D. - University of California
    (Economics)
Everard Lofting, Ph.D., University of California
    (Water Resource Economics)
Harvey O. Banks, Consultant
    (Water Resources Planning)

Case studies were drawn from the experience of WRE staff and special consultants. The study setting, problem definition, and solution(s) were developed by a discussion leader and participants in groups ranging from 4 to 12 persons depending on subject matter and relevance to the participant(s) interests and responsibilities in the Vistula Project. Case studies actually covered in Phase I included:

(1) Economics: Input-Output (Leontief) Models
(2) Stream Quality Models
(3) Pumped Storage and Low-Flow Augmentation
(4) Waste Treatment Optimization
(5) Reservoir Operating Rules
(6) Hydropower Optimization
(7) Watershed--Streamflow Routing and Estuary Hydrodynamics
(8) Numeric Multisite Package
(9) Sequence Selection
(10) Linear Programming for Reservoir Regulation
(11) Texas Simulation Model
(12) Stage Development Model
(13) Plan Evaluation Procedure

Model development was initiated simultaneously at a preliminary level by both the Polish team members and their WRE counterparts. Modeling activities focused on the following:

·Stochastic-Dynamic Programming for Reservoir Operations in Vistula
·Dynamic Programming for Hydropower Production in Vistula
·Waste Treatment Optimization by Linear Programming
·Reservoir Management by Linear Programming and Out-of-Kilter Algorithm
·Simplified Channel Routing Model

Initial model development progressed along two parallel lines in the matter of optimal allocation of water resources of the Vistula River Basin. One alternative proposed by the

Polish group involved the development of a set of three models in a package subsequently called the "Three-Step Method." Another drawn from the experience of WRE in Texas water planning involved the application of the Out-of-Kilter Algorithm to multi-reservoir systems.(1) A program of testing these model packages on a trial case was devised, with the final selection of the model deferred until the team was established "on-site" in Poland.

Accomplishments

Phase I was considered generally successful by all participants in achieving its general goals--(2) acquainting the Polish team with mathematical modeling techniques currently in use in the U.S., and (2) initiating development of models for application in Poland. Deficiencies, if any, lay in the presumptions by WRE prior to contact with the Polish team concerning the levels of preparation and expertise in computer applications. There existed an understandable lack of familiarity with third generation high-speed computers and some programming skills were lacking. Nevertheless, capacity to adapt to new technological innovation was at a high level and the team returned to Poland with high capability and confidence that the modeling approach was feasible of implementation in the Vistula Project.

Phase II. Model Implementation in Poland

Strategy and Organization - Phase II was aimed primarily at achievement of practical working tools, e.g., mathematical models and programs, with which the Polish water resource planners could evaluate alternative systems and strategies. This had to be accomplished in a period of about six working months, a rather short period when compared to previous experience in model development in the United States. Clearly, this requirement called for a transfer of proven methodology whenever possible and the use of experienced personnel to the maximum practical extent. WRE was called on to provide much of this methodology and expertise, specifically related to the computer. The Polish team, while contributing substantially in computer skills, made its greatest input to the Project during this period in the development of realistic planning alternatives and the basic hydrologic and water use data needed for evaluating them.

In early November 1970 the Polish team and four of the WRE counterpart team met in Warsaw to review the general water resource planning strategy with the Vistula Project Advisory Panel and to initiate work on Phase II. The approved strategy and the models proposed for development are shown in the schematic of Figure 1. Some 34 project tasks were identified,

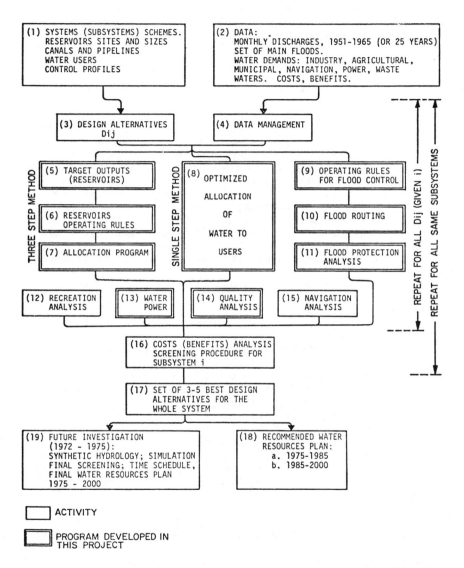

Figure 1.   General Water Resource Planning Strategy in Vistula
            Basin.

scheduled, and responsibilities were assigned to Polish team
members backed up by WRE advisor consultants. The two junior
authors served as advisor consultants in residence for the six
months duration of Phase II, and four other WRE staff members
and Dr. Deininger participated for periods of three to six
weeks over the period from November 1970 through April 1971.

Assignments

The Phase II work assignments to the WRE members of the
team were:
1. Develop the One-step Method of water resources allocation.
2. Advise and consult on development and adaptation of
   flood routing techniques and programs.
3. Adapt water quality models for application to the
   Vistula River System.
4. Assist in testing of all models with real data
   developed for planning alternatives and variants.
5. Adapt all programs to ICL (British) computers.
6. Advise and consult on all matters of computer usage
   and mathematical model development.
7. Maintain liaison with the UN manager of the Vistula
   project.
8. Assist in documenting models, programs, and project
   accomplishments.

The Polish team took major responsibility for the following work assignments:
1. Develop the Three-Step Method of water resource
   allocation.
2. Develop flood routing techniques and programs.
3. Develop single project power optimization program(s).
4. Develop planning alternatives and variants.
5. Assemble and prepare basic data for computer application.
6. Test all models on real data.
7. Screen alternatives and variants.
8. Document models, programs and project accomplishments.

Accomplishments

Most of the development targets of Phase II were met
although significant difficulties were encountered in staying
on the present schedule, largely due to uncertain access to
computers of required capability. A workable planning package
was developed and the more critical models and programs to be
used in the screening process (see Figure 1) were operational
by the end of April 1971. Although it had been hoped that
production runs on some 150 variants, involving 12 subsystems
of the Vistula System, would be well underway by this time,
this goal was not quite achieved. However, the Polish team

carried the production work forward and completed runs on all variants by mid-summer 1971. This work was carried out under the auspices of Hydroprojekt, the Polish national water resource consulting organization.

It was recognized in developing the planning strategy that two alternatives might be available to deal with the problem of optimal water resource allocation. As agreed in Walnut Creek, program development continued in Poland along parallel lines with responsibility for the Three-Step Method assigned to the Polish team and the lead in developing the One-Step Method being taken by WRE personnel. Production runs were targeted to begin in late April at which time a decision would be reached as to which package would be used. As it turned out, the single-step technique was selected and employed in making production runs. This was perhaps the most singular and innovative contribution to water resources planning that re-sulted from the international cooperative effort on the Vistula Project.

The flood routing models proved to be more difficult to develop and apply than was anticipated. Final development was deferred to Phase III.

Water quality modeling, per se, was not a major project effort although successful adaptation of a WRE stream model for temperature prediction was accomplished.

The major problems encountered in Phase II centered around the computer itself. While good access was possible for low speed computers (Polish ODRA), access to high speed large capacity hardware was very limited. British ICL 1904 and 1905 computers were available, but not at the level of convenience required for model and program development. This situation is improving gradually in Poland as new machines, including IBM 360 series, are installed.

Phase III. Model Improvements

Phase III was implemented by an extension on the original contract to extend the capabilities of the models developed in Phase II and to initiate some new areas of mathematical modeling. It was carried out over the period from October 1971 to June 1972 and involved short-term visitations, one to two months, of seven Polish engineers to the Walnut Creek offices of WRE and 14 man-weeks of counterpart effort in Warsaw.

Principal activities included:
1. Extend development of the One-Step Method (VISSIM)
2. Test sensitivity of VISSIM to hydrologic and econometric variables

3. Develop and adapt water quality model(s) to Vistula temperature problems
4. Extend and complete development of flood routing models
5. Document all models
6. Install models on computers in Warsaw.

The objectives of Phase III were generally met although schedules were compromised substantially by administrative problems and by the perennial computer access problem.

Conclusions

The mathematical modeling phases of the Vistula Project were carried out fairly successfully overall. Problems were encountered throughout the project with computer hardware, particularly convenience of access. However, it is expected that this may be less of a restraint in the future. A high degree of rapport and mutual respect for technical competence of model team participants was developed. Substantial advances in the mathematical modeling art were made in the project, especially in the development and refinement of the One-Step Water Resource Allocation Model, VISSIM.

Other notable contributions were in the development of a versatile power optimization program by the Polish team* and the initial application of a stream temperature model to the Vistula River System. As an exercise in the interchange of water resources planning knowledge, the experience was rewarding to all.

References

(1) WRE, Inc., "Systems Simulation for Management of a Total Water Resource," Report to the Texas Water Development Board, August 1969, 132 pp.

(2) Orlob, G. T., D. F. Kibler, and I. P. King, "Mathematical Models for Planning the Future Development and Management of the Vistula River System in Poland," Final Report Phases I and II, United Nations Office of Technical Cooperation, December 1971, 66 pp.

---

*This task was the responsibility of Dr. K. Jackowski, Associate Professor of the Warsaw Technical University.

METHODS OF TRANSFER OF WATER RESOURCES KNOWLEDGE
FROM DEVELOPED TO DEVELOPING REGIONS WITH SPECIAL
EMPHASIS TO ON-FARM WATER MANAGEMENT

By

Omer J. Kelley
Director, Office of Agriculture
Bureau for Technical Assistance
Agency for International Development
Washington, D.C.

Introduction

The importance of water for agriculture can hardly be
over-emphasized. Agricultural crops require an average of
about 5,000 gallons per acre per day, with extremes on hot,
dry days reaching as much as 15,000 gallons. There's really
no alternative resource that can take the place of water, and
without water most all animals and plants would die in a few
days. It makes little difference to the plants whether the
water needed for plant use comes from natural precipitation,
is applied as irrigation water, or is extracted from the
moisture stored within the soil root zone, thus the scope of
on-farm water management includes the management of all sources
of water (precipitation, soil moisture storage, and applied
irrigation water) so as to use the available resource effectively to optimize agricultural production. It is quickly apparent
that water management is compounded with soil, climate, crop,
fertilizer, capital, and energy; however, social, cultural,
political, economic, legal, and religious considerations often
have a bearing on what is done with or to the water. In a
recent seminar before the technical staff of the Indian
Agricultural Research Institute, A.I.D.'s water management
specialist defined on-farm water management as follows:

"Modern 'On-Farm Water Management' is a complex combination of art and science requiring the application
of our best knowledge of water, soil, climate, and
crops and their interactions, together with inputs
of nutrients, pesticides, capital, power (energy),
and management for agricultural production. It
extends from the production of water as precipitation
(either in the water shed or at the farm) to the
disposal of the remnants after use. It gives emphasis
to timely and sufficient delivery of water to the
farm including the conjunctive use of surface water

and groundwater and the re-use of irrigation return
flow or the sequential use of waters reclaimed from
industrial, municipal or other uses. It includes
the preparation of the farm land to enhance its
efficiency to receive and to store water. It employs
the necessary water removal systems (drainage works)
to control the water table, provide leaching requirements, and dispose of unwanted water whether coming
from excessive precipitation, excess irrigation, or
otherwise. It involves the design and construction
of devices and structures for the efficient application of water to the land such as field ditches,
pipelines, furrows, borders, and sprinkler systems.
It involves the design and construction of complicated engineering works such as dams, reservoirs, canals,
and appurtenances for control and modification of
the space-time availability of natural water supplies
so delivery and application to the farmland can be
made on a timely basis. In modern society the need
for proper concern for the environment, erosion,
pollution, water quality, and factors affecting the
quality of life are also recognized. Apparent also
is the knowledge of and need for institutions,
organizations, legislation, laws, and regulations
providing for an orderly and acceptable development
and use of the water resource to meet societal goals."

This definition of on-farm water management, although
somewhat lengthy, does emphasize the complexity of water
management for agriculture.

You may be interested to know that A.I.D. has sponsored
a number of international seminars concerned with on-farm
water use. Perhaps the longest and most complete series of
seminars are those of the Near East South Asia Irrigation
Practices Seminars held biennially in the Near East South Asia
regions beginning in 1956. In the eight biennial seminars
during the period 1956 to 1970, inclusive, a major item of
discussion in practically every seminar was the concern for
improving the use of water on the farm. It was emphasized
time and time again that the integration of the production
resources for agriculture takes place at the farm. The fact
that a water resource is partially developed with reservoirs
and canals does not necessarily imply that the water resource
is used. Therefore, in recent years A.I.D., FAO and many other
international and national agencies have been concerned with
the utilization of the resource at the farm level. At the
present time there is almost a total global commitment to
emphasize the use of the resource at the farm level rather
than the traditional water development policy of "developing an
idle resource".

In a recent paper presented at the Seminar on Tropical Soils Research, Ibadan, Nigeria, the writer mentioned the importance of water management for agriculture. Water management consists of manipulation of the water resource to alter its space-time-quantity-availability and thus improve the environment for crop production. Three broad categories of water management have been established as follows:

A. "Management of a natural water supply (precipitation) where it reaches the land to conserve it and increase its immediate and future availability for utilization by crops."

B. "Artificial application of water to the soil (irrigation) to augment natural precipitation and insure availability when needed by crops."

C. "Removal of excess surface water, or subsurface water (drainage), whether coming from natural or artificial causes to protect and maintain the root zone moisture environment required for maximum yields."

The application of these three categories of water management or combinations of the three will be different depending upon the nature of the problem involved as discussed below.

To discuss the methods of transfer of water resource knowledge from the more developed to the less developed regions, it is necessary to understand the nature of various aspects of the problem and the individual components that vary with climate, soils, vegetation, etc. Therefore some background on this variation seems appropriate.

Scope of the Problem (Physical Problems and Manpower Problems)

The physical problems of water management may roughly be divided into those concerned with high rainfall areas, those involving low rainfall areas, and those concerned with irrigated areas.

High Rainfall Areas - Here the main water problem is usually concerned with too much water, limiting the type of crops that can be grown, and placing serious limitations on the physical system to remove the excess water without erosion or crop damage. Although the high rainfall problem may be continuous throughout the year in some areas, it is usually typified by excess rainfall during a particular season (monsoon) followed by dry seasons in which there's not enough precipitation to maintain plant growth. Large areas in Asia, South America, and Africa have the problem of high rainfall during part of the year, during which time the production is essentially limited to rice or crops that can be grown under wet conditions, followed by dry seasons during which time there may not be enough precipitation to continue crop production.

Improving water management in the high rainfall areas may involve:
Land management.
Construction of storage facilities.
Improvement of natural drainage channels.
Construction of water removal systems.
Water application system.

1. Land management. This includes treatment of soil or land surfaces to improve infiltration, provide surface retention, increase soil moisture storage, restrict overland flow and reduce erosion. The land management practices include contour farming, deep tillage, subsoiling, strip cropping, terrace construction, benching, and leveling. The nature of the soil, the topography, and the intensity and duration of the precipitation are all important in the selection of the land management practices or combination of practices for moisture management.

2. Construction of storage facilities. Storage facilities are important in all water management. The alteration of the space-time-quantity distribution of the water resource can only be achieved by storage. Storage may consist of soil moisture storage, small farm tanks or large reservoirs, the impact on the distribution of the water resource depending upon the storage capacity in relation to the area and precipitation intensity.

3. Improvement of natural drainage channels. Removal of excess surface waters quickly and safely depends upon the efficiency of the natural drainage in conjunction with man-made structures for water removal. Natural channels often become overgrown with vegetation or restricted by encroachment of structures which greatly reduce their carrying capacity. Protection of the channel area to maintain its efficiency is constantly needed.

4. Construction of water removal systems. Man-made drainage facilities are essential in maintaining high production levels and safeguarding agricultural land. Drainage terraces, surface drains, and sub-surface drains are all essential in providing and maintaining the proper soil moisture environment for maximum production.

5. Water application systems. Droughts of short duration are common even in the high rainfall areas and water application during the drought period coupled with good agronomic practices (fertilizer, variety and pest control) can have dramatic impacts on production levels.

Low Rainfall Areas - In the low rainfall areas or during the low rainfall seasons, the problem involves the management of the natural precipitation so as to retain as much moisture in the soil root zone as possible and make it available for use by the crop. The intensity and distribution of the precipitation play an important role in how the water management is achieved. Distribution of the rainfall often causes serious problems of erosion and damage when the precipitation intensity exceeds the ability of the soil to absorb water. Water management in the low rainfall areas includes fallow, terracing, contour farming, tillage, weed control, and strip cropping used in conjunction with improved varieties and fertilizer practices to optimize the available resources.

Irrigated Areas - "Irrigation is the artificial application of water for crops drawn from rivers or streams or from ground water supplies to supplement or replace rainfall". In the irrigated areas of the world, irrigation is considered to be the sole source of water for crops; however, in both high rainfall areas and low rainfall areas, the inadequacy of precipitation during short periods often results in serious reductions in yields, and improved water management to these areas through irrigation is expanding rapidly. Irrigation itself is a complex problem, almost always requiring community involvement for the development of the resource, the operation and management of the system, and proper scheduling of the water supply to the on-farm system to satisfy the water requirements of crops. Irrigation requires more techniques for the high rainfall and low rainfall areas; although a large technical input is required for all water management.

Water management also involves a number of problems not connected with the physical manipulation of the water resource itself but concerned with the manpower requirements of the management of the resource.

Manpower Problems - The manpower problems include lack of trained scientists, lack of administrators who understand the problem, and lack of education.

1. Lack of trained scientists and institutions. Especially in the developing countries there is a lack of trained scientists to collect the necessary basic water resource data, to identify and deal with the problems, to plan the needed on-farm improvements, and to render the necessary technical assistance required by the farmers to be able to introduce modern on-farm water management techniques to their particular farming area. This usually requires some institutional arrangement. In the '30s and '40s this job was done in the U.S. primarily by the Soil Conservation Service of the U.S. Department of Agriculture; in the U.S. today it is done by business or engineering firms. Most LDCs lack these institutional capabilities.

2. Lack of administrators who understand the problem.
Throughout the world water is considered to be the property of
the public, thus belonging to everyone and owned by no one.
Water management, therefore, involving especially diversions
from water courses, or ground water, must be in accordance
with some plan acceptable to society. There must be, therefore,
a public policy. This requires administrators who understand
the problem to initiate the government program, to support the
required legislation, to lead in needed reforms, to initiate
educational programs, and to organize and lead training programs.
There must also be sufficient political muscle to present the
farmers' problems and to secure support for water management
policies.

3. Lack of education. The level of literacy in the
developing countries is also a serious problem standing in the
way of modern on-farm water management. Traditional farming,
although not viewed by many as water management, is substantially
a water management technique that is based upon the transfer of
knowledge in a "father-to-son relationship." Over the centuries
the water management information and the development of the
traditional farming in a given region have largely developed
in this way. Within this framework it is very difficult to
insert modern technology or modern methods. All of us resist
change. In order to emphasize, one need only to point the
resistance to change that occurs even with the highly educated
groups. Less than one hundred years ago the doctors and
dentists strongly opposed the use of anesthetics or drugs to
relieve pain, yet today they are looked upon as absolutely
essential in the practice of modern medicine. Another important
factor in dealing with traditional agriculture is the risk
factor. The uneducated farmer is relatively sure of the
production he can obtain by following traditional methods. By
introducing new techniques he is dealing with methods and procedures unfamiliar to his method of operation; he feels insecure
and unsure of the results. In addition, costs must be incurred,
and the farmer may lack the credit or capital required for the
necessary improvements.

Methods of Transfer of Water Resource Knowledge

The transfer of water resources knowledge is perhaps no
different than the transfer of knowledge of any kind. In
effect, the methods employed will vary over a wide range,
depending upon the needs of the developing country, the
resources available, and the nature of the technology to be
transferred. Traditional methods of knowledge transfer
include: (1) educational systems; (2) demonstrations and pilot
projects; (3) adaptive research; (4) training of counterparts
and gifted individuals; (5) publications; (6) seminars; (7)
short courses; (8) field observations; (9) consultants and
experts; (10) legislation; (11) development of institutions;

and (12) development of incentives and improving markets. Over the years A.I.D. has been involved in all of these processes and within the past five years has developed energetic and rather massive programs in certain of these areas. In commenting on the need for technical assistance and the problems of transfer of technology, the President's Science Advisory Committee had this to say: "The products of technology and know-how cannot be transferred directly to the developing nations." And stating further, "...there is an urgent need to carry out adaptive research, to establish strong indigenous institutions, and to develop the manpower that will enable the poor, food deficient nations to carry out the self-sustaining, continuing programs of research and development that are essential to modern food production."[1]/ A.I.D. was involved in many of these programs long before the subject report was published. A brief discussion of A.I.D.'s involvement would probably be in order.

Educational Systems - A.I.D. has contracts with a number of United States universities to improve the competence of the educational institutions in the developing nations. A good deal of this emphasis has been focused on the problems of managing the natural resources, especially water. The emphasis has been on developing classroom work and laboratories for the training of native technicians to cope with the problem and thus build the manpower staff needed by the developing country who will be required to make the transfer of technology within the framework of the socio-economic cultural system of their native land.

Demonstrations and Pilot Projects - More than ten years ago A.I.D. made plans for establishing demonstration projects and pilot projects in the developing countries to specifically focus on the wise utilization of water on the farm. Specific representative areas were selected and contracts made with U.S. institutions, both government and private, to supply technicians to carry out the work in the developing country. An integral part of this pilot project idea was that each foreign technician should have assigned to him a counterpart within the developing country so that the transfer of knowledge could take place on an "eyeball-to-eyeball" basis. It was envisioned that this method of knowledge transfer would indicate those particular practices that had immediate applicability to the particular situation of the developing country and could be used for the training of administrators who must initiate the necessary reform in the drafting of the necessary legislation and the formulation of policies. Unfortunately the pilot projects have been only mildly successful.

1/The World Food Problem, a Report of the President's Science Advisory Committee, Volume 1, Report of the Panel on World Food Supply, The White House, May 1967, p. 20.

Adaptive Research - Nearly five years ago A.I.D. began
negotiating with United States universities to conduct adaptive
research in the field of water management to discover the
alterations necessary to transfer the advanced technology
available in the United States to the conditions of the developing countries. Contracts with Colorado State University and
Utah State University have been in force for a little more than
three years, and A.I.D. Missions and the developing countries
are cooperating in this program. It has been the policy to do
the research within the socio-economic framework of the
developing country. The building of indigenous institutions
and the training of local people who fully understand the
limitations of the developing country has been the "modus
operandi" of these projects.

Colorado State University is carrying out its research
program in Pakistan with concern for the regional problems of
the Near East and South Asia. The broad scope of the work at
the present time covers land grading techniques, water course
improvement, soils management and agronimic practices, water
quality problems, engineering problems of water measurement,
water delivery, sediment control, and others including legal,
social and economic concerns.

Utah State University has concentrated its efforts on the
regional water management problems of Latin America with
emphasis on water requirements of crops, water removal systems,
water laws, water-soil-crop-fertilizer interactions, and
timing and uniformity of water applications.

Both Colorado and Utah have produced results which are
already being put to use in these two large areas of the world
and a biannual meeting is held to seminar the research findings
of these two institutions.

Training of Counterparts and Gifted Individuals - An
important facet of the educational programs, the demonstration
and pilot projects, and the adaptive research has been the
selection of counterparts and gifted individuals for training
in the United States to work with the modern technologies within
the framework of the United States, and to return to their
country to adapt those applicable practices to the conditions
of the developing country. Over the years literally hundreds
of individuals have been selected within the A.I.D. program
for training outside of their home country. These people
have participated in short courses of two to three months
duration, they have participated in formal education at the
universities obtaining advanced degrees, they have worked with
the Bureau of Reclamation and the Soil Conservation Service in
the office and in the field to observe the approach to the
problem within the United States. These individuals are then

400

returned to their home country to adapt the modern technologies to the local conditions. Since the Foreign Training Program was initiated about 1950, the Foreign Training Division of USDA has processed more than 50,000 participants from nearly all foreign countries who have come to the United States for special training in all fields of agriculture. A.I.D.'s sponsorship of these trainees has ranged from 2,000 per year to more than 4,000 per year with many others being sponsored by their own government, FAO, and organizations such as the Ford Foundation and Rockefeller Foundation. In addition, a number have been sponsored by contract groups and universities whose programs have not been developed or supervised by the U.S. Government. Among these trainees are more than 1,000 people who have received advanced degrees in some field of agriculture.

Publications - The printed page is a recognized method of information transfer. However, it is probably more of a convenience in recording knowledge transferred "eyeball-to-eyeball" than a transfer mechanism. Most books, technical papers, and similar publications are used by the author to record his ideas and findings and for reference in the knowledge transfers that take place on an individual basis. Nevertheless, A.I.D. has strongly supported the building of the library facilities of the developing countries and has systematically tried to provide the most recent literature to the A.I.D. Missions for distribution and use in the LDCs. It is estimated that nearly 100,000 publications per year are supplied to the LDCs by TA/AGR, involving some 15,000 subject matter items. These estimates do not include a large number of technical papers and publications supplied directly to the LDCs by A.I.D. contractors and other government agencies such as USDA and the Department of Interior.

Seminars - As mentioned earlier, A.I.D. has sponsored a number of seminars and at least ten in the water management field. These seminars provide an excellent opportunity for the participants to exchange knowledge on a personal basis, to share their ideas, and to seek solutions to their common problems. In the Near East South Asia Irrigation Practices seminars mentioned above, more than 500 participants representing top level administrators from twenty different countries have met to focus on the irrigation problems of the region. The proceedings of these eight seminars total more than 2,500 printed pages. A.I.D. has also sponsored irrigation seminars in the Far East and Latin America, the latter group continuing the seminars without A.I.D. support since the first one was held.

It has been the policy in these seminars to encourage, indeed insist, that the nations of the LDCs personally participate in the presentation of technical papers and discussions.

401

Foreign experts were used only in an advisory capacity and did not dominate the program but remained in the background. It is interesting to note that in the last five NESA Irrigation Practices Seminars all of the technical papers were presented by the nationals of the participating countries, and the Chairmen of all panels, technical sessions, and discussion groups were nationals of the participating LDCs.

Short Courses - Of special interest in water management are the irrigation short courses designed for foreign participants to observe and study modern irrigation methods being practiced in the United States. The first course held in 1953 at Utah State University had 35 participants from 17 different countries many of whom are now in top administrative positions in their home country. The short course has been an annual affair at Utah State since 1953, and during the period more than four hundred foreign engineers and agronomists have received special water management training at USU. Irrigation short courses have also been organized recently at Colorado State University and the University of California at Davis.

A course closely related to irrigation problems has been conducted at the U.S. Regional Salinity Laboratory at Riverside, California where each year 24 scientists from foreign countries have received special training in drainage and salinity. Over the past 12 years, 288 scientists have received this special training.

Field Observation - Often an integral part of seminars and short courses is a planned program of field observations to see modern water management in action. Such field trips are an important tool in knowledge transfer whether taken to a pilot project in the developing country, a specific project in a neighboring country or an extensive trip. Field days at experiment stations and research centers also provide a similar experience.

Consultants and Experts - Professional people possessing outstanding ability and having international prestige have been used to introduce modern techniques to the developing countries and to aid in selecting those particular practices that have apparent applicability. Both FAO and A.I.D. have used consultants with some degree of success in achieving a transfer of technology and the adoption of modern on-farm water management. The best success is obtained when the introduced technology is adapted and modified to suit the local conditions of the LDC rather than attempting to change the local conditions to match the introduced technology. For example, in introducing land leveling as a condition for improving water management, it is natural for the expert to want to use the heavy equipment techniques geared to the large farms typical of the United

States. This simply will not work in many of the LDCs at this time. The farms are small, often with irregular boundaries, and the equipment, capital, and know-how that is essential to this mechanized method just isn't available. However, alternatives to the use of very heavy equipment have been developed and have proved to be successful, especially in Turkey.

In Turkey, with the technical help and other assistance of A.I.D., a small wheel scraper of about one cubic yard capacity was developed for land grading to be used with the smaller (50 h.p.) tractors available in Turkey. The technology for operation and maintenance of the tractors was available and the tractors were being used as a power source for other jobs. The land leveling with this scraper was first introduced under the sponsorshop of TOPRUKSU, but now many contractors in the private sector are bidding for the land leveling work.

Legislation - It is a well known fact that water laws or the lack of any water law often inhibits the adoption of modern concepts of water use. A.I.D. has assisted the LDCs needing water laws and legislation by providing experts and consultants to help draft the necessary water codes. Legal processes are often successful in achieving desired changes when other methods of knowledge transfer fail to do the job.

Development of Institutions - It was indicated earlier that modern on-farm water management requires considerable technical input beyond the capacity of most cultivators. Strong institutions are needed in the developing countries to provide this service and A.I.D. has supported the development of such institutions. Of special interest to A.I.D. is the development of the DSI and TOPRUKSU in Turkey. DSI is very similar to the U.S. Bureau of Reclamation, and TOPRUKSU is like the U. S. Soil Conservation Service. Both of these organizations are now well staffed, equipped, and qualified to render the technical assistance and develop the sophisticated designs essential in an efficient modern irrigated agriculture.

It should be noted also that a fair number of rather prestigious international institutions have been developed recently with the concern for agricultural production of the LDC. These institutions -- IRRI, CIMMYT, CIAT, IITA, CIP, and ICRISAT -- although not specifically concerned with water, do have water management included in a prominent position.

Incentives and Markets - Often the incentive for transfer from the traditional to modern water management is not visible to the cultivator although the information seems to be understood. An important activity of A.I.D. has been to assist the developing country with the necessary credit and to help provide incentives to farmers. In the water management field an attractive incentive is cost-sharing for the needed physical improvements or other facilities necessary to use the modern techniques of on-farm water management. Most of the money provided by A.I.D. has been in the form of a loan to the developing country for a specific purpose. At the present time some of the A.I.D. Missions are considering rather sizeable loans to focus on the problems of on-farm water management and to provide the necessary incentives to accomplish the physical improvements necessary to do the job. Closely related to the credit and cost-sharing needed for physical improvements is the development of markets and marketing organizations to insure that the farmer gets a top price for his product.

What is the Focus of Knowledge Transfer

As indicated earlier in this paper, there is no direct step in the transfer of knowledge and technology from the developed to the developing country. In the field of water management it is recognized that the ultimate target of any knowledge transfer is the individual farmer, for it is on the farm land where the production resources, including water, climate, soil, crop, fertilizer, and management, are all integrated into an agricultural production system, and the concern in the developing world is to obtain more production per unit of water on each individual farm. Good water management is an indispensable part of modern agriculture. Indeed, the high-yielding varieties, especially wheat, require water at specific times if they are to perform to their potential. The President's Science Advisory Report quoted earlier says, "... the transition from traditional farming to modern agriculture will be difficult and expensive for the hungry nations but it is absolutely essential if their food needs are to be met. There is no alternative." Part of this expensive process will be the preparation of the farm land to receive and store water involving land grading (leveling), construction of farm ditches, and the improvement of the water courses and the available water supply to make it available on a timely basis. The improvement of the physical system as a necessary requisite of modern water management should receive high priority.

The ultimate target of the knowledge transfer as mentioned above is the farmer. However, in order to reach the farmer it is often necessary to train farm advisors, system operators, and administrators, and to develop production processes and institutions. A useful tool that has been employed in the United States, but to a lesser degree in the developing country, is the device of production contracts in which the processing and marketing institution enters into a contract with the farmer to buy his particular produce at a given price if it meets certain standards. In this contractual situation the farmer is provided with the necessary technical advice, seed, fertilizer, and management procedures that must be followed to obtain the quality desired by the processor. This arrangement has not been used to any considerable extent in the developing countries, and marketing and quality control are one of the chief problems. Markets do, however, provide a direct contact with the farmer and must receive greater emphasis as a mechanism for knowledge transfer.

A considerable problem that is apparent to all people working with the transfer of modern technology to the developing country is the selection and adaptation of the technologies that can be adapted to the local conditions within their constraints. Modern on-farm water management technology in developed countries and especially in the United States is highly capital-intensive, highly energy-intensive, and has a low labor requirement. In developing countries such as India and Pakistan, the energy simply is not available; likewise capital is very scarce and labor is abundant. A modern high-pressure sprinkling system which is fully automatic would, therefore, have only limited application in countries with limited available energy, whereas in the United States, although the system is highly sophisticated, it has many advantages for special conditions. The focus must, therefore, be on the applicability of the technology to the conditions that can be achieved in the LDC.

It is believed that modern on-farm water management will require considerable inputs of technology, large amounts of capital, but in general will require less labor. A well prepared farm, even for a low energy requirement system, such as surface irrigation, requires much less labor for irrigation than one which has not had the input of technology and the land preparation and other physical works necessary for the modern practices. There needs to be even more emphasis on the training of technicians to provide the necessary technical services. Capital or credit must also be provided, although to a limited extent available labor may sometimes be substituted for capital. The reduced labor requirement of lands better prepared will only slightly reduce the farm labor requirements if at all, since many other labor jobs will be created by new technology -- including cultivation and fertilizer practices.

A particular advantage of modern water technology that has not been mentioned heretofore is the advantage of built-in decisions that a well-designed system has for correct water application. A well-designed modern system has a considerable amount of management built into it, and the farmer is automatically led to the correct decision in the application of water to his land. The farmer will make fewer mistakes with a well-designed well-built system than he will with one which does not have the technology input. Where the farmer makes the right decisions regarding water management, the overall efficiency of the system will be greatly improved. Continued focus on modern technology to achieve designs with built-in management components is essential.

Since the water resource problems are highly 'site specific', one might postulate that the adaption of modern on-farm water management techniques will also be limited by local conditions. However, most of the methods for the transfer of knowledge outlined above will have applicability and can be used for appropriate conditions and ultimately concern the farm or the farmer.

GUIDELINES FOR TRANSFER OF PRACTICE TO
APPLICATIONS FOR OPTIMUM ON PLANNING OF KEY ITEMS
OF WATER RESOURCE PROJECTS

By

D.R.Sikka
B.E.(Hons.), F.I.E. (India)
M.Am. SCE., M.I. SRM
Secretary
Control Board for Major Projects
Madhya Pradesh State Government
BHOPAL (M.P.) INDIA

Synopsis

Overall requirements for the development of Water Resources and the Transfer of Knowledge have been indicated. The utilization of knowledge from research to practice on actual construction and implementation of Water Resources Structures like large irrigation and hydro-electric dams has been stressed. In addition classification of items, on the identified projects, methods for compilation and codification of data, and a central control on irrigation at the head-quarters of the organization have been suggested. Also an international classification of items in the prescribed area of operations has been emphasized. The present methods and procedures of the American Society of Civil Engineers has been commended. Also obstacles to the transfer of knowledge have been examined. As a result organizations and financing for these activities have been recommended.

Introduction

The well known saying, "The thirst of civilized man is insatiable, the more sophisticated the thirstier he grows, and in developing countries as little as 20 litres of fresh water per head per day sometimes suffices, in developed areas 150 to 250 litres," suggests that the criteria for planning and harnessing surface and sub-surface water resources in a developing area of a country, keep in view the priorities. The short and long term needs of its citizens must be considered. But are suitable norms available and will unpredictable operation and construction costs wait for the time involved in investigations and execution of the scheme and the role of political decisions? Therefore, what should be the effective organization for management and implementation of water resources projects involving millions and millions of dollars/rupees investment? Why should not the knowledge and experiences gained at similar places where results have been most productive at economical costs be available? Thus, an effective documentation and communication system has to exist if the transfer of knowledge from research to practice is to be achieved.

407

Planning with more alternatives and undertaking time bound construction programs which fit in the pre-determined socio-economic programs of prime use of water resource such as irrigation, hydro-electric power development including pumped storage, domestic and industrial water supply, artificial recharge, desalination of sea-waters, reservoirs multiple uses, water conveyance and distribution system considered suitable for the needs of the finalized area, require adequate finance, men, and material resources to harness for optimum utilization at minimum cost. Under the 'systems attack-action', the best could be achieved only if the 'efficiency factors' gained in other projects in similar circumstances are applied by a trained staff.

Some Key Factors for Classification and Codification on Construction Projects

There are, of course, many other aspects, physical, socio-logical, biological, economic, political, legal agricultural etc. and all these quantitative and initially nondeterminate dimensions need first integration to arrive at a particular plan: the most important requirement for the effective transfer and receipt of knowledge - project formulation at the time of preparation and then at the level of implementation. At present difficulties arise due to the size of the State or country, types of public and private sector efforts, economic conditions, availability of sophisticated data compilation and transmission equipments, existing means of communications, different objectives for water resource planning and applications, single project or a comprehensive plan under industrial or agricultural use within political boundaries or within the boundaries of river-basin or sub-basin. Then the designs and execution, involving concrete or stone masonry dam based on conventional methods, play a leading part. This generally results in individual project approach rather than a whole.

The prime requirement for developing water resources is to insure that the investigation and construction of projects is done under a crash program. Minimum time involved in completion means minimum investment and maximum benefits; this has to be the rule rather than exception. But, how can it be achieved in construction of large irrigation and hydro-electric dams and canal systems? The wire construction engineer knows that he should come out of the river bed at once, after successfully completing the foundation job of the gigantic hydraulic structure if he expects to complete the superstructure involving valuminous quantities in concrete or masonry in the remaining period left for completion. The prime requirements would be to complete the spillway arrangements including erection of spillway gates; as before he could simultaneously release the partial benefits with the raising of dam. How can this be achieved in practice more timely and effeciently if the project

manager of design and construction indicated is not aware of
the results achieved elsewhere in similar circumstances? It
is of paramount importance that transfer of the knowledge be
achieved with a "time base" and should be available to those
responsible for implementation of particular items. This would
require classification of items. Types of rocks, Exploration,
Foundations, Drilling, Grouting, Geological Constants, Spillway
gates sizes etc. their codification on field results, compiled
and released for reference elsewhere. Supposing a dam is completed in a country in 1972 and its case history report is
documented and published in 1978, there is not much use to dams
under construction between 1972-1978. However, after 1978, the
construction requirements would have changed considerably. It
is the time which is the essence for transfer and availability
of knowledge. Thus if foundations of a large dam involving
considerable public funds and requiring intensive drilling and
grouting construction of high R.C.C. Spillway piers or erection
of Gates are being tackled, the data collected on the same type
of rock and job should be available for studying alternatives
and working out economics, particularly in a system where
Engineers in a Government Organization are the designers and
supervisors, and contractors are only to execute accordingly.
We should, therefore, emphasize first the need for a classified
list of items under each of the main heads and sub-heads of
water resources projects and the hydraulic structures and appurtenant works and allot "signs and symbols" to it. It should be
prescribed that all documentation of research work or field data
collected in investigation during construction should be compiled
under these classified items. This would require each sizable
project to have a cell only for data collection, documentation,
and release. Component break-ups of a Water resources Plan of
the 'area' will have to be done, so that common components
could be referred everywhere under similar circumstances.

In addition, it is necessary to encourage standardization
in designs of components of hydraulic structures looking to the
requirements of benefits proposed, method of constructions based
on the type of equipment and labour employment methods proposed.
For example in case of Barrage, the Components above the crest
level could be standardized in respect to size of piers, size
of spillway gates, and items connected with block out concreting
of gates embedded parts. Also the method of estimating each
project should be done under the classified items, so that it
results in synchronization during implementation and codification.

The basic difficulty in achieving some of the above
objectives is the lack of effective organization, finance, and
initiative. It would, therefore, be essential to provide a
micro-percentage say 0.001 for this work, so that transfer
of knowledge could be released simultaneously with the completion of an item to the Central Information or Central Room

of the Organization for further compilation and documentation. This Control Room would have to be located at the headquarter office of the organization.

At present it has not been decided at what level the transfer of knowledge has to be released to those engaged upon investigations and construction. The circumstances would vary in case of those employed by contractors and by Government agencies like State's Irrigation Department. Ultimately, the present system of engineering cadres, particularly in Government departments may have to be replaced by areas. Specialist cadres for each of the classified items at levels other than the top or topmost level are essential so that the "Knowledge flow line" proceeds ahead uninterrupted in a chain series.

Need for Effective Planning - Implementation Body

Water Resources Projects involve millions of rupees/dollars investment. These have to be executed with confidence under time-bound operations, requiring quick and correct decisions at sanction and implementation levels, so that society is not deprived of benefits when even a 1 to 5% saving would mean substantial gains to exchequor. Let this be the first policy decision of the administration. This could only be possible scientifically not by undertaking projects in isolation but by making full use of transfer of knowledge from research to practice, proper evaluation of construction specifications, and Cost Curves based on results, wherever necessary crossing the international barriers.

Since a number of major projects are under investigation and execution, much effective transfer of knowledge takes place making decisions in meetings.

However, the real difficulty arises, because of the number of publications, books, journals etc. being released by the various national and international Organizations and Societies. Timely referencing is not possible, and not everybody concerned has the means to avail it. In this connection, however, the excellent work being done by American Society of Civil Engineers needs to be commended for its data collection, compilation, and releases through their Journals and Transactions.

Yet the greatest bottleneck is the absence of an overall body for investigating, planning, construction, and management of water resources plans. While efforts are made to have an integrated approach and organization for infrastructure development in the command areas of projects, there is yet to develop effective organization for development of upstream protection measures, fisheries, wildlife, water supply, antipollution measures and environmental effects. Multiple organizations all

410

over the country under different departments and agencies deal with water resource development creating difficulties in water budgeting and optimum utilization of projects constructed, what to talk of transfer of knowledge which should release as a 'flow' based on plans actually implemented by each except whenever seminars or conferences are held on a particular item.

Free flow and exchange of useful scientific data between private and public organizations rather than compartmentalization is also essential. More than that, the existing syllabus of University Courses, in many cases are becoming a bottleneck in proper appraisal of problems and requirements of the water resources planning and implementation schemes by our young planners and Engineers. Drastic changes are needed.

As soon as an effective body for planning overall water resource development with or without implementation of projects, is established for a region or river basin of the State in a country again with an apex body at the Central or Federal level, it is suggested that categories of projects should be prepared for those in which data collection and compilation would be made.

In this connection, it is worthwhile to mention that in Madhya Pradesh State, the Control Board for Major Projects has been constituted to be in charge of overall planning, investigation and construction of all major irrigation, hydro-electric and multipurpose projects, and the development of water resources for the whole State. This is to be governed by Chief Minister and its Progress Reviewing Committee and presided over by Chief Secretary, the highest Civilian of the State.

However, it is desirable to prescribe suitable norms and criteria for launching a program of transfer of knowledge on Water Resources Projects, under a phased categorized program, looking to the funds available for each of the pinpointing organizations in the area of action. If the Conference is able to high-light some of the important issues with the presence of several experts from all over the world, very useful steps would have been initiated for achieving most economical and efficient execution of public projects in this vital sector for the welfare of the Society.

For example I was engaged in the construction of Hasdeo Barrage, a huge hydraulic structure constructed across River Hasdoe with a catchment area of 3000 sq. miles and a designed flood discharge of 0.8 million cusecs. While tackling its complicated foundations involving foundation treatments and comprising of facture and fissured granite rocks, I derived the following result:

Average consumption of cement after final plugging of grout worked out:

Type of grouting	@ foot of hole	@ unit area
(a) Curtain-45 lbs. per sq. inch Mix. 1:12 to 1:6.	21 lbs.	1.54 lbs.
(b) Consolidation 20-30 lbs. per sq. inch Mix. 1:4 to 1:6.	24 lbs.	1.65 lbs.

The yardstick for, depth of holes/pressures in grout holes, which could thus be worked out, is

$$D = \frac{H}{4 \text{ to } 5} \times Z$$

D = depth of holes required in ft.
H = Height of maximum flood level -upstream above hole
Z = Constant varying on Geological conditions.

Value of 'Z' in the above cases worked out to zero for semiconsolidated sandstones, 1 to 1.25 for curtain grouting, and 0.75 to 1 for consolidation grouting. The final grouting pressures were to be 1.5 to 2 times the depth of the hole, but the fissures and seams about the rocks took limited intakes at 0.751 times of the depth. Mechanical extramination of such type of rocks in search of harder varieties would increase considerably the cost of projects. Thus this should serve as a guideline for construction planning on our projects in similar situations.

The following should be carefully analyzed: 1) whether to use blanket or consolidation grouting in a particular type of rock, depending on their intake and porosity; 2) whether we could eliminate grouting to save time and costs; 3) whether such an elimination would result in improvement of foundation drainage? The above results at Hasdeo Barrage would satisfactorily tend to establish that operations on this item could be avoided or at least kept to bare minimum.

Experiences mentioned above clearly show an urgent need for an international standardization and classification of rocks from the practical and construction point of view, so that their treatments are considered, only where absolutely necessary. Thus one could come above the river bed as quickly as possible. The 'key' to successful, economical, and timely completion of river valley projects involving capital outlay of crores of rupees.

The classification/codification, if done by collecting data on all the sizable dams constructed all over the world, and by determining geological constants and ranges would allow useful knowledge derived from practical results achieved on efficiently planned and implemented projects to be diverted for use elsewhere particularly for those where water development projects are the lifetime of the society's needs. Similar action would be called for in respect to other items indicated earlier.

NEW FRONTiERS IN DRAINAGE AND RECLAMATION ENGINEERING IN THE INDUS PLAINS

By

Mohiuddin Khan, S.K.

Engineering Advisor

Synopsis

This paper discusses the success and failures of some of the world's largest projects for drainage and reclamation. The story of drainage and reclamation in West Pakistan is a fàscinating story of transfer of knowledge not only from developed countries to developing countries but also from research and local experience to practical implementation in the last two to three decades. Progressively new concepts have been evolved in West Pakistan.

Introduction

The Indus Plain has the largest contiguous system of irrigation in the world with a gross commanded area of 37.4 million acres and a culturable commanded area of 33 million acres. According to recent surveys more than 17 million acres of agricultural land in the Indus Plain has a water table within 10 feet of the groundwater, which is a potentially hazardous limit. An area of 11 million acres is affected by salinity. An area of about 40,000 to 100,000 acres is being damaged annually due to waterlogging and salinity, and about 14 million acres have fresh groundwater where salinity is 1000 ppm T.D.S. Approximately 5 million acres have groundwaters ranging from 1000 to 3000 ppm which can be used by mixing it with river and canal waters, whereas 11 million acres have saline waters above 3000 ppm which cannot be used for irrigation even by mixing with canal water. As these statistics show, waterlogging and salinity are a serious problem in a country which is essentially agricultural and where 80% of the people depend on agriculture.

Systematic irrigation in the Indus Plain has a history of about 100 years when inundation canals from rivers were beginning to be converted into weir control. The annual irrigation at present is about 30 million acres and is restricted mostly due to shortage of supplies. Higher intensities are possible with better water availability and drainage and reclamation. Unfortunately, when this large system of irrigation was developed, drainage and reclamation were not given the necessary importance; thus the Indus basin has suffered from the menace of salinity and waterlogging on such a large scale. The problem was realized in the Twenties when the Irrigation Research Institute, Lahore was set up. A Directorate of Land Reclamation was also created for the

414

Punjab in 1946 to reclaim salt affected lands. This
Directorate had started a program of reclaiming the soil by
means of leaching by rice crops with flood supplies. Crop
rotation and green manuring were also adopted.

The Sukkur Barrage in the lower Sind, which has a
commanded area of 7.5 million acres, was opened in the early
Thirties; however, a few years later serious waterlogging
conditions developed. The Northern areas in the Punjab were
already facing the problem of waterlogging and salinity. In
these early stages the only measures conceived were open
drains. Drains did not prove a success as they have a limited
influence for drainage of seepage water and for removing
waterlogging conditions. Serious efforts could only be started
after independence in 1947.

Work by F.A.O. Experts

Apart from the studies carried out by the Irrigation
Research Institute, Lahore, and the Directorate of Land
Reclamation, help was sought from agencies such as F.A.O.
as far back as 1950. Mr. Milo B. William of F.A.O. visited
Pakistan in 1950 followed by other experts from F.A.O. and
made a number of suggestions with regard to tubewells for
drainage, reclamation by installation of tile drainage, etc.
The main recommendation of F.A.O. experts was to carry out
more survey and investigation and to select a few pilot areas.
They did select a small area in the Punjab and 20 tubewells
were constructed in the Chuharkana area, which formed the
first pilot project. This area had also been selected by the
Punjab Soil Reclamation Board for experimentation. Dr. Frank
Eaton of the River Side Laboratory of the U.S.A., who was
sent by the F.A.O. to study the salinity and alkalinity in the
Irrigated Lands in the Indus Valley, submitted a report in
1953. He made detailed recommendations about the quality of
irrigation waters in West Pakistan, the control of groundwater
table by open drains, and tile drains, the pumping of water
from tubewells, and the use of gypsum to overcome sodium
hazard, etc.

Advice by U.S. Bureau of Reclamation

Mr. Maierhofer of U.S. Bureau of Reclamation discussed
the proposals of F.A.O. to start pilot schemes and made his
own suggestions. In his opinion the country needed an action
program much more than simple experimentation which, unless
very closely supervised, can become too academic and specialized for practical application. Pilot projects, in his view,
are operated by skilled technicians, whereas farms are operated
by farmers who in Pakistan are uneducated. Therefore, the
education of farmers should take place on the farm by
actually "doing" and through irrigation extension among

agriculturists. After the lands are made fit for more
productive farming and after sufficient water is available,
they will learn much more than they could have from occasionally
viewing a pilot project.

According to him the technical problems which exist are
not new. They have all been encountered before and successfully solved. Therefore, there should be no great need for
pilot projects to develop answers. The energies and funds,
instead, should be directed towards actual work on the lands.
We have reliable irrigation and reclamation for estimating
the amount of water they require and the best methods of
application for designing the irrigation system to meet these
requirements, for designing and constructing drainage works
to prevent waterlogging and salinization and to remove the
salts, for the most favorable land use for given conditions of
soils and climate, and for developing the groundwater potential.
This suggestion by Mr. Maierhofer coming as far back as 1952
is remarkable as it is by actually undertaking large projects
that transfer of knowledge has been possible in Pakistan. In
fact the demonstration of public tubewells has significantly
accelerated the development of tubewells in the private
sector in West Pakistan which is responsible for the green
revolution.

Help by U.S. AID

In 1954 the United States International Co-operation
Agency offered assistance in the program of drainage and reclamation so urgently needed by West Pakistan. A contingent
of groundwater and soil experts of the United States Geological
Survey came to West Pakistan and planned a major program of
investigations on groundwater resources as well as land
capabilities for reclamation purposes. Large scale investigations were carried out by exploratory drillings in the
Punjab to determine the geological formation of the areas and
the groundwater quality both from deep and shallow resources.
The permeability and storage coefficient of the formation was
also determined by actual pumping tests. This work was done
by a special organization of the Irrigation Department Punjab
known as the Groundwater Development Organization which in
1958 prepared its first Salinity Control and Reclamation
Project (SCARP) for about 1.25 million acres of the Central
Rechna Doab.

W.A.P.D.A. Programme

In 1958 West Pakistan Water and Power Development
Authority, W.P.WAPDA, came into being. Assisted by consultants such as Tipton and Kalmbach, Harza, Huntings and
MacDonalds etc., it took over the problem of waterlogging
and salinity and prepared a program for the whole of West

Pakistan in 1961. The program had 26 projects which would benefit 29 million acres under the command of existing irrigation systems. They comprised 10 reclamation schemes in the northern part of the Indus Plain and 16 projects in the southern area. The reclamation schemes of the Northern Zone embody primarily the utilization of tubewells for subsoil drainage combined with drainage for the removal of storm runoff. In the Southern Zone the reclamation schemes consisted primarily of open drains for the removal of subsoil and surface water supplemented with tubewells in those areas where it is feasible to provide subsoil drainage by this means. In all, the program embodied the construction of some 31,500 tubewells, 7,500 miles of major drainage channels, and 25,000 miles of supplemental drains.

U.S. White House Expert Panel Report

The President of Pakistan visited the U.S.A. in 1961 and requested the President to send a team of experts to study the problem of waterlogging and salinity in Pakistan. A mission headed by the Scientific Adviser to the President of the U.S.A. and followed by Dr. Revelle went into the problem in great depth and prepared a report.

The 1964 report on Land and Water Development in the Indus Basin by the U.S. White House Department of Interior Panel on waterlogging and salinity in West Pakistan popularly known as the Revelle Report is a comprehensive document for agriculture, drainage, and reclamation of West Pakistan. The engineering aspects of the report were on the lines of WAPDA program, but the panel laid great emphasis on the agricultural aspects. The panel felt that agriculture in West Pakistan is both a physical and human problem. It is a problem of land, of water, of people, and of the interactions among them. The panel brought out that waterlogging and salinity is only one of the problems besetting agriculture. They stated that there are various other problems such as need for additional irrigation water, more fertilizer, improved seed and crop varieties, pest and disease control, better cultivation, and salt free soil. Each can increase yields 10 to 30 percent when applied singly, but in combination they can give increase of 200 to 300 percent. The panel suggested dividing West Pakistan into project areas of not less than a million acres and taking up integrated development of these project areas. On the administrative side the panel recommended a shift from a structure based on function to one based on area. Their view was that the shift would permit a coordinated attack on all aspects of the agricultural problem in regions of managable size. The panel considered that transfer of technology to farmers is especially important. They also suggested that the study of techniques of transfer of knowledge should be given high priority.

In practice considerable benefit has been derived from these suggestions in Central Rechna in the Northern Indus Plain and in the Khairpur project in the South. The administrative setup had to be changed to make it more economical and to fit it with the functions of the existing Government Departments after experience of the two projects. Suggestions of this panel underwent a major change with respect to the proposal of mining water as it was considered that mining water up to 100 feet as suggested by the panel would cause serious problems. There was severe criticism by the Irrigation and Agriculture Departments and other Pakistani experts. The World Bank Team carefully examined objections by various sources and came to the conclusion that the water should be depressed by only 10 to 15 feet below ground. Lowering the water table to 100 feet would increase seepage losses and cause intrusion of saline water from adjoining areas.

Views of Dr. Kovda of UNESCO

Dr. Victor Kovda, Director of the Department of Natural Sciences of UNESCO, visited Pakistan in 1964 and studied the problem of drainage and reclamation of the Indus Plains. Though the visit was only for 10 days he gave certain useful suggestions and took part in the F.A.O. Seminar held at Lahore in 1964. He reported that the idea of installation of huge networks of pumping tubewells with cyclic circulation of saline groundwater and soluble salts was being studied. Also, the reserves of accumulated toxic soluble salts be reported by artificial means outside the irrigated land. The existing balance of growing accumulation of soluble salts should be destroyed and replaced by new type of balance of desalinization with permanent outflow of any excess of soluble salts. This task most effectively could be done by heavy leachings and washing out of soluble toxic salts from both saline soils and saline groundwaters.

He also stated that there is a sharp increase of salinity of groundwater with depth, and the absence of mapping of the groundwaters makes it difficult to predict the effect of using groundwaters on the soils. He was not clear about the hydrological and chemical relationship of the fresh groundwater with the deep basic stratum and the mineralized groundwater both in the horizontal and vertical directions. He concluded that it would be difficult to predict the long term conclusion of pumping fresh groundwater on the basis of existing scientific information. This warning of Dr. Kovda has proved correct. For example, in the sweet water zones in the Punjab where large scale pumping of groundwater has taken place, the quality of water has deteriorated fast and many of the tubewells had to be abandoned.

418

Horizontal Drainage Versus Vertical Drainage

The controversy regarding the horizontal versus vertical drainage has been going on ever since serious technical study of drainage and reclamation in the Indus Plains was undertaken. The Lower Indus Project Consultants consisting of Hunting Technical Services and Sir Macdonald and Partners examined the economics of tubewells and tile drains. According to them the capital cost of drainage by tubewells is Rs. 174/- per acre for a 3 cusec tubewell and Rs. 112/- per acre for a 4 cusec tubewell. The annual cost is Rs. 39/- to Rs. 24/- per acre. The capital cost of drainage by tile drain is Rs. 640/- per acre and the annual costs Rs. 49/- per acre. It was thus felt that in sweet water zones drainage by tubewells is the most suitable method. Even in semi saline and saline areas compound tubewells and skimming wells were suggested.

The F.A.O. Seminar of 1964 held in Lahore debated the various aspects of reclamation and drainage, and the consensus was that in the sweet water zones the most economical method of reclamation and drainage is to sink tubewells which would not only depress the water table but make available water for leaching of salts and increase the cropping intensity. Mixing with canal water in suitable proportion was considered a solution where the groundwater had concentration higher than permissible. By and large the salinity and reclamation projects in West Pakistan followed this concept.

Suggestions by World Bank Study Group

The World Bank Team headed by Peter Lieftinck and assisted by international consultants such as Sir Alexandar Gibb and Partners, Hunting Technical Services and International Land Development Consultants undertook preparation of a Master Plan for Water and Power Resources in West Pakistan. Drainage and Reclamation formed an important part of the water program.

The first phase of the action program was for the development of a total of 10,118 public tubewells in the on-going V SCARPS. It was necessary to undertake 12 additional tubewell projects in which 11,403 tubewells need to be installed. The capacity of 4,867 tubewells would be 4 cusecs and of 6,556 tubewells equal to 3 cusecs. These were to serve about 12 million acres. 8000 public tubewells 3 to 4 cusecs and 200 to 250 feet deep with imported materials have been completed and about 2,500 remain to be electrified.

In the saline groundwater zones, however, a separate and specific drainage system would be required, and the effluent would have to be disposed of through the river system into the desert or sea, according to circumstances. In the Punjab Doabs the outfalls can only run into the river channels; thus

419

excessive salinization of river water, it would be necessary for saline tubewell effluent to be discharged only during periods of high river flow. In the IACA's (World Bank Consultants) view this would make the annual cost of tubewell drainage comparable with that of tile drainage. In areas where direct disposal facilities to the sea or to the desert are proposed and where the aquifer is suitable for tubewells, tubewell drainage is more economical than tile drainage because large capacity drainage wells could be pumped throughout the year. This applies to the Lower Indus, where large outfall drains are planned, and to the Sutlej Left Bank, effluent would be dispersed into the adjacent desert.

Suggestions for Future Projects

After the experience of the first 5 SCARPS and the development of about 90,000 private tubewells, it is now felt that private tubewells will be more economical and could be encouraged in the sweet water zones, whereas public tubewells should be concentrated in the saline water zones. The World Bank Review Mission of 1970 also agreed that private tubewells of about 1 cusec capacity were as good as public tubewells for lowering the water table and making water available at economical cost. This is a great departure from the previous thinking of the foreign consultants and the World Bank itself which had a public tubewell orientation in the action program. In fact, the review mission suggested reduction in the size of the public tubewell program in the action program up to 1975 due to financial constraints and the above factors. In addition the following suggestions are being considered by the government for future SCARPS:

(i)   The size of the public tubewells may be reduced from 3-4 cusecs to about 2 cusecs which is more manageable and is near to the discharge of outlets where mixing is done. This is the size of the departmental tubewells which were being constructed before the foreign aided projects were undertaken in Pakistan. With this discharge there is less danger of pumping saline water. The depth of tubewells which varies from 200 to 300 feet was mainly responsible for higher salinity of the water as the salinity of water increases with depth. The ratio of horizontal permeability to vertical is 50 to 100 in the area; thus deep tubewells pumped more saline water.

(ii) Mild steel and fibre glass strainers have not proved a success. We may have to revert back to the departmental brass strainers or alternatively try P.V.C. and asbestos cement for economy.

420

(iii) As mining of water is not to be done, ordinary
centrifugal pumps which are locally manufactured
may be installed instead of turbine pumps, except
where required by special cases. The cost of operation and maintenance of centrifugal pumps would be
smaller.

(iv) Greater attention should be paid to soil reclamation
in the SCARP Project areas as soils have deteriorated
due to use of deep tubewell water.

(v) Detailed planning, engineering, and design of SCARPS
should be carried out by local design organizations.
Electrification and installation of tubewells should
be done by a single agency to avoid delays.

Conclusion

It can be seen from the above that the transfer of
knowledge in the Indus Plain with respect to drainage and
reclamation has been a two-way traffic, not only from the
developing countries to developed countries but also from
developing countries to the general pool of knowledge. The
experience of SCARPS in West Pakistan is unique as these are
some of the largest reclamation and drainage projects in the
world. Thus, Pakistan has achieved the necessary break-through
in the new frontiers in drainage and reclamation engineering
by undertaking the SCARPS at great cost and by associating the
developing countries. Large problems require large solutions.
Mistakes have been made and lessons learned, but Pakistan and
the World are the wiser for it.

Greater success in transfer of knowledge would have been
facilitated by adopting the following methods:

(a) Intimate association with local experts who know
the area and problems, and proper check on consultants
of foreign aided projects.

(b) Restriction on large scale transfer of sophisticated
techniques of developed countries to developing
countries without thorough analysis of all technical
and socio-economic aspects.

(c) Seminars and symposia at different stages of
investigation planning, project preparation, operation,
and maintenance.

(d) A more thorough post project monitoring and evaluation.

References

1. Reports of the Irrigation Research Institute, Lahore; Directorate of Land Reclamation, Lahore; and Irrigation, Drainage, and Flood Control Research Council.

2. Reports of the Groundwater Development Organization, Irrigation Department, Punjab.

3. Reports of WAPDA's Consultants:

   (i)   Tipton and Kalmbach

   (ii) Harza Engineering Company;

   (iii) Hunting Technical Services, and

   (iv) Sir Macdonald and Partners.

4. Report prepared by the World Bank Study Group headed by Pieter Lieftinck, 1967.

5. World Bank Review Mission Report.

SESSION VI - COMMENTS

DISCUSSION by R. G. Thomas*

Once again, I would like to emphasize the complexity of
the problems not only of the UN system, but of the world wide
problem of levels of competance, level of problems etc. It
should be emphasized, however, that the basic principle of
the UN assistance is that all requests for assistance come
from the countries themselves. Details of what to do must
then be worked out by the experts of the countries (where
they exist) and experts of the UN system. It should not be
forgotten, however, that nations have available many other
sources of assistance to choose from.

DISCUSSION by J. A. Cunge**

I would like to support very strongly the idea expressed
by Prof. Nemec that it is dangerous to use one single contractor
or one school of thought. The Vistula project was in
difficulties because there were not used computers of 3rd
generation. I think that international organizations should
impose to contractors the application of their customary
techniques to the local conditions. This was done for Lower
Mekong Project by UNESCO and it worked all right.

DISCUSSION by A. R. LeFeuvre***

With reference to the development of mathematical models
to the Vistula River, Canada had a similar experience of model
technology transfer. In this case a Canadian consultant
employed a U.S. Specialist in mathematical models as a sub-
contractor with the proviso that an employee of the Canadian
consultant be trained in the technique and participate in the
execution of the project. Additionally, the contract required
a number of seminars to educate both private sector and
government staff in the Math Model techniques using the actual
project as a timely example.

DISCUSSION by Paul-Marc Henry****

As a reaction to Mr. Nemec's presentation, I would like
to remark on the "Polish" project.

1. Assert the value of the project to act as a catalyst
in requesting more than twenty different authorities in Poland
to agree on a joint approach.

2. Sub-contractors had to report to an International
Advisory Board with leading experts from several institutions

*F.A.O., Rome, Italy
**Engineering Research Center, Colorado State University
***Box 5050, Burlington, Ontario
****O.E.C.D., Paris, France

423

and different countries.

3. Emphasize the value of the tour of most advanced institutions by related groups of experts, from countries of the project prior to the implementation of the projects.

DISCUSSION by W. W. Doyel*

With regard to standards, there is a Federal Interagency Work Group presently developing recommended procedures for water-data acquisition. The National Bureau of Standards recently issued a large publication listing activities in the field of standards development.

With respect to the subject of transfer of knowledge and with particular reference to the area of technical assistance, one aspect that plays a vital role has not been mentioned. Maybe it is understood, but I feel it needs to be identified clearly. In any exchange there is the element of anticipation - what the recipient expects to receive and what the giver expects to give. Expectation can be either positive or negative, but it is a filter through which communication takes place, and it influences both the giver and the receiver. When the expectations are not met an adverse reaction can result. The role of expectation should be fully recognized in technical assistance, especially because of this inherent problem in communication across cultural, idealogical and language boundaries.

DISCUSSION by Dr. Omer J. Kelley**

It seems to me that the reviewer missed at least part of the issue in his reference to "the printed page." Obviously, AID recognizes "the printed page" as a major means of general transfer of knowledge as is indicated in the paper. This particularly works well on an individual basis. Also, as indicated in the paper, just in our office alone we transmit more than 100,000 publications yearly for the LDCs. The point being made in the paper refers to the solutions of "on-farm water management problems." It has been our experience that more than just knowledge of the printed page is necessary to accomplish what is needed for good on-farm water management practices. Hence, we have found other methods of knowledge transfer seems to be quite important. Further, many "printed pages" have been available to LDC scientists and administrators relating to on-farm water management practices for many years, from the almost complete lack of development programs in this area or good land leveling and water management practices on individual farms, it would seem almost axiomatic that "the printed page" has not been fully effective.

*U.S. Geological Survey, Washington, D.C. 20242
**Agency for International Development, Washington, D.C. 20523

INTERNATIONAL ORGANIZATION TRANSFER EXPERIENCE

Chairman: Victor Koelzer

Rapporteur: Bruce Anderson

● *The last session offers an appropriate concluding
note as to the global requirements and larger
bodies involved in water resources knowledge.   The
common concern revolves around the crucial aspects
of development and of the benefits that accrue to
mankind from the extension of knowledge.   Knowledge
transfer and water resources policies must be integrated with an overall social and economic development.   To do otherwise, it will be an exercise in
academic sterility, rather than a vital element in
the common effort towards the betterment of mankind.*

Rapporteur: Bruce H. Anderson
Director, International Programs
Utah State University
Logan, Utah, USA

Seven papers are considered in this summary report. Six
of the seven papers come from the United Nations system of
organizations with the seventh paper from the United States
Army Corps of Engineers. Two of the six papers come from personnel of the Water Resources Section, Resources and Transport
Division, United Nations Headquarters, New York; and two from
the Water Resources and Development Division, Rome, Italy. One
paper from the Office of Hydrology, United Nations Educational,
Scientific and Cultural Organization, Paris, France; and one
from World Meteorological Organization, Bogota, Colombia.

The summary report will consist of a brief review of each
paper on an individual basis followed by elaboration and discussion of some of the key points raised and emphasized by the
papers. The general reporter will highlight areas that, in his
opinion, need further discussion, clarification and debate, in
an attempt to stimulate reaction from the participants, with
the authors and between the authors.

An IHD Project for Technology Transfer to Developing Regions

This paper is considered as an informative progress report
on a specific project undertaken by the U. S. Army Corps of
Engineers. As such, it stands somewhat apart from the other
papers in this group.

The objective of the project is to develop, test, and
document "methods suitable for practical applications in
hydrologic engineering." Special attention is given to methods
and procedures where hydrologic records are deficient in time,
accuracy and general coverage.

The work will consist of 12 volumes, a description of which
is provided in the paper. A training workshop is reported which
will provide training in efficient use of the most effective
techniques from hydrologic engineering studies.

The full impact and contribution of the work will, of
course, only be known after the volumes are completed, tested,
revised and put to use. The completion of this project should
be of interest to all of us.

The Role of FAO in the Transfer of Water Resource Knowledge to Developing Regions

This paper contends that we must be concerned with the benefits that accrue to mankind. Development is a slow process and the major role in its achievement must come from within the country itself. External inputs can be catalytic, but must be carefully selected to meet the complex needs and absorption capacity of the country. The variables affecting knowledge transfer and its impact are many and need consideration. It must, however, be site specific.

The function of FAO to fight proverty, malnutrition, and hunger through the Regular Programme which includes world surveys, conferences, seminars, and publications and contact with new technology, and its Field Programme of providing advisors and other technical assistance is explained. The process and problems of knowledge transfer under the above programs provides some insight into the experience of FAO.

The conclusions and summary provided express the authors ideas that knowledge and wisdom transfer is the best form of aid, that it is a human process, and that care in selection and adaptation of knowledge is essential. The selection and preparation of persons who receive and those who give is of crucial importance, and that greater support, recognition and esteem should be accorded those who provide the bridge between available knowledge and its practice. Finally, the authors make a plea for more lucid scientific writing and some means to discourage work that apparently is of little worth in problem solving and that which benefits man.

Technical Activities by FAO in the Transfer of Water Resources Knowledge to Developing Regions

The authors make the point that water is a major factor in controlling man's destiny, that it is a fixed supply and the demands upon it are increasing, necessitating careful planning and attention to an efficient use of the resource. The hunger problem has always been with us but the gap between rich and poor is widening. There is a great manpower resource of well-trained people available to work on problems, but the inability to get knowledge to the user, the practitioner, is a major obstacle.

The paper considers many of the factors which must be considered in a transfer of knowledge about water, its development and management. The planning of water programs must involve a complex array of factors including environmental factors in the hope of finding some optimal path to minimize nonproductive activities and maximize productive and efficient utilization criteria.

A wise management of water probably can do more toward increasing food supplies and agricultural income than any other agricultural practice. The barriers to good use include traditional practices, which must be changed. The concepts of the interrelationships between water, fertilizers and good seeds must be part of knowledge transfer in addition to good design organization and administration of systems and farmer education. The integration of such factors into the economic-socio-political structure of a country must all be part of comprehensive planning to achieve an optimization of the inter-relations between key factors. The authors stress the need for knowledge transfer to reach the user and a recognition that those involved therein should not be relegated to what they call a "secondary citizen" role.

Transfer of Knowledge in Water Resource Policies From Developed to Developing Countries

Water resources policy is defined as "the shaping of basic guidelines, organizational principles, and fundamental procedures under which water is managed and utilized within any given society and in relation to neighboring societies." A chart is provided listing some of the basic constraints affecting policy formulation as well as implementation actions.

Knowledge transfer programs should be conditioned to meet specific country needs, priorities and alternatives as defined by local institutions and agencies. A basis for such decisions should be a comparative survey on available supplies and future demands.

Knowledge transfer must consider integration with overall social and economic development and the bias naturally held by water oriented experts should be avoided by selecting policy formulators who are not water oriented. Recognition of rapid change in use patterns and needs is essential and a broad look must be taken of alternative uses. Then the level of technology applicable to the region can be determined. The functions of United Nations organizations is considered and a listing of some of their activities provided.

Transfer of Water Resources Knowledge Through The United Nations Technical Assistance Activities

The United Nations Department of Economic and Social Affairs Headquarters in New York, bears responsibility for the exploration, assessment and development of mineral, water, and energy resources and primarily for the resources located underground. Emphasis has been given to feasibility type studies and approximately 19 are in progress or have been completed, usually through private contracts. Publications consultant panels, seminars and symposia, experts and consultants have been used for knowledge dissemination purposes.

429

Training of personnel at all levels is of major concern in knowledge transfer. This is done through many types of programs from on the job training to formal academic programs at the post-graduate level.

In recent years, emphasis has changed from "nonoperational" activities to operational activities. Experience indicates that "technical and scientific knowledge on water cannot be transmitted directly from industrialized countries to developing countries. It has to be adapted to local conditions taking into account natural and economic conditions as well as the human factor."

Examples are provided of specific problems that have arisen due to lack of understanding of local conditions. Two pitfalls are pointed out: academism and empirism. Undue pressures are sometimes placed on countries by consulting firms and foreign technicians to follow practices or techniques not suited to the countries capability.

Trained personnel are limited and ofttimes courses are provided to persons without the background needed to absorb the information provided. Experience indicates that a proliferation of water agencies should be avoided. Cooperation should replace assistance in the near future and the relationships between donor and recipient will than change for the better.

A listing of UNDP/UN sponsored water resources projects is provided.

Recent Development of Hydrological Services in Colombia

This paper provides a specific example of a knowledge transfer project in hydrology and meteorology in Colombia. A massive transfer of knowledge is considered necessary to help reduce the differences between developing and developed countries. Prerequisite to such a transfer is a receptive infrastructure to gather the necessary technical competence and establish policy for development.

Colombia took the necessary steps and established the Colombian Meteorological and Hydrological Service. The steps in its progress are indicated including the decisions necessary to adapt modern technological methodologies to Colombian conditions. Automated data processing was bypassed in favor of manual data processing procedures. The author provides examples of the relationships and physical characteristics of various parameters in the Colombian case and indicates how these affected the decisions made in developing policy and programs for Colombia.

Transfer of Water Resources Knowledge Aspects of the Work of the
United Nations System

The paper discusses knowledge transfer from one country to
another or horizontal transfer. Alternative ways of promoting
inflow of knowledge are stated, with due consideration to the
goals desired by the country. Factors affecting a country's
ability to absorb the transfer successfully include financial
resources, capable people, management capacity, knowledge and a
proper political and social infrastructure. Assistance to
achieve the infrastructure required to successfully absorb knowledge is available through the United Nation Advisory Committee
on Application of Science and Technology (UNACAST).

The United Nation system provides assistance in knowledge
transfer through Regular Programs and through United Nations
Development Program. Examples of types of programs available
are listed for both programs.

DISCUSSION

Since the title of the general summary report is International Organization Transfer Experience, it is unfortunate that
more papers outlining the experience of other international
organizations and agencies were not included as a basis for comparison. Perhaps they are provided in another set of papers.
As indicated above, the work presented here is almost exclusively
that of the organization of the United Nations. However, a wide
spectrum of water resources is considered and the papers provide
food for thought and warrant consideration by the conference
members.

A very important area of consideration is introduced by
Mr. Szesztay, that of Policy Formulation for Water Resources.
The definition as approached by the United Nations covers aspects of water management and utilization. It adequately covers
the problems that arise within a given society and its neighbors
in relation to the above aspects, but seems to omit the element
of developing water for management and use. The area of identifying the resources and preparing it for management and use
should perhaps be included in a comprehensive definition of
Water Resource Policy.

The point is well made that the responsibility for defining
needs and priorities for knowledge transfer emphasis, rests with
the persons or institutions charged with the responsibility of
policy formulation and implementation. It may be, however, that
some advice and assistance is needed from outside sources to
provide a proper perspective. It is the experience of this
author that the identification of needs and priorities is a

rather difficult task and one often neglected by many nations.
Mr. Szesztay stresses the differences that will and do exist
from country to country which determines the degree of sophistication required in knowledge transfer programs.

To aid decision makers in policy formulation, a comparative
survey on available supplies and future demands upon water is
recommended. It is stressed that such a survey will also condition the choice of alternatives in a development program.
Twelve areas are listed by Mr. Szesztay that may affect policy
formulation in the choice of alternative programs.

The case of Colombia in developing Hydrological Services
as given by Wulf Klohn and Silviu Stanescu illustrates what can
happen when policy makers decide on a program and put the necessary resources to work to make it go. Important here is the
fact that the country must be ready to develop the infrastructure required to assure a successful program.

The above point leads naturally into the area of planning
of water resources. The Houston, Horning paper emphasizes
overall integrated planning. All factors involved in water development must be integrated in the hope of finding an optimal
path to minimize nonproductive activities and maximize productive activities and efficient utilization of the resource.

A total approach to planning requires a large allocation
of resources of all kinds to provide adequate data for decision
making. It is indicated, however, that some initial water development can usually proceed rather rapidly using underground
water resources. A program of full development would require
time and a good look at the problems which may arise as development proceeds. The above approach is also indicated in Dijon's
paper. He places more emphasis on a rapid pay-off from planning. He indicates that priorities should be given to projects
which can lead to practical results within a short period of
time.

Mr. Verhoog indicates that a country faces a choice. It
may choose a fast payoff using developed country assistance
and procedures, or it may choose to move more slowly with
less dependence economically, socially and culturally on a
developed country. The United Nation system places greater
emphasis on the latter according to Mr. Verhoog. There is a
difference in point of view expressed in Mr. Dijon's paper.

The approaches to planning indicated above raises some
interesting challenges when considering knowledge transfer.
First, integrated planning requires a great deal of expertise,
and an ability to be able to see how all the factors of water
resources blend and interact together. Of interest is how do

432

we handle such a complex transfer of knowledge to a country whose resources are limited and where institutions are developing but perhaps not yet ready for such sophistication. It is hard to argue with the concept, but it is also difficult to see how all factors can be adequately handled when resources to apply to the task may be in short supply. This is especially true of experienced personnel. Many have received good academic training, but many lack experience in project formulation and decision making with respect to project development. Perhaps it is for the above reasons that Dijon presses for a fast return from development projects. But here again, projects designed for fast returns may have adverse effects farther down the time scale, and these may outweigh the advantages of fast pay-off. All of which seems to argue that the need for knowledge transfer is of great importance and must proceed as rapidly as possible. The question as to how and at what level must then be asked.

A common thread running throughout the papers is that care must be exercised in the level of technology and knowledge transferred. The criteria seems to be that this is a site specific problem and must be handled on a region by region basis. Only in this way can factors such as the socio-economic levels be considered, and the human factor be brought prominently to the forefront.

Mr. Klohn and Mr. Stanescu's paper on Colombia provides good evidence that the country was ready for a knowledge transfer program. It made resources available and made policy decisions commensurate with the requirements of the program. Noteworthy is the discussion on the decisions that were made to keep the program on a level commensurate with actual country situations. Perhaps the conference would be well advised to reflect on this point and react to how you can actually determine the technology level and what are the implications of setting your sites too low or too high in this respect. An interesting statement is made by Mr. Dijon to the effect that "technical and scientific knowledge on water cannot be transmitted directly from industrailized countries to developing countries." He indicates that, "It has to be adapted to local conditions taking into account natural and economic conditions and the human factor." Many of the other papers seem to agree with Dijon. They do, however, emphasize the second part of the statement, and provide illustrations and examples to substantiate the point of view expressed. It may be of value though to examine the first statement. Perhpas it is a question of semantics, but it is difficult for this writer to accept the statement as made.

Is it true that we cannot transfer technical and scientific knowledge on water directly from industrialized countries to

developing countries? This author contends that you can, in
fact, you must transfer scientific knowledge directly. Let me
illustrate this to the extent that Darcy's Law doesn't change
because one country is less industrialized than another, factors
that affect water movement through soils or the coefficient of
friction for a given pipe size for a given flow for the material
used does not change, rather it is how we apply knowledge, the
technology that we transfer that is in question. Mr. Dijon's
example indicates that the wrong knowledge was applied to the
problem - scientific knowledge per se was not at fault.

There is an implication in the statement of Dijon and his
examples that there needs to be a better orientation of those
who are involved in knowledge transfer. A careful selection
of professional people should be made before they are used in
programs of knowledge transfer. This point is also made by
others.

Again, clarification is needed on the "two pit falls"
"academism and empirism" discussed in Dijon's paper. A proper screening of personnel for a particular job seems to be
the issue he raises. Again, the real problem seems to be in
how academism is applied not in academism itself, or in how
empirism is handled, not in the process of empiricism.

There appears to be a difference in the way Houston and
Horning view the trained manpower available in developing
countries and the way Mr. Dijon views it. The former claim
that there is a substantial pool of manpower available while
Dijon considers there is only a modest number of trained
people. It may well be that an overabundance of trained personnel will be needed to get personnel working at the user
level.

Underhill, etal., treat the subject of knowledge transfer
by pointing out that country development is a slow process and
at best development aid can play only a marginal role. But
notwithstanding this, they contend that knowledge transfer at
the right time, at the right level is a major key to development
success. They consider that knowledge can't be transferred in
bulk, and that in reality, it is wisdom and judgment that
should have emphasis in the transfer process. This point of

Mr. Klohn's paper indicates that empirism was used to
check out empirical formulas established in other countries before using them in the Colombian case. He indicates that "the
method followed was verification and possibly adjustment to
specific local conditions of the results of investigation in
other countries before these results were applied to practice."
This seems to indicate empirism was the way they worked. Perhaps the conference should consider this point further.

view tends to agree with the argument made above that it is the technology that is the questionable item in the transfer. We must, therefore, be concerned with the process of transfer so that we emphasize that which is needed to those ready to receive it at a level they can absorb.

The same authors illustrate the principle behind what they call "intermediate technology" with interesting examples of actual experiences. And again, they bring out that each situation is site specific and must be treated accordingly. These points illustrate the need for not only training local people, but there needs to be a better training and orienting of those who work in knowledge transfer organizations of all kinds. Sending an expert into an area to do work for which he is not qualified reflects on the administrators who sent him and the lack of orientation necessary to alert him as to real situations existing there.

The analysis of FAO's experience by Underhill, etal., describes the process of knowledge transfer as (a) the translation of knowledge in the mind of the knower into some form of output, written or spoken work or physical action. (b) Actual transmittal to the receiver through one of the common mechanisms. (c) The retranslation and assimilation by the receiver into his own frame of understanding and storage. (d) The use he makes of it. It takes the complete process to result in a successful transfer of knowledge.

Perhaps as we analyse the experience of the past it may be that there has been too little follow through on the intricacies and complexity of the last point made by Underhill, etal. It is the end use of knowledge transfer that must result in a benefit of mankind. Further emphasis on the importance of the user is given by Houston and Horning. A great deal of effort can be expended on the process of transfer, but unless there is something that happens as a result of all this effort it may not have a benefit to mankind. It may have been a great exercise intellectually, but never produce any lasting benefit other than in the minds of those involved. The user is the final target in many knowledge transfer programs, but in reality he seems to be the "forgotten man." It is easier to work at other levels, relegating the user role to the future.

Houston and Horning in considering the user in irrigation projects, point out many of the serious problems that face the world with respect to water, namely, its amount is fixed; the competition for its use is intensifying; the effeciency of use is still very low, and that food production is still short of needs. These situations have existed for a long time, yet we have the knowledge and technology to do better, to produce double the world food supply by 1980 "if" farmers generally were to make better use of presently known production methods. This highlights one of the major weaknesses that exists in the knowledge transfer system, namely, that knowledge is not getting to the user in a way that results in its application. Emphasis now needs to be placed on the use of knowledge, on the "forgotten man," for he is the only one who can apply the knowledge to increase production and eventually, hopefully, help to close the gap between rich and poor.

Another point Houston and Horning make in their paper is that those working in the area of turning applied research and extension of research information into practical use must be given greater importance in the knowledge transfer process. By so doing, more effort will be expended in getting essential knowledge into the minds of the user. Then perhaps, greater benefits can accure to mankind from knowledge transfer programs and water resource development projects.

It would be difficult indeed to overlook the final comment by Underhill, etal., in which a challenge is made to the scientists, the researchers in the field of water resources, to exercise care in how research is presented, indeed the very kind of research that is done. Here I would only comment that the degree of abstraction in approaching a problem and its solution varies considerably, and it might be dangerous to try to dictate at what level an individual works. What seems to be of importance in this day and age is that we try to strike a balance in our search for truth, our quest for knowledge, and our concern to see the application of scientific knowledge provide a better way of life for all mankind. In the pursuit of this balance, with so many of the human race still in impoverished conditions, perhaps now is the time to give increased emphasis to programs of knowledge transfer that will reduce the inequities that universally exist between rich and poor and recognize the problems, the status, the right of the "forgotten man."

The analysis of experience outlined in the papers reviewed in this summary report reflects the enormity of the task confronting us in water resource knowledge transfer. The experience of the past should be a good stepping stone for more progress in the future. The authors are to be commended for sharing their experience with us, and contributing to a realistic discussion of programs for the future.

In conclusion, perhaps we can say that the process of education--knowledge transfer if you will--with respect to water is a continuous one and like the hydrologic cycle it must go on and on. It must go on at all levels, from the policy level that shapes guidelines, (that must be somewhat flexible), organizational principles, and procedures under which water is developed,

436

managed and utilized within any given society and in relation
to neighboring societies, to the level of the user, the "forgotten man" who finally determines the end benefit to man.
Due recognition must be given to the integration of all factors
possible to work out as efficient a program as can be done
within the limits and constraints that exist, so that practical
results can be obtained within a reasonable time span. Finally,
let us heed the plea that we are entering a new era of cooperation in the exchange of knowledge and experience. Through
cooperative effort science and technology can effectively be
used for the common good.

AN IHD PROJECT FOR TECHNOLOGY TRANSFER TO DEVELOPING REGIONS

By

Edward F. Hawkins
Engineer-In-Charge, IHD Project
The Hydrologic Engineering Center
U. S. Army Corps of Engineers
Davis, California, U.S.A.

Synopsis

As part of the United States program for the International Hydrologic Decade (IHD), the U. S. Army Corps of Engineers developed a project entitled "Hydrologic Engineering Methods for Water Resources Development" and assigned it to The Hydrologic Engineering Center. The objectives of the project are to develop and test methods suitable for practical applications in hydrologic engineering and to document these methods in a report. Special attention is given to circumstances under which there are deficiencies in the length, accuracy, and general coverage of hydrologic records.

Volume 1 of the 12-volume report describes the general requirements and procedures for the major types of hydrologic engineering studies, and the remaining volumes describe specific hydrologic engineering methods and procedures usually required in studies associated with water resources development. The report is being published in provisional form to allow some time for review of the report and use of the methods including computer programs in other countries. The report will be updated, revised as necessary, and published in final form near the end of the Decade in 1974.

Recognizing one of the other objectives of this project - that of training in efficient use of the most effective techniques for hydrologic engineering studies - the HEC is also sponsoring an International Workshop in Hydrologic Engineering on 7 August - 1 September 1972 in cooperation with the U. S. National Committee for the IHD. The primary objective of the workshop is to provide engineers engaged in day-to-day planning, design, and operation of water resources projects with a thorough understanding of the application of a comprehensive variety of hydrologic engineering techniques. The workshop will also serve as a primary test of the utilization of the report, since it will be relied upon heavily as a training document.

The workshop is divided into four major areas: (1) fundamental considerations in water resources development; (2) statistical and mathematical techniques for hydrologic engineers;

(3) analysis of natural hydrologic systems; and (4) analysis of water resources development.

The Project

Early discussions leading to initiation of the International Hydrological Decade (IHD) stressed the objective of stimulating "scientific research in hydrology." There was some reluctance to include in the IHD program any proposals that emphasized practical applications of techniques to problem solutions. It was argued that the IHD program should be designed to avoid risks and that resources needed to stimulate worldwide activity in fundamental "scientific hydrology" might be diverted to the solution of immediate problems relating to water resources development.

The need for emphasizing "scientific research in hydrology" as the primary objective of the IHD program has been generally accepted, and this emphasis has generally prevailed in the formulation of IHD programs, particularly in the United States, (1)(2). However, it has been recognized that attention should also be given to improving methods and criteria required to utilize available information and new findings from research efforts in order to facilitate more efficient planning, design, and operation of water resource projects and systems. It is reasoned that "methods" research and testing, as well as the training of personnel in efficient use of the best techniques, should parallel efforts to acquire new knowledge through research in scientific hydrology.

The U. S. Army Corps of Engineers has actively participated in the International Hydrological Decade (IHD) and supported the U. S. National Committee for the IHD since its inception. As a result, the Corps began early in the Decade to develop studies that would contribute to the overall IHD program of the United States. One of these, the project entitled "Hydrologic Engineering Methods for Water Resources Development," was adopted by the Corps of Engineers as a part of its contribution to the IHD and was indorsed by the U. S. National Committee for the IHD as part of the United States IHD program.

The objective of this project is to develop, test, and document "methods suitable for practical applications in hydrologic engineering." The methods and procedures selected

(1) U. S. National Committee for the International Hydrological Decade, "International Hydrological Decade: Phase 1 - Proposed United States Program," Washington, D. C. May 1965.

(2) U. S. National Committee for the International Hydrological Decade, "International Hydrological Decade: Framework for the U.S. Program," Washington, D. C., April 1966.

for this project are those that would be required for efficient planning, design, and operation of water resources developments, giving special attention to circumstances under which hydrologic records are deficient in time, accuracy, and general coverage.

In 1966, the Office of the Chief of Engineers assigned primary responsibility for the project to The Hydrologic Engineering Center (HEC) in Davis, California. It was decided that to accomplish the primary objective of the project, a report would be prepared to describe the hydrologic engineering methods and procedures that have been used successfully in Corps of Engineers studies or were believed to be of significant interest. The report would not attempt to be a compedium of all known hydrologic engineering methods and procedures, but rather would concentrate on selected, practical methods and procedures, but rather would concentrate on selected, practical methods and procedures that are essential for complete analysis and have been demonstrated as satisfactory in the light of experience in the HEC.

It is intended that this report will be distributed widely to all other nations cooperating in the IHD and to interested individuals, universities, and water resources development agencies within the United States. It was believed that for the report to be of maximum value it would be desirable to publish it in provisional form, invite comments, and then publish it in final form near the end of the Decade in 1974. This procedure would provide time for the review and testing of the report procedures under actual working conditions and should bring to light any major deficiencies.

In addition to the procedure of publishing the report in provisional form, it was felt that other means of testing the methods and procedures should be initiated. Accordingly, cooperative studies were developed with water resources agencies in Guatemala and Peru. These studies were designed to test (and modify if necessary) specific procedures presented in the report while also yielding usable information to the cooperating agencies. Both of these studies are nearing completion, and final reports, jointly written by the cooperating agencies and the HEC, will be published as contributions to the IHD. Professional papers dealing with various phases of these studies have been presented elsewhere and will not be

440

discussed here (3)(4)(5). Recognizing that additional testing and evaluation of the proposed techniques should be initiated, arrangements are being made for new cooperative projects, and plans are underway to delineate mutually beneficial projects with other countries.

Another objective of this project is to provide training in efficient use of the most effective techniques for hydrologic engineering studies. Accordingly, the HEC is also sponsoring the International Workshop in Hydrologic Engineering in cooperation with the U. S. National Committee for the IHD. The workshop is open to hydrologic engineers from any country except the United States. The primary objective of the workshop is to provide engineers engaged in day-to-day planning, design, and operation of water resources projects with a thorough understanding of the application of a comprehensive variety of hydrologic engineering techniques.

The Report

The report, under the general title "Hydrologic Engineering Methods for Water Resources Development," consists of 12 volumes. The first volume discusses hydrologic engineering problems generally associated with water resources development and the general procedures used in their solution. Each of the other volumes contains detailed discussions of hydrologic engineering methods and procedures as well as computer program descriptions of programs that can be used in the application of these methods and procedures. The title of each of the 12 volumes is given in table 1.

Each volume generally consists of a brief description of the basic theory and underlying assumptions of the methods and procedures being presented, discussions of data requirements, detailed explanations of the techniques and how they are applied, discussions of the applications to areas of sparse data, typical examples to illustrate the techniques presented, computer applications, and generalized computer program descriptions.

(3) Beard, Leo R. and Augustine J. Fredrich, "Maximum Utilization of Scarce Data in Hydrologic Design," Second CENTO Seminar in Hydrology, Teheran, Iran, March, 1969.

(4) Beard, Leo R., Augustine J. Fredrich, and Edward F. Hawkins, "Estimating Streamflows Within a Region," ASCE National Meeting on Water Resources Engineering, Memphis, Tennessee, January, 1970.

(5) Feldman, Arlen D., "Evaluation of Drought Effects at Lake Atitlan," Second International Symposium in Hydrology, Fort Collins, Colorado, September, 1972.

Table 1. Volume Titles of the IHD Report

Volume No.	Title
1	Requirements and General Procedures
2	Hydrologic Data Management
3	Hydrologic Probabilities
4	Hydrograph Analysis
5	Hypothetical Floods
6	Water Surface Profiles
7	Reservoir Operation for Flood Control
8	Reservoir Yield
9	Reservoir System Analysis
10	Principles of Ground-Water Hydrology
11	Water Quality Determinations
12	Sediment Transport

Traditionally, the HEC's work in the systemization of methods and procedures used in hydrologic engineering has concentrated on the development of a library of generalized computer programs. Program descriptions for the programs are included in the report, and they constitute a significant portion of the report. In general, techniques used in the programs are described in the report, and information pertaining to the application of the programs to typical problems is also included as a part of the report. Table 2 shows the computer program descriptions included in each volume.

Table 2. Computer Program Descriptions Contained in the IHD Report

Volume No.	Computer Program Descriptions
1	Flood Hydrograph Package
	Water Surface Profiles
	Reservoir System Analysis--Conservation
2	Monthly Streamflow Simulation
	Daily Streamflow Simulation
3	Frequency Statistics of Annual Maximum or Minimum Flow Values
	Regional Frequency Computation
4	Basin Rainfall and Snowmelt Computation
	Unit Hydrograph and Loss Rate Optimization
5	Unit Graph and Hydrograph Computation
	Hydrograph Combining and Routing
	Balanced Hydrograph
	Streamflow Routing Optimization
6	Backwater--Any Cross Section
	Channel Improvement Sections for Backwater Program
	Gradually Varied Unsteady Flow Profiles

Table (cont)

Volume No.	Computer Program Descriptions
7	Conduit Rating--Partial Gate Openings
	Spillway Rating--Partial Tainter Gate Openings
	Spillway Rating and Flood Routing
	Spillway Gate Regulation Curves
8	Reservoir Area-Capacity Table by Conic Method
	Reservoir Yield
9	
10	Finite Element Solution of Steady State Potential Flow Problems
11	Reservoir Temperature Stratification
12	Suspended Sediment Yield
	Deposit of Suspended Sediment
	Reservoir Delta Sedimentation
	A Movable Bed, Digital Model for Calculating Aggradation and Degradation

A brief description of the subject matter coverage of each volume of the report follows:

.Volume 1, "Requirements and General Procedures," describes the general nature of water resources improvements and the general procedures used in hydrologic engineering studies. It is structured around various types of water resource improvements such as local protection projects, flood control by reservoirs, water supply by reservoirs, hydroelectric power development, multipurpose reservoirs, and water resources systems. For each type of improvement, the general characteristics of the improvement, the types of hydrologic engineering studies that may be required, and the general study procedures are described. This volume is intended to provide the hydrologic engineer with an overview of various types of problems and appropriate solution techniques as a general introduction to the other volumes which contain specific methods and procedures.

.Volume 2, "Hydrologic Data Management," describes methods and procedures for managing hydrologic data in a systematic manner, for estimating missing portions of hydrologic records, and for generating synthetic hydrologic data. Discussion is centered around the processing of basic data, data storage and publication, adjustment of runoff data, regional analysis as applied to hydrologic engineering problems and hydrologic simulation.

.Volume 3, "Hydrologic Probabilities," describes the use of probability theory and statistical methods as they apply to

443

hydrologic engineering problems. The volume discusses general probability concepts and definitions, hydrologic frequency curves, graphical and analytical techniques for computing frequency curves, analytical adjustments to hydrologic frequencies, volume-frequency computations, and regional frequency analysis.

.Volume 4, "Hydrograph Analysis," is concerned primarily with practical techniques for analyzing precipitation, snowmelt, infiltration, and the runoff process as they relate to the computation of flood hydrographs. Topics discussed in this volume include: estimation of the areal depth and distribution of precipitation; calculation of runoff from snowmelt; determination of loss rates by linear and nonlinear functions; unit hydrograph theory and derivation; hydrograph reconstitution; and the estimation of unit hydrograph and loss rate coefficients for ungaged areas.

.Volume 5, "Hypothetical Floods," describes different types of hypothetical floods and general guidelines for their development and use in hydrologic engineering studies. Some of the subjects covered are: standard project floods; probable maximum floods; balanced hydrographs; the routing of floods through river channels; and flood computations for stream systems.

.Volume 6, "Water Surface Profiles," describes the procedures necessary to determine water surface profiles in river channels. The volume discusses the one-dimensional energy equation as applied to open channel flow, the classification of open channel flow, basic data requirements, the calculation of steady flow profiles, and unsteady flow in open channels.

.Volume 7, "Reservoir Operation for Flood Control," discusses the basic principles involved in operating a reservoir for flood control. The volume discusses controlled reservoir releases, regulation of design and expected floods, outlet capacity considerations, spillway operation, seasonal operation variations, conditional rain-flood and snowmelt-flood reservation, and multiple reservoir operation for flood control.

.Volume 8, "Reservoir Yield," describes procedures for determining storage-yield relationships for a single reservoir. The volume describes simplified methods for yield determinations and the use of detailed sequential analysis and optimization techniques for obtained yield estimates.

.Volume 9, "Reservoir System Analysis," discusses the planning, design and operation of a system of reservoirs for multiple purposes. Subjects covered are the determination of study objectives, multipurpose operation considerations, effects of constraints, complementary and competitive services, computer analyses, study results analysis, and optimization techniques.

.Volume 10, "Principles of Ground-Water Hydrology," differs from the other volumes in that step-by-step procedures for use in solving ground-water problems are not presented. Instead, the fundamental concepts which govern the analyses of the occurrence and movement of ground water receive the major emphasis. This volume presents the basic principles of hydrology, geology, hydraulics, and physics as they relate to ground water; this information can be used as a guide for hydrologic engineers in the identification and initial considerations of ground-water aspects of water resources development studies.

.Volume 11, "Water Quality Determinations," examines the technology of the water quality field as it applies to water resources planning, design, and operation. The volume discusses physical, chemical and biological parameters, water quality requirements for beneficial uses, causes of water quality degradation, water quality calculations, water quality surveys, and the control of water quality in riverine and limnological systems.

.Volume 12, "Sediment Transport," describes the occurrence, aggradation, and degradation of sediment in rivers and reservoirs. It discusses sediment characteristics, the determination of sediment yields from watersheds, sediment movement in rivers, and reservoir sedimentation.

The status of the report, as of 1 July 1972, is that Volumes 1 and 2 have been completed and published, Volume 10 has been approved and is being published, final drafts have been completed for Volumes 4, 6, 7, and 11, and first drafts are near completion for the remaining volumes. It is anticipated that all of the volumes will be completed, published, and ready for distribution by January, 1973.

Workshop

Increasing national and international interest in water resources has stimulated much new activity and progress in hydrologic engineering, since hydrology is basic to an understanding of water resources problems and to planning for water resources development. In addition, the advent of electronic computers has enabled hydrologic engineers to develop new techniques and procedures that were not previously available. Accompanying this increased interest is an urgent world-wide need for transferring this technology to developing regions, as exemplified by this conference and by the International Hydrological Decade, itself. Probably one of the most effective ways of transferring this knowledge is through training courses for hydrologic engineers from developing nations. That UNESCO and the U. S. National Committee for the

IHD has supported this method of transferring methods is evidenced by their sponsorship of the International Seminars for Hydrology Professors and the IHD Fellowship program.

Accordingly, the International Workshop in Hydrologic Engineering was developed and will be held in Davis, California, on 7 August - 1 September 1972. The major overall objective of the workshop is to present modern techniques and procedures of hydrologic engineering, emphasizing electronic computer applications.

Because of the need to apply modern concepts and technologies to the development and utilization of the limited supply of water resources throughout the world, it is important to provide hydrologic engineers with the skills necessary to apply these techniques. Accordingly, the specific objectives adopted for the workshop are:

·To review techniques and procedures currently being used in hydrologic engineering and to illustrate their applications by electronic computers.
·To introduce some of the more advanced techniques that are being used in the planning design, and operation of water resources projects and systems.

As previously noted, the workshop was open to hydrologic engineers from any country except the United States. The workshop is a contribution by the United States to the IHD, and no fee or tuition is charged. Since the course is a contribution to the IHD, preference was given to representatives from countries that are actively participating in the IHD. The workshop is designed to provide engineers engaged in day-to-day planning, design, and operation of water resource projects and systems with a thorough indoctrination in a comprehensive variety of hydrologic engineering techniques. Consequently, working-level and supervisory engineers were encouraged to apply rather than administrators and executives. Preference was given to applicants who had experience in hydrologic engineering or closely related fields and who had current working assignments as hydrologic engineers. Since all workshop instruction will be in English, another requirement was that all participants should have the ability to read, write, speak, and understand English. As of 1 July 1972, there are 40 engineers representing 25 different countries enrolled in the workshop.

The workshop is structured to incorporate a combination of lectures, discussions, field trips to nearby water resources development projects, and problem-solving sessions that will give each participant the opportunity to use available computer programs and to evaluate the resulting solutions. The majority of the instruction will be by the staff of the HEC, but guest

446

lecturers have been invited to discuss topics of general nature that are related to the course content.

The subject matter coverage for the workshop has been divided into four major areas - roughly corresponding to each week of the 4-week workshop:

·The first week of the workshop will include such considerations as water resources management concepts, hydrologic data management, social, economic, and cultural considerations in water resources development, rainfall-runoff relationships, unit hydrograph theory and derivation, flood routing, hypothetical flood computation, and basin modeling by computer.

·The second week will concentrate on hydrologic probabilities and frequency determinations. Some of the subjects to be covered are probability theory, statistical distributions and measures, graphical and analytical frequency methods, linear regression theory and its application to hydrology problems, regional correlation analyses, stochastic hydrology, and uncertainties and risk in water resources development.

·The third week will deal with river hydraulics, hydraulics of sediment transport and deposition, and ground water as related to hydrologic engineering studies. Subject matter includes computation of gradually varied flow profiles, fluvial hydraulics including sediment transport, scour, and deposition in rivers and reservoirs, the occurrence and movement of ground water, and ground water management.

·The fourth week will include such areas of consideration as systems analysis in water resources development, the operation and simulation of multipurpose projects and systems, the analysis of flood control, irrigation, and hydroelectric power projects and systems, and water quality considerations.

Since a major part of the workshop is devoted to the application of the electronic computer to the solution of hydrologic engineering problems, each participant should be somewhat familiar with computers and computer programming. Therefore, to insure that each participant receives the maximum benefit possible from the workshop, evening sessions will be offered during the first 2 weeks on computer applications for engineers. These sessions will be mandatory for all participants who have not had working experience with computer utilization and will be optional for all others.

Conclusions

It is difficult to draw conclusions at this point since the project is still continuing. However, the initial reactions to the project and to those portions that are complete (such as Volumes 1 and 2) have been gratifying, and the comments that have been received have been very helpful. It is realized that the only true tests of the success of the project will be the tests of time and of use of the report and workshop techniques by hydrologic engineers in developing countries. The hope is that the objective of the project - that of transferring technology on practical methods and procedures in hydrologic engineering to developing regions - will be useful and beneficial to other countries.

Acknowledgment

The project described herein is being conducted by The Hydrologic Engineering Center of the Corps of Engineers. It is authorized by the Corps of Engineers as a contribution to the IHD and has been indorsed by the U. S. National Committee for the IHD. Consequently, it is impossible to identify each of the persons who have made significant contributions to the project, but the importance of their contributions must be acknowledged.

The opinions expressed herein are the author's, and the methods and procedures described in the report and presented in the workshop do not necessarily reflect the official policies and procedures of the Corps of Engineers.

THE ROLE OF FAO IN THE TRANSFER OF WATER RESOURCES KNOWLEDGE TO DEVELOPING REGIONS

By

H. W. Underhill, Hydrologist, R. G. Thomas, Hydrogeologist
Water Resources and Development Service
Land and Water Development Division

and

D. Salomons, Fellowships Officer
Fellowships and Training Branch
Personnel Division
Food and Agriculture Organization of the United Nations
Rome, Italy

Synopsis

The transfer of knowledge is not an end in itself; the end is to benefit mankind. This benefit will only be achieved if the knowledge is suitable, is adequately transmitted to a well motivated recipient, and is correctly applied. Every situation demands a different solution. FAO has wide experience in this sphere and believes that the transfer of knowledge of the right kind and at the right level to be immediately absorbed and applied is the key to development. The choice and preparation of the individuals - those who are to transmit, and those who are to receive and apply the knowledge - are crucial.

Transfer of Knowledge is the Key to Development - But Only When it Fits the Lock...

The dream of instant development has faded long ago. Rich and poor countries alike have learned to face the harsh reality: development is an agonizingly slow process, and development aid can only play a marginal role. The days are gone when massive transfusions of capital or equipment were considered an adequate answer to poverty; it is now realized that at best developing countries can be helped to help themselves, that development must grow from within a country and external assistance is only useful if it stimulates this process and if it fits the current situation (economic and social structure, educational level). As with all growth processes, the external input must be absorbed and digested before it can have beneficial effects. It must be suited to the needs of the receiver as well as to the resources of the donor. Thus the effectiveness of outside help is limited by the capacity of the receiving country to accept innovations and to adapt them to its own needs. The pace of this absorption process is set by the amount of skilled and motivated manpower available; therefore, transfer of knowledge is one of the most effective forms of aid, for it

449

increases the number of people who can handle innovations and material assistance.

Knowledge, however, is a very special commodity, and it cannot be shipped in bulk; it can only very gradually be transferred. Before teachers or extension workers can reach the people, they themselves must be trained. This will take time and the number of people able and willing to respond to this training may initially be small. On the other hand, useful knowledge potentially has an immense multiplier effect once it has been transmitted - even though initial results may not be stunning, the outcome on the long run can be impressive.

What kind of knowledge, however, can be regarded as useful? It is clear that knowledge can only be useful if it is the right kind of knowledge and if it is correctly applied. A degree in law is of little use in fighting a smallpox outbreak, or a knowledge of extremal probability distributions in using a current meter. On a wider scale, much of the disillusion with aid programs has resulted from inadequate understanding of the difference between the resources and, therefore, between the needs of the donors and the recipients. The donor countries, capital-intensive, have tended to export the capital-based technology which they have found effective in their situation but which may be unsuitable in countries with small capital but surplus labor resources. Even if the right type of knowledge is transmitted, there is no guarantee that it will be effective: the recipient may lack the motivation to use it as intended and find a more congenial or better paid job. Moreover, even if the motivation is there the application may be faulty through a lack of understanding of wider issues. For example, tractors may be introduced in place of hand labor or bullock power and show an economic benefit to the costing of the works, but a loss to the country suffering from rural poverty and unemployment.

Thus to be effective, knowledge should be of the right type, transmitted to a well motivated recipient, and be correctly applied. In fact, what we are really trying to transfer (if we accept the Concise Oxford Dictionary) is wisdom and judgment; for wisdom is defined as "experience and knowledge together with the power of applying them critically and practically" and judgment is "critical faculty or discernment." Here, the environment of the potential recipient plays a major role as well: some societies have rewarding incentives to offer, not so much financially as socially in offering "job satisfaction," but others reject possible innovators. The whole issue of "brain drain" from the developing countries, which has been found to be as much related to political and psychological factors as to financial reasons, illustrates the problem.

FAO - What it is and Does

After this discussion of the philosophy and pitfalls of transferring knowledge, we should raise the question: what is FAO's approach? First a few words about what FAO is and does.

In the words of an official pamphlet on FAO (1) "The Food and Agriculture Organization of the United Nations is an agency for international action, to fight the poverty, malnutrition, and hunger which afflict about half the people in the world. It is an independent organization in the United Nations family of specialized agencies...a cooperative of 121 governments."

Its program of work is carried on mainly through two separately financed channels - the Regular Programme, and the Field Programme. The former is financed directly from FAO's own budget; the work includes world surveys, conferences, seminars, and publications, and keeping in touch with new ideas in technology so as to make these available, when and where applicable, to staff in the field. The second is financed principally by the United Nations Development Programme, which channels requests for assistance from UN member countries to the most suitable UN agency for their execution. Assistance under this program usually is given in the form of either individual advisers or "projects" involving a team of UN/FAO technical specialists working alongside a government team for a specific job. To quote the pamphlet: "A condition of every project is that the country must assign its own counterpart specialists to work with the international team. Thus, when a project ends, its achievements should be twofold - direct progress in the chosen field of activity and an enhancement of knowledge and skill enabling the "home" experts to undertake more development work of a similar kind. These national technicians are often given fellowships by FAO for further study abroad." Water resources studies are of course an essential part of FAO's activities, as the development of agriculture includes large investments in irrigation, flood protection, and drainage schemes, as well as activities in soil and water conservation, watershed management, and inland fisheries. Examples of particular water resources techniques which have been transferred to developing countries through FAO field projects are rainfall-runoff models, groundwater models, stochastic hydrology, reservoir operations studies, systems analysis in irrigation planning, and the use of computers in data processing and in other standard water resource techniques.

---

(1) "FAO - what it is, what it does, how it works," FAO, Rome, 1970.

It should be realized that other UN agencies are also involved in water resources. Routine or "operational" hydrology, including networks and services, is the responsibility of the World Meteorological Organization (WMO). Unesco is concerned with scientific research and education, and with the International Hydrological Decade. The World Health Organization (WHO) is responsible for city and village water supply, though FAO is also involved in water supplies for rural communities and livestock. The Resources and Transport Division of the UN is concerned with industrial supplies, hydropower and navigation. The family of UN technical agencies covers the whole field of water development; however, in terms of field projects in developing countries, FAO has probably played the major part.

The Place of Hydrology in FAO's Field Activities

When the end use is agriculture, including rangelands, forestry, and fisheries, FAO is responsible for water; however, when FAO resorts to water resources technology as a means to bring about agricultural development, it does not concentrate only on the construction of dams, canals, tunnels, pipelines, wells, sprinkler systems and so forth. FAO is interested in an understanding of the resources available, of the uses to which the water will be put, of the many alternatives available to a given government for a particular area, and the processes of local planning, design, and operation as well as national planning. Simply constructing a dam and major canals does not necessarily mean successful irrigation, nor does drilling a well and providing pumps. In addition, FAO insists not only on the technical soundness of its projects but also on their effectiveness given their agronomic, economic, and social implications. The transfer of technology is complemented by the transfer of insight into the large scale consequences of the use of new techniques.

Previously the point was made that the knowledge which is to be transferred must be suitable to the conditions in which the recipient finds himself. He must be assisted to move forward one step at a time; he must be confident that each step is within his capabilities and that each step is an improvement on the last. This is the principle behind "intermediate technology." As an example the case may be quoted of water lifting devices from a river to a canal consisting of a beam with a horizontal pivot actuated by the worker walking backward and forward on the beam to raise water in a bucket attached to the far end. There may be several of these in line, employing perhaps 10 or 20 men. The irrigation expert rightly sees that one petrol pump would save all this labor. However, an intermediate technology expert suggests a number of bicycle-powered pumps. With the petrol pump the profit would go largely to the pump manufacturer and the petroleum company - both outside the country - and 20 men would become unemployed; with the second method the equipment could be manufactured locally, output would still be greatly increased, and 20 men would continue to be usefully employed. However, intermediate technology requires an uncommitted approach to a problem, a willingness to experiment and be unconventional. This is difficult for the donor expert, who has his well tried techniques, and also for the recipient engineer who may feel cheated at being offered only half measures, and who may be understandably impatient to make the greatest "progress" in the shortest time.

In FAO's experience, no two situations are alike. In one country computer services are available and the local well-experienced hydrogeologists can quickly absorb and apply groundwater modeling techniques. In another country the one engineer trained abroad may be eager to introduce computerized hydrological data processing, but below him there may be no one who understands a stage-discharge curve. On a less dramatic level many cases could be quoted of errors resulting from inadequate understanding of the basic scientific principles - for example, a least-squares fit to a scatter of non-homogeneous discharge measurements, or an extreme value probability distribution fitted to a series of data which show, when plotted, a sharp break in slope suggesting a sample drawn from two different populations. This kind of error is of course not exclusive to the developing countries. The point is that the transfer of knowledge is in the last resort a human activity with humanistic goals, and if it is to be effective each situation must be approached anew. This is why the personal qualities of technical assistance specialists, discussed further in Chapter V, are so important.

Transfer of Water Resources Knowledge by FAO

The means for the transfer of knowledge used by FAO can be considered under the following headings:

Mainly "Regular Program" activities:

  - Seminars
  - Regional Research
  - Panels of Experts, Study Groups, and Consultants
  - Publications

Mainly "Field Program" activities:

  - Technical assistance (advisers)
  - Projects
  - Consultancies
  - Fellowships

These will be discussed briefly in turn.

Regular Program - Seminars are usually financed jointly by FAO and the host country, and bring together specialists from other countries in the region to discuss, under the guidance of outside specialists in the subject, problems specific to the region which concern water resource development for agriculture.

Experience has shown that such seminars need careful preparation if they are to be worthwhile. It is now an essential part of FAO's seminar policy that the host country should make a major contribution to the technical as well as administrative aspects; it should have some useful experience to offer. Since problems differ so widely over the world (human, legal, economic, and institutional as well as physical), the subject of the seminar must be sharply defined to be of interest to, and the participating countries should be limited to, those sharing the particular problem which is to be discussed. The FAO regional officers play a key part in seminars, both in the contacts and planning beforehand and in the follow-up after.

A step further from seminars is the regional research programme, in which a number of countries sharing a similar environment and similar problems cooperate in research and dissemination of knowledge under a common programme, financed partly from their own resources, partly by FAO, and partly, in some cases, from other sources of external funds (for example bilateral aid channelled through FAO).

"Panels of Experts" are another form of spreading knowledge on key problems of interest to developing countries. They consist of small groups of highly qualified specialists selected individually for their knowledge and experience in a specific field and working under contract with FAO. Their task is to research into what is already known - and sometimes the available knowledge is conflicting - to collate, and to process the data and then present it, usually through publications and seminars, in the most readily usable form for the recipients. A current study of this type is the panel on Crop Water Requirements under varying climatic and other conditions, whose report is expected next year.

Other panels of experts or study groups may operate within the framework of cooperative programs with universities or other scientific bodies, or they may consist entirely of specialists from within FAO itself. An example is the group which prepared, with the assistance of field staff and national governments, the provisional FAO Indicative World Plan for Agricultural Development which attempted to assess expected future developments and to suggest overall policy measures as well as detailed programs. The important part of this survey and planning which concerned irrigation was undertaken jointly with the International Commission on Irrigation and Drainage, and is now to be developed with the aid of a university contract to a study in depth of the irrigation situation and potential of the African continent south of the Sahara.

It goes without saying that the forms by which knowledge is transmitted are interrelated, and this is particularly clear in the case of publications. Though these are sometimes prepared entirely by FAO staff, more often they are the means for disseminating knowledge prepared and processed by groups or individuals working under one of the other activities mentioned above - seminars, regional research programs, panels of experts, and consultants. Since the new series of "Irrigation and Drainage Papers" of the Water Resources and Development Service of FAO was started in early 1971, ten papers have appeared, to which should be added the series by the Fisheries Department (for titles see Appendix).

Field Program - Under the field program the oldest form of the transfer of knowledge is the provision of Technical Assistance experts. They serve, at the request of Member Governments, as advisors to technical departments of governments and, in special cases (under the Operational Assistance Programme) actually undertake operational and executive duties, filling a post in the government establishment.

In its early years the UN Expanded Programme of Technical Assistance, founded in 1950, was concerned almost entirely with individual TA experts as advisors. However, it soon became apparent that the need was greater than could be met through this kind of assistance, and in 1959 the UN Special Fund was established to give assistance through teams of UN experts working with government counterparts in clearly defined projects. Since January 1972 the two programs of Technical Assistance and Special Fund have been merged. More than 200 projects of the Special Fund type that concern water resources and irrigation have been completed by FAO or are in progress since this program started in 1959.

Transfer of knowledge through these projects should be principally by example. This is demanding, and the partial failures have shown up the weaknesses - in project preparation, in planning and clarification of objectives, in recruiting suitable UN/FAO experts, and in government interest and support. Some UN/FAO projects - about a third perhaps - are let out under contract to consultants rather than being operated by a "direct recruitment" team of FAO, which has both advantages and disadvantages (see Chapter V).

Individual consultancies, as opposed to contracts with consulting firms for major work, play an important part in field projects. The team on the ground cannot be expected to be fully up to date in all aspects of the wide range of sciences they must cover, and short term, usually some days or weeks, consultancies for individual highly qualified specialists are a valuable form of technical support.

Fellowships for national counterparts are another means for transmittal of knowledge and normally form an important element in field projects; a few are also available, for advanced level study, through the Regular Programme. In the past twenty years FAO has awarded some 10,000 individual fellowships for study abroad to nationals of developing countries.

How Effective are FAO's Methods to Transfer Knowledge?

It may be convenient at this point to see the transfer of knowledge as a four stage process. The first is the translation of knowledge in the mind of the knower into some form of output - written word, spoken word, or physical action. The second is the transmittal of this to the receiver - through a fellowship, consultancy, seminar, library, or whatever. The third is the retranslation and assimilation by the receiver into his own frame of understanding and storage, and lastly the use he makes of it. Failure at any point may negate the whole process.

The process of transferring knowledge and wisdom may be summed up under "guidance." But for guidance to be effective there are three requirements: (a) the guide and the guided are agreed on their objective, (b) they start from the same point, and (c) the guidance is practical and realistic. Though these requirements are general in any form of training, they are especially important in the transfer of technical knowledge to developing countries.

Of the means for the transfer of knowledge described in Chapter IV, the main ones are seminars, field projects, and fellowships; the effectiveness of these will be discussed briefly. With regard to seminars, it can be said that this method of transfer of water resources and water use knowledge by FAO is working well. The budgetary difficulties of FAO, along with other UN agencies, may in a way have contributed to this by forcing more reliance on the host country; divided responsibility always entails risks, but these can be minimized by careful selection and preparation, and in any case are the price of self-help.

The effectiveness of UN/FAO direct recruitment field projects is a much debated subject. An evident weakness is that the team is multi-national and, therefore, without a common background - scientific, linguistic or cultural. This weakness is perhaps overstated for the world has moved far towards a common understanding, if not synthesis, in this respect and the type of person who would apply and be recruited to a field team is likely to have an international outlook and scientific training, and must of necessity be fluent in the international language to be used on that project. The letting of projects under contract to consulting firms avoids this real or apparent weakness but introduces others - the possible entanglement in commercial interests, less concern with training, and outside pressure to give contracts to unsuitable firms.

The second of these points is particularly important and is at the root of the dilemma in which a project manager finds himself. On the one hand he has a specific and detailed plan of operation to which he must adhere, and on the other he is expected to undertake training. On the one hand, he is expected to operate with the speed and efficiency regarded as normal in developed societies, and, on the other, he is not independent but must rely on local counterpart services and work at every step with the government of a country where customs and methods may be totally different. He is, in fact, caught between an upper millstone turning at the speed of modern methods and a lower millstone often of medieval design which may show no apparent movement at all. Under such circumstances it is little wonder that the fulfillment of the technical requirements of the project frequently is given priority at the expense of training. This is a pity for the major element that should distinguish a UN project from a normal commercial one is the element of training, of building up knowledge, experience, and judgment in the country until it is able to undertake its own development works without external help. Because of their unique nature, the UN agencies are particularly suited to build up scientific and managerial capability in the developing countries. Field projects on specific development schemes offer a particularly good way of doing this by demonstration, especially when project plans and timing schedules are realistic and not over-ambitious and the managers and members of such project teams are selected both for their teaching and their scientific qualities; in fact teaching should have priority, for additional scientific support can always be provided as necessary through highly qualified consultants in a special field, and the selection of individual UN/FAO field staff who are motivated and able to motivate, remains the crucial factor.

Fellowships, awarded to nationals of developing countries within the framework of UN/FAO projects, have proved to be a very effective means of transferring knowledge. As stated previously, FAO has awarded more than 10,000 individual fellowships in the twenty years of this program, and during this period it has learned much about the factors which can make a fellowship into a success or cause failure.

In early days it was thought that the awarding of fellowships, particularly for study in the developed countries, was the quickest and most effective means for the transfer of knowledge. However, experience has shown that fellowships should only be awarded when other ways to transfer knowledge are blocked or when they are clearly insufficient; on-the-spot training and institution building should have priority whenever possible. Moreover, national or regional fellowships should have preference over international ones; for a fellow must have reached a high scientific level and must have considerable international experience to be able to profit to the full extent of training in an environment totally different from his own.

The following considerations are taken into account in the planning of FAO's fellowship program.

(1) Precise timing of the fellowships within the total time schedule of the related project is essential to achieve the ideal aim of gradual take-over of responsibilities from the international experts by their national counterparts.

(2) The fellowships should be planned with the manpower requirements of the recipient country and especially the particular needs of the project in mind.

(3) Unless a candidate has a more than average command of the proposed language of instruction, he should not be sent on a fellowship; there is a close correlation between a fellow's language proficiency, or lack of it, and the results of his study. It may be interesting to learn that FAO fellows who study in developing countries, mostly in their own region, usually have far less serious communication problems than those who carry out their program in an industrialized country. Apart from the language itself, the "cultural shock" effect of living and working in a totally alien environment plays a role in this respect.

(4) FAO is hesitant to send fellows to study in developed countries because the conditions under which they work and study are different from their usual environment and they find it hard to adapt the acquired knowledge to their own particular circumstances.

The purpose of an FAO fellowship reaches beyond the direct personal interest of the fellow involved; the primary objective of such training is to contribute to the social and economic development of the fellow's country. This objective demands an extra motivation on the part of the fellow to bring about change, a strong personal involvement, which can be even more strengthened by giving the fellow a voice in the shaping of his study program. This may reinforce his feeling of personal responsibility to make his study a success. A paternalistic approach of those who are responsible for the planning and execution of the study program can be fatal.

Conclusions

(1) The transfer of knowledge is the best form of aid for it leads to the only form of development which is ultimately effective, that is helping people to help themselves. In the sphere of water resources FAO has had considerable success in transferring modern techniques.

(2) The transfer of knowledge is a human to human process. It cannot be shipped in bulk.

(3) The knowledge and experience of the developed countries are seldom suitable without modification to the developing countries. The final purpose of the transfer of knowledge - the benefit of mankind - requires that each situation must be judged according to the local infrastructure, history, and culture. However, these factors are not static, and both the type of knowledge to be transferred and the method of transfer should be continuously reexamined.

(4) FAO, as an international agency to fight the poverty, malnutrition, and hunger which afflict about half the people of the world, puts the highest priority on this form of aid.

(5) The means of transfer of water resources knowledge by FAO include:

FAO financed:

- Seminars
- Regional Research
- Panels of Experts, Study Groups and Consultants
- Publications

UN financed:

- Technical Assistance (Advisors)
- Projects
- Consultancies
- Fellowships

Each of these has its place in FAO's overall training philosophy.

(6) In FAO's experience the selection and preparation of the individuals - both donors of knowledge and those who receive and apply it - are of crucial importance.

459

(7)   The art of the bridge builder (pontifex of classical times) should once again be esteemed in society, and encouragement should be given to the interpreters of science who lie between researchers and practitioners, and between developed and developing countries.

(8)   As part of the bridge-building process, scientific writers should be encouraged to be intelligible. It should be accepted that "obscurity is the refuge of incompetence" (2) rather than a sign of erudition. Scientific groups such as national associations for the advancement of science might sponsor annual awards for the most lucid paper and booby prizes for the most needlessly incomprehensible.

Acknowledgment

The authors are greateful to FAO for permission to present this paper; however, the views expressed are their own.

Appendix

Recent FAO publications concerning water resources:

I.   Irrigation and Drainage Papers

1.   Irrigation practice and water management, 1971.

2.   Irrigation canal lining, 1971.

3.   Design criteria for basin irrigation systems, 1971.

4. .Village irrigation programs: a new approach in water economy, 1971.

5.   Automated irrigation, 1971.

6.   Drainage of heavy soils, 1971.

7.   Salinity seminar, Baghdad, 1971.

8.   Water and the environment, 1971.

9.   Drainage materials, 1972.

10.   Integrated farm water management, 1971.

II.   Fisheries Department Papers

Doudoroff, P. and Shumway, D. L., Dissolved oxygen requirements of freshwater fishes, 1970.

U.S. Department of the Interior, Federal Water Pollution Control Administration, Facsimile of Section III; Fish, other aquatic life and wildlife, of Report of the Committee on Water Quality Criteria, 1969.

---

*Robert Heinlein, "Stranger in a Strange Land."

EIFAC, Water quality criteria for European freshwater fish, Report on finely divided solids and inland fisheries, 1964.

EIFAC, Water quality criteria for European freshwater fish, Report on extreme pH values and inland fisheries, 1968.

EIFAC/CECPI, Water quality criteria for European freshwater fish, Report on water temperature and inland fisheries based mainly on Slavonic literature, 1968.

EIFAC/CECPI, Water quality criteria for European freshwater fish, List of literature on the effect of water temperature on fish, 1969.

EIFAC, Water quality criteria for European freshwater fish, Report on ammonia and inland fisheries, 1970.

Fraser, J. C., A partial annotated bibliography on water levels, fluctuation, and minimum pools in reservoirs for fish and other aquatic resources, 1970.

Fraser, J. C., An annotated bibliography on the establishment of acceptable flows for fish life in controlled streams, 1970.

Lennon, Robert E., Hunn, Joseph B., Schnick, Rosalie A., and Burress, Ralph M., Reclamation of ponds, lakes, and streams with fish toxicants: a review, FAO Fisheries Technical Paper No. 100, 1970.

Allen, George H., A preliminary bibliography on the utilization of sewage in fish culture, FAO Fisheries Circular No. 308, March 1969.

Dill, William A., Kelley, D. W., and Fraser, J. C., The effects of water- and land-use development on the aquatic environment and its resources and solutions to some of the generated problems, FAO Fisheries Circular No. 129, August 1971.

Welcome, Robin L., Preliminary list of the inland waters of Africa and their characteristics, FAO Fisheries Circular No. 134, December 1971.

TECHNICAL ACTIVITIES BY FAO IN THE TRANSFER
OF WATER RESOURCES KNOWLEDGE TO DEVELOPING REGIONS

By

C.E. Houston, Chief

and

H.M. Horning, Senior Officer
Water Resources and Development Service
Land and Water Development Division
Food and Agriculture Organization of the United Nations
Rome, Italy

Synopsis

Water has always been important to man's production of
food. To provide food requirements by the end of the next
decade will require the utilization of 300 thousand million
cubic meters of new water.

Water must be studied, developed, and used as a single
resource. Technical manpower for study and development of
water resources in many developing countries is of a high
caliber, but as with many developed countries the utilization
of the end product is the gap leading to success or failure.
FAO is attempting to fill that gap through field projects,
seminars, and publications. The first step in this process
is to create an awareness with Governments, then with Technical
Services, and finally with the water users. The success or
failure of the end user determines the success or failure of
an irrigation project, not the engineering design and construction.

Introduction

Since the dawn of civilization water has controlled man's
destiny. There was never enough for everyone, and there has
never been a time when there was sufficient food. There have
always been rich countries and poor countries. A gap has
always existed, but it is now becoming wider. More human lives
hang in the balance today due to lack of food than all lives
destroyed in all wars. Two main reasons why people are hungry
are: they do not produce enough food and they have no money to
buy it. Giving food will not solve a country's problem. It
may temporarily alleviate a situation, but unfortunately it
may also retard a country's development.

We have enough knowledge in the sciences of food production to double the world's food supply by 1980 if farmers
were to make better use of present production methods. The
farmer, like everyone else, must have his reward, particularly
the small farmer in developing countries who risks losing
everything, or at least getting into debt for many years, if he

462

makes just one big mistake while trying to apply the results of modern agricultural research.

From the practical standpoint, agricultural production limitations throughout the world are more likely to be socio-economic-political than physical or biological. These limiting factors range from deep seated rural traditions to government policies. Traditions are slow to change and extremely difficult to attack through government.

Civilization first developed in an environment requiring irrigated agriculture. Only during the past 1,500 years has the scene shifted from the dry areas to the more humid regions. It is in these humid areas that the great population centers of the world have developed today; thus most of the arable soils of the areas are now used for crop production. To increase further food and fibre production for the world, we are again returning to the arid and semi-arid lands that comprise over 50 percent of the earth's land surface. The majority of the developing countries are located in the arid or semi-arid zones, and nearly one half of the world's population depends upon food production under some degree of irrigation.

FAO's Indicative World Plan states that to provide the food requirements of the developing countries by 1985, it will be necessary to increase the irrigated area by about 30 million ha. This will require the utilization of approximately 300 thousand million cubic meters of water.

The total water supply of this planet is essentially fixed. Although man has been able to manipulate the supply in regard to location and time of use, the total supply has changed very little over the past thousands of years.

But the demand for water, as population has increased and uses have multiplied, has risen tremendously. Thus, man must find ways to increase food production and meet other requirements of water by more efficient development and use of the world's limited supply.

Over half of the world's population consists of farmers, who own, use, or manage most of the land and water resources in rural areas. In the developed countries the numbers are decreasing, while in the developing countries they are increasing. This requires a change in perspective in transfer of technology from developed to developing countries. Whereas specialists in developed countries have been trained and are operating on the principle of labour-saving devices in resource utilization, they have to seriously consider labour-intensification programs of resource development and utilization in developing countries.

463

Quite often the research staff of various organizations in the developing countries are the academic equals of their counterparts anywhere in the world, at least within the narrow confines of their parent discipline. They usually have been educated in the best schools in the world and are ready and able to contribute to their share of high quality agricultural research.[1]

However, the processes of research dissemination and application present an altogether different picture in most developing countries. Applied research and extension of research information into practical use has assumed the status of a second-class activity. This is, of course, wrong for, at least in developing countries, any research which is not used may be considered a waste of time and money.

Water - The Resource and Its Development

It is now accepted that all water is a single resource, and neither surface nor groundwater development can be considered in isolation. The scientific approach to the determination of the water resources of any natural unit is an integrated one in which a water balance is resolved. In other words, the total precipitation on the watershed or unit must equal or be balanced by evapotranspiration, surface runoff, infiltration to the groundwater basin, and changes in surface and groundwater storage.[2]

Successful management of all water in a unit or basin requires the conjunctive operation of surface and groundwater. Under such management, groundwater can be used to supplement a scarce surface water supply during dry periods. Surface water can be used mostly during medium and high runoff times to satisfy agricultural and other users and to recharge aquifers through percolation in natural or artificial basins and channels and occasionally through wells.

An ideal water conservation and source allocation system, with conjunctive use of surface and groundwater, may include a number of streams or creeks, surface reservoirs, several aquifers and recharge ponds, and a network of wells, pipelines, or canals supplying water to dispersed areas. Such multiple systems, although efficient from the standpoint of water conservation, may require large capital outlays for the

[1]/Pomeroy, C. R. (1970) The Field Support Function of the Agricultural Experiment Station in the Developing Countries. In Journal of the Post Graduate School, Vol. 8, No. 1.

[2]/Houston, C. E. (1971) Some Factors Influencing Groundwater Development and Use for Agriculture, Seminar on Groundwater, FAO, Granada, Spain.

required structures. All of these elements of operation, plus the possible orientation of importance of one to the other, plus expansions and contractions or other improvements, present a multitude of potential operational schedules. These are far too involved and tedious for standard mathematical formulation and must be referred to simple computerization.

In traditional and in recent irrigation development, preference had been given to the use of surface water resources. But in several areas, and on an increasing scale, existing surface waters are already surveyed, known, developed, or allocated for future development. There remain the groundwater resources, larger than generally recognized and available for initial rapid development, though full development may be more difficult and fraught with possible dangers of over-development and of salination. There has been a general tendency to ignore or overlook groundwater as a potential source for large irrigation development. Four major reasons for this neglect are: (i) the full implications of the hydrological cycle are a relatively recent discovery; (ii) efficient pumps and low-cost power are only recently generally available; (iii) hitherto, agriculture relied on traditional surface sources for water supply; and (iv) groundwater science and technology have developed only recently.[1]

So, in the field of hydrogeology and groundwater resources investigation and development, technical assistance from FAO aims at helping to match the demands for water for irrigation and other hydro-agricultural purposes with the resources of both surface and groundwater available in the area.[2] In all cases, the final aim is the integrated use and management of total water resources to achieve more and improved production of food, timber, and other agricultural outputs, thus raising the standard of living and social-economic level of the people of that region.

The term hydrogeology now embraces all aspects of hydrology and the use of geophysical, hydrochemical, drilling, aquifer testing, simulation models, and other means of investigating and determining the groundwater resources of an area or region. The tremendous increase in the number and complexity of the tools now available for groundwater investigations, development, and management are of great

[1] Ambroggi, R.P. (1969) "The Management of Water Resources with Reference to the Role of Groundwater", ITC-Unesco Centre for Integrated Surveys, Delft, Netherlands.

[2] Burdon, D.J. and Thomas, R.G. (1971) Importance of Geology to Water Resources Projects in Developing Countries, XXIV International Geological Congress, Serial No. 01009.

potential value to the developing - as well as to the developed - countries of the world. Groundwater lives and moves and has its being in a geologic environment, and a knowledge of this environment is basic to a knowledge of the groundwater it contains. Therefore the inputs to and the answers received from such tools as analog and mathematical models must be tempered by a sound understanding of their geological meaning.

In helping developing countries to use these techniques to identify groundwater resources which can be developed and used for hydro-agricultural purposes, FAO is always conscious of the end purposes, and avoids undirected investigations. Integrated use of groundwater with other water supplies is a basic principle. In the case of groundwater investigations, where the natural hydrogeological unit may be a large basin, yet where the groundwater is required for use in limited areas where soil surveys indicate optimum returns, there can be a clash of interests between regional and local approaches. Such are usually solved by carrying out a reconnaissance type survey of the whole groundwater basin, but concentrating the investigation - and often pilot development - on the zone where development will take place.

Continued improvement in the integration of surface and groundwaters will require further research in the many hydrological, geological, and water use conditions. Simple computerization and mathematical models are necessary for general relationships and planning but the study of more complex systems will require the use of electrical analogy or other methods. The more complex systems must be analysed, taking into consideration legal and economic limitations in addition to physical factors. This should include the types of organizations which may be best adapted to carrying out the planning, financing, and, finally, the management and operation of the highly integrated system. The determination of the costs and how they should be distributed throughout the entire operation is, of course, of major importance.

This type of water development planning is a highly complex undertaking. It includes a long sequence of steps and involves a large number of widely differing activities. It is this complexity which makes timing important. "Time is money" is a widely used slogan and nowhere is this more applicable than in the planning, construction, and operation of irrigation systems costing large sums of money and resources. Good planning of water development will have to create an optimal path of activities which will keep at a minimum the time for which non-productive investments have to be made. It will also have to specify measures which will speed up the process of reaching full utilization of the facilities constructed, thus enabling an early flow of benefits.

The effect of all of this on the natural environment must be studied more than it has been in the past. Regarding planning development and use of water, a new approach must be taken which includes the environmental aspects and the promotion of a new attitude to integration with other aspects of water planning. Alternatives need to be explored and optimum solutions sought, using new methods of evaluation and analysis of the environmental quality.[1] This new concept must be based on the correct understanding of the interrelationship between the development and management of water and the environment as a whole, taking into account the different phases of water occurrence in the atmosphere, on the land, in the soil, and underground.

There are many examples of planning studies and even execution of projects where it seems to be assumed that application of modern technology alone will suffice. The technology is, of course, available but the problem much more often lies in how to apply it in a given socio-economic situation than in the determination of what particular inputs are necessary. Far too much planning in resource development is unrelated to the human factor or to the overall needs and objectives of the country. The result is production of plans that never get off the shelf, or partial or complete failures because the plans, however sound technically, have not been related to the ultimate users - the farmers - and have not been conceived with the understanding of what the latter can or will do.

Of course, any development planning must be based on a realistic assessment of available physical resources. In most parts of the world some information is available, but it is surprising how seldom it is found to be systematically recorded or used in such a way as to point towards important development potential.

Usually there are some kinds of existing climatic records and often also records of stream flows. Both may be much less than complete but may go back over a considerable period of years. Rainfall and stream flow are variable, both within and between individual years. Agricultural development requires accurate assessment of distribution and probability, neither of which can effectively be determined without reasonably long-time records. Inferences derived from plant or wider biological communities can sometimes be valuable as a basis for determining general climatic zones, in the absence of reliable meteorological data in the particular area being studied. Robertson et al. stressed the importance of evaluating the water resource as an integral and indeed primary aspect of

1/Cheong Chup Lim (1971) Integrated Farm Water Management, FAO Irrigation and Drainage Paper No. 10.

land resource evaluation. The view was advanced "that much development expenditure can be wasted, especially in the early stages of exploration and planning, if examination of water resources - whatever their nature - is not given equal or higher priority to investigation of other physical resources. For example, an assured rainfall in an area is a good reason for seeking to exploit it. A country with a wide range of sunshine hours could well direct its enquiries first to areas with the better radiation figures. For investment, the user is interested in the difference between present production and potential production, with due regard to the growth pattern between the two and the associated cost. Although it may be valuable - and academically satisfactory - to have a systematic coverage of a country by regional first stage surveys, time and funds are in practice usually both in short supply. There is usually information available about climate and the water resource (though often very little in connection with groundwater) so that it is possible to direct first stage land resource surveys to regions where the water resource shows some promise."[1]

Funding agencies have found through experience that resource surveys should not be undertaken as a survey per se. There should be a major end use in mind such as for agriculture, industry, urban, or combinations of uses. Major funding agencies and major operating organizations have also found that resource investigations should be undertaken by those organizations most closely allied with the major end user.

Water Management

Improved water management is as important to successful irrigation as is water development. In fact, irrigation and drainage workers in developing countries generally agree that improved water management probably can do more towards increasing food supplies and agricultural income in irrigated areas than any other agricultural practice. Experience has shown that if a country took the money to be used for a new irrigation scheme and used it to train irrigation technicians in water management, who in turn would train the farmer, the returns from increased production and income would be several times the return to be gained from the new scheme.

In most developing countries, very little is known as to the amount of water to apply at an irrigation or the frequency

---

[1]/Robertson, V.C., Jewitt, T.N., Forbes, A.P.S. and Law, R.D. (1968) The Assessment of Land Quality for Primary Production. In Land Evaluation: Papers of a CSIRO symposium organized in cooperation with UNESCO, ed. G. A. Steward, MacMillan, Canberra.

of irrigations for maximum crop returns. Usually only by the
appearance of the crops is it indicated as to where too much
or too little water is applied.

Under traditional irrigation practices water use usually
is high whereas yields are low. The water-use/crop-yield ratio
can be as unfavorable as 5,000 tons water/1 ton yield for wheat
and 15,000 to 20,000 tons water/1 ton yield for rice. Land
and water resources which easily can be developed for agriculture
are becoming short. New irrigation and drainage require higher
investments which can be economically made only with high crop
returns. In addition, water shortage in many areas calls for
a better water/yield ratio. It has been proved that ratios
as low as 1,000 tons water for 1 ton of wheat and 3,000 tons
water for 1 ton of rice are possible under irrigated conditions.

Better water management, use of fertilizers, and better
seeds are the three main elements for better yields and improvement of the water-use/crop-yield ratio. The advantages of
proper fertilizer application and use of high-yielding varieties
can easily be demonstrated to the farmers and in most cases
are readily accepted by them. In contrast to this, measures
to improve water management are often opposed by tradition, be
it traditional irrigation practices which have been developed
over centuries, or be it traditional rain-fed agriculture.
However, differences in average rice-yields, as shown in Fig.
1, demonstrate the advantage of the improved combination of
water management, fertilizers and seeds and the progress which
has been made in their introduction in Asia.

Improvement of water management practices in irrigation
and drainage schemes requires:
    (i) projects be designed and constructed to meet the
water requirements at the farmers' fields, to allow sufficient
flexibility for changes in cropping pattern, and to permit the
efficient operation of the scheme; traditional irrigation
systems have to be provided with control structures, improved
distribution networks, and, in most cases, field lay-outs will
have to be re-designed;
    (ii) organizations for scheme operation and administration
be established, and
    (iii) farmers be educated in proper water management at
the field.

The introduction of improved water management in agriculture is a complex problem involving the whole of rural society
and agricultural administration, and often has consequences
which reach as far as the national legislative bodies who have
to effect the required changes in land and water laws. The
main problem, however, will be to educate farmers to use water
properly: a tremendous task as ultimately millions and millions
of farmers are involved.

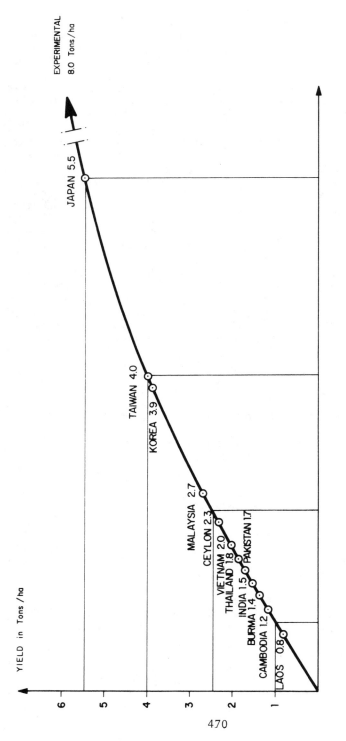

Fig. 1 The Role of Watercontrol and Use of Additional Imputs on Rice Yields on a Country Wide Basis.

470

To make governments and experts aware of the problems
of water management in agriculture, FAO is operating a series
of seminars and training courses at the regional and national
levels. It is encouraging to note that the recent UN Conference
on the Human Environment in Stockholm recommended that FAO
create regional water management centers for the promotion
and scientific backstopping of improved water management and
use in agriculture.

It is clear that measures to accelerate benefits from
water development projects for agriculture must necessarily
be grouped around the farmer's field, as the success of investments depends ultimately on the effectiveness with which the
water is used by the farmers. It is clear that if water is to
be effectively used by the farmer he must have adequate means
to do so. He must also know how to do it. Finally, there
must be sufficient incentive in material terms for him to be
productive and sustain his effort.

Apart from improving crop yield and ensuring economic use
of water, good water management also has a significant effect
on the economy of a project. This is because low irrigation
efficiencies result in demands for a larger quantity of water
which calls for greater storage capacity, larger structures
and larger canals and, therefore, heavier capital investment.
Furthermore, water so wasted may considerably reduce the area
that can be irrigated with a given amount of water, thus
raising the construction cost per unit area and reducing the
overall project returns.

The answer to these problems may be provided by a new
approach towards water development projects: The allocation of
scarce water resources and the planning of costly water
development projects should no longer be based on empirical
formulae; effective water use in agriculture calls for a new
type of complex planning of water resources development in
relation to the utilization of other resources, soil fertility,
cropping pattern, and crop returns which might be termed water
use planning. This modern approach to effective water use in
agriculture seeks to maximize the efficiency of input use, such
as water management, fertilizer application, seeds, and land
preparation. This new approach is parallel to similar movements
in other disciplines which also seek to optimize the inter-
relations between key factors.[1]

Of the over 50 active FAO field projects dealing with
water, at least half contain water management at the farm level
as the main emphasis.

---

[1]/Horning, H.M. (1970) The Role of Water Management at the
Field. FAO TA 2964.

FAO is the responsible UN Organization for water in regard to agriculture. The Water Resources and Development Service is the responsible Service for water in FAO. Our interest and activities in water begin with the formation of clouds and extend throughout all the ramifications of the resource, its development and its management until it finally passes into the oceans.

Being an international organization, our overall approach must be on a world-wide basis. Although the field projects are usually confined to a country and a basin or sub-basin, our regular program takes on broader aspects. Our consitutional charge is to assist in improving rural conditions in the world through the utilization of water.

TRANSFER OF KNOWLEDGE IN WATER RESOURCES POLICIES FROM DEVELOPED TO DEVELOPING COUNTRIES

By

K. Szesztay
Water Resources Section
Resources and Transport Division
United Nations, New York

Synopsis

Fields and types of knowledge in which transfer and assistance may be needed depend largely on projected demands and strategies for water resources development and management. Policy formulation is itself, therefore, an important field for consideration by the Conference. Possibilities and limitations for transferring knowledge in this sector are discussed in the light of recent United Nations experiences and programs. The selection of the proper level of technology corresponding to future investment capabilities and manpower resources is particularly emphasized.

There are rather well developed forms and channels for transferring scientific and technological knowledge in the field of water management. It is usually more difficult to transfer knowledge and provide assistance for the formulation of overall water resources development policies and programs. The possibilities and limitations of this type of assistance are discussed below taking into account recent United Nations experience.

Water Resources Policies

In a United Nations draft report, water resources policy has been defined as "the shaping of the basic guidelines, organizational principles, and fundamental procedures under which water is managed and utilized within any given society and in relation to neighbouring societies" (U.N. 1971a, p.3).* The scheme in the Annex lists some of the basic constraints (social, economic and physical) which affect policy formulation as well as functions and major fields of action by which the water resources policies are adopted and put into effect.

Regarding the subject of this Conference, persons and institutions formulating and implementing water resources policies are expected to define fields and types of knowledge in which transfer is required, as well as the priorities among the requirements. The extreme differences, from country to country, and from region to region in the socio-economic and

---

*See list of references.

physical conditions listed in the introductory portions of the Annex, suggest that similar differences exist with respect to scope and orientation of water resources policies, as well as in their significance and role within overall national (regional) development policies.

Regarding policy-formulation for a specific region, a comparative survey on available supplies and future demands, referred to in the Annex, should serve as the very basis of this complex and iterative exercise (U.N. 1962). The results of this survey, i.e., the assessment of overall relative abundance or scarcity of supplies within the foreseeable future, will be the principal guide to further efforts in policy formulation. It also conditions a selection among the basic alternative of water resources development, such as:
-The increase of available supply by storage, artificial recharge of groundwaters, construction of regional or inter-regional water grid systems;
-The decrease of the demand by changes in water use technologies, changes in production processes, introduction of economic incentives and regulatory measures for increased water quality treatment or for land use alterations;
-Search for new sources of water supply;
-Revision or reallocation of economic objectives.

Studies and decisions on alternative measures for achieving a decrease in flood losses, as well as those affecting developing lands and other natural resources of the region; or guidelines for overall environmental management are further aspects closely inter-related with water resources policy formulation and referred to in the Annex.

Types of Knowledge Needed and Problems of Transferability

Integration with overall social and economic development - The formulation of water resources strategies requires a full knowledge and close personal contact with the basic facts, traditions, and goals of the overall social and economic development of the region. It is also an endless iterative process in which continuity may be maintained only through a reasonable stability in the top leadership.

All this suggests that the most important criterion for policy formulation should stem from experts native to the region, whose personal judgement and knowledge can best benefit from the experience of more advanced regions (through studies, visits and personal contacts prior to and during their term of service).

474

Preference for generalists - Decisions on basic questions
of water resources policy should be based on a well balanced
consideration of many elements covering almost all sectors
of the region's economic structure and motivated by advances
in many different fields of science and technology. It is
usually more difficult to arrive at a reasonable balance of
the various elements, as the number of specialists involved
increases. This certainly does not mean that governments
of developing countries should hesitate to initiate or accept
advice in the different specific fields of water resources
management. It only means that suggestions for significant
changes in specific aspects of water management should be
undertaken in consultation with experts having broad orientations in water resource problems.

Such "generalists" can usually be found in countries or
regions of water scarcity where the achievement of an overall
balance in water resources development strategies is conditioned
by a physical and economic limitations.

The primary economic orientation of water resources
policies - The rapidly changing patterns of water use, and more
particularly its increased use for waste disposal, indicate that
man is currently in a transition phase from the days of assumed
water plenty to the immediate future, which will be governed by
much greater care and efficiency in use. Although subsidies
for certain water uses from local, regional, or national budgets
will certainly remain significant features of water resources
policies, there should be an increasing awareness and adaptation to the fact that the efficient use and rational conservation
of water resources may be achieved only through an economically
oriented approach.

A clear differentiation between total annual cost and
revenue should frequently lead to changed rate patterns, and
to an increased role for economic incentives. The expertise
of economists with overall experience in natural resources
management may greatly facilitate the assessment of the actual
and potential role of economic incentives in water resources
development and management.

Search for a full range of alternatives - One of the
lessons from the experiences of most of the industrialised
countries, which may greatly benefit the water resources
development strategies of the developing countries, concerns
the attention and incentives devoted to the identification of
a full range of choices in developing and managing the region's
water resources. In a great number of industrialized countries,
water resources policies were biased by the predominance of
structural (engineering) approaches. The construction of dams
and other structural measures for increasing the regions
natural water supply to its physical limits, were too often

accepted as primary policy objectives without proper consideration of other possible alternatives aiming at the reduction of
demand or the more efficient use of water.

This could be achieved through changes in technology or
production processes, as well as by introducing regulatory
measures or economic incentives (White 1970, U.N. 1972b). The
consideration of such non-structural measures is particularly
relevent to the conditions of the developing regions where
capital and skilled manpower are usually scarce and investments should assure rapid returns.

Selection of the proper level of technology - Developing
countries have the potential to adapt and apply the most
advanced technologies from the early phases of their development. An evaluation of the requirements brought about by
these technologies in terms of investments and skilled
personnel, however, usually suggests that the most advanced
level is not necessarily the most appropriate level for the
given conditions. One of the most responsible and difficult
aspects of a water resources strategy is the identification
of place and timing for the application of the various types
and levels of new technology. Small scale pilot experiences
and testing operations may greatly facilitate decisions on
large scale application. Applied research should be considered
as an important and direct tool of decision-making in this
respect.

Programs for fellowships and technical assistance can be
meaningful and effective only if they are based on the results
of the above policy decisions, with respect to fields and
levels of technology to be studied. It should also be emphasized that in order to promote the transfer of technology,
the developed countries should facilitate access to new
technologies under fair and reasonable terms and conditions
(U.N. 1972a).

The data base for policy formulation - There are good
opportunities for transferring knowledge and technology from
industrialized to developing countries as regards the methods
and facilities for collecting, processing and storing data on
water resources and water use. Here again policy decisions
and guidelines on the overall structure and operation of the
information system should precede studies and consultation on
technologies to be applied.

An early agreement on basic concepts and methods is
particularly important in cases of water resources common to
more than one regional or national administration. Even the
most simple elements of policy (e.g. per capita water use or
economic losses caused by a given flood) will not be comparable

among the different parts of the region unless careful consideration is given to common interpretation of the concepts
and data involved.

Role of the United Nations Organizations

The most direct ways by which the organization of the
United Nations system contributes to the transfer of knowledge
on water resources policies, from the industrialized to the
developing countries, are those interlinked with the formulation
and execution of UNDP (Special Fund) projects. The various
phases of the country programming exercise offer regular opportunities for such contributions, and these are frequently
supplemented by special advisory missions on overall water
resources administration and policy formulation. These preliminary contacts may identify the need for special projects
in the field of institution building, water law and water
resources administration. Six projects of this type are
presently under execution by the Resources and Transport
Division of the United Nations in Asia and Latin America.

The promotion of an exchange of national knowledge and
experience in water resources policy is one of the principal
aims of a number of non-operational activities of the United
Nations organizations. The World Health Organization and the
Food and Agricultural Organization regularly convene meetings
of high level experts responsible for national policy formulation in their respective fields of water resources management. The Regional Economic Commissions of the United Nations
also convene regular or occasional meetings to review and discuss basic problems of overall national water resources policies
of common interest to countries of the region.

The following may be referred to from among the recent
activities of the Water Resources Section of the Resources
and Transport Division among the activities closely related
to transfer of knowledge in water resources policy formulation:
    -A panel of Experts on Water Resources Policies was
established in 1970. The preliminary text of the report of
the Panel was recently published (U.N. 1971a) and a revised
version is expected to be finalized by the end of this year.
    -An interregional survey on National Systems of Water
Resources Administration was initiated and conducted in 1969
in six countries (Algeria, Hungary, India, Israel, Mexico and
Spain). A preliminary version of a comparative study was
prepared for the first session of the Committee on Natural
Resources (U.N. 1971b) and a revised version of the study is
in print.
    -An interregional seminar was held in October 1969 in
Tbilisi, USSR on flood damage prevention measures and management as important components of water resources policies (U.N.
1972b).

-An Expert Group meeting was held from 10 to 17 May 1972 in Budapest, Hungary, on one of the most difficult problems of policy formulation, the forecasting of future demands for water. The 17 working papers prepared by the participants of the meeting are available from the Secretariat, and a concise report is expected to be published on this subject by the end of 1972.

References

ECE 1970 - Trends in water resources use and development in the ECE region, A survey prepared under the auspices of the Committee on Water Problems of the United Nations Economic Commission for Europe, ST/ECE/WATER/1.

FOX, I.K. 1971 - Water Resources Law and Policy in the Soviet Union, The University of Wisconsin Press, Madison, Milwaukee and London.

UN 1962 - Approaches to water resources development in developing countries, Report A. 213 of the UN Conference on the Application of Science and Technology for the Benefit of the Less Developed Areas.

UN 1971a - Report of the United Nations Panel of Experts on Water Resources Development Policies, ESA/RT/AC.2/1.

UN 1971b - National Systems of Water Administration: A Comparative Study (A preliminary version).

UN 1972a - Committee on Natural Resources, Report on the Second Session, E/5097.

UN 1972b - United Nations Interregional Seminar on Flood Damage Prevention Measures and Management (in printing).

University of Wisconsin 1971 - Public Water Resource Project Planning and Evaluation: Impacts, Incidence and Institutions, D. W. Bromley, A. A. Schmid, W. B. Lord.

WHITE, G.F. 1970 - Strategies of American Water Management, The University of Michigan Press, Ann Arbor, 155 p.

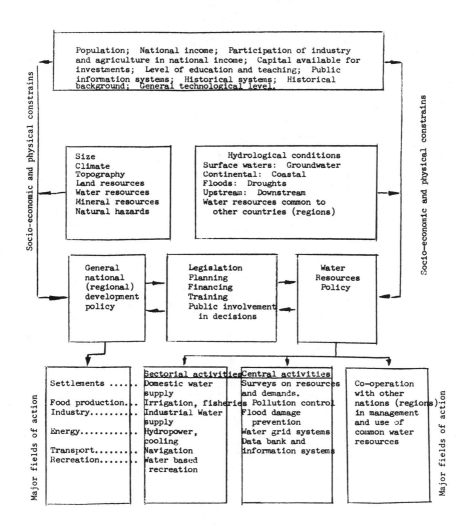

Water resources policies: Constrains, functions
and major fields of action.

TRANSFER OF WATER RESOURCES KNOWLEDGE THROUGH THE
UNITED NATIONS TECHNICAL ASSISTANCE ACTIVITIES*

By

Robert E. Dijon
Technical Adviser
Water Resources Section
Resources and Transport Division
United Nations Headquarters, New York

Synopsis

The United Nations has provided technical assistance in
the field of water resources to many developing countries,
especially as an Executing Agency of the United Nations
Development Program.

The United Nations is particularly interested in activities
centered on Institution Building and Training. Training is
provided on a on-the-job basis, as well as through fellowships abroad; some examples of the results, which were obtained,
are given.

The following conclusions can be drawn from the experience
of the U. N. in the transfer and exchange of water resources
knowledge:

- local national conditions have to be considered: what
  is relevant for temperate regions does not necessarily
  apply to tropical areas.

- a first priority is to be given to projects which can
  lead, within a short period of time, to practical results.

- the human factor is essential; training programs should
  be adapted to the academic and professional background
  of the local personnel.

- more is to be done for the dissemination and exchange
  of information, not only from developed regions to
  developing regions, but also on a broad regional and
  international basis.

Many organizations of the United Nations family have,
from the very beginning, been engaged in activities related
to water resources development. These activities were greatly
increased in recent years with the establishment of the First
U. N. Development Decade and the United Nations Development
Program (UNDP).

---

*This article is published with the authorization of the U.N.
The opinions expressed are not necessarily endorsed by this
organization.

About 50 million dollars of UNDP funds, are committed each year to the study and development of water resources in developing countries, through projects which are entrusted' to a number of U. N. agencies for execution. The activities of the specialized agencies of the United Nations: UNESCO, FAO, WMO, WHO and IAEA, in the field of water resources are generally well known. This paper will limit itself to briefly illustrating the activities of the United Nations Department of Economic and Social Affairs in New York, in the field of water resources which are not limited to a specific end use for water, or to strict scientific and technical aspects, as is the case of the specialized agencies. In broad terms it can be said that the fields of interest and competence of the U.N. have mainly related to overall economic, social, and institutional aspects. With respect to natural resources, the United Nations Headquarters bears responsibility for the exploration, assessment, and development of mineral, water, and energy resources, and primarily for the resources located underground. The activities of the U. N. in the field of groundwater are quite significant. Out of a total of some 30 UNDP projects having as a main objective (or as the only objective) the exploration and development of groundwater resources, a total of 19 was or is currently being carried out by U. N. Headquarters. The present paper will put some emphasis on the activities in groundwater, as most of these projects are of the technical assistance type, and thus fit exactly into the theme of this meeting; since they are the feasibility study type, the majority of surface water projects are carried out through subcontracts awarded to private firms.

Water resources development is handled at U. N. Headquarters by the Resources and Transport Division of the Department of Economic and Social Affairs. The activities in the field of water have been implemented in a number of ways including: the preparation of publications, the organization of consultant panels, seminars and symposia, the assignment to developing countries of instructors, experts and consultants, within the framework of technical assistance programs, and through the award of fellowships in the water resources field to scholars from developing countries.

The UNDP has entrusted U. N. Headquarters with the execution of a number of water resource development projects, of which a listing is provided in an annex to the present paper - this enumeration shows how diverse and widely distributed geographically were these operations; 61 projects, of which 28 are completed, are spread over 36 countries in all continents.

One of the major objectives of the projects is the training of personnel at all levels, from the specialized laborer (mechanic, tool-pusher), up to the engineer and the post-graduate scientist. This training is provided both by on-the-job basis, through lecturing and demonstrations in the country itself, and through fellowships overseas. After some 10 years of operation, it appears appropriate to try to draw some conclusions on the results which were obtained in transferring water resources knowledge to the countries bene-fitting from UNDP/UN sponsored water resources projects.

U. N. Publications on Water

Water-resources knowledge is being transferred by the United Nations in many ways. First, United Nations is issuing sales publications, which are directly or indirectly related to water resources. Among such publications the following may be noted: "Water for Industrial Use" (1958); "Integrated River Basin Development" (1958 and 1970); "Large-Scale Ground Water Development" (1960); "Water Desalination in Developing Countries" (1964); "The Design of Water Supply Systems Based on Desalination" (1968); "Solar Distillation as a Means of Meeting Small Water Demands" (1970); "Ground Water in Africa" (1971). Some of these publications are the direct outcome of panel meetings and seminars, which were organized by the United Nations and were attended by international consultants and also experts, officials, and scholars from developing countries. These meetings represent a good opportunity for exchanging information and comparing the results of projects. It would be erroneous to think that the transfer of knowledge always goes in the same direction. It often happens that the experience which is gained in developing countries is of significance to industrialized countries.

The U. N. work program for 1972 and following years includes the following publications of which some are already in an advanced stage of preparation: "Assessing Water Uses and Minimal Requirements," "Manuals on Flood-Damage Prevention," "Use of Contaminated Waters," "Ground Water in the Western Hemisphere." Within the framework of UNDP/UN country projects, a number of documents of general interest were prepared such as a bibliography of water resources, papers of general interest, and manuals, such as a water-well drilling manual in Spanish, compiled for the use of drillers in Central America. In addition to its own meetings and publications, the United Nations participates in and contributes information at water conferences sponsored by government or international professional associations such as the Water for Peace Con-ference, held in Washington (USA), in 1967, and meetings of such nongovernmental organizations as the International Commission for Irrigation and Drainage. A number of United Nations experts and scholars have published in a number of scientific periodicals. These publications do not engage the responsibility of the U. N., but they are sometimes rendered public under the author's responsibility, with U. N. approval. Some results of U. N. water projects have been brought to the attention of the public in this manner.

Operational Activities

The above mentioned activities which are termed "non-operational," have, however, given way in recent years to a steadily growing flow of "operational activities," of the technical assistance type, undertaken on an interregional, regional, or country basis. Interregional water experts based in the headquarters of the regional economic commissions (Geneva, Santiago, Addis Ababa, Bangkok), whose assignments are being financed by the regular budget of the United Nations, have accomplished a great number of missions advising countries on water related issues and policies, on a short term basis.

The United Nations Development Program has financed the assignments, on a country basis, of many Technical Assistance and Special Fund projects. Each international expert on these projects is in general working in close cooperation with a national "counterpart" professional, who will take over the duties of the expert at the end of the project. The transfer of knowledge is made directly in this case, on a daily and on-the-job basis. The U. N. expert is sometimes an adviser to the government; sometimes he has direct responsibilities for operations (as in the case of OPAS experts). He might be a project manager or a member of a team. In all these cases, the principle of having a counterpart professional working with him remains valid. If necessary, the training of the counterpart is complemented by means of an overseas fellowship for graduate or post graduate courses, work in a specialized institution, government service, or private firm. U. N. experts are also lecturing in Universities on water matters (Central and South America) and training local workers and technicians (well-diggers and well-drillers in Africa). On U. N. water projects, knowledge is also transferred by experimenting and demonstrating new methods and processes, preparing reports, and organizing documentation units for water.

A good framework for such action is provided when the project is focused on Institution Building, Training, Water Law, and Water Management, which is the case for an increasing number of projects. International river basin projects also provide an excellent opportunity for comparing the approaches and solutions to water problems between neighboring countries.

With respect to the listing of water projects entrusted for execution to the United Nations (presented in an annex to this paper), the major categories of operations include:

water-management studies, surface water and hydropower
resources surveys and planning, groundwater exploration and
pilot development, international river basin feasibility
studies, strengthening Government services, Institutes for
Research and Training, Engineering and Surveys.

Methods

It appears appropriate after some 10 years of activities
in all these fields, to draw from the experience gained some
principles and guidelines regarding the transfer of water
resources knowledge to developing countries. A first overall
remark is that the technical and scientific knowledge on water
has to be adapted to local conditions taking into account
natural and economic conditions and the human factor.

In general, industrialized countries are located in the
temperate climatic zone, while most of the developing countries
are in the tropical zone. As a result, experts who have
no experience of tropical areas have sometimes incorrect ideas
on what can be expected there in terms of water resources.
For instance a young Scandinavian hydrogeologist was looking
for gravels of glacial origin in the crystalline regions of
East Africa. Such gravels are good aquifers in crystalline
regions of Scandinavia, but do not exist in East Africa, which
has not experienced quaternary glaciations. A yearly rainfall
of 800 millimeters is a good average in a temperate-humid
climate, while it is much less significant in a tropical area
due to the high evaporation ratio. Hydrological systems, which
include flow resulting from snowmelt, are quite different from
those which are mainly supplied with water by tropical rain-
storms. Quality standards for water consumption cannot be
the same: in industrial countries pollution resulting from
industrial waste, which is expressed by the contents in oligo-
elements (such as lead, mercury, phenol), is the limiting
factor for human consumption. In such countries special
standards are defined for water utilized in industry, and
consumers can afford to pay for a water low in dissolved
solids with a good taste. In developing countries it is the
bacteriological content which is important for human consumption, while a water somewhat high in salt contents and having
a bitter taste is not harmful. On the contrary in arid cli-
mates, it is preferable to drink water containing up to 1500
ppm in Sodium chloride, in order to avoid a harmful dehydra-
tion, which can be fatal to small children. It is therefore
essential that the specific conditions prevailing in equatorial,
tropical, and desert areas be taken into consideration by
experts originating from industrialized countries. This applies
to the installation of gaging stations, analysis of hydrographs,
water-balance calculations, flood warning systems, protection

of river banks, ground water exploration, and water quality studies.

Economic Aspects

Another important factor to be taken into account is related to economic conditions. In developing countries the needs are immense and the financial resources are very limited. The format of any study or survey must be properly adapted to its objectives. Research must be limited to the essential and should not deal with subjects which in spite of their scientific interest do not have a bearing on the social and economic conditions. For instance, in a tropical country where the rainfall is currently 4000 mm/year, and where surface water resources are very abundant there is no need for a laboratory model study of sea water intrusion in a coastal aquifer, as is happening in a given African country. Research studies are justified, however, when concrete and urgent problems are to be solved. Detailed surveys are justified only for pilot or experimental areas; their results can be extrapolated in order to cover a region; the use of air photography is to be maximized, while land surveying - slow and costly - is to be minimized, especially in regions where communications are difficult. The use of costly and delicate imported equipment is to be reduced to a minimum especially when maintenance and repairs cannot be secured appropriately; this applies in particular to river-gaging, water analysis, and waterwell-drilling equipment.

In broad terms, two pitfalls are to be avoided: academism and empirism. On one hand, many water resources experts mainly from Continental Europe (West and East) would tend to be oriented towards academic studies on water resources without giving sufficient consideration to the utilization aspects. On the contrary, many experts and firms from other countries including Great Britain, the U.S.A. and Northern Europe would tend to be oriented mainly towards the engineering aspects of water resources development. In both cases developing countries are submitted to strong pressure, either for carrying out studies and surveys which are not really proportioned to their needs, or for constructing water works, which are not adapted to local needs and local resources. It is therefore essential to develop an integrated and balanced approach which, while taking into consideration both the water resources and water engineering aspects, is to be oriented towards economic solutions. Officials and technicians of developing countries must be made fully aware of this type of approach, in order to be able to reject offers emanating from firms and institutions which are not likely to help substantially in the overall improvement of the economic and social conditions (and on the contrary might generate deficits and debts). The

United Nations is doing its best through its various projects
to promote this philosophy. In particular, the best possible
use is made of the existing documentation, including aerial
photography, water analyses, hydrologic records, geophysical
diagrams, which are carefully reviewed, evaluated, and if
necessary corrected, thus avoiding costly and useless new
surveys. It should also be noted that the assessment of water
resources in a developing country cannot be made on an accurate
basis, due to the small number of years for which reliable
hydrologic data are available. This consideration should not
delay indefinitely the execution of water resources projects.
Methods have been developed for assessing water resources
availability using data which are relevant to a small number
of years of observation, provided proper extrapolation is done.

Training

The human aspects must also be considered. In many
developing countries, in spite of the considerable efforts
which were made in recent years in the field of education,
the number of educated people at the graduate level is still
modest, while illiteracy is still quite widespread. As a
result, and considering that not many educated people are
available for the water sector, water resources knowledge is
communicated to a number of sub-professionals, undergraduates,
and even illiterate people, frequently in a language which
is not currently spoken in industrialized countries (Swahili,
for instance). It happens also that special training courses
have to be organized with a view to bringing high school
students up to the levels of engineer or scientist. For
instance, in the School of Geology, operating in Bamako (Mali)
for young French-speaking Africans, a training in geology
which includes identification of rock samples, structural
geology, laboratory experiments, microscopic studies, field
mapping, and lecturing at the B. Sc. level is provided to
high school students. They do not, however, have the basic
level of instruction in mathematics and physics, which is
normally reached by graduates.

One of these technicians, who was working on a U. N.
project was granted a fellowship. This enabled him to acquire
the basic scientific level which he needed, through correspondence courses, while working in a hydrogeological service,
where he was dealing with practical problems. By the end of
his fellowship, his reports showed that he had reached the
level of a qualified hydrogeologist.

Fortunately in some developing countries there are now
a number of graduates who are available for training in the
water resources field. However, the training of high-level
technicians does not meet all the needs. One water resources

engineer, when his work involves field operations, usually
needs several sub-professional assistants, such as hydro-
metrists, operators, surveyors, etc., and field workers, a
car (jeep-type), and a driver, some equipment, the part-time
services of a secretary, a draftsman, and laboratory
technicians. Deprived of these means, he will only be able
to sit behind a desk and do paper work. It happens also that
water resources experts from developing countries, unsatisfied
with their position, due to the lack of means, are moving to
other professions where managerial positions are vacant,
especially in the industry sector. This means that the long
years which were spent in training them in the water resources
field were lost. Such cases are fortunately the exception,
but they should not even exist. They show that the best way
of transferring water resources knowledge is to carry out in
the country itself, projects which have practical objectives
and which provide an opportunity for training governmental
teams, including personnel of diverse levels and skills, from
the specialized worker up to the scientist and the engineer.
Such projects, if they are Institution Building oriented,
provide also the institutional framework, which will create
the conditions for continuing the action after the completion
of the project. When such projects include experts from
several countries, they enable a fruitful exchange of views.
In projects which are contracted to specialized firms, the
technical assistance apsects are in general not considered a
priority. However, the contracts often bear obligation to
the firm for including government-paid nationals in their
teams.

Need for World-Wide Cooperation

One mistake to avoid, when water resources knowledge is
provided through Technical Assistance to developing countries,
is the multiplication of water agencies with all the resulting
duplication, rivalry, and neutralization of efforts. Such an
unfortunate situation exists sometimes in industrialized
countries, but this is not a valid reason for creating similar
conditions in developing countries, which cannot afford such
a waste. There should not be any competition between several
government agencies for doing the same thing in the water
field. From another point of view, it happens sometimes that
antagonism develops between water specialists, who have been
trained through various bilateral assistance programs. Such
programs should not instill into the minds of the scholars
a parochial spirit. More than a certain type of knowledge,
it is the willingness to learn about water matters, which is
to be taught. In developing countries the water resources
specialists, must be versatile people, of many talents: they
should not have narrow, sectorial views. They should take
an interest in the water problems of the neighboring countries,
which are relevant to their own. It has to be emphasized

that the transfer of water resources knowledge gains most of its efficiency through the exchange of information at the level of the regions, especially when it is institutionalized by the creation of regional centers for information and studies such as the INTERAFRICAN COMMITTEE FOR HYDRAULIC STUDIES. The U. N. by means of its international teams of experts and its regional projects is helping to broaden the views of a number of countries in the field of water resources.

In the field of water resources, as in many others, times are soon coming when cooperation will effectively be substituted for assistance which means that the former relationship between donor and recipient countries will disappear, and a broader system of world-wide cooperation instituted. The International Water Conference, which may be convened in 1975, or shortly thereafter, by the United Nations, will represent a significant step in this direction.

ANNEX I

UNDP/UN SPONSORED WATER RESOURCES PROJECTS

Groundwater
component: (*) minor, (**) substantial, (***) major or exclusive

COUNTRY AND PROJECT'S SYMBOL	PROJECT	APPROVED BY GOV. COUNCIL, DURATION
AFGHANISTAN		
AFG-4	Groundwater Investigation (***)	completed 12/69
AFG-18	Establishment of a Water Management Department (*)	1/68 - 4½ yrs
ARGENTINA		
ARG-13	Groundwater Research in the Northwest (***)	completed 12/70
ARG-44	Water economy, Law and Administration Research and Training Institute	1/71 - 3 yrs
BOLIVIA		
BOL-14	Groundwater Development in the Altiplano (***)	1/68 - 4 yrs
BURMA		
BUR-5	Mu River Irrigation Survey	completed 10/69
BUR-13	Development of the Sittang River Valley	1/68 - 3½ yrs

488

ANNEX I - (Continued)

COUNTRY AND PROJECT'S SYMBOL	PROJECT	APPROVED BY GOV. COUNCIL, DURATION
CAMEROON		
CMR-16	Groundwater Investigations and Pilot Development (***)	1/71 - 3 yrs
CHILE		
CHI-35	Water Resources Development in the Norte Grande (**)	6/69 - 4 yrs
CHINA		
CHA-3	Hydraulic Development Projects	completed 2/62
CHA-17	Comprehensive Hydraulic Development Survey of the Choshui and Wu Basins	completed 3/67
COSTA RICA		
COS-2	Groundwater Surveys in Three Selected Areas (***)	6/65 - 4½ yrs
CYPRUS		
CYP-2	Survey of Groundwater and Mineral Resources (**)	completed 9/69
ECUADOR		
ECU-11	Survey of Hydrological Resources of Manabi Province (*)	completed 6/65
EL SALVADOR		
ELS-2	Groundwater Survey of the Metropolitan Area of San Salvador (***)	1/65 - 3½ yrs
GREECE		
GRE-23	Power Development Planning	6/68 - 2¼ yrs
ICELAND		
ICE-1	Survey of Hydroelectric Power Development in the Hvita and Thjorsa River Basins	completed 12/66
INDIA		
IND-20	Survey of Potential Hydropower Sites	completed 1/67
IND-15	Cavitation Research, Cavitation Research Centre, Poona	12/60 - 3 yrs

489

COUNTRY AND PROJECT'S SYMBOL	PROJECT	APPROVED BY GOV. COUNCIL, DURATION
IND-101	Coastal Engineering Research Center and Development of Hydraulic Instrumentation	1/71 - 4 yrs
IND-49	Groundwater Project in Rajasthan (***)	1/64 - 4 yrs
IND-58	Groundwater Investigations in Madras State (***)	completed 6/69
IND-98	Groundwater Investigations in Madras State - Phase II (***)	6/68 - 2½ yrs
IND-114	Groundwater Surveys in Rajasthan and Gujarat (***)	1/71 - 3 yrs
INDONESIA		
INS-27	Institute of Hydraulic Engineering	1/70 - 4 yrs
IRAN		
IRA-1	Geological Survey Institute(*)	completed 6/68
ISRAEL		
ISR-16	Electrodialysis Pilot Plant, Mashabei Sade	6/66 - 3 yrs
JORDAN		
JOR-4	Goundwater Survey of the Azraq Area (***)	completed 5/64
KUWAIT		
KUW-2	Water Resources Center, Kuwait City (*)	1/68 - 5 yrs
LEBANON		
LEB-7	Groundwater Survey (***)	completed 6/69
MADAGASCAR		
MAG-3	Surveys of the Mineral and Groundwater Resources of Southern Madagascar	completed 9/69
MALI		
MLI-5	Invesitgation of the Selingue Dam Site on the Sankarani River	1/70 - 2 yrs

COUNTRY AND PROJECT'S SYMBOL	PROJECT	APPROVED BY GOV. COUNCIL, DURATION
MLI-7	Strengthening Government services for groundwater exploration and development (***)	6/67 - 3 yrs
MAURITANIA		
MAU-2	Strengthening Groundwater Services (***)	6/67 - 3 yrs
NEPAL		
NEP-2	Hydroelectric Development of the Karnali River	completed 2/65
NICARAGUA		
NIC-8	Groundwater Investigations in the Pacific Coastal Area (Chinandega) (***)	1/67 - 3¼ yrs
PANAMA		
PAN-1	Water Resources Survey of the Chiriqui and Chico River Basins	completed 11/64
PARAGUAY		
PAR-16	Investigation of Groundwater Resources in Central and North-eastern Chaco (***)	1/69 - 3 yrs
PHILIPPINES		
PHI-19	Feasibility Survey for the Hydraulic Control of the Laguna de Bay Complex and Related Development Activities	completed 6/70
POLAND		
POL-9	Planning the Comprehensive Development of the Vistula River Systems (*)	6/68 - 2 yrs
SOMALIA		
SOM-4	Mineral and Groundwater Survey - Phase I (*)	completed 3/68
SOM-14	Mineral and Groundwater Survey - Phase II (**)	1/68 - 3 yrs
SOM-23	Mineral and Groundwater Survey - Phase III (**)	1/72 - 2 yrs

COUNTRY AND PROJECT'S SYMBOL	PROJECT	APPROVED BY GOV. COUNCIL, DURATION
YUGOSLAVIA		
YUG-6	Studies on the Regulation and Control of the Vardar River	completed 7/69
YUG-7	Regulation and Management of the Sava River	completed 12/70
SURINAM		
NET-4	Public Water Supplies and Sewerage (in Cooperation with WHO)(**)	1/70 - 3 yrs
TOGO		
TOG-4	Survey of Mineral and Ground- water Resources (**)	completed 4/71
TOG-11	Groundwater Exploration in the Coastal Region (***)	6/70 - 2½ yrs
TUNISIA		
TUN-28	Intensification of Groundwater Exploitation in Northern and Central Tunisia (***)	1/69 - 2½ yrs
UGANDA		
UGA-5	Karamoja Groundwater Survey (***)	completed 5/68
UPPER VOLTA		
UPV-4	Mineral and Groundwater Survey (**)	completed 9/68
UPV-10	Hydrological and Railway Studies in Connection with Mineral Development in the Northeast (**)	1/69 - 2 yrs

REGIONAL PROJECTS

AFRICA		
REG-28	Integrated Basin Survey of the Mono River	completed 4/66
REG-53	Feasibility Study for the Diversion of the Logone River Floods	completed 6/69
REG-60	Hydrological and Topographical Studies of the Gambia River Basins	1/70 - 3 yrs

REGIONS

REG-80	Design of a System of Water Management in the Upper Senegal River Catchment	completed 10/70
REG-147	Planning the Development of the Kagera River Basin	1/71 - 2 yrs
REG-251	Technical Studies of the Trans-Saharan Road (**)	6/71 - 2½ yrs

ASIA

REG-7	Hydrographic Survey of the Lower Mekong	completed 1/64
REG-2	Survey of Four Tributaries (Mekong)	completed 12/64

EUROPE

REG-203	Integrated Development of the Vardar/Axios River Basin	1/71 - 3 yrs

LATIN AMERICA
BRA-61 Integrated Development

and URU-18	of the International Yaguaron River Basin	1/72 - 1½ yrs

RECENT DEVELOPMENT OF HYDROLOGICAL
SERVICES IN COLOMBIA

By

Wulf Klohn
Expert Hydrologist
World Meteorological Organization
Bogotá, Colombia

and

Silviu Stanescu
Expert Hydrologist
World Meteorological Organization
Bogotá, Colombia

Synopsis

Hydrological investigation was limited in Colombia until
1968 when a national hydrological and meteorological service
was started as a joint project of the Colombian Government, the
World Meteorological Organization, and the United Nations
Development Programme. Technical assistance in hydrology,
offered by an international team of experts, was directed
mainly towards hydrometrical network design and construction
of the stations, personnel training on hydrological techniques,
and introduction of procedures for data collection, processing,
analyzing and interpretation. This is a typical case of transfer of knowledge from developed regions to a developing country.
However, knowledge was not transferred uncritically but screened
for applicability under the specific local conditions, as is
explained with selected examples. Automation of data collection
and processing was examined, and as a consequence, the use of
digital recorders rejected. For the Colombian network, long-
range strip-chart recorders were selected as the most suitable
type. Further automation was examined as a means to obtain a
rapid access to stored data. For network design and as a
method of hydrological synthesis and extension, ample use was
made of the relationship between the hydrological regime and
the physical characteristics of the basins. Since a great
extension of Colombia land use is changing rapidly from forest
to cattle raising and agriculture, the hydrological regime of
most rivers is changing towards more extreme flood peaks and
low waters. Therefore, theoretical frequency is not applicable
indiscriminately, and graphical empirical methods offer definite
advantages. Data on water temperature are sparse but it will
be possible to obtain useful information by correlation to air
temperature. On variation of precipitation with altitude, no
general relation is applicable; these must be deducted from
local data. As a general conclusion, transfer of knowledge
should be selective.

Introduction

In most developing countries, hydrological investigation is limited or does not exist at all. To solve local problems, results of investigation and experience of countries with greater economical and technological resources are applied. In this sense, the Colombian case is representative. The aspects here discussed derive from application of a United Nations technical assistance program in Colombia.

Creation of a National Hydrological and Meteorological Service

Massive transfer of knowledge is necessary to reduce the distance that separates developing and developed countries. This statement is also true for hydrological knowledge that, for the convenience of developing countries, should be used more extensively. For a flow of knowledge at national scale, a strong receptive structure able to concentrate the existing capacity and establish a policy for development of the activity is required. Such a sub-structural organism was created in Colombia in 1968 as the main subject of a joint project of the Colombian Government, the World Meteorological Organization (WMO), and the United Nations Development Programme (UNDP). The Project which is entitled "Colombian Meteorological and Hydrological Service" (CMHS), initiated consolidation and development of existing facilities in hydrology and meteorology, and created a national service of the same denomination. The WMO, as the international executing organism, administers the funds provided by UNDP for purchase of equipment and instruments not manufactured locally, and furnishes the services of international experts whose duties typically include: help to locate and execute measuring stations, train local personnel in the installation and use of equipment, and introduce convenient methods for data processing and interpretation (1). More generally expressed, the expert should be an agent of transfer of knowledge in his special field.

On the basis of positive experience in other countries, the creation of a unified hydrological and meteorological service was initiated in Colombia (1,7). Unification of these activities offers some definite advantages, notably in developing countries where neither of both activities has a strong tradition. Conceptually, collection, processing, and analysis of elements of information about the environment in general and water resources in particular are centralized. Operationally, more rational and intense use of personnel and material is obtained, and duplicity of functions is avoided. Moreover, coordinated and harmonic development of both areas is secured by exploring the possibilities of using available information more efficiently.

Ways of Knowledge Transfer

The creation of the Colombian Meteorological and Hydrological Service as a governmental agency, and its development in the frame of the United Nations multilateral technical assistance, have notably accelerated the flow of experience and knowledge to Colombia. Technical assistance by WMO, exercised through the experts charged with the execution of the project, is imprinted in multiple aspects belonging to the development of hydrological activity at a national scale. In the first years, assistance was directed mainly towards projection and execution of hydrometrical networks, personnel training at the operational level, and interpretation of basic data. In addition, some studies of hydrological synthesis were elaborated.

Transmission of knowledge and experience by personal contact may be efficient at the individual level but is insufficient to reach all the potentially interested, because the duration of a mission is limited and stages of development follow each other rapidly. To break the limitations of direct communication, the most convenient way is to prepare and distribute documents on each matter (8). In the Colombian case, most of these documents were prepared by the WMO experts, having in view the need for material in Spanish, selected according to specific local conditions. It was generally found that only national personnel of the highest professional level were able to benefit directly from technical literature in English. Thus the training of intermediate technical and junior professional personnel, essential for a service in the formative stage, is only possible in the language of the country.

Preparation of professional personnel is completed in other countries with more experience in hydrology. The graduate specialization courses organized in diverse countries in the frame of the IHD have been used profitably. Participation in international technical and scientific meetings and seminars has also contributed to the transfer of knowledge and has completed the formation of hydrological personnel of the higher level. Possibly one of the most important effects of this kind of meeting is the opening of new ways of communication, thus contributing to overcome the scientific isolation of developing countries.

Screening of Foreign Experience

Since the start of the activities to organize the CMHS in Colombia, the conviction has been that before applying results of foreign hydrological experience, these should be screened and their viability in the local conditions verified. For this reason it was avoided to introduce empirical formulas established under conditions specific to other countries (9). Various types

of appliances and instruments were experimentally tested before
introducing greater quantities, and in certain cases modifications to the design were introduced according to necessities
discovered during experimentation. The same caution was applied
to data collection and processing, analyzing in each case the
technical and economical implication of the change.

Technological and economical conditions of Colombia do not
allow to advance basic investigation of remote application and
benefit. However, specific applicative investigation with
short and intermediate term results are essential, since
hydrological knowledge and experience in tropical areas are
limited. The method followed was verification and possibly
adjustment to specific local conditions of the results of
investigation in other countries, before these results were
applied to practice. Some examples will illustrate this process
of knowledge filtration and adjustment.

Automatized Collection and Processing of Data

In technologically advanced countries with a high level of
salaries, automated data processing is applied to several
aspects of hydrological activity. Developing countries may
profit from this experience, proceeding however cautiously to
adapt the new possibilities to local reality. Doubtless the
greatest difficulty is control of data quality. This requires
wide application of human insight and is difficult to automate,
particularly in view of low network densities and limited hydrological knowledge of the diverse regions. For any manual or
automatized data processing procedure, the concurrence of
experienced personnel for analyzing and interpreting data is
required. Such professional staff can only be formed in the
course of years.

In the Colombian case, automation of data processing was
examined in diverse phases (4). Acquisition of data by means
of digital recorders was discarded owing to higher cost of
these instruments and additional difficulties, as compared
with analogical recorders, for interpreting the records in the
field. Revision in situs of the records and earliest correction of any deficiency belong inseparably to the method of
hydrological network operations established in Colombia,
according to local realities such as difficult and costly access
to most stations and scarcity of adequately trained observers.
For the Colombian network long-range strip chart recorders were
selected as the most suitable type. For similar reasons the
automized calculation of discharge measurements was not
considered attractive. In fact, it is always indispensable
for the river gaging technician to calculate discharge in the
field immediately upon measurement and to decide on the need
for repeated further measurements. On the other hand, it is
considered attractive to develop hydrometrical statistics by

computer, using a program for processing instantaneous water
levels through rating curves defined by manual methods. As a
result, test tabulations of characteristic discharges for
quality analysis and definitive tabulations for the Hydrometrical Yearbook are obtained (Fig. 1). This program is actually
under experimentation (4). A powerful argument to replace the
present manual calculations by automated processing is that the
last one will allow establishment of digital data storage. It
is expected that rapid, computer-compatible access to stored
data will further complete use of hydrological antecedents
disposable in Colombia, with the consequent benefit to national
economy.

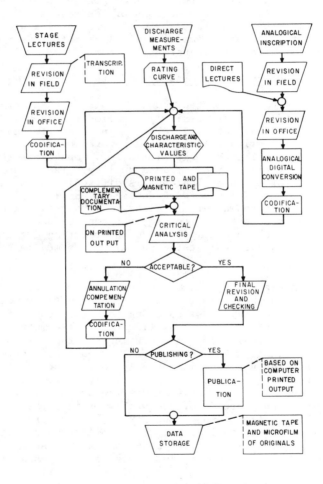

Figure 1. Flux Diagram of Automatized Processing of
Hydrometrical Data in Colombia.

Relation Between Hydrological Regime and Physical Characteristics of the Basins

In mountainous regions of several continents it has been found that the main hydrometeorological parameters, such as mean precipitation, and mean minimum and maximum runoff vary according to the main physiographical and morphometric characteristics of the basins, such as area, mean elevation, mean slope, etc. For this reason, a register of the main morphometrical and physiographical characteristics of the hydrographical basins was one of the first activities advanced by the CMHS (8,9). At this time, areas and mean elevations of basins as well as river lengths determined upon maps at scale 1:100,000 are available for most of the national territory. At the same time, determination of other characteristics, such as slope of basins and streams, drainage density, coefficient of forest cover, etc., are advancing.

This information was applied, in the conditions of Colombia, mainly to two areas of activity: 1) projecting of hydrometrical networks; and 2) interpretation, generalization, and indirect calculation of hydrometeorological data. In the projection of basic hydrometrical network in mountain regions, distribution of stations according to area and mean elevation of basins was used as a fundamental criterium (8,9). By applying the network density criteria recommended by the WMO for minimum basic networks (16), and siting the stations in a morphologically and hydrographically representative way, it is expected to define the main traits of the hydrological regime of the Colombian rivers at the least cost (2,7,8,9). Interpreting, generalizing, and calculating indirectly hydrometeorological data are based mainly on definition of graphical relations that indicate territorial variation of the main hydrological and meteorological parameters as a function of morphometrical and physiographical factors whose variation is known (3,8,9). The first attempts of approximation developed in Colombia in the described way (10-13) yielded encouraging results, even though based upon relatively poor information (Fig. 2).

Relation Between Hydrological Regime and Forest Situation of the Basins

By general theoretical considerations and through experiences affected in Europe and North America, it is known that vegetation is one of the main determinant factors of the hydrological regime. Deforestation has a sensible incidence upon regime characteristics, extending the amplitude of variation of water levels, discharge, and sediment discharge.

In Colombia, deforestation is advancing in most of the national territory, due to colonization and the use of former forest lands for agriculture and cattle raising. In regions

499

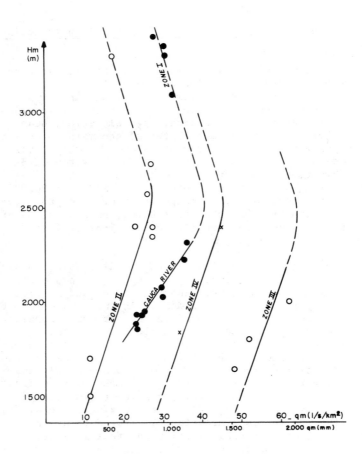

Figure 2.   Variation of Mean Runoff (1951-1970) with Mean
            Elevation in the Upper Cauca River Basin (Colombia).

where deforestation is progressing, it is not possible to
process hydrometrical information by classical methods of
statistics.   Maximum and minimum discharges may be determined
empirically by means of the superior and inferior envelope of
the frequency curve, without adjusting the population of events
to theoretical curves (Fig. 3).   Through this procedure it is
possible to obtain more realistic frequency curve extrapolations
corresponding to a future situation expected to be characterized
by greater maximum and lesser minimum discharges.

Relation of Air and Water Temperature

    Investigations advanced in several countries have
demonstrated satisfactorily that variation of water temperature

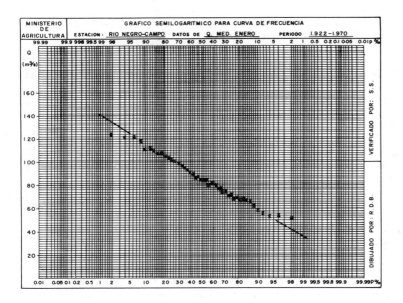

Figure 3.   Adjusting Frequency Curve by Superior and Inferior
            Envelopes in Case of Progressing Deforestation.

is related to variation of air temperatures measured in the
basin. These last are measured regularly in meteorological
stations, and past information is generally satisfactory.
Scarcity of direct measurements of water temperatures has
hindered a study of its regime. However, the experience of
other countries suggests that previous knowledge of air
temperature regime may be conducive to determination of the
main traits of termical regime of water, with a reduce expense
in direct measurements of water temperatures. For this reason,
a synthesis study of the air temperature regime in Colombia has
been elaborated (12). On the other side, water temperature
measurements are effected in representative points to define
the relation to the air temperature. By graphical relation it
is expected to obtain knowledge on the termical regime of water.

Variation of Mean Precipitation with Altitude

Preparation of coordinated runoff, precipitation, and
evaporation maps is a widely used method to verify hydrological
data and determine regime characteristics. On the basis of
measurements realized in several countries of the temperate
zone, it has been verified that mean precipitation increases
with altitude until a certain level corresponding approximately
to the basis of the rain-yielding clouds. Upon this level,
quantity of precipitation diminishes with altitude. The shape

501

of the precipitation versus altitude is essential to calculate
the water balance of a territory.

   In recent years, results of foreign investigation based
upon limited data apparently demonstrated that the precipitation-
altitude relation in the Colombian mountains was inverse, i.e.,
that precipitation was generally diminishing with altitude (14).
A detailed examination of this aspect, based upon more information (10,11,13) demonstrated that the said conclusion may be
valid only in a macrogeographic appraisal. In relatively
reduced areas, however, the variation are similar to those
found in temperature regions but invest a more complex
character. For instance, in the Bogotá River Basin, of some
6000 km² and equipped with a relatively dense pluviometrical
network, not less than 4 regressions of precipitation against
altitude were found, depending mainly on position and exposition
of parts of the basin (Fig. 4). Similar aspects have been
noted in other basins. Hence it is concluded that water
balances cannot be based on macrogeographical generalizations
or relations found in other regions. On the contrary, it is
essential to apply the data of each region and precipitation
versus altitude relations based upon direct local information.

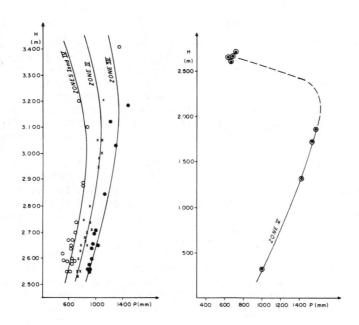

Figure 4.   Variation of Mean Annual Rainfall (1951-1970) with
            Altitude in the Bogota River Basin (Colombia).

502

Conclusions

As found in the Colombian case, to transfer hydrological knowledge to a developing country it is necessary previously to strengthen a receiving substructure. This can be obtained by creating and developing a unique national hydrological and meteorological service, in which all available personnel trained or specializing in the subject is centralized. All possible effort should be made to strengthen this staff through training in the country with assistance of international experts, and abroad, utilizing graduate courses offered in the developed areas. Imported knowledge generally should be screened, tested, and adjusted to specific conditions of the country. This should be one of the main duties of the national professional staff. In this way, activity of the international experts is directed towards the aperture of channels of communication and the development of critical and applicative sense of national hydrologists.

Bibliography

1. Plan de Operaciones del Proyecto OMM/FE - Servicio Colombiano de Meteorología e Hidrología, Bogotá, Colombia, 1968.

2. Klohn, W., Criterios de la OMM para la red mínima de aforos y su aplicacion a Colombia, Publicación Aperiódica No. 1, SCMH, Bogotá, Colombia, 1969.

3. Klohn, W., Magnitudes fisiográficas e índices morfométricos relacionados con la hidrología, Publicación Aperiódica No. 12, SCMH, Bogotá, Colombia, 1970.

4. Klohn, W., Procesamiento automatizado de datos hidrométricos Publicación Aperiódica No. 25, SCMH, Bogotá, Colombia, 1971.

5. Nordenson, T. J., Preparation of co-ordinated precipitation, runoff and evaporation maps, Reports on WMO/IHD Projects, Report No. 6, WMO, Geneva, Switzerland, 1968.

6. Rodda, C. J., Hydrological network design - needs, problems and approaches, Reports on WMO/IHD Projects, Report No. 12, WMO, Geneva, Switzerland, 1969.

7. Sanchez De La Calle, A., and Stanescu, S., Hidrologia en Colombia, Publicación Aperiódica No. 19, SCMH, Bogotá, Colombia, 1971.

8. Stanescu, S., Problemas principales actuales de la organización de la red nacional de estaciones

hidrológicas en Colombia, Publicación Aperiódica No. 1, SCMH, Bogotá, Colombia, 1969.

9. Stanescu, S., Determinación práctica de las principales características morfométricas y fisiográficas de las cuencas hidrográficas y su aplicación en cálculos hidrológicos, Publicación Aperiódica No. 12, SCMH, Bogotá, Colombia, 1970.

10. Stanescu, S., and Sanchez, F. D., Estudio de las precipitaciones medias en la cuenca hidrográfica del río Bogotá, Publicación Aperiódica No. 21, SCMH, Bogotá, Colombia, 1971.

11. Stanescu, S., and Sanchez, F. D., Evaluación preliminar de datos pluviométricos e hidrométricos en las cuencas hidrográficas Zulia, Sardinata y Catatumbo hasta la frontera con Venezuela, Publicación Aperiódica No. 23, SCMH, Bogotá, Colombia, 1971.

12. Stanescu, S., and Diaz, J. R., Estudio preliminar de la temperatura del aire en Colombia, Publicación Aperiódica No. 26, SCMH, Bogotá, Colombia, 1971.

13. Stanescu, S., and Rodriguez, G., Estudio hidrológico preliminar de la cuenca hidrográfica del Cauca Superior, Publicación Aperiódica No. 27, SCMH, Bogotá, Colombia, 1972.

14. Weischet, W., Klimatologische Regeln zur vertikalverteilung der Niederschläge in Tropengebirgen, Die Erde, Zeitschrift der Gesellschaft für Erkunde zu Berlin 100, Jahrg. 1969, Heft 2-4, S.287-306, F.R. Germany, 1969.

15. World Meteorological Organization, Organization of Hydrometeorological and Hydrological Services, Reports on WMO/IHD Projects, Report No. 10, WMO, Geneva, Switzerland, 1969.

16. World Meteorological Organization, Guide to Hydrometeorological Practices, WMO - No. 168, TP. 82, Geneva, Switzerland, 1967.

TRANSFER OF WATER RESOURCES KNOWLEDGE
ASPECTS OF THE WORK
OF THE UNITED NATIONS SYSTEM

by

Frederik H. Verhoog
Programme Specialist - Office of Hydrology
United Nations Educational, Scientific and
Cultural Organization
Paris, France

Synopsis

This article describes, in a general and schematic way,
the work of the United Nations system in the transfer of water
resources knowledge with most emphasis on Unesco's* role. The
Agencies of the United Nations System put considerable effort
into the transfer of knowledge from the developed to the
developing countries. The volume, expressed in dollars, spent
by United Nations on water resources knowledge transfer is only
a fraction of the total world volume; therefore, United Nations
effort is especially directed towards incentive action and
assistance in planning.

Aspects of the Work of the United Nations System

The transfer of knowledge, both vertical transfer, that is
from research to practice and horizontal transfer from one
country to another, is something that concerns all fields of
science and technology. We will, therefore, discuss the problem
of horizontal transfer of knowledge in general as it cannot be
done otherwise, if our conclusions are to be realistic and
within their proper context.

A country can promote the inflow of knowledge by one or a
combination of the following ways:

1) Purchase of complete solutions, procedures, equipment,
and manpower without any national scientific effort;
2) Recruitment of foreign specialists to teach and train
nationals;
3) Sending nationals abroad to obtain the required knowledge;
4) Procurement of published information from one or more
developed countries.

---

* The facts presented and the opinions and views expressed do
not imply the expression of any opinion whatsoever on the
part of Unesco or any other UN agency.

When promoting the transfer of knowledge, the following should be taken into account:

1) the best for the economic development of the country;
2) the most happiness for the population of the country;
3) the best international co-operation and understanding, and thereby world peace;
4) the best for the world as a whole.

An important dilemma in this context is:

1) do we promote the self development of a country, implying slow economic development in the beginning but resulting in more independence economically, socially, and culturally;

or

2) do we promote quick economic development, adjusting the economy of the developing country to the needs of the developed countries taking over procedures and techniques resulting, of course, in dependence in all fields.

In the UN system emphasis is put on the encouragement of self-development in the country.

To start self-development of a country the following are necessary:

. Energy and natural resources;
. Schooled, capable, and practical people;
. Management capacity;
. Technical knowledge;
. A physical infrastructure;
. Political and sociological infrastructure.

Three out of these six requirements, that is people, management, and knowledge are influenced directly by transfer of knowledge.

In order to make the transfer of knowledge as effective as possible, a certain basis is required at the receiving end: financial resources, capable people, management capacity, knowledge, and a proper political and social infrastructure.

These are, more or less, the same needs as those for starting the self development of a country or any economical or functional entity. This is exactly the reason why transfer of knowledge from one developed country to another developed country is much more effective than from a developed to a developing country. If we follow the premise that: a) we want to promote self development and/or adjustment development of a country, b) we need a transfer of knowledge for this, and

506

c) a certain infrastructure to make this transfer of knowledge effective then the national structures for science and technology in the field of water resources as well as of the utmost importance. The United Nations System is directing much effort in this direction, especially in the framework of the UN Advisory Committee on the Application of Science and Technology to Development (UNACAST).

Based on the experience obtained during the first development Decade, UNACAST adopted in 1970 a frame for the so-called stage II of the world plan of action. Part I of the plan includes a sector on Science and Technology Policies and Institutions for which Unesco is responsible.[1] The plan contains recommendations to Governments on how to improve the scientific and technological infrastructure and how to integrate national science policy with development planning. The scientific and technological infrastructure includes:

- the governments structure for science policy making;
- the country's scientific community, including university set-up, career possibilities etc.
- the allocation of human and financial resources to research;
- experimental development and related activities;
- the national network of scientific and technological institutions;
- international, scientific, and technological cooperation.

First the government of each country has to decide between vertical and horizontal transfer of technology. In other words, a proper balance should be found between the pursuit of original indigenous research versus the importation of foreign technology. The formulation of criteria necessary to make this choice needs to be considered by sectors of economic activity, for instance, when the overall national development plans are being worked out on the basis of the general economic situation of the country and its national, scientific, and technological potential. As applied research and experimental development are great resource consumers, not only in terms of scientists and engineers, but also in terms of financial resources, it is clear that the sectors for independent and indigenous science development have to be carefully chosen. There is a strong relationship between Research and Development, but we are not able to predict a definitive and direct cause and effect relationship in most cases, nor can governments do it. Thus it is not really possible to predict the economic

---

1. Contribution of Unesco to Stage II of the World Plan of Action of Science and Technology to Development (Science and technology policies and institutions) Unesco, Paris, 1970.

and social benefits of a Water Resources Research Institute or a Hydrology Chair in a university.

It is up to national governments to decide how they want to develop their country, but if Unesco is requested to assist in planning the scientific and technological infrastructure, it uses the Technology Assessment method. This method is based on a single mission science matrix. The relatedness of each science or technology to each mission, and to one another within each mission, is indicated by a series of relevance ratings. By completing and summing up the matrix, a relevance profile is developed. A capability profile is derived in a similar way. The ratings are given by the people in the country who make or influence decisions concerning the allocation of resources for institutional buildup in science and technology. The sciences and technologies related to water resources on one side of the matrix are: Agricultural Engineering, Sanitary Engineering Transportation Engineering, Public Health, Meteorology, Climatology, Ecology, Geography, Hydrology, Limnology, Weather Analysis, and Forecasting and Fluid Mechanics. In the profiles, the general field of sciences is divided into 8 in which Environmental Sciences and Engineering Sciences are included.

In the framework of UNACAST, the technology assessment method for the survey of science and technology needs in developing countries was used for the first time in 1970 in four countries in four continents. The results were positive and what is especially interesting, water resources sciences rate very high on the priority lists. This means that for the first time we can prove what we knew intuitively already, that is, that water resources development and research and education are extremely important for the development of a country.

When discussing and evaluating UN assistance to developing countries, we have to take into account the fact that this assistance is, in terms of money, only a small fraction of the total volume of assistance in transfer of water resources knowledge.[2] With this in mind, it is clear that the UN effort is especially directed towards incentive projects, exchange of information, promotion, and assistance in planning.

The UN system assists the transfer of knowledge in two ways, one through the Regular programs of the UN agencies and the other through the execution of pre-investment projects for the United Nations Development Programme. The regular programs are mostly directed towards exchange of information and promotion and the UNDP program towards pre-investment projects

[2]ACC Sub-Committee on Water Resources Development - Annual Report on Water Resources. Edited and compiled by the UN Resources and Transport Division UN, New York, 1969.

which include in this case assistance to Universities and Government services. Under the regular programs, Unesco and other agencies organize various international courses in the developed countries.

Unesco supports the post-graduate International Courses in Hydrology in Budapest, Delft, Graz, Jerusalem, Madrid, Moscow, Padua, Prague and Roorkee. These courses are mainly attended by engineers and scientists from developing countries. Since 1966, these courses have had more than 1,000 participants. Unesco only pays from $3.5 to 8,000 per year for each course, while all other expenses are covered by the respective governments. This is a good example of how Unesco works, that is by convincing richer governments to spend money on subjects which are given priority internationally. The Delft course, which has a duration of 11 months, converts civil engineers and sometimes geologists into hydrologists. The other Unesco sponsored postgraduate courses for hydrologists are of shorter duration.

Due to the fact that Unesco's financial contribution is only marginal we have little or no influence on the curriculum of the courses or on the way the teaching is performed. In most cases we are very satisfied, and a strict control would only lead to difficulties in the transfer of knowledge. On the other hand, it is Unesco who decides which courses it will support. Unesco also supported international summer schools in hydrology in the Netherlands, at various places in the USA and in the USSR. The summer schools are intended for people with a wide experience in the water resources field. The Unesco contribution is used primarily for travel and the subsistence allowance for participants from developing countries and guest lecturers.

In general, the courses for engineers and scientists are held in the developed countries because of the availability of a larger number of capable people and facilities for training purposes. On the other hand, courses for technicians and undergraduates are best held in the developed countries because local teachers can then be used and the local environment can be used as a training ground. Unesco has organized technician training courses and courses in special subjects at a high level for hydrologists several times, partly with the support of UNDP in Chile, Kenya, Mali, Tunis and in preparing further courses to be held in Argentina, Ghana, Japan, Lebanon and Turkey, etc. Other UN agencies do the same in other related fields. The main purpose of these courses is the transfer of knowledge, but they are also inspiring. They give or should give the people confidence in themselves and a new way of looking at problems.

As you know the UN system organizes many conferences in the field of water resources. The UN and the Regional Economic Commissions in the field of water management, FAO -- land and water, WMO in "meteorology and operational hydrology," the International Atomic Energy Agency in the use of nuclear techniques in hydrology, WHO in water quality, and Unesco for educational aspects and scientific hydrology. The direct transfer of knowledge is not of first priority at conferences; however, conferences do enable participants from all countries to meet and discover what other countries are doing.

The United Nations agencies have established many working groups and panels dealing with water resources subjects. In most working groups, experts from developed and developing countries discuss a specialized subject together. The transfer of knowledge is direct and fruitful because the best specialists from both the developed and the developing countries are invited. The Co-ordinating Council of the International Hydrological Decade has working groups on the following subjects: Water Balances, Representative and Experimental Basins, Hydrology of Carbonate Rocks of the Mediterranean Basins, Information and Publications, Nuclear Techniques, Floods and Low Flows, Education and Training, Groundwater Studies, the Influence of Man on the Hydrological Cycle and on the Quality of Water. International Hydrological Decade panels exist on the subjects: hydrological mapping and legends for maps, hydrologic information systems, glossary of hydrologic terms. The preparation of guide books, manuals and reports, are also the tasks of the working groups and panels.

The primary objective of the symposia is the exchange of knowledge. Unesco organizes or sponsors around two or three symposia every year in the field of water. Most of these symposia are organized in co-operation with the International Association for the Hydrological Sciences and with the World Meteorological Organization. One of the ways Unesco and other UN agencies support symposia is by providing for travel costs and living allowances for participants from developing countries. Also, Unesco often makes it possible to publish the proceedings.

Since 1965, Unesco has been involved in the following symposia, among others: Water in the Unsaturated Zone, Wageningen, 1966; Floods and their Computation, Leningrad, 1967; The Use of Analog and Digital Computers, Tucson, Arizona, U.S.A. 1968; The Hydrology of Deltas, Bucarest, 1969; World Water Balance, Reading, 1970; Hydrometry, Koblenz, Federal Republic of Germany, 1970; Nuclear Techniques in Hydrology, Vienna, 1970; The Use of Mathematical Models in Hydrology, Warsaw, 1971; The Hydrology of Marshridden Areas, Minsk, 1972.

All UN agencies have the possibility of granting fellowships in the field of water from their regular budgets. These are primarily used for obtaining additional training abroad and not for what could be called regular education. The duration can be from one to twelve months. There are no restrictions as to where or how the training should be performed, it can take place in Universities, Institutions, or private firms. The candidate may, in principle, choose what he wants and we, of course, help him. Besides the overall support for the courses, the total amount of man months of fellowships awarded by Unesco in the field of hydrology, through the regular program, is rather small, not more than 15 man months per year in fact. The reason for this is that many fellowships are awarded through bilateral and UNDP assistance.

The UN system has a large number of publications in the water field. Since 1965 the following IHD publications with the transfer of knowledge as primary objective have been issued, among others: Flood Studies, an International Guide for Collection and Processing of Data, Unesco, Paris, 1971; Representative and Experimental Basins, 1970; Textbooks on Hydrology, Unesco, Paris, 1971; Seasonal Snow Cover, Unesco, Paris, 1971; Hydrologic Information Systems, Unesco/WMO, Paris, 1972; Groundwater Studies: An International Guide for Research and Practice, Unesco, Paris, 1972.

The World Meteorological Organization guide on hydrometeorological practices and the UN/ECAFE flood control series are also well known. The publications are international, that is, they are prepared and checked by many specialists from several countries. In this way they give generally accepted knowledge and procedures. The publications are destined to be useful to the majority of countries and situations, which implies that they are especially useful for the developing countries who form the majority. It also implies that in most cases they do not give the latest available information. This is probably unavoidable for this kind of publication, but they at least form an excellent introduction.

Another form of transfer of knowledge is the transfer of high-level specialists to developing countries. As high level specialists are very busy in their own countries, they are never able to spend more than four or five weeks at a time in a developing country. Thus, the specialist does not have the time to carry out a specific study but can only look around, discuss the problems and programs, and give advice. These kind of missions are, therefore, called Advisory Missions. The short Advisory Missions by internationally well known specialists are very popular in many of the developing countries. One of the reasons is that these advisory missions are a great help to the local specialists as they are backed up by an authority and can ensure that their projects are sound scientifically and technically. Another factor which leads to success is that the high level specialist nearly always has a large international experience, and, because of the short time available, he does not try to impose his own way of working but is more inclined to accept a given situation and see in which way it can be improved by the country itself. The annual number of advisory missions for the whole UN system is considerable; in the water resources field alone it is about 100.

One of the cheapest ways by which knowledge can be obtained is through reading. Unesco and other UN organizations provide books and other publications to developing countries, mostly in the framework of developing projects. At the moment the flow of publications to the developing countries is insufficient. Unesco is developing a program, in collaboration with ICSU (International Council of Scientific Unions) called Unisist, an abbreviation for United Nations Information System, which is meant to provide an international framework in which the flow of information can take place.[3]

The greatest deficiency exists in the field of periodicals; one of the main reasons is that aid giving governments do not favour giving assistance in the form of recurring costs. The only solution is to convince governments of developing countries that it is worth the money in hard currency to subscribe to water resources periodicals.

In international meetings it is often shown that much time is wasted and much confusion created by misunderstandings about the meaning of water resources terms. During the coming years the UN agencies will publish several international glossaries. One of them will be the Unesco/WMO International Glossary of Hydrology.

The prime objective of the United Nations Development Programme (UNDP) is to assist governments of developing countries with pre-investment projects which also include the establishment of universities and institutes. UNDP sometimes finances regional training courses and the like. The UNDP finances a project but leaves the execution of it to the Government and an executing UN specialized agency such as, FAO, Unesco, WMO etc. The UNDP contribution to a project consists of all items that can only be obtained with foreign currency. It can be divided into the chapters experts and consultants, fellowships and training, equipment and subcontracts.

A UNDP project has two main objectives, the first is to assist the Government to execute a given work and the second is to teach the national engineers how to continue the project alone and how to execute similar projects without foreign assistance in the future. A UNDP project can thus be regarded as a way of transfer of technology by which the giver and receiver work together every day for a few years. Quite often subcontracting with a specialized firm is necessary. In by far

---

[3]Unisist, Study Report on the Feasibility of a World Science Information System, Unesco Paris, 1971.

the most cases these firms quickly understand the special
character of UNDP projects and accept the training component of
their work. The total yearly budget of UNDP is about 400
million dollars. It is not always easy to decide if a project
is primarily a water resources project; thus all figures given
are somewhat subjective. In April 1971 the total amount for
projects in execution in the water resources field was about
110 million dollars. An average duration is about 3 years, so
that about 38 million was spent yearly.[4] If we take into
account that about 5% of this is spent on training through
fellowships; then this is 1.9 million a year. The standard
figure for a fellowship is about $5,000 for 12 man months; so
that per year about 4,700 man months are available for training in the field of water resources.

The total number of large scale SF water resources projects
in execution is about 90. The following are breakdowns of UNDP
funding:

Institution building: 18%
Groundwater surveys: 28%
River and Basin surveys: 11%
Coastal problems: 1%
Flood and river control and forecasting: 7%
Master plans for water supply: 13%
Lakes and limnology: 3%
General Water Surveys: 19%

As can be seen from the figures, most of the work, including
the transfer of knowledge carried out in the developing
countries by the UN system, is done through UNDP funding.

In addition to the training component inherent in every
UNDP project, there is the idea that national and foreign
experts work closely together. This seems to be the best way
to transfer technology because all factors needed for success
are available. After training abroad the national engineers are,
if necessary, given an interesting job in their own country
together with a foreign expert from whom they can learn everything necessary. It can be said that 2 or 3 national experts
have a private teacher. All equipment and literature necessary
is purchased by UNDP for the execution of the project and
remains in the country, so that it can be used afterwards for
the same or similar projects.

A new venture for UNDP is the promotion of interinstitu-
tional links in Science and Technology between scientific
institutions in developed countries and similar institutions
in developing countries. It is expected that the Inter-
institutional links projects will prove valuable in cases

---

[4]Status of Approved Projects - United Nations Development
Programme, DP/SF Reports, Series A, UN, New York.

where large scale UNDP projects have been terminated while
the young institution thus established still needs continuing
support for a number of years in order to build strength
and experience.

DISCUSSION by Fred Hotes*

I want to refer to the first sentence, paragraph 3, of the Rapporteur's remarks on Mr. Szesztay's paper "...the bias naturally held by water oriented experts should be avoided by selecting policy formulators who are not water oriented."

Indeed, I cannot find this statement in my copy of the Szesztay paper, nor such a implication. As a matter of fact at the top of the third page of Szesztay's paper, he implies the contrary, i.e., "The formulation of water resources strategies requires a full knowledge and close personal contact with the basic facts,...."

If the statement were made, I would have to disagree with it. (I do agree with all of Szesztay's comments on page 3 of his article.) I do agree that policies should be formulated by a broad range of experienced people from several disciplines, and certainly could include people who are not water oriented, as long as the latter are intelligent, relatively unbiased, persons.

DISCUSSION by Paul-Marc Henry**

I would like to elaborate some general points on international organizations.

1. The U.N. as a complete system is an institutional problem - not a technical one.

2. Any agency is using the following procedures

- individual experts

- team of _directly_ recruited experts

- contributing to private (or public) consultants, engineers or firms

3. It is entirely difficult to combine in any one project, aspects of efficiency in implementation and long term problems of training and updating in hydrology.

4. This is not an academic question as we are supposed to act quickly, i.e., increase food production by 9% a year at least during the next 10 years.

---

*Enviro-Engineers, Inc., Berkeley, California 94710

**O.E.C.D., Paris, France

DISCUSSION by Glenn Schweitzer*

As a general observation, it may be useful to note that
bilaterally the trend is to use intermediary institutions and
not directly hire experts in institution building efforts.
Also there is less interest in surveys for the sake of surveys since many surveys lie unused on shelves.

DISCUSSION by Nguyen Quang Trac**

Let me present a personal experience of a successful
transfer of water resources knowledge: the UNDP/FAO hydrogeological investigation of the Guadalquivir basin in Spain.
From 1966 to 1971 a team of experts has realized the complete
investigation of an area of 60,000 km^2, trained their Spanish
counterparts in all the technics of groundwater investigation
and exploitation including mathematical and analog simulations,
water systems analysis, water resources feasibility studies.
The concrete results of the project are reflected in the
decision of the Spanish Government to extend the investigation
to all the southeast area of the country in the framework
of five projects, and to exploit groundwater for the irrigation of 30,000 in the Guadalquivir basin, all those operations
to be realized during the Third Plan of Development (1972-1975).

The success of the Guadalquivir Project is due to the
following main factors:

1. The background of the receiver country which can be
translated by a brief figure: the Spanish GNP was already
600 $/pc in 1966 and 900 $/pc in 1971. This could arise the
question of the necessity of using such a country as Spain as
an intermediate step of knowledge transfer to gain in
efficiency.

2. The experts all had extensive experience in arid
and semiarid regions like Spain.

3. From the beginning, the experts went through the
language barriers not only in order to communicate with
their counterparts and to arrive to a perfect cooperation,
but also to be able to understand and to learn their proper
approach of their own problems.

---

*10414 Democracy Lane, Potomac, Maryland   20854

**UNDP/FAO, Madrid 3, Spain

DISCUSSION by Lourival A. Oliveria*

Speaking to the points raised by Mr. Hawkin's paper, I would like to acknowledge the valuable contributions given by the Corps of Engineers to the International Workshop that took place in Davis in August 1972. Practical and updated matter was presented during four weeks in a well organized course.

It would be very useful for the purpose of the transfer of knowledge (the object of the present meeting) if such a workshop would be done in the future with the same care as the first one.

DISCUSSION by V. Yevjevich**

This session is related to transfer of water resource knowledge by international organizations only, mainly because the number of specific papers submitted on knowledge transfer by general bilateral activities, consulting firms, academic institutions and non-profit organizations was limited. The possible reasons for more papers on knowledge transfer related to international organizations are: (1) those related to activities of international organizations are more eager to tell their story; and (2) the present public scrutiny in some countries on the efficiency of using international organizations for knowledge transfer requires this story to be told.

Administrators and specialists working with various international agencies or organizations likely find themselves in the same position at present as the technologists in the United States and in other developed countries have found themselves in recent years, namely under the public scrutiny. However, it is useful to have large international agencies or organizations under scrutiny from time to time. They build with time an apparatus and internal administrative mechanism. The premises of organization and the performance of staff may easily come at variance with basic and evolving objectives expected to be fulfilled by these organizations.

It is not unusual for ideas or investigations, generated in a particular country, to be taken over by specialists of international organizations, and presented as proposals for solving various problems around the world. This approach of "skimming ideas and results" from various countries is often carried out by a temporary hiring of leading specialists from those countries as short term experts. Because large investments are needed for producing new scientific and technological

* Electrobra's Avenida Presidente, Vargas 642 - 6° andar
   Rio de Janeiro, Brazil

**Colorado State University

results, and new ideas are best generated in a creative
environment at significant cost, this skimming with a minimum
effort represents in fact the indirect additional subsidies to
these international organizations.

Many individuals are reluctant to criticize the performance of international organizations and their officials or
specialists. Factual critical observations usually do not
go public. For example, many international agencies have
become perfected in writing reports to represent as successes
the relatively meager performance or failures. Built-in
administrative procedures are often used for the self-
preservation of an international apparatus rather than for
stimulating a continuous review of premises and for drawing
in the new blood. Simplified methods of performance, easy to
implement by short training courses, would facilitate the
inflow of new blood and expertise.

Some international experts are often very critical of
officials in developing regions, contending that they can not
identify their problems or goals. This should be expected
since these are difficult tasks. An international expert
who criticizes the knowledge user in developing regions
usually neglects the mechanism and procedures of problem
diagnosis and goal setting. When a patient with a problem
goes to a physician of general practice, he expects him to
help in finding expertise for diagnosis and for curing the
disease. The medical profession has succeeded in emphasizing
both the diagnostic and curative sides of practice, usually
through the appropriate specialists. It looks as if the
international knowledge transfer should follow these two
emphases, the identification of problems with goal setting,
and the solution of problems. Because the two functions
are often interwoven in the knowledge transfer, they are
rarely performed in an efficient manner by the same individual.

Many difficulties are encountered in water use and in
translation of modern water resource technology into practical
techniques. There are several optimizations in any water
resources project, which may not have anything to do either
with the water availability or with the translation of
knowledge into techniques. A classical example is the
reluctance of farmers to use irrigation water and modern
irrigation techniques, when they optimize income. Because
the superproduction of a commodity usually leads to a decrease
of the unit price, the total income may be the same or even
lower for a larger effort in using the best irrigation
techniques. The income optimization by a farmer is a function
of agricultural and pricing policies. Only when several
levels of optimizations, such as the individual, local, regional, national, and even international, agree that given
technologies should be used, do the use of water and modern

technology have a good chance of being implemented, as the examples of the Green Revolution have demonstrated.

Though the objective of organizers of this Conference was to limit the problem of transfer of water resource knowledge from research to practice and from developed to developing regions, the tendency in discussions has been to cover much broader subjects, involving the political, social, economic, and other aspects of knowledge transfer. The problem of general education has been emphasized as the prerequisite of knowledge transfer. Practically, there are a small number of developing regions in the world, which do not have a university or other high learning institutions. Similarly, the regions without some specialists trained in the best schools are rare. It is axiomatic that the effects of political, social, economic, cultural and other factors of a social system and the influence of both the general and specialized educations on knowledge transfer should not be neglected. The premise of this Conference is that the ways and means of transferring research results to practice and water resources science and technology from developed to developing regions can be made under the given conditions of social systems, economic developments and potentials, while treating the specific aspects common to all systems. However, the transfer of knowledge is a function of all environmental factors at both sides, having knowledge and needing knowledge.

The particular field of transfer of water resource knowledge is an example of how this transfer can be most effective under different constraints and conditions. The transfer of knowledge can always be a two-way avenue, namely from research to practice as well as from practice to research (in the reverse order in the sense of defining useful research topics and potential implementation), and from developed to developing as well as from developing to developed regions with the experience going in the reverse direction.

ROUNDTABLE DISCUSSION

● *A special panel convened during the last day of the Conference to summarize major points, explicate issues, and raise questions in order to provoke final comments from both authors and participants. The panel chaired by Professor Henry P. Caulfield, Jr. of the Political Science Department at Colorado State University included the following individuals:*

H.P. Caulfield CSU	R. Hagan Univ. of Cal.	W. Shaner CSU
R. Dijon U.N.	P.M. Henry OECD	D.R. Sikka India
M. Gaus N.S.F.	M. Miller World Bank	F.H. Verhoog UNESCO
C.Q. Gois Portugal	G.E. Schweitzer AID	E. Vlachos CSU

The panel discussion ranged over a wide array of topics, issues, and specific problematic situations. It would have been impossible to include all the interesting points raised throughout the discussion. While this would have added an inordinately lengthy document to the present volume, it was considered as more useful to summarize the central arguments as a joint contribution of the panel members and the actively participating audience. With the exception of the initial and closing remarks of the panel moderator, the rest of the text is comprised of excerpts and comments with no particular identification. Similarly, although the presentation follows more or less the evolution of argument throughout the discussion, there is no strict adherence to a time perspective, but more an emphasis on parallel arguments.

Discussions by this panel are as important to future readers of proceedings as they are to participants of this conference. Because the bulk of conference materials is well presented by authors, general reporters, and participants, the panelists have an opportunity to air their individual views by looking at the transfer of water resources knowledge from their particular vantage points. This transfer is not conceived as a general knowledge transfer which depends on social and environmental conditions, but as the transfer of water resources knowledge of mutual interest to all partners. It includes the transfer from researchers to practitioners, so that the research results may be more relevant to social problems; from practitioners to researchers so that relevant problems can be investigated; from developed to developing, and in return from developing to developed regions, as mutually beneficial ventures in a continuous process of improving the efficiency of science and technology in solving social problems. The fact which most impressed participants at this conference was the high stress on human dimension in knowledge transfer in general, and in the water resource knowledge transfer in particular.

However, practitioners and responsible officials in developing regions of the world have been criticized for not showing a broader interest in the use of the most modern knowledge. This is a question of optimization and caution. Valid points can be made for practitioners in developing regions who are reluctant to allow their regions to serve as test grounds for theories, ideas, research results and new technology which have not been tested elsewhere. However, the principle is sound when large undertakings in water resource developments are preceded by investments for reviewing, adapting, and developing a better technology for solving problems posed by these developments. These efforts may decrease the total cost and risks, and increase the benefits to amply pay for the investigation cost. However, the chances should be sufficient to insure that this cost is compensated by the overall economy and other benefits of this enterprise.

The social accountability for activities in producing and implementing water resource knowledge will be more and more required as the competition for limited public funds becomes tougher. The knowledge transferred and applied is the best way of accounting socially for investments in research and development.

In opening this panel discussion we expect to hear stimulating ideas and new points of view from panelists. The ideas expounded and questions raised will be useful also for planning the subjects of the Second International Conference for Transfer of Water Resource Knowledge to take place at this University in 1977.

-In the several sessions of this Conference the transfer of water resources knowledge has already been discussed from the points of view of international transfer in general, of multi-lateral transfer through the United Nations and its Specialized Agencies, of bilateral transfer between nations and of intra-national transfer. In addition, mechanical means of transfer, through publications, libraries, computerized information retrieval systems, etc., have been discussed.

-This panel session, in effect, provides a summary dis-cussion from all of these points of view toward the transfer of water resources knowledge: first by initial remarks of each member of our distinguished panel, and then by discussion between panel members and through questions and comments from the audience.

● One should be careful to make some pertinent, systematic distinctions in the transfer of knowledge. To start with, concerning the modality of transfer there are such crucial elements as: -Level
                           -Agent
                           -Purpose
As indicated elsewhere there are different principles, methods, and conditions of awareness, training, and intervention at various levels of technology for knowledge transfer. On the larger or macro-level one is preoccupied with general issues, decision-making, planning etc. On the intermediate level, emphasis is placed on the middle-echelon personnel, basic principles of design, and especially managerial capabilities. Finally, on a micro level, all efforts are directed towards application, field practice, everyday exigencies and technology. We should be aware of all such differentiations and avoid the indiscriminant mixing of universal awareness, strategic planning, practical considerations, folklore, etc. Simply, we should not expect to have for all levels the same degree of sophistication, extent of training, and time requirements.

● In terms of the transfer of knowledge itself one may also distinguish four levels:
    a. transfer of technical information per se;
    b. transfer of planning information;
    c. citizen participation, or citizen preferences;
    d. education.

-At the same time in transferring knowledge we need to sort out the role of the various players in the game, as well as to what system could be used for evaluating the effective-ness of the transfer.

● When we talk about levels of transfer we also talk about different modalities. There is the university transmission, where scholars go out and scholars come from developing countries and then go back. There is also the modality where institutions are involved, such as the World Bank. It may be extremely important here to distinguish between the responsibilities of different institutions in transferring knowledge or expertise.

● While the discussions on the various topics have started out in the area of water resources technology, before long we have heard about experiences in other areas--highways, sociology, organization of the U.N., and library procedures. It would seem, then, that the transfer of knowledge in water resources is made up largely of the transfer of technical knowledge in general and only to a lesser degree in the areas that are unique to water resources. If this is the case, then it behooves us to investigate what is taking place in the transfer of technology in other disciplines.

● A key question is, what kind of knowledge are we transferring? Very little attention was paid to the related question of who identifies the kind of needs that various countries have for knowledge and, then, who can best deliver it. Some examples may eliminate such questions. If you look in the water field, Mexico went to the World Bank for help with respect to its National Water Planning Studies, India to the United Nations, while Ceylon preferred the FAO. You would be put hard to distinguish in any fundamental way the kind of knowledge they needed. In essence, they needed a package: different combinations of talents, from data collection to the analysis of data that ultimately could be turned into something identified as a project. To sum up: there is no modality by which we know, or we can transmit how countries can get the kind of knowledge they need, for what they want to do.

● One more point on modality: the question of whether we pick individual experts or whether we do it in terms of packages, consulting firms and so forth. A project is often no better than the people sent out to do it. You can have the most beautiful terms of reference, the kinds of things that have to be transmitted, train people to do it. Yet when people or combinations of people are sent, it does not quite get done the way it ought to be done. Now we have a tremendous repository of talent in the world. One finds it when we go out to search for people who might do a certain kind of job or people who compliment each other to form a team. We often failed to do what we thought we would do because the men we selected did not turn out to be as good as they might have been. To track down the proper men, implies a simple technology, of getting a repository of talent, put on punch cards, and then retrieving it according to the best fit. Such a selection could be done in terms of scientific fields and then break them down by types of leadership (whether they are mature and have leadership roles, or whether they are just second level people who have to work under somebody) and on to this get a short list of talent. We ought to think very hard about concrete proposals to improve our method of sending in people just because it is much more easy to send a man who has a range of talents than trying to get an assemblage of specialists.

● What we have been hearing essentially in most of the presentations and discussions involved is knowledge in the sense of technical knowledge or technical data. But there is also the question of the transfer of policy. These two get into completely different realms of activity. More important, water resources is part of the overall picture in which decision makers have to make decisions. There would be a lot of other factors that enter into the picture such as transportation, housing, and general utilization of natural resources.

● In connection with the transfer of knowledge one should point out transferring of knowledge is not in itself sufficient; there must also be some way of estimating what has happened as a result of such a transferring, and a feedback from the people who are using the knowledge to the people who are generating the knowledge.

● Positions have been taken in discussion that one should talk about the general knowledge transfer through education rather than the transfer of water resource knowledge. However, the fact that every field of technology and socio-economic activity has some specific problems and aspects of knowledge transfer, should not be neglected. A meeting of specialists is useful if it is contained within the specific aspects of their discipline. The general principles of knowledge transfer may neither be useful nor be practically implemented if the constraints and specific conditions of particular fields are not taken into account. The relationship between theory and practice has been the subject of much investigation throughout history. Whenever theory and practice have been rigidly separated, the progress of science and technology has been impeded. A division of theoreticians and practitioners may be useful for looking at a problem from different points of view, but not if the knowledge must be applied to find the socially acceptable solutions to important problems.

● Throughout the Conference an important distinction was made between basic research and applied research. The fear was also expressed that we are entering a period of retrench-ment, especially in applied research. While this may be somehow true for "hard" sciences, the social sciences are only now beginning to participate in research generally and they have quite a way to go. This is more true as new questions have arisen concerning the "quality of life", development, and growth. In this respect we need to provide a distinction between "underdevelopment" and "undevelopment". The first can be understood in the context of social and political circumstances, while the second refers to the lack of exploring natural resources and the threat of plain survival.

● At least once during the discussions the statement was made that the developing countries lacked rational decision-makers. Webster says that "rational" is something "based on, or derived from reason."

-There are few in the less developed countries, or else-where, who acted contrary to their reasoning. And often their reasoning in their given set of circumstances was quite as good as that of anyone else. It is more likely that those in the less developed countries act differently from us because we perceive the problems differently.

-For example, our experience may convince us correctly that a farmer should adopt a new method of farming. But to the farmer, who runs the full risk of the change in technology and who may be living on the edge of poverty, it may be quite rational to be very cautious about experimenting with something new. This follows a well known economic principle--that the value of additional consumption is worth less than the loss of an equal amount. And, as we know, not all agricultural innovations and schemes have proved successful.

-The same hesitancy can be justified by local economists who are aware of the relative scarcities of productive factors in their country, by local engineers who are concerned about the lack of skills and service facilities to support complex factories, by the local sociologist who appreciates the traditions of his countrymen, and by the politician who is reluctant to disturb a delicate political balance.

-The task confronting those who wish to offer new technical knowledge to those in the developing countries therefore would be both to learn the background of the various situations there and to understand the reasoning behind the choices made by the local decision-makers. Then, realistic means could be devised for influencing them.

● A strong point has been made that we should listen and heed the wishes of planners in the less developed countries, at least within the limits of sound technology. Perhaps we should go even further by saying that such sensitivity to the aspirations of those in these countries is probably the only way we from the technically advanced countries can substantially influence their decisions. An example of this is the failure of a certain country to significantly use, as yet,

a million dollar study of its agricultural sector, mainly because that study was not formulated with the active participation of those in that country. On the other hand, advisors have
been keenly sought, over worked, or what you will, in trying to
meet the needs of the government in solving the problems of its
daily activities--e.g., how to improve the poor financial position of its nationally-owned shipping company, or where to
locate the next cement plant. Thus, in the successful transfer
of technology the question of its relevance to the recipients
is obviously of paramount importance.

● Three types of schemes in the transfer of knowledge can
be visualized. The first involves the training of scholars or
a few people or the higher echelon, and provide them with the
background, library facilities, and institution for spreading
the "gospel" around. The second involves the development of a
major project with no consideration of specific population,
where all stages of research (including broad principles of
economic feasibility) are involved, with the hope that the
"contagion" will spread all over the country. Finally, a third
type ignores most of the population through the development of
a pilot project which can later spread social benefits to the
rest of the country.

● A note on the training and education of the various
specialists. Very little thought has been given to intermediate transfer of knowledge and the specialized institutions
or universities. It would be advisable to bring people into
universities, but not offer them degrees. Let them come to the
universities and take specialized seminars under an intensive
program of two or three months (which, by the way, is the time
that valuable people from developing countries can afford to
spend in a host institution). Otherwise, you get perennial
students with a possible mutual enrichment.

More than anything else, we need to train managers for
problems of water, as well as other, resources. We need to
transfer both the capacity to make an inventory according to
certain basic criteria, and managerial knowhow for managing
resources. Still, we should not forget that we are dealing
with countries of totally different tradition of their water
management. It is important to find out what kind of society
are we dealing with, the kind of management we are talking
about, and finally, the transfer of knowledge in the context
of various levels of technology. There are countries with long
history and far-reaching tradition of water management, China,
India, Egypt, etc. If, on the other hand, one is dealing with
a society that has no or limited water management traditions
(such as countries in Africa), it will be extremely difficult
to transfer the extensive hydrologic management of other nations.
The same is also true for completely empty lands. Thus, we
need to evaluate projects in a broad context of resources,

management, and historical traditions in order to become more
sensitive and develop also guiding principles.

● The transfer of science and technology is often characterized as a supply and demand problem. The supply for knowledge
and a demand for knowledge. During the last few years, developing countries have been working very hard on the supply side.
There are very many first class scientific and technological
people, research institutions are in place and operating and
there is quite a capability that did not exist a number of
years ago. But, there has not been quite as much effort on the
demand side, of science and technology. Everyone can recognize
that there is a gap between what is being generated and what is
being used. It can be argued that the weak link in the transfer
of knowledge system is the genuine demand for science and
technological knowledge which means that there is a desire for
and a capability to use it, whether the demand is for knowledge
that has been generated indigenously or the demand is for knowledge which has been imported from abroad.

● Unless we have plenty of time to wait until everybody is
capable of participating actively in water resources work, we
may have to take shortcuts. Many countries may need direct
assistance without bothering too much as to the capacity to
actually make the inventory themselves. Many occasions occur
when the country will ask for a quick assessment of their
resources. In this case, the transfer of knowledge is really
just a transport of technology from one point to another in order
to make this inventory quickly and efficiently according to this
method. Time, then, is an extremely important constraint.
There is no question that water is becoming quickly expensive
and difficult to get, no question that the users are increasing in numbers, and that the rate of use by the human being
is much greater than it was, say 100 years ago.

● There are many examples of how transfer of knowledge can
be accomplished. A novel approach is that used in the establishment of two counterpart teams in Europe and Africa. The first
was the design team, while the second was in charge of data
collection and field requirements. There is an intimate
cooperation between the teams who work locally and the designers.
For example, the collecting team works in Africa and the future
designers of the proposed project provide continuous advice and
general orientation as to the required data. This operation
established early the fact that while it was easy to solve
technical problems, the application that the particular region
was a much more formidable problem. This is why among the first
sub-teams established was the "social team", which before even
topographic and geologic information, provided a thorough
investigation of local socio-cultural conditions. Thus, during
the design and execution of the project, the "social team"
was also able to explain to the local people what was happening,

providing, at the same time, the opportunity for public participation (and they themselves getting additional advice from
the natives).

● When one speaks of various agencies, it is tempting to
recall the simple giving of money for a variety of projects.
But conditions are changing. The World Bank, for example,
although it gives money, the real value comes in the knowhow
that comes along with it. In answer to those who say to the
Bank: "just give us the money", the answer is "we want to know
what you want to use if for, because when we give you our
opinion on how you intend to use it, we are imparting knowledge."
Thus, the Bank talks about enhancing and developing a country
in a certain manner, i.e., the distribution of benefits shall
accrue to the poor as well as to the rich.

● The tools of economics should be more widely used in
investment decision. One notices a marked increase in the
number of well-known economists who have become interested in
investment analysis during the past several years. Earlier,
this subject was left to only a few. Moreover, one favors
the effort to try to impute values to benefits that are difficult to quantify. It is hoped that economists--especially
those with such interests and abilities--and engineers will
expend more effort in learning how they can contribute to
better decision-making in this area. There certainly seems
to be a natural complementarity of the two disciplines at this
point. Moreover, proper economic analysis can add much to
evaluating the merits of "slogans" such as: use labor intensive
methods, apply a simple technology, or look for projects with
rapid pay-back periods. The variables common to each of these
slogans are costs, benefits, and time--which are the normal
inputs of the cash-flow method of benefit-cost analysis.

● A great problem that can be encountered many times in
several countries is the lack of self confidence of engineers
and consequently the fears to design something that will be
executed. This has three main reasons:
    a. Their professors and bosses also have never done it.
    b. A failure of the construction will have great con-
       sequences personally.
    c. The fear that in the last year in the professional
       journal there will have appeared a better way of how
       to solve the problem. And this is a real good argu-
       ment because the next foreign consultant or expert
       will let him and his boss know this.

● There is no doubt that systematic documentation is a
key to solving many problems. Institutes are very important in
the transfer of knowledge, although many governments do not
believe in them, but place more faith in contracts or projects.
Despite the existence of quite a few universities and specialized

organizations there is an inherent danger in the very spread
of numerous centers of excellence and the consequences of
fragmentation. The answer to such multiplication can be the
International Institute approach.

Concluding Remarks of Moderator (Prof. Henry P. Caulfield, Jr.).

-I would like, if I may, to make a few observations of my
own regarding the transfer of water resources knowledge.

-The calling of a Conference on Transfer of Water Resources
Knowledge and the willingness of each of us to attend implies
the existence of a widespread intuition that there is a problem
about water resource knowledge transfer in particular and
possibly about knowledge transfer generally. The problem we
believe is that there are bodies of knowledge in one location
that somehow are not becoming assimilated readily and widely
and are not being used where applicable. But its discussion
has tended to focus here upon the transfer of water resource
knowledge from developed to less developed areas of the world
as though this were the most fundamental aspect of the problem--
as though there were no intranational transfer problem within
developed nations.

-This is not the most fundamental aspect. The problem of
transfer of water resource knowledge, or the transfer of
knowledge generally, needs to be viewed in more fundamental
terms as involving at least four, and probably more subproblems:

-Subproblem of Perspective - The academic frame of
reference in observation and thinking, regardless of discipline,
is clearly different from the frame of reference of one primarily engaged in action to achieve certain ends. The academic
frame of reference is a discipline, each with its basic premises
and its own specialized language. The words may be the same as
common speech, but the meanings are often substantially different. Moreover, reality is perceived and analyzed in terms of
each discipline. In action to obtain policy development and
implementation, humanistic, behavioralistic and technical
considerations are involved in understanding one's actions
and goals and in relating them to the actions and goals of
others. One calls upon all of his knowledge and experience
which, in a fragmentary way, may be said to be widely multi-
disciplinary. The differences in perspective upon reality of
the many academic disciplines and the language of their
expression makes communication in depth often difficult among
academics. This is true despite their common academic posture
toward reality. When this problem is compounded by the shift
in perspective to that of one engaged in action, transfer of
knowledge can become even more difficult.

531

-Subproblem of Modeling - Unidisciplinary and interdisciplinary research, the modern modes of the production of
knowledge, involve the development of models in which the
parameters contributed by one or more disciplines are appropriately related. The common language and form of modeling is
often that of mathematics. Full intellectual understanding
thus involves a rather full, if not necessarily complete,
knowledge of the mathematics involved. Yet many disciplines
relevant to interdisciplinary research are not yet expressed
generally in mathematical form. Moreover, there is a "generation gap" among academicians as well as practitioners of the
same discipline where that discipline over the years has
increasingly become expressed in mathematical form. And this
is not just a language problem. Mathematical form also
introduces a new level of rigor to disciplinary thinking and
expression. Thus the form of expression and rigor of disciplinary and interdisciplinary knowledge has a bearing upon the
ease of its transferability and assimilation in some respects
facilitating and in others inhibiting.

-Subproblem of Values - In the behavioralistic mode
now dominating economic, sociological and political research
and in the traditional scientific method of physical and
biological research, unidisciplinary and interdisciplinary
research in the production of knowledge is conceived as
"valueless"--so far as possible. But in the world of governmental action the determination of water and related land use
involves value commitments and their weighting by the planner/
decision-maker. Failure to use new knowledge may be due to
perceived inconsistency between its value premises in use and
with the prevailing values that it would disturb or displace.
Thus its transfer from production through research to its use
in practice is inhibited or blocked.

-Subproblem of Sensory Experience - If one has ever
tried to explain, or imagined the task of explaining, what
color is to a person who always has been blind, one obtains
insight on the subproblem of sensory experience. Trying to
explain New York City to a native in the back country of Kenya
is another example. These examples are far-out, but to a
lesser extent the problem of knowledge transfer, particularly
knowledge of depth and subtlety is always with us. On the
other hand, relative ease of communication is evident when
conversing with persons of common background, understanding
and experience. When one cannot presuppose such background,
understanding and experience, one faces the problem of knowledge
transfer. No doubt this subproblem is a part of certain of the
other subproblems identified above, but I believe it warrants
separate identification.

-These subproblems, and thus the overall problem of transfer
of knowledge, are all present, obviously, in developed countries.

They are not just involved in the transfer of knowledge between developed and less developed countries. That they are involved in a developed country, and specifically with respect to the transfer of water resources knowledge in the United States, is indicated by amendments enacted by the Congress last year to the Water Resources Research Act of 1964.[1] Those amendments, together with the Act as previously amended, recognize the transfer problem by providing that each water resources research institute located at a university within each state and supported by Federal funds authorized by the Act shall provide "means for improved communication regarding...research results, including prototype operations, ascertaining the existing and potential effectiveness of such for aiding in the solution of practical problems, and for training qualified persons in the performance of such scientific information dissemination." Moreover, the Act now provides that university water research institute programs are to be "developed in close consultation and collaboration with leading water officials within the State to promote research, training and other work meeting the needs of the State." In other words, the problem of water resources knowledge transfer is perceived by the Congress as a problem of research relevance to practical needs and of communication of relevant research result to practitioners. This view is in accord with my own perception, when Executive Director of the U.S. Water Resources Council between 1966 and 1969, of the great multi-dimensional gulf that exists generally between those who undertake water and related land resource research and those engaged in planning and obtaining action for such resource developmental use.

-Finally, I would like to make two points about the transfer of knowledge between developed and less developed countries: There are many cultural, social, political and economic reasons why a less developed country may not desire to utilize knowledge produced in a developed country. This inhibition in the utilization of knowledge, however, is not a problem of the transfer of knowledge per se; it is a problem of utilization. If the knowledge produced in a developed country becomes known to, and is accepted as potentially useful by, a cultural, social, political or economic change agent in a less developed country, then it is possible that the knowledge will eventually become utilized in the less developed country. In other words utilization of knowledge by a less developed country may be more a function of cultural, social, political or economic change which, in turn, may be a function in part of the transfer of knowledge to a change agent.

---

[1] See P. L. 88-379 for Water Resources Research Act of 1964 and P. L. 92-175 for amendments enacted in 1971.

-Lack of utilization of knowledge, for example certain
types of technological knowledge, may also be mistaken as a
knowledge transfer problem per se. Technological knowledge
produced in developed countries, and particularly in the
United States, tends to be labor saving. Capital is cheap
relative to labor in the United States. The opposite is now
true in most, if not all, less developed countries. Thus the
present problem for them is often a lack of technological
knowledge most appropriate to a labor surplus economy rather
than a problem of knowledge transfer. New knowledge is needed.

PARTICIPANTS
FIRST INTERNATIONAL CONFERENCE ON TRANSFER
OF WATER RESOURCES KNOWLEDGE

Colorado State University - September 14-16, 1972

Agnew, Allen F.
Water Research Center
Washington State University
Pullman, WA   99163

Albertson, M. L.
Colorado State University
Fort Collins, CO   80521

Anderson, Mr. Bruce
Utah State University
Logan, UT   84321

Andrew, John W.
Colorado State University
Fort Collins, CO   80521

Antonio, Delzirene de V.
DNAE-MME
Rio de Janeiro, Brazil

Barros, Cecilia Maria de
Dept. of National Water &
  Electrical Engineering
Rio de Janeiro, Brazil

Basso, Eduardo
University of Chile
Avenida 4, Calle Central
San Jose, Costa Rica, A.C.

Benson, Manuel A.
4506 N.W. 39th Street
Fort Lauderdale, FL   33313

Boschman, Wilmar
3512 Wenatchee
Bakersfield, CA   93306

Browzin, B. S.
Ebasco Services, Inc.
21 West Street, 11th Floor
New York, NY   10006

Buras, Professor Nathan
Technion
Haifa, Israel

Burnash, Robert J. C.
1641 Resources Building
1416 9th Street
Sacramento, CA   95014

Butcher, William S.
Office of Science and Technology
Executive Office of the President
Washington, D.C.   20550

Castro, Fabio De Gennaro
Centrais Electricas de Sao Paulo
  S.A. - CESP -
  Av. Paulista, 2064-17
Sao Paulo, Brazil (C.P. 1035)

Caulfield, Henry P.
Colorado State University
Fort Collins, CO   80521

Chamberlain, A. Ray
Colorado State University
Fort Collins, CO   80521

Chaudhry, M.
Colorado State University
Fort Collins, CO   80521

Chiang, Sie Ling
854 Bethel Drive
Harrisburg, PA   17111

Chin, Hubert
P.O. Box 91
Kingston 7, Jamaica

Chitwood, Jack K.
3424 D Willowrun Drive
Austin, TX   78704

Guerrero, Pedro
Colorado State University
Fort Collins, CO   80521

Guillen, Juan Coma
Spain

Haftorsen, Roy
AID
Washington, D.C.   20550

Hagan, Dr. Robert
University of California
Davis, CA   95616

Halpenny, Leonard C.
3938 Santa Barbara
Tucson, AZ   85711

Hamalaway, Mahmoud El
5, Soliman Mohamed Abaza Street
Hilliopolis 2nd district
Cairo, Egypt

Hasfurther, Dr. Victor
University of Wyoming
Laramie, WY   82070

Hashino, Michio
University of Tokyshima
1, 2-chome, Minamijosanjima
Tokushima, Japan

Hawkins, Edward F.
609 Second Street, Suite 1
Davis, CA   95616

Henry, Paul-Marc
President, OECD Development
  Centre
94 Rue Chardon-Lagache
75775 Paris Cedex 16, France

Herbst, P. H.
Private Bag X313
Pretoria, South Africa

Herr, Lester A.
Federal Highway Administration
400 Seventh Street, SW
Washington, D.C.

Hotchkiss, Bill
Colorado State University
Fort Collins, CO   80521

Hotes, F. L.
3527 South Silver Springs Road
Lafayette, CA   94549

Ikebushi, Shuichi
Kyoto University
Yoshidahonmachi Sakyoku
Kyoto, Japan

Jawed, Kahlid
Colorado State University
Fort Collins, CO   80521

Kadoya, Mutsumi
Disaster Prevention Research
  Institute
Kyoto University
Uji-City, Kyoto, Japan 611

Karplus, Alan
Colorado State University
Fort Collins, CO   80521

Kay, John A.
4100 Southwest Freeway
Suite 402
Houston, TX   77027

Kelley, Dr. Omer J.
Bureau for Technical Assistance
Agency for International
  Development
Wasington, D.C.   20523

Keyes, Conrad G., Jr.
Box 3 CE
New Mexico State University
Las Cruces, NM   88001

Khan, Mohuiddin
Government of Pakistan
98-A, Satellite Town
Rawalpindi, Pakistan

Klohn, Wulf
World Meteorological Organization
CH-1211, Geneve 20
Switzerland

537

Laurenson, E. M.
P.O. Box 793
Lae, New Guinea

LeFeuvre, A. R.
Box 5050
Burlington, Ontario, Canada

Longenbaugh, R. A.
Colorado State University
Fort Collins, CO   80521

Lopez, Oscar
Colorado State University
Fort Collins, CO   80521

Luedtke, John R.
1324 W. Dayton Street
Madison, WI   53716

McGuire, R. A.
1416 9th Street
Sacramento, CA   95814

McKerchar, Dr. A. I.
Purdue University
Lafayette, IN   47907

McMahon, Dr. T. A.
Monash University
Clayton, Victoria, 3168
Australia

McPherson, M. B.
23 Watson Street
Marblehead, MA   01945

McWhorter, David B.
Colorado State University
Fort Collins, CO   80521

Mahmood, Khalid
Colorado State University
Fort Collins, CO   80521

Malik, Sarfraz Khan
President's Secretariat
  Planning Division
Pakistan Secretariat Block-P
Islamabad, Pakistan

Maniak, Prof. Dr.-Ing. Ulrich
Technical University Braunschweig
3300 Braunschweig, West Germany

Mashayekhi, Taghi
Colorado State University
Fort Collins, CO   80521

Mattich, A. K.
521 Federal Building
269 Main Street
Winnipeg, Manitoba, Canada

Miller, John F.
13420 Oriental Street
Rockville, MD   20853

Miller, Morris
International Bank for Reconstruction and Development
1818 H Street NW
Washington, D.C.   20433

Naas, Seddik
1917 S. Shields #k-6
Fort Collins, CO   80521

Neilson, Frank
P.O. 631
Vicksburg, MD   39180

Nemec, J.
World Meteorological Organization
CH-1211 Geneve, Switzerland

Newton, Donald W.
TVA
218 Evans Building
Knoxville, TN   37902

Nir, A.
Weizmann Institute of Science
Rehovot, Israel

Nordin, Carl F.
Colorado State University
Fort Collins, CO   80521

Oliveira, Almeida Lourival
1346 Connecticut Avenue
Washington, D.C.   20036

Ong, Ming
1416 9th Street
Sacramento, CA   95814

Onstad, Charles A.
North Central Soil Conser-
  vation Research Center
Morris, MN   56267

Pao, Richard H. F.
Cleveland State University
Cleveland, OH   44115

Pinkayan, Subin
Asian Institute of Technology
Henri Dunant Street
Bangkok, Thailand

Poblete, J. A.
Universidad de Chile
Santiago, Chile

Prakash, Anand
Colorado State University
Cort Collins, CO   80521

Rattie, John J.
Box 360 - 25 State Police Drive
Trenton, N.J.   08603

Rechard, Paul A.,   WHO-WRRI
P.O. Box 3038
University Station
Laramie, WY   82070

Remington, Stanley M.
3815 Ridgeview Road
Arlington, VA   22207

Rhoades, Marjorie
Colorado State University
Fort Collins, CO   80521

Ribney, F. M. J.
3 Kurang Place
Cooma North, N.S.W. 2629
Australia

Richardson, E. V.
Colorado State University
Fort Collins, CO   80521

Rodier, Jean
International Association of
  Hydrology
19, rue Eugene-Carriere
Paris 18º, France

Sarma, Barada C.
Texas Water Rights Commission
Sam Houston Office Building
Austin, TX   78711

Schmidt, Fred C.
Colorado State University
Fort Collins, CO   80521

Schwarz, Francis K.
5909 Holland Road
Rockville, MD   20851

Schweitzer, Glenn E.
Office of Science and Technology
Agency for International
  Development
Washington, D.C.   20523

Shaner, W. W.
Colorado State University
Fort Collins, CO   80521

Shaw, William
Panama City, Panama

Sikka, D. R.
D-16, 74 Bungalows
T. T. Nagar
Bhopal (M.P.), India

Simmons, Wm. P.
U.S. Bureau of Reclamation
Denver Federal Center
Denver, CO   80225

Simons, D. B.
Colorado State University
Fort Collins, CO   80521

Soemantri, Bambang
Directorate of River and Swampy
Tromolport 23 Kot. Kebajoran Baru
Djakarta, Indonesia

Stanescu, Silviu - WMO/UNDP
  Expert
Apartado Aereo 3868
Bogota, Columbia

Stephens, Larry D.
Rm 490, Building 67
Denver Federal Center
Denver, CO   80215

Tai, P. K.
Colorado State University
Fort Collins, CO   80521

Taylor, Donald C.
Manager, Research Services,
  ASCE
345 East 47th Street
New York, NY   10017

Taylor, George C., Jr.
Room 331, Arlington Towers
Washington, D.C.   20242

Taylor, O. James
1838 S. Van Gorden Court
Lakewood, CO   80228

Thaemert, R. L.
Colorado State University
Fort Collins, CO   80521

Thomas, Mr. R. G.
FAO
Via delle Terme di Caracalla
00100 Rome, Italy

Thompson, Theodore R.
Agency for International
  Development
Washington, D.C.

Tirtotjondro, Rachmat
Institute of Hydraulic
  Engineering
2 Djalan Kidang Panandjung
Bandung, Indonesia

Trac, Nguyen Quang
International Training, E.R.S.
So. Building USDA
Independence Avenue
Washington, D.C.

Verhoog, Frederick H.
Office of Hydrology, UNESCO
Place de Fontenoy
Paris VII, France

Villela, Swami M.
1465 Carlos Botelho
Sao Carlo, Sao Paulo
Brazil

Vlachos, Evan
Colorado State University
Fort Collins, Co   80521

White, Gilbert
University of Colorado
Boulder, CO   80302

Whitford, Peter W.
International Bank for Reconstruction and Development
1818 H Street NW
Washington, D.C.   20433

Yevjevich, Vujica
Colorado State University
Fort Collins, CO   80521

Zuberi, F. A.
Colorado State University
Fort Collins, CO   80521